MATHEMATICS TODAY

FOR ICSE

CLASS – VIII

O.P. MALHOTRA
M.A. (*Gold Medallist*)
Head of the Maths Department (*Retd.*)
The Doon School, *Dehra Dun*

S.K. GUPTA
Principal (*Retd.*)
Birla Vidya Mandir
Nainital

ANUBHUTI GANGAL
M.A. (*Gold Medallist*) *M.Ed.*
Formerly, Senior Faculty Member
The Daly College, *Indore*
Birla Vidya Mandir, *Nainital*

S. CHAND & COMPANY LTD.

(AN ISO 9001: 2000 COMPANY)
RAM NAGAR, NEW DELHI -110 055

S. CHAND & COMPANY LTD.

(An ISO 9001 : 2000 Company)

Head Office: 7361, RAM NAGAR, NEW DELHI - 110 055
Phone: 23672080-81-82, 9899107446, 9911310888
Fax: 91-11-23677446
Shop at: **schandgroup.com**; e-mail: **info@schandgroup.com**

Branches :

AHMEDABAD : 1st Floor, Heritage, Near Gujarat Vidhyapeeth, Ashram Road, **Ahmedabad** - 380 014, Ph: 27541965, 27542369, ahmedabad@schandgroup.com

BENGALURU : No. 6, Ahuja Chambers, 1st Cross, Kumara Krupa Road, **Bengaluru** - 560 001, Ph: 22268048, 22354008, bangalore@schandgroup.com

BHOPAL : Bajaj Tower, Plot No. 243, Lala Lajpat Rai Colony, Raisen Road, **Bhopal** - 462 011, Ph: 4274723. bhopal@schandgroup.com

CHANDIGARH : S.C.O. 2419-20, First Floor, Sector - 22-C (Near Aroma Hotel), **Chandigarh** -160 022, Ph: 2725443, 2725446, chandigarh@schandgroup.com

CHENNAI : 152, Anna Salai, **Chennai** - 600 002, Ph: 28460026, 28460027, chennai@schandgroup.com

COIMBATORE : No. 5, 30 Feet Road, Krishnasamy Nagar, Ramanathapuram, **Coimbatore** -641045, Ph: 0422-2323620 coimbatore@schandgroup.com **(Marketing Office)**

CUTTACK : 1st Floor, Bhartia Tower, Badambadi, **Cuttack** - 753 009, Ph: 2332580; 2332581, cuttack@schandgroup.com

DEHRADUN : 1st Floor, 20, New Road, Near Dwarka Store, **Dehradun** - 248 001, Ph: 2711101, 2710861, dehradun@schandgroup.com

GUWAHATI : Pan Bazar, **Guwahati** - 781 001, Ph: 2738811, 2735640 guwahati@schandgroup.com

HYDERABAD : Padma Plaza, H.No. 3-4-630, Opp. Ratna College, Narayanaguda, **Hyderabad** - 500 029, Ph: 24651135, 24744815, hyderabad@schandgroup.com

JAIPUR : A-14, Janta Store Shopping Complex, University Marg, Bapu Nagar, **Jaipur** - 302 015, Ph: 2719126, jaipur@schandgroup.com

JALANDHAR : Mai Hiran Gate, **Jalandhar** - 144 008, Ph: 2401630, 5000630, jalandhar@schandgroup.com

JAMMU : 67/B, B-Block, Gandhi Nagar, **Jammu** - 180 004, (M) 09878651464 **(Marketing Office)**

KOCHI : Kachapilly Square, Mullassery Canal Road, Ernakulam, **Kochi** - 682 011, Ph: 2378207, cochin@schandgroup.com

KOLKATA : 285/J, Bipin Bihari Ganguli Street, **Kolkata** - 700 012, Ph: 22367459, 22373914, kolkata@schandgroup.com

LUCKNOW : Mahabeer Market, 25 Gwynne Road, Aminabad, **Lucknow** - 226 018, Ph: 2626801, 2284815, lucknow@schandgroup.com

MUMBAI : Blackie House, 103/5, Walchand Hirachand Marg, Opp. G.P.O., **Mumbai** - 400 001, Ph: 22690881, 22610885, mumbai@schandgroup.com

NAGPUR : Karnal Bag, Model Mill Chowk, Umrer Road, **Nagpur** - 440 032, Ph: 2723901, 2777666 nagpur@schandgroup.com

PATNA : 104, Citicentre Ashok, Govind Mitra Road, **Patna** - 800 004, Ph: 2300489, 2302100, patna@schandgroup.com

PUNE : 291/1, Ganesh Gayatri Complex, 1st Floor, Somwarpeth, Near Jain Mandir, **Pune** - 411 011, Ph: 64017298, pune@schandgroup.com **(Marketing Office)**

RAIPUR : Kailash Residency, Plot No. 4B, Bottle House Road, Shankar Nagar, **Raipur** - 492 007, Ph: 09981200834, raipur@schandgroup.com **(Marketing Office)**

RANCHI : Flat No. 104, Sri Draupadi Smriti Apartments, East of Jaipal Singh Stadium, Neel Ratan Street, Upper Bazar, **Ranchi** - 834 001, Ph: 2208761, ranchi@schandgroup.com **(Marketing Office)**

SILIGURI : 122, Raja Ram Mohan Roy Road, East Vivekanandapally, P.O., **Siliguri**-734001, Dist., Jalpaiguri, (W.B.) Ph. 0353-2520750 **(Marketing Office)**

VISAKHAPATNAM: Plot No. 7, 1st Floor, Allipuram Extension, Opp. Radhakrishna Towers, Seethammadhara North Extn., **Visakhapatnam** - 530 013, (M) 09347580841, visakhapatnam@schandgroup.com **(Marketing Office)**

First Edition 1979 with Subsequent Edition and Reprints
First ICSE Edition 2006
Subsequent Editions and Reprints 2007, 2008 (Twice)
Revised Edition 2009, Reprint 2010
Reprint 2011

ISBN : 81-219-2716-1   **Code : 14C 515**

PRINTED IN INDIA
By Rajendra Ravindra Printers Pvt. Ltd., 7361, Ram Nagar, New Delhi -110 055
and published by S. Chand & Company Ltd., 7361, Ram Nagar, New Delhi -110 055.

A NOTE ON THE NEW 2009 EDITION

The text matter and answers have been thoroughly re-checked.

AUTHORS

A NOTE ON THE NEW 2008 EDITION

The authors wish to express their satisfaction and gratitude for the warm welcome accorded to this series.

1. The text matter has been completely revised to help better understanding and the number of questions and exercises have been reduced wherever it was felt to be advisable to do so.

2. Keeping in view the age group for which the books are meant, the layout and font size has been changed to facilitate easy reading.

3. The books have been thoroughly checked for any printing mistakes and all the answers have been checked by the authors themselves after solving each and every question. Hopefully, the books will now be error-free.

4. The authors are grateful to all those teachers and students who have provided valuable feedback for the improvement of the series.

A NOTE FOR THE TEACHERS

Dear friends,

We feel happy to be able to present for your perusal and consideration the new and thoroughly revised and updated edition of our **Mathematics Today Series for classes VI, VII and VIII**. It has no doubt been possible as a result of the motivation and feedback received in the form of valuable comments, suggestions and criticism from the learned teachers. We strongly feel that a textbook howsoever good it may be is only a tool to help teachers to teach effectively. It is the teacher and only the teacher who is competent to decide his/her teaching strategies in the classroom and is the best judge of how to use the textbook to meet the special needs of his/her class. It is earnestly hoped that this series will be able to supplement your efforts effectively to create interest of your pupils in the subject and make the study of mathematics interesting and enjoyable and gain mastery over the subject.

Howsoever best one performs or creates there is always scope for improvement.

We would be very happy rather grateful to receive your comments, appreciation/criticism and suggestions for further improvement of the books.

With regards

Yours sincerely,
Authors

PREFACE TO THE REVISED EDITION

It gives us great satisfaction to be able to bring out this new version of our old Maths Today series for classes VI to VIII. The old series has been rehashed and redesigned incorporating the current global trends and International practices and the latest philosophy and policy of providing stress free education.

The **salient features** of this series are :

1. It follows strictly the new syllabus of the ICSE council.

2. All the mathematical concepts have been presented in a very simple and lucid form and loading the course content with unnecessary and irrelevant details has been avoided. The approach and orientation is to lay a strong foundation for the students through adequate emphasis on the fundamentals.

3. It aims at complete involvement of the pupils in the learning process. The emphasis throughout the text is on a student-centered performance and the **activity approach** is freely used relating the mathematical concepts to real life situations.

4. Every unit is introduced by a motivating paragraph or story.

5. To facilitate easy and better understanding each unit is divided into a number of subunits with short & separate practice exercises on each subunit.

6. **An attempt has been made to expose the children more fully to the 'Why' of various operations and made abundant use of diagrams, illustrations, cartoons, tables and charts to stimulate the student's interest in the subject and to clarify more difficult concepts.**

7. Colour panels are used throughout as a teaching aid to emphasize important terms and relationships and present useful tips.

8. The problems given in the books avoid tedious calculations and help in strengthening the understanding of basic principles honing the faculties of thinking and reasoning.

9. Each chapter contains a **unit summary of key points** at the end. It reviews the main points covered and helps the students in remembering them.

10. **Unit review exercises** help in evaluating the assimilation of the concepts learnt in a unit.

11. **Mental maths** exercises have been given to help the students acquire speed and sharpen their intellect.

12. **Historical Notes, Quizzes, Just For Fun, Puzzles and Enrichment Material** offer further intellectual challenge to sharp students and help them not only to maintain their interest in the subject and widen their horizon of knowledge but would also be of immense help in preparing for such competitions such as Mathematics Olympiad at various levels.

It is hoped that this series of books will meet more than adequately, the needs of the students they are meant for. Any suggestions for the improvement of the books would be most welcome and gratefully acknowledged.

AUTHORS

SYLLABUS

1. Sets
   Revision of work done in Classes VI and VII
   Idea of a set   Well defined collection of distinct objects.
   Notation   Roster method (listing elements) and set builder method.
   Finite/ Infinite set   Denoting sets by capital letters and elements by small letters.
   Universal set
   Revision of work done in Classes VI and VII
   The empty set   Candidates will be expected to be familiar with the terms and symbols
   Equivalent sets   connected with sets, namely,
   Equal sets   Sets of numbers : N, W, I or Z, Q and R
   Cardinal number of a set   General : $\in, \notin, \xi, \varnothing$ or $\{\}$, $n(A)$.
   Subsets   Operational : $A', \cup, \cap$.
   Complement of a set   Relation : $= \neq, \leftrightarrow, \Leftrightarrow, \subset, \supset, \subseteq, \supseteq$.
   Union of sets Intersection of sets
   Venn diagrams   Venn diagrams as illustrations to bring out relationship in sets and their use in simple logical problems.

2. Numbers
   Numbers   Natural numbers, whole numbers, integers, rational and irrational numbers, real numbers,
   The real Number line   Prime and composite numbers, odd and even numbers. Factors, H.C.F., Multiples, L.C.M.
                                                   Four fundamental operations. Simplification of expressions involving fractions and decimals (Use of principle of BODMAS).

                                                   Symbols : $=, \neq, >, <, \geq, \leq, +, -, \times, \div$ of, brackets.

   Directed numbers   Four fundamental operation involving directed numbers.
   Ratio, fractions,   Conversion of one to the other.
   decimals and percentage
   Squares and Square roots   Square root by factors and division method.

3. Arithmetical Problems
   Simple Interest   Calculation of Interest and Amount only.
   Compound Interest by Simple Interest method   Calculation of Interest and Amount only.
   Percentage, Profit and Loss   Elementary (Simple and direct question) only.
   Time and work   Pupils must be fully conversant with the measures of money length, areas, volume weight and time.

   Time and Distance Proportional parts

4. Algebra
   Fundamental concepts   Pupils will be expected to be familiar with algebraic terms such as term monomial, binomial, trinomial, polynomial degree of a polynomial, coefficient, variable, constant, linear, algebraic fractions.

   Fundamental operations   Addition, subtraction and multiplication.
                                                   Division of a polynomial by a monomial or a binomial of first degree.
                                                   Simplification by removal of brackets (Use of principle of BODMAS).
   Substitution   Substitution in polynomials (degree 2 or 1) involving at most three unknowns.
   Exponents   Positive, integral and zero indices only.
                                                   Laws of exponents :
                                                   $$x^m . x^n = x^{m+n}; x^m / x^n = x^{m-n}; \ (m > n \text{ only})$$

                                                   $$\left(x^m\right)^n = x^{mn} \text{ and } x^0 = 1$$
                                                   Proofs of the laws will not be required.
   Formulae   Framing of formulae (simple cases). Change of subject of formula.
   Products and $(x \pm a)(x \pm b)$
   Expansions $(x \pm a)^2$
   Factorisation   Taking common; $ax + bx, a(x + y) \pm b(x + y)$
                                                   Grouping and taking common : $ac + bd + ad + bc$
                                                   Difference of squares $x^2 - y^2$

                                                   Trinomials $ax^2 + bx + c$ $(a, b, c \in N)$

   Linear equations   Solution of :
                                                   (i) simple linear equation and problems leading to them.
                                                   (ii) pairs of simultaneous linear equations in two variables. Simple problems leading to them,
                                                   Candidates will be expected to find a solution set in a given replacement set for the variable.
   Graphs   Graphical representation of a linear equation in two variables. Solution of a pair of simultaneous linear equation in two variables graphically.

5. Mensuration
   Area and perimeter of a triangle, rectangle,   Problems on paths inside or outside a rectangle or a circle may be
   trapezium and circle   included.
   Volume and surface of cuboids   Pupils should be familiar with the abbreviations; cm, m, km, cm^2, m^2, cm^3, m^3.
6. Geometry   **Note :** In the Geometry section of the syllabus, pupils will not be expected to prove theorems.
                                                   Question should be set to test simple logical deductions, from geometrical properties.

Fundamental concepts	Candidates will be expected to be familiar with line, plane, space, line segments, polygons as a set of points.
Lines	Parallel, intersecting, perpendicular, bisectors of angles, bisectors of line segments.
Angles	Acute, right, obtuse, straight and reflex. Adjacent angles, vertically opposite angles. Complementary and supplementary angles. Alternate, corresponding and interior opposite angles (with reference to parallel lines).
Properties	(a) If two straight lines intersect, the adjacent angles are supplementary and vertically opposite angles are equal.
	(b) If two angles having a common arm are supplementary the other two arms lie in a straight line.
	(c) If two parallel lines are cut by a transversal line,
	(1) the alternate angles are equal,
	(2) the corresponding angles are equal,
	(3) the interior opposite angles on the same side of the cutting line are supplementary.
	(d) The converse of (c).
Polygons Triangles	The angle sum property - interior : $(2n - 4)$rt. angles, exterior; (4 rt. angles).
Kinds	Scalene, isosceles, equilateral
Properties	(a) Congruency : SAS, ASA, SSS, RHS.
	(b) The angle sum property.
	(c) If one side of a triangle is produced, the exterior angle formed is equal to the sum of the interior opposite angles.
	(d) If two sides of a triangle are equal, the angle opposite to them are equal; and the converse.
	(e) if two sides of a triangle are unequal, the greater side has the grater angle opposite to it; and the converse.
	(f) Pythagoras' theorem.
Quadrilaterals, Parallelogram	(a) If a pair of opposite sides of a quadrilateral are equal and parallel, it is a parallelogram.
	(b) The opposite angles of a parallelogram are equal and adjacent angles are supplementary.
	(c) The diagonals of a parallelogram bisect each other, and each diagonal bisects the parallelogram.
	(d) Parallelogram on the same base and between the same parallels are equal in area.
Area propositions	(e) The area of a triangle is half that of a parallelogram on the same base and between the same parallels.
Rectangle	(f) The diagonals of a rectangle are equal and bisect each other.
Square	(g) The diagonals of a square bisect each other at right angles and are equal.
Rhombus	(h) The diagonals of a rhombus bisect each other at right angles.
Constructions	Using ruler and compasses **only** :
Angles	An angle equal to a given angle.
	Bisection of a angle.
	Construction of angles of 60°, 30°, 90°, 45°.
Lines	Bisector of a line segment. Perpendicular bisector of a line segment.
	Construction of a perpendicular to a line (i) at a given point in the line and (ii) from an external point.
Triangles	Simple data corresponding to congruency conditions (Question on constructions of triangles given sum/difference of sides/angles **not** to be asked)
	Opposite angles are supplementary.
Rectangles, Squares and Rhombus	From simple data.
Circle	From simple data. Circumcircle and in circle of a triangle.

1. Arithmetic/Algebra

Approximation	Significant figures, rounding off to a specified unit (e.g. to the nearest mm, nearest g, nearest paisa, etc.) and decimal places.
Power and roots	Use of tables in computing square, cubes, square roots and cube roots of natural numbers.
(tables and approximation)	Using the division method to find the square roots of a non-perfect square natural number to a specified number of decimal places e.g. find $\sqrt{27}$ correct to 2 decimal places.
H.C.F. and L.C.M.	Using factors only.
Inequations	Simplification of algebraic fractions (cancelling the H.C.F. / in Nr. and Dr.) Addition and subtraction of simple algebraic fraction by finding the L.C.M. of the denominators.
Quadratic equations	Solution of quadratic equations in one variable, using factors only. *Problems leading to quadratic equation excluded.*

2. Mensuration

Area and perimeter of a trapezium	Use of the formula for area; direct problems only.

3. Geometry

Circles	Terms : radius, diameter, circumference, chords, arcs, semicircle, major arc, minor arc, sectors, segments, central angle, tangents, $\angle$ in a semicircle = 90°.
Symmetry, Reflection, Rotation	Figures having symmetry, line symmetry, rotation through 90°.

4. Statistics

Tabulation of raw-data. Frequency tally. Frequency distribution and column graphs based on frequency distribution and not frequency density. Introduction to grouped data - tabulating data and finding mean. Introducing median and mode, revising earlier concepts.

CONTENTS

UNIT 1 : SET THEORY

UNIT 2 : PURE ARITHMETIC

UNIT 3 : COMMERCIAL MATHEMATICS

UNIT 4 : ALGEBRA

1. Sets

1.1 Introduction

You have already studied 'sets' in classes VI and VII. All the topics in 'Set Theory' mentioned in the syllabus were covered in these classes. Here we shall review and strengthen these concepts further. We shall also take up the properties of operations on sets in detail.

1.2 What is a Set ?

A set is a **well defined collection of objects**. By 'well defined' we mean that it must be possible to tell beyond doubt whether or not a given object belongs to the collection under consideration.

For example :

1. If we consider the group of months whose names begin with **M**, then you know that March is included in this group, but June is not. This collection of months is well defined and so is a set.

    The following are also well defined collections and so are examples of sets.

2. The set of numbers 1, 3, 5, 7 and 9.

3. The set of pupils in your class.

    The following **do not describe a well defined collection and so are not sets.**

1. **The vegetables which taste good to all.**

    As tastes differ from person to person, different persons will include different vegetables in this collection.

2. **All good movies**

    You may like a particular movie but your friend may not.

    Sets are usually denoted by the capital letters $A, B, C, ...$ etc.

1.3 Sets of Numbers

You are familiar with the sets of natural numbers, whole numbers, integers, rational numbers. About the sets of irrational numbers and real numbers you will learn in the next chapters. We have

N = set of natural numbers, i.e. $N = \{1, 2, 3, ...\}$

W = set of whole numbers, i.e. $W = \{0, 1, 2, 3, ...\}$

Z = set of integers, i.e. $Z = \{ ..., -3, -2, -1, 0, 1, 2, 3, ...\}$

Q = set of rational numbers

R = set of real numbers.

1.4 Members of a Set and Symbol '∈' for 'belongs to'

The objects that belong to a set are called members or **elements** of the set. Elements of a set are usually denoted by small letters $a, b, c, ...$

For example :

1. $7 \in$ the set of odd numbers.

2. $8 \notin$ the set of odd numbers.

3. $-20 \notin$ the set of whole numbers.

4. $\dfrac{1}{3} \notin$ the set of integers.

5. $-\dfrac{1}{3} \in$ the set of rational numbers.

6. $a \in \{a, b, c\}, b \in \{a, b, c\}, c \in \{a, b, c\}, d \notin \{a, b, c\}$.

7. $1 \notin \{0, 2, 4, 6, 8\}$

8. $9 \in$ set of square numbers.

9. $4 \notin$ set of multiples of 3.

1.5. How to Describe a Set ?

There are two ways to name a set

(*i*) **The Roster method.**

In this method, the elements of the set are listed within braces. For example,

$$A = \{1, 2, 3, 4, 5\} \text{ or } A = \{5, 3, 1, 2, 4\}$$

The order in which elements are listed is unimportant. If P is the set of counting numbers less than 100, you may list the members as $P = \{1, 2, 3, 4, ..., 99\}$. The three dots after 4 means that the numbers after 4 continue in the same manner until 99 is reached.

Let N be the set of counting numbers. You can list N this way

$$N = \{1, 2, 3, 4, ...\}$$

Here the three dots mean that the numbers continue in the same manner without end.

Let B be the set of letters in the word 'floor'. You can list B this way.

$$B = \{f, l, o, r\}$$

Note that repetition is not done while listing the elements.

(*ii*) **The Rule (or property) method or the Set-builder form.**

The rule method denotes the set by using words, formulas, or properties. Thus, set A, P and N described above by roster method can be denoted by rule method as under :

$$A = \text{The set of natural numbers less than 6.}$$
$$N = \text{The set of natural numbers.}$$
$$P = \text{The set of natural numbers less than 100.}$$

More concisely, when the members of a set S possess a property P and x is any element of S, then we write the set S as

$S = \{x \mid x$ has a property $P\}$ or $S = \{x : x$ has a property $P\}$ and read it as, S is the set of elements x, such that x has the property P. The vertical line or the colon means *'such that'*

This is called the **set builder form.**

For example :

(*i*) Let A be the set of colleges affiliated to Delhi University.

Then $A = \{x \mid x$ is a college affiliated to Delhi University$\}$.

(*ii*) Let E be the set of even whole numbers less than twenty.

Then, $E = \{n : n$ is an even whole number less than 20$\}$

or $\qquad\qquad\qquad E = \{x \mid x = 2n, n \in W \text{ and } n < 10\}$.

(*iii*) Let P be the set of reciprocals of natural numbers. Then $P = \left\{x : x = \dfrac{1}{n}, n \in N\right\}$.

Ex. 1. *Write the following sets in roster form :*

(a) $A = \{x \mid x = 7n, n \in Z \text{ and } -3 \leq n < 3\}$,   (b) $B = \{x : x \in W, 5x - 7 < 19\}$,

(c) $C = \left\{x : x = \dfrac{p}{p+3}, p \in N \text{ and } p < 7\right\}$.

Sol. (a) Given $n \in Z$ and $-3 \leq n < 3$, *i.e.* n can take up values $-3, -2, -1, 0, 1, 2$ (Note that n being less than 3, it does not take up the value 3).

Also, $x = 7n$, putting $x = -3, -2, -1, 0, 1, 2$, we obtain $x = -21, -14, -7, 0, 7, 14$.

Hence, the given set can be written in the roster form as $A = \{-21, -14, -7, 0, 7, 14\}$.

(b) Given $5x - 7 < 19$, $x \in W$ or $5x < 19 + 7$, $x \in W$ or $5x < 26$, $x \in W$ or $x < \dfrac{26}{5}$, $x \in W$

The whole numbers less than $\dfrac{26}{5}$ are $0, 1, 2, 3, 4, 5$

∴ $B = \{0, 1, 2, 3, 4, 5\}$.

(c) Given $p \in N$ and $p < 7$ so p will take up the values $1, 2, ..., 6$

so $x = \dfrac{1}{1+3}, \dfrac{2}{2+3}, \dfrac{3}{3+3}, \dfrac{4}{4+3}, \dfrac{5}{5+3}, \dfrac{6}{6+3} = \dfrac{1}{4}, \dfrac{2}{5}, \dfrac{3}{6}, \dfrac{4}{7}, \dfrac{5}{8}, \dfrac{6}{9}$ or $\dfrac{1}{4}, \dfrac{2}{5}, \dfrac{1}{2}, \dfrac{4}{7}, \dfrac{5}{8}, \dfrac{2}{3}$

Hence, $C = \left\{\dfrac{1}{4}, \dfrac{2}{5}, \dfrac{1}{2}, \dfrac{4}{7}, \dfrac{5}{8}, \dfrac{2}{3}\right\}$.

Ex. 2. *Write the following sets in set builder form.*

(a) $F = \left\{\dfrac{5}{12}, \dfrac{6}{13}, \dfrac{7}{14}, \dfrac{8}{15}, \dfrac{9}{16}, \dfrac{10}{17}\right\}$.   (b) $G = \{0, 1, 16, 81, 256, 625\}$

Sol. (a) Do you observe that in the given set, the denominator of each fraction is 7 more than the numerator ?

∴   In the set builder form,

$$F = \left\{x : x = \dfrac{n}{n+7}, n \in N \text{ and } 5 \leq n \leq 10\right\}.$$

(b) Do you observe that elements of the given set are the fourth powers of the first five whole numbers ?

∴   In the set builder form

$$G = \{x \mid x = n^4, n \in W \text{ and } n \leq 5\}.$$

EXERCISE 1 (a)

1. Which of the following collections are sets ?

(a) Planets of our solar system.

(b) Interesting books in the library.

(c) Colours of rainbow.

(d) Beautiful girl students of your school.

(e) Top five wicket takers in Test Cricket.

(f) Smart and handsome boys of your class.

(g) Presidents of India.

(h) Good football players.

2. Re-write the following statements, using set notation :

(a) 3 is an element of set of natural numbers.

(b) -5 is not an element of the set of natural numbers.

3. Let A = {Prime numbers ≤ 19}.

Insert the appropriate symbol '∈' or '∉' in blank spaces :

(a) 4 ... A   (b) 7 ... A   (c) 9 ... A   (d) 13 ... A   (e) $\sqrt{3}$ ... A   (f) 1 ... A.

4. **Answer true or false :**

   (a) $0 \in W$ (b) $0 \in N$ (c) $12 \in$ set of factors of 24.   (d) If $V =$ set of vowels, then $k \in V$.

5. **Specify each of the following sets in the roster form :**

   (a) The set of prime numbers less than 10.   (b) The set of letters in the word 'SATELLITE'.

   (c) The set of natural numbers less than 0.

6. **Specify each of the following sets by stating a rule :**

   (a) $\{15, 16, 17, 18, ...\}$ (b) $\{5, 10, 15, ...\}$ (c) $\{0, 2, 4, 6, ...\}$ (d) $\{-5, -3, -1, -2, -4\}$

7. **Specify each of the following sets in the set builder form :**

   (a) $A = \{4, 8, 12, 16, 20, 24, ...\}$ (b) $B = \{4, 9, 16, 25, 36, 49, ...\}$ (c) $C = \{..., -4, -3, -2, -1, 0\}$

   (d) $D = \left\{\dfrac{1}{2}, \dfrac{2}{3}, \dfrac{3}{4}, \dfrac{4}{5}, ...\right\}$ (e) ϕ

8. **Write the following sets in roster form**

   (a) $\{x \mid x \in N, x < 6\}$ (b) $\{d \mid d$ is a digit in the number $5354725\}$ (c) $\{y \mid y = 3x - 1, x \in N\}$

   (d) $\{x \mid x = n^2, n \in N, 4 \leq n \leq 10\}$ (e) $\left\{x \mid x = \dfrac{p+1}{2p+3}, p \in W \text{ and } p \leq 6\right\}$

TYPES OF SETS

1.6 Finite and Infinite Sets

If the members of a set can be counted with the counting coming to an end, the set is a **finite set,** *e.g.* $A = \{1, 3, 5, 7\}$ is a finite set. If the process of counting the members of a set cannot come to an end, the set is said to be an **infinite set**. The set of natural numbers is an infinite set.

For example : The following are finite sets :

  (i)   The set of oceans.

 (ii)   The set of human beings living on earth.

(iii) $\{x : x = 3n + 1, n \in Z, -2 \leq n < 2\}$

The following are infinite sets

  (i)   Set of rational numbers between 0 and 1

 (ii)   Set of all points on a line segment

(iii) $\{x : x \in Z, x < 0\}$.

1.7 Singleton Set

A set containing only one element is called a singleton set.

For example: $\{7\}$ is a singleton set, containing only one element, namely, 7.

1.8 The Empty Set

A set that has no members is called the empty set or the null set. It is denoted by the symbol $\{\ \}$ or ϕ.

    Note : There is only one empty set and it is called 'the empty set'. There is nothing like 'an empty set', or 'empty sets.'

For example:

Each one of the following is the empty set :

  (i)   The set of people who have landed on Mars.   (ii) $\{x \mid x \in Z, 0 < x < 1\}$.

(iii) $\{x : x \in R \; x \neq x\}$.   (iv) $\{x \mid x \in R, x^2 = -1\}$.

    Caution : $\{0\}$ and $\{\phi\}$ are not empty sets because each of these sets contains one element.

1.9 Cardinal Number of a Finite Set

The number of members in a set is called the **cardinal number** of the set. The cardinal number of a set A is denoted by $n(A)$.

For example :

(i)   Let $A = \{0, 1\}$ then $n(A) = 2$

(ii) Let $B = \{$months of the year$\}$, then $n(B) = 12$

(iii) Let $C = $ set of letters in the word 'BOOK', then $C = \{B, O, K\}$ and $n(C) = 3$

(iv) Let $M = $ set of months having 32 days, then $M = \phi$ and $n(M) = n(\phi) = 0$

> **Note that**
> 1. Cardinal number of an infinite set is not defined.
> 2. Cardinal number of the empty set is zero, *i.e.*, $n(\phi) = 0$.

1.10 Equal Sets

Two sets A and B are called **identical** or equal sets, written as $A = B$, when they have exactly the same elements. For example, if $A = \{p, q, r\}$ and $B = \{q, r, p\}$, then $A = B$.

Equivalent sets

Two sets are called **equivalent sets** if they contain the same number of elements, which may not be exactly the same elements. The equivalence of two sets A and B is expressed by writing $A \leftrightarrow B$. Obviously, the equivalent sets have the same cardinal number. For example if $A = $ set of letters of the word '*MAN*' and $B = $ set of letters of the word '*BOY*', then $A \leftrightarrow B$, as both contain 3 elements. They are not equal sets as they contain different elements.

> **Do you observe that**
>
> All equal sets are equivalent sets while all equivalent sets are not equal sets ?

For example:

(i) Let $A = $ set of the letters of the word '*PRAM*'; $B = $ set of the letters of the word '*RAMP*'
     $C = $ set of the letters of the word '*MARE*' Then, $A = B, A \neq C, B \neq C$.
     Also, since $n(A) = n(B) = n(C)$, we have $A \leftrightarrow B, A \leftrightarrow C, B \leftrightarrow C$.

(ii) Let $A = \{$all digits of the natural number system$\}$, $B = \{$Number of players in a baseball team$\}$,
     then $A \leftrightarrow B$, since $n(A) = n(B) = 9$
     Note that, $A \neq B$, since both the sets contain different elements.

1.11 Overlapping Sets

Two sets are called overlapping sets if, they have at least one element in common.

For example : The sets $A = \{5, 6, 7\}$ and $B = \{7, 8, 9\}$ are overlapping sets, since the element 7 is common to them.

1.12 Disjoint Sets

If two sets A and B have no elements in common, then we say that A and B are **disjoint sets.** For example, let $A = \{7, 11, 13\}$, $B = \{6, 8, 10\}$

Then A and B are disjoint sets, since no element is common to them.

EXERCISE 1 (b)

1. State which of the following sets are finite and which are infinte.

(a) $\{$The men who have orbited the Earth$\}$.   (b) $\{$The men who have landed on the moon$\}$.

   (c) {The integers between –5 and 5}.   (d) $\{x \mid x = 2y, y \in W\}$.

   (e) {The infants in your class}.   (f) $\{x : x \in R, 4 < x < 5\}$.

   (g) The set of atoms in the Earth.   (h) The set of multiples of ten.

   (i) The set of points on a line segment.   (j) The set of grains of sand on the beach.

2. **Which of the following are singleton sets?**

   (a) {Capital of India}.   (b) {Mountain peaks more than 8000 m high}.

   (c) $\{x \mid 5x - 3 = 7, x \in N\}$.   (d) $\{x \mid x^2 = 25, x \in Z\}$.

3. **State which of the following are empty sets :**

   (a) {odd numbers divisible by 2}   (b) {prime numbers which are even}   (c) {cubes with 8 faces}

   (d) $\{x \mid x \in W, x + 3 < 3\}$ (e) {days with 1440 minutes}

4. **State the cardinal number of the following sets**

   (a) $P = \{$planets of our solar system$\}$ (b) $C = \{$consonants of the English alphabet$\}$

   (c) $K = \{$letters in the word 'MADAM'$\}$ (d) $A = \{x \mid x + 3 = 0, x \in N\}$

   (e) $B = $ set of numbers whose square is 16.   (f) $M = \{x \mid x$ is a prime number, $1 < x < 30\}$

5. **Determine whether the two sets specified below are equivalent :**

   (a) $\{a, b, c, d\}$ and $\{-3, -7, -8, 0\}$ (b) $\left\{\dfrac{1}{2}, \dfrac{1}{3}, \dfrac{1}{7}, \dfrac{1}{9}, \dfrac{1}{10}\right\}$ and the integers between $\dfrac{5}{8}$ and 10

   (c) {months of a year} and $\{x \mid x < 12, x \in W\}$ (d) $A = \{$the even integers x between 1 and 9$\}$,

                                               $B = \{$the negative integers between –8 and –2$\}$.

6. **State whether the following pairs of sets are equal or not.**

   (a) $A = \{x : x$ is a letter of the word 'paper'$\}$ (b) $A = $ set of digits in the number 59678.

      $B = \{x : x$ is a letter of the word 'pear'$\}$ $B = $ set of digits in the number 7568896.

   (c) $A = \{x \mid x \leq 5, x \in N\}$ and $B = \{x \mid x \leq 5, x \in W\}$

   (d) $A = \{x \mid x < 1, x \in W\}$ and $B = $ set of cows having 5 legs

7. **From the following pairs of sets, identify the disjoint and overlapping sets.**

   (a) $A = $ set of letters in the word '*MAD*'   (b) $P = $ set of digits in the number '3150'

      $B = $ set of letters in the word '*OLD*' $Q = $ set of digits in the number '2468'

   (c) $L = \{x \mid x = 6p, p \in W, 0 \leq p \leq 8\}$ (d) $E = $ set of months having 30 days

      $M = \{y \mid y = 8q, q \in W, 0 \leq q \leq 6\}$ $F = $ set of months having 31 days.

1.13 Subsets

Let A, B be any two sets, then A is called a **subset** of B if every member of set A is also a member of set B. This is expressed by the symbols $A \subseteq B$ read "A is a subset of B". B is called the **superset** of A and we write it as $B \supseteq A$.

If there exists at least one element in A which is not a member of B, then A is not a subset of B. We express it as $A \nsubseteq B$ (read as A is not a subset of B).

For example :

   (i) Let $A = \{2, 3\}$, $B = \{1, 2, 3, 4, 5\}$, then $A \subseteq B$ because every member of A is also a member of B.

  (ii) Let $A = \{1, 3, 5\}$, $B = \{2, 3, 4, 5, 6\}$ then $A \nsubseteq B$, since element '1' of A is not contained in B.

 (iii) Let $P = \{$letters of *TAME*$\}$ and $Q = \{$letters of *MATE*$\}$.

      Do you observe that every member of P is a member of Q and every member of Q is a member of P?

      So, $P \subseteq Q$ and $Q \subseteq P$. Also, the elements being the same in these two sets, we have $P = Q$. From this example, we infer that

| **Every set is a subset of itself.** |

Remark. Since the empty set has no elements, **empty set is a subset of every set**. Thus, for any given set A, $\phi \subseteq A$.

1.14 Number of Subsets of a Given Set

(1) The subsets of $\{a\}$ are ϕ, $\{a\}$.

∴ Number of subsets = $2^1 = 2$.

(2) The subsets of $\{a, b\}$ are ϕ, $\{a\}$, $\{b\}$, $\{a, b\}$.

Number of subsets = $2^2 = 4$.

(3) The subsets of $\{a, b, c\}$ are ϕ, $\{a\}$, $\{b\}$, $\{c\}$, $\{a, b\}$, $\{a, c\}$ $\{b, c\}$, $\{a, b, c\}$.

Number of subsets = $2^3 = 8$.

| **A set containing 'n' elements has 2^n subsets.** |

1.15 Proper Subsets

The subsets of a given set other than itself are called proper subsets of the given set and the symbol '$\subset$' is used to denote a proper subset.

For example : If $A = \{c, a, p\}$, then each of the sets ϕ, $\{c\}$, $\{a\}$, $\{p\}$, $\{c, a\}$, $\{c, p\}$, $\{a, p\}$ is a proper subset of A; Note that the given set A itself is excluded from the list.

Obviously, the number of proper subsets of a set containing n elements is $2^n - 1$.

Remarks. The empty set is a proper subset of every set except itself, *i.e.,* **the empty set has no proper subset.**

1.16 Power Set

The set of all possible subsets of a set A is called the power set of A. It is denoted by $P(A)$.

If A contains n elements, then the number of elements in $P(A)$ is 2^n.

For example : let $A = \{g, o\}$, then the subsets of A are ϕ, $\{g\}$ $\{o\}$, $\{g, o\}$

∴ $P(A) = \{\phi, \{g\}, \{o\}, \{g, o\}\}$

EXERCISE 1 (c)

1. **Tell in each of the following, whether first set is a subset of the second set or not :**

   (a) A = set of letters in the word '*LATE*' B = set of letters in the word '*PLATE*'

   (b) P = set of even prime numbers $Q = \{x \mid x = 2p, p \in N \text{ and } 1 \leq p \leq 3\}$

   (c) L = set of digits in the number 1590 M = set of digits in the number 178902

   (d) E = set of triangles having 4 sides F = set of digits in the number '100'.

2. **Write all the subsets of the following sets :**

   (a) $\{0\}$ (b) $\{1, 2\}$ (c) $\{a, b, c\}$ (d) ϕ.

3. **Write the proper subsets of the following sets.**

   (a) $\{5\}$ (b) $\{p, q\}$ (c) $\{c, a, b\}$ (4) ϕ.

4. **How many subsets do the following sets have?**

   (a) A set having 5 elements   (b) The set of letters of the word '*CENTENARY*'.

5. **How many proper subsets do the following sets have ?**

   (a) The set of factors of 12   (b) The set $\{x \mid x \text{ is a prime number, } x < 20\}$.

6. **Answer true or false :**

   (a) $3 \subseteq \{3, 0\}$ (b) $\{3\} \subseteq \{3, 0\}$ (c) $\phi \in \{3, 0\}$ (d) $0 \in \{3, 0\}$ (e) $\phi \subset \{3, 0\}$ (f) $\phi \subseteq \{\phi\}$.

7. **Find the power set of each of the following sets**

   (a) A = {digits in the number 98}   (b) B = {letters in the word '*KID*'}

8. **Answer true or false :**

   (a) For any two sets A and B either $A \subseteq B$ or $B \subseteq A$ (b) Every set has a proper subset

   (c) Every subset of a finite set is finite   (d) Every subset of an infinite set is infinite.

1.17 Universal Set

Sometimes for a particular discussion, we form sets by selecting some or all of the elements of a fixed set S. This fixed set S is called **universal set** for that discussion. It is obvious that all sets under consideration in a certain discussion are subsets of the universal set for that discussion. The nature of the universal set is determined from the context and it may not always be specifically given, but can be suitably chosen. We shall denote the universal set in this book by the symbol ξ.

For example :

   (i)   In plane geometry, the universal set consists of all the points in a plane.

   (ii) For the set of prime numbers, composite numbers, positive odd numbers and positive even numbers, the universal set can be taken as the set of natural numbers.

   (iii) For the set of players of football eleven of your school, the universal set may be taken as the set of all pupils of your school.

   (vi) Suppose we have to solve the inequation $\{x \mid x < 5, x \in W\}$. The solution will be $\{0, 1, 2, 3, 4\}$. If the universal set were the set of integers, *i.e.* $\{x \mid x < 5, x \in Z\}$ then the solution would be $\{ \ldots -3, -2, -1, 0, 1, 2, 3, 4\}$. It will be an infinite set.

1.18 Complement of a Set

If A is a subset of a universal set ξ, then the set of all those elements of ξ which do not belong to A is called the

complement of A and is denoted by A' or $\overline{A}$ or A^C. Thus, $A' = \{x \mid x \in \xi, x \notin A\}$ [Note that $A' = \xi - A$]

$$n(A') = n(\xi) - n(A).$$

For example:

   (i)   Let ξ be the set of all pupils of a class and A the set of all girls in that class, then A' is the set of all boys in that class.

   (ii) (a) Let $\xi = \{1, 2, 3, 4, 5, 6, 7, 8\}$ and A = $\{1, 3, 5, 7\}$, then $A' = \{2, 4, 6, 8\}$.

   Also, $n(\xi) = 8$, $n(A) = 4$, $n(A') = 4$

   (b) If $n(\xi) = 30$, $n(A) = 16$, $n(B) = 21$, then $n(A') = n(\xi) - n(A) = 30 - 16 = 14$

   $$n(B') = n(\xi) - n(B) = 30 - 21 = 9 .$$

It is obvious that the complement of A' is A, that is, $(A')' = A$. The **complement of the universal set is the empty set,** that is $\xi' = \phi$ and the complement of the empty set is the universal set, *i.e.*, $\phi' = \xi$.

EXERCISE 1 (d)

1. **Suggest a universal set for each of the following :**

   (a) {Jaipur, Chennai, Bangalore, Itanagar}   (b) {Narmada, Cauvery, Mahanadi, Jhelum}

   (c) {Asia, Europe, Antarctica}   (d) {Earth, Mars, Venus}

   (e) {0, 5, 10, 15, 20, 25}

2. Solve the following equations :

   (a) $\{x \mid 2x + 6 = 0, x \in Z\}$ (b) $\{x \mid 5x + 16 = 1, x \in N\}$ (c) $\{x \mid 2x - 3 < 7, x \in W\}$

   (d) $\{x \mid 4x - 25 > 13, x \in Z\}$ (e) $\left\{y \mid \dfrac{5y}{3} - 7 \le 13, y \text{ is a prime number}\right\}$

3. **List the elements of A' if**

   (a) $\xi = \{\text{alphabet}\}$, $A = \{\text{consonants}\}$ (b) $\xi = \{2000, 2002, 2004, 2006\}$

                                                          $A = \{\text{leap years}\}$

   (c) $\xi = $ set of letters in the word '*RUSSIA*'

      $A = $ set of letters in the word '*AIR*'

4. **List the elements of A' and B' if**

   (a) $\xi = \{1, 2, 3, 4\}$, $A = \{1, 4\}$ $B = \{1, 3\}$ (b) $\xi = \{0, 4, 9, 16, 25, 36, 49\}$

                                                            $A = \{4, 25, 36\}$, $B = \{0, 9, 16\}$

   (c) $\xi = \{\text{Days of the week}\}$

      $A = \{\text{Sunday, Wednesday}\}$

      $B = \{\text{Tuesday, Friday}\}$

5. If $n(\xi) = 75$, $n(A) = 38$, $n(B) = 45$, find $n(A')$ and $n(B')$

OPERATIONS ON SETS

1.19 Union of Sets

    The union of two sets A and B is a set C formed by combining the elements of A and B. It contains all elements in either of the sets A or B. Elements that are common to both A and B need to be listed only once in set C. The symbol $A \cup B$ means the union of A and B and is read "A union B".

    $A \cup B = \{x \mid x \in A \text{ or } x \in B \text{ or } x \in \text{ both } A \text{ and } B\}$

For example:

 (i) If $A = \{1, 2, 3,\}$ and $B = \{4, 5, 6\}$, then $A \cup B = \{1, 2, 3, 4, 5, 6\}$

 (ii) If $A = \{a, b, c, d\}$, $B = \{a, b, x, y, z\}$, then $A \cup B = \{a, b, c, d, x, y, z\}$

(iii) If $A = \{\text{factors of } 12\}$, $B = \{\text{factors of } 16\}$ then

      $A = \{1, 2, 3, 4, 6, 12\}$, $B = \{1, 2, 4, 8, 16\}$ and $A \cup B = \{1, 2, 3, 4, 6, 8, 12, 16\}$

(iv) If $A = \{x \mid x = 3p, p \in N\}$, $B = \{y \mid y = 4n, n \in N\}$ then

      $A = \{3, 6, 9, 12, 15, 18, 21, 24, ...\}$, $B = \{4, 8, 12, 16, 20, 24, 28, ...\}$

    So $A \cup B = \{3, 4, 6, 8, 9, 12, 15, 16, 18, 20, 21, 24, 28, ...\}$

            = $\{x \mid x \in N, x \text{ is divisible by 3 or by 4}\}$

 (v) If $A = \{2, 3, 5, 7, 11\}$, $B = \{1, 3, 5, 7, 9\}$, $C = \{0, 1, 2, 3\}$ then,

      $A \cup B = \{1, 2, 3, 5, 7, 9, 11\}$.

      $(A \cup B) \cup C = \{1, 2, 3, 5, 7, 9, 11\} \cup \{0, 1, 2, 3\} = \{0, 1, 2, 3, 5, 7, 9, 11\}$ ...(1)

          $B \cup C = \{1, 3, 5, 7, 9\} \cup \{0, 1, 2, 3\} = \{0, 1, 2, 3, 5, 7, 9\}$

      $A \cup (B \cup C) = \{2, 3, 5, 7, 11\} \cup \{0, 1, 2, 3, 5, 7, 9\} = \{0, 1, 2, 3, 5, 7, 9, 11\}$ ...(2)

    Do you observe from (1) and (2) that $(A \cup B) \cup C = A \cup (B \cup C)$?

1.20 Properties of Union of Sets

> **Let A, B, C be any sets, then**
> 1. $A \cup B = B \cup A$ (Commutative law) 2. $(A \cup B) \cup C = A \cup (B \cup C)$ (Associative law)
> 3. $A \subseteq A \cup B$ and $B \subseteq A \cup B$ 4. If $A \subseteq B$, then $A \cup B = B$
> 5. $A \cup \phi = A$ 6. $A \cup A' = \xi$

1.21 Intersection of Sets

The intersection of two sets A and B is a set that contains elements that are both in A and B. The symbol $A \cap B$ means the intersection of A and B.

$$A \cap B = \{x | x \in A, x \in B)$$

For example :

(i) If $A = \{1, 2, 3, 4, 5, 6\}$ and $B = \{1, 3, 5, 7, 9\}$, then $A \cap B = \{1, 3, 5\}$. Do you observe that $A \cap B \subseteq A$ and $A \cap B \subseteq B$?

(ii) If $A = \{1, 3, 5, 7\}$ and $B = \{2, 4, 6, 8\}$, then these two sets do not have any common members. They are disjoint sets. Their intersection is the null set, that is, $A \cap B = \phi$.

(iii) Let $A = \{2, 4, 6, 8, 9, 10, 12\}$, $B = \{1, 6, 7, 10, 11, 12\}$, $C = \{2, 5, 8, 12, 15\}$ then

$A \cap B = \{2, 4, 6, 8, 9, 10, 12\} \cap \{1, 6, 7, 10, 11, 12\} = \{6, 10, 12\}$.

$B \cap A = \{1, 6, 7, 10, 11, 12\} \cap \{2, 4, 6, 8, 9, 10, 12\} = \{6, 10, 12\}$

$\therefore \quad A \cap B = B \cap A$.

Now, $(A \cap B) \cap C = \{6, 10, 12\} \cap \{2, 5, 8, 12, 15\}, = \{12\}$.

Again, $B \cap C = \{1, 6, 7, 10, 11, 12\} \cap \{2, 5, 8, 12, 15\} = \{12\}$

$A \cap (B \cap C) = \{2, 4, 6, 8, 9, 10, 12\} \cap \{12\} = \{12\}$

$\therefore \quad (A \cap B) \cap C = A \cap (B \cap C)$.

(iv) Let $A = \{x : 2x + 9 = 0, x \in N\}$, $B = \{1, 2, 3, 4\}$

$2x + 9 = 0$ gives $x = -\dfrac{9}{2}$ which is not a natural number.

$\therefore \quad A = \phi$.

$\therefore \quad A \cap B = \phi \cap \{1, 2, 3, 4\} = \phi$.

(v) Let $\xi = \{$letters of *FREEDOM* $\}$

$A = \{$letters of *FEED* $\}$ then

$\xi = \{f, r, e, d, o, m\}$, $A = \{f, e, d\}$, $A' = \{r, o, m\}$

$\therefore \quad A \cap A' = \{f, e, d\} \cap \{r, o, m\} = \phi$.

1.22 Properties of Intersection of Sets

> **Let A, B, C be any sets, then**
> 1. $A \cap B = B \cap A$ (Commutative law) 2. $(A \cap B) \cap C = A \cap (B \cap C)$ (Associative law)
> 3. If $A \subseteq B$ then $A \cap B = A$ 4. For any sets A and B, we have
> $\qquad A \cap B \subseteq A$ and $A \cap B \subseteq B$
> 5. $A \cap \phi = \phi$ 6. If $A \subseteq \xi$, then $A \cap A' = \phi$.

1.23 Difference of Two Sets

Let A and B be two sets, then $A - B$ is the set of elements which belong to A but do not belong to B.

Thus

$$A - B = \{x \mid x \in A \text{ and } x \notin B\}$$

Similarly, $$B - A = \{x \mid x \in B \text{ and } x \notin A\}.$$

For example :

(i) Let $A = \{1, 2, 3, 4, 5\}$, $B = \{3, 4, 5, 6, 7\}$ then $A - B = \{1, 2\}$, $B - A = \{6, 7\}$

Note that $A - B \neq B - A$

(ii) Let $A = \{1, 3, 5, 7, 9, 11, 13, 15\}$, $B = \{3, 5, 7, 9\}$ then $A - B = \{1, 11, 13, 15\}$, $B - A = \phi$

Note that $A - B \neq B - A$

EXERCISE 1 (e)

1. Let $\xi = \{1, 2, 3, 4, ..., 8, 9\}$, $A = \{1, 2, 3, 4\}$, $B = \{2, 4, 6, 8\}$, $C = \{2, 3, 7\}$, $D = \{3, 6, 9\}$, $E = \phi$. Find :

(a) $A \cup B$ (b) $B \cup C$ (c) $C \cup D$ (d) $D \cup \phi$ (e) $A \cup D$

(f) $B \cup D$ (g) A' (h) B' (i) $A' \cup B'$ (j) $(A \cup B)'$

2. Find $A \cup (B \cup C)$ and $(A \cup B) \cup C$ in the above and verify that $A \cup (B \cup C) = (A \cup B) \cup C$.

3. Let $A = \{\text{factors of } 16\}$, $B = \{\text{factors of } 24\}$, find $A \cup B$.

4. Let $L = \{\text{letters of } CRICKET\}$ $M = \{\text{letters of } CATERPILLAR\}$ $N = \{\text{letters of } CARETAKER\}$

Find :

(a) $L \cup M$ (b) $M \cup N$ (c) $L \cup N$

5. **List the elements of $A \cap B$ if**

(a) $A = \{2, 3, 5, 7, 11\}$, $B = \{1, 3, 5, 7, 9, 11\}$

(b) $A = \{\text{Birds}\}$, $B = \{\text{flightless birds}\}$

(c) $A = \{\text{letters of } CHENNAI\}$, $B = \{\text{letters of } CHAIN\}$

(d) $A = \{\text{colours of rainbow}\}$, $B = \{\text{Black, Purple, Violet, Green}\}$

(e) $A = \{\text{Odd numbers}\}$, $B = \{\text{Even numbers}\}$

(f) $A = \{\text{Even numbers}\}$, $B = \{\text{Even prime numbers}\}$

(g) $A = \{x \mid x + 3 = 0, x \in N\}$, $B = \{x \mid x \leq 3, x \in W\}$

(h) $A = \{\text{Factors of } 24\}$, $B = \{\text{Factors of } 36\}$

Verify that $A \cap B = B \cap A$.

6. $A = \{4, 6, 9, 15, 20, 21\}$, $B = \{6, 15, 20, 23\}$

Find $A \cup B$ and $A \cap B$ and verify that $n(A) + n(B) = n(A \cup B) + n(A \cap B)$.

7. $A = \{5, 7, 9, 11, 13, 15\}$, $B = \{7, 8, 11, 15, 20\}$, $C = \{5, 8, 9, 11, 13, 15, 17, 20\}$

Verify that : $A \cap (B \cap C) = (A \cap B) \cap C$.

8. **Find $A - B$ and $B - A$ in the following :**

(a) $A = \{a, b, c, d, e, f\}$ (b) $A = \{\text{letters of } 'FIGHT'\}$ (c) $A = \{\text{Factors of } 8\}$

     $B = \{a, e, f, g, h\}$ $B = \{\text{letters of } FRIGATE\}$ $B = \{\text{Factors of } 12\}$

(d) $A = \{7, 8, 9, 10, 11, 12, 13\}$ (e) $A = \{\text{letters of } COMPLEMENT\}$

     $B = \{8, 10, 12\}$ $B = \{\text{letters of } COMPLAIN\}$

VENN DIAGRAMS SHOWING RELATIONSHIP BETWEEN GIVEN SETS

1.24 Venn Diagrams

The English logician Venn used diagrams to show relationships between sets. These diagrams are called **Venn diagrams.** A set is represented by a region enclosed by a circle or a rectangle. The elements of the set are written inside this region. We shall represent the universal set by a rectangle and its subsets by circular regions inside this rectangle.

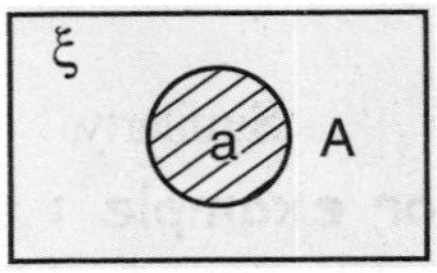

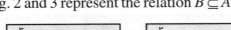

Fig. 1 shows (1) The universal set x (Rectangle)

(2) The set A (Circle)

(3) The elements $a \in A$

Fig. 1

1.25 Venn Diagrams Showing Relationships Between Given Sets

Type 1. Showing subsets

Fig. 2 and 3 represent the relation $B \subseteq A$.

Type 2. Showing complement of a set

Fig. 4 shows A', the complement of A.

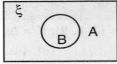

Fig. 2   **Fig. 3**

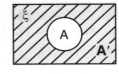

Fig. 4

Type 3. Showing union of sets

The shaded portions in the following diagrams illustrate the union of two sets A and B.

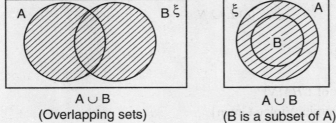

A ∪ B
(Overlapping sets)

A ∪ B
(B is a subset of A)

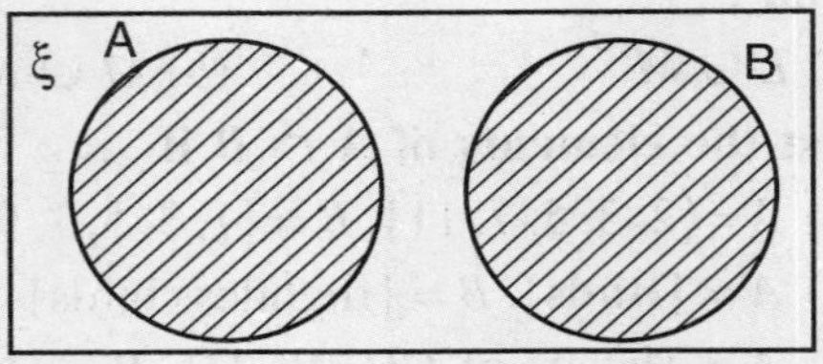

A ∪ B
(Disjoint sets)

Fig. 5   **Fig. 6**   **Fig. 7**

Type 4. Showing intersection of sets

The intersection of two sets A and B can be shown by the following Venn diagrams.

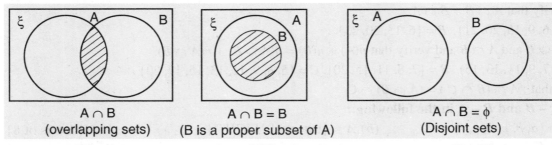

A ∩ B
(overlapping sets)

A ∩ B = B
(B is a proper subset of A)

A ∩ B = φ
(Disjoint sets)

Fig. 8   **Fig. 9**   **Fig. 10**

The shaded portions in the above diagrams represent the intersection of A and B.

Type 5. Showing difference of sets

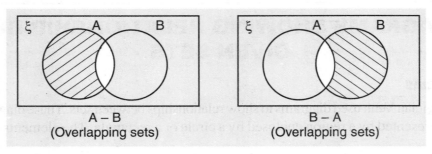

A – B
(Overlapping sets)

B – A
(Overlapping sets)

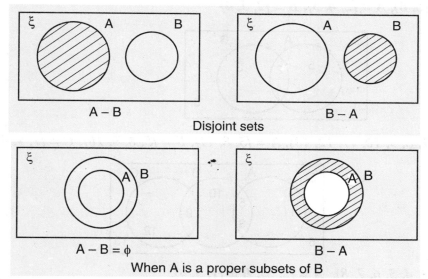

Type 6. Showing $(A \cup B)'$ and $(A \cap B)'$

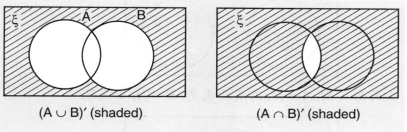

Type 7. Showing $A \cup B \cup C$ and $A \cap B \cap C$

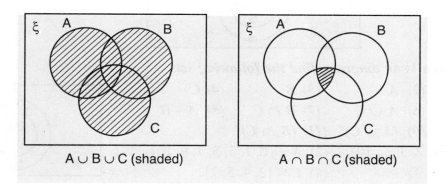

1.26 Examples

Ex. 1. *Illustrate the given information on a Venn diagram.*

    $\xi = \{4, 5, 6, 7, 8, 9\}, A = \{5, 7, 8\}.$

Sol.

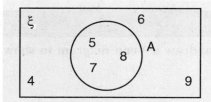 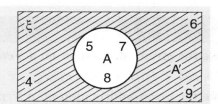

    Remark : A' will be represented by the shaded region as shown.

Ex. 2. $\xi = \{1, 2, 3, 4, 5, 6)$, $A = \{2, 4, 5\}$, $B = \{2, 3, 4\}$

Sol.

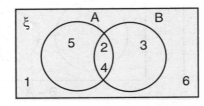

Ex. 3. *Let* $\xi = \{5, 6, 7, 8, 9, 10, 11, 12, 13)$, $A = \{5, 8, 11\}$, $B = \{5, 8, 9, 10\}$, $C = \{7, 9, 12\}$.

Sol.

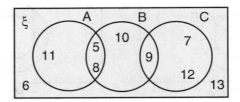

Ex. 4. *Let* $\xi = \{1, 2, 3, 4, 5, 6, 7, 8)$, $A = \{2, 5\}$, $B = \{1, 3, 4\}$.

Sol.

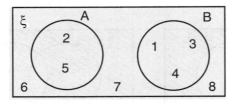

Ex. 5. *Let* $\xi = \{1, 2, 3, 4, 5, 6, 7, 8\}$, $A = \{1, 3, 4, 5, 6, 7\}$, $B = \{1, 4, 5, 7\}$.

Sol.

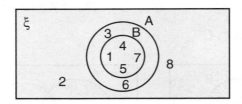

Ex. 6. *From the given Venn diagram, find the following sets.*

    (1) ξ (2) A (3) B (4) C

    (5) A' (6) $A \cup C$ (7) $B \cap C$ (8) $A - B$

    (9) $C - B$ (10) $(A \cup C)'$ (11) $(B \cap C)'$.

Sol. (1) $\xi = \{0, 1, 2, 3, ..., 10\}$,   (2) $A = \{0, 1, 3, 5, 7, 9, 10\}$,

      (3) $B = \{3, 5, 9\}$,   (4) $C = \{2, 4, 5, 7\}$,

      (5) $A' = \{2, 4, 6, 8\}$,   (6) $A \cup C = \{0, 1, 2, 3, 4, 5, 7, 9, 10\}$,   (7) $B \cap C = \{5\}$,

      (8) $A - B = \{0, 1, 7, 10\}$,   (9) $C - B = \{2, 4, 7\}$,

      (10) $(A \cup C)' = $ Those elements of ξ which are not in $A \cup C = \{6, 8\}$

      (11) $(B \cap C)' = $ Those elements of ξ which are not in $B \cap C = \{0, 1, 2, 3, 4, 6, 7, 8, 9, 10\}$

EXERCISE 1 (f)

1. Illustrate the given information on a Venn diagram. Also, draw a Venn diagram to show A'.

   $\xi = \{a, b, c, d, e, f\}$, $A = \{a, c, e\}$

2. Illustrate the given information on a Venn diagram

   (*a*) $\xi = \{1, 2, 3, 4, 5, 6, 7, 8\}$, $A = \{2, 3, 4, 7\}$, $B = \{3, 5, 7, 8\}$

   (*b*) $\xi = \{1, 2, 3, 4, 5, 6, 7, 8, 9, 10\}$, $A = \{1, 3, 4\}$, $B = \{1, 4, 5, 7\}$, $C = \{5, 7, 9\}$

(c) ξ = {letters of *TAMILNADU*}, P = {letters of *TAMIL*}, Q = {letters of *MAT*}

(d) ξ = {1, 2, 3, 4, 5, 6, 7, 8}, A = {2, 7}, B = {3, 4, 8}

(e) ξ = {2, 4, 6, 8, 10, 12, 14, 16, 18}, G = {2, 4, 8, 12, 14, 16}, H = {4, 12, 14}

3. In each of the following diagrams describe the shaded area.

(i) 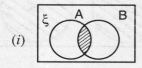 (ii) 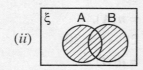 (iii)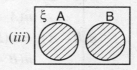

(iv) 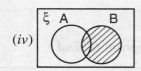 (v) 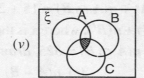 (vi)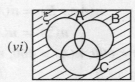

4. Use a diagram similar to the following, to show the following sets.

(a) A' (b) B' (c) $(A \cup B)'$

(d) $(A \cap B)'$ (e) $A' \cap B$ (f) $A \cap B'$

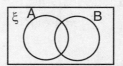

5. From the given Venn diagrams list the following sets.

(i) $A \cap B$ (ii) $A \cup B$ (iii) A' (iv) B' (v) $A - B$ (vi) $(A \cap B)'$ (vii) $(A \cup B)'$

(a) 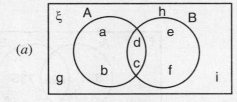   (b)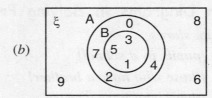

6. From the given Venn diagram, list the following sets :

(a) ξ   (b) A   (c) B   (d) C   (e) $A \cap B \cap C$

(f) $A \cup B \cup C$ (g) $(A \cap B \cap C)'$ (h) $A \cap B'$ (i) $B - C$ (j) $(B \cup C)'$

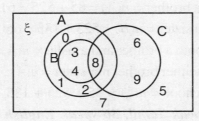

1.27 Cardinal Properties of Sets

The diagram shows two intersecting sets A and B and the number of elements in them. From the diagram, we find that

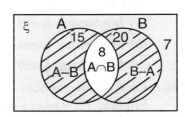

$$n(A \cap B) = 8, \ n(A) = 15 + 8 = 23$$
$$n(B) = 8 + 20 = 28$$

Note that $n(A \cup B) = 15 + 8 + 20 = 43$

Also, counting the elements of $A \cup B$, the elements of $A \cap B$ are counted twice, so

$$n(A \cup B) = n(A) + n(B) - n(A \cap B) = 23 + 28 - 8 = 43$$
$$\boldsymbol{n(A \cup B) + n(A \cap B) = n(A) + n(B)}$$

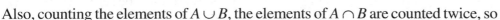

If A and B are non intersecting sets and

$$n(A) = 10, n(B) = 25, \text{ then since } A \cap B = \phi, n(A \cap B) = n(\phi) = 0$$

$\therefore \qquad n(A \cup B) = n(A) + n(B) = 20 + 25 = 45$

Also, it is clear from the first Venn diagram that

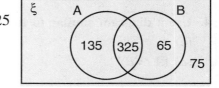

(1) $\qquad n(A - B) = n(A) - n(A \cap B) = 23 - 8 = 15$

$\qquad$ i.e. $n(A - B) + n(A \cap B) = n(A)$.

(2) $\qquad n(B - A) = n(B) - n(A \cap B) = 28 - 8 = 20$

$\qquad$ i.e. $n(B - A) + n(A \cap B) = n(B)$

(3) $\qquad n(A \cup B) = n(A - B) + n(B - A) + n(A \cap B) = 15 + 20 + 8 = 43$

(4) $\qquad n(\xi) = n(A) + n(A') = n(B) + n(B')$, where x is the universal set.

Ex. 1. *If $n(\xi) = 600, n(A) = 460, n(B) = 390,$ and $n(A \cap B) = 325,$ draw a Venn diagram to find :*

$\quad$ *(a) $n(A \cup B)$* $\qquad\qquad$ *(b) $n(A \cup B)'$* $\qquad\qquad$ *(c) $n(A - B)$*

Sol. Given : $\qquad n(\xi) = 600, n(A) = 460, n(B) = 390, n(A \cap B) = 325$

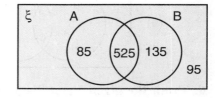

$\qquad\qquad n(A \cup B) = n(A) + n(B) - n(A \cap B)$

$\qquad\qquad\qquad\qquad = 460 + 390 - 325 = 525$

The given sets are intersecting sets. The Venn diagram is as shown.

$\qquad\qquad n(A \cup B)' = n(\xi) - n(A \cup B) = 600 - 525 = 75$

$\qquad\qquad n(A - B) = n(A) - n(A \cap B) = 460 - 325 = 135.$

1.28 Use of Venn Diagrams in Solving Problems

Ex. 2. *The Venn diagram shows*

$\qquad \xi$ = *{pupils in a school}*

$\qquad A$ = *{those who have a brother}*

$\qquad B$ = *{those who have a sister}*

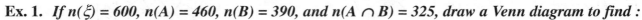

Write down the number who :

(a) have a brother $\qquad$ *(b) have a sister* $\qquad$ *(c) have both a brother and a sister*

(d) have neither brother nor sister $\quad$ *(e) are in the school altogether.*

Sol. (a) Number of pupils who have a brother = $n(A) = 85 + 525 = 610$

$\quad$ (b) Number of pupils who have a sister = $n(B) = 525 + 135 = 660$

$\quad$ (c) Number of pupils who have both a brother and a sister = $n(A \cap B) = 525$

$\quad$ (d) Number of pupils who have neither brother nor sister = $n(A \cup B)' = 95$

$\quad$ (e) Total number of pupils in the school = $n(\xi) = 85 + 525 + 135 + 95 = $ **840.**

Ex. 3. *In a group of 70 people, 48 speak Tamil, 36 speak English and all the people speak at least one language. Find :*

$\quad$ *(a) how many speak both the languages;*

$\quad$ *(b) how many speak only Tamil;*

$\quad$ *(c) how many speak only English.*

Sol. Let A denote the set of people who speak Tamil and B the set of people who speak English. Then $n(A) = 48, n(B) = 36$

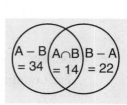

'$A - B$' represents the set of people who speak only Tamil. '$B - A$' represents the set of people who speak only English and $A \cap B$ the set of people who speak both languages. We have

$n(A \cup B) + n(A \cap B) = n(A) + n(B)$

∴ $n(A \cap B) = n(A) + n(B) - n(A \cup B) = 48 + 36 - 70 = 84 - 70 = \mathbf{14}$

∴ Number of people who speak both languages = 14

Number of people who speak only Tamil = $n(A - B) = n(A) - n(A \cap B) = 48 - 14 = \mathbf{34}$

Number of people who speak only English = $n(B - A) = n(B) - n(A \cap B) = 36 - 14 = \mathbf{22}$.

Ex. 4. *Out of 100 candidates who appeared in an entrance test in English and Mathematics, 80 passed in at least one subject. If 60 passed in English and 65 in Mathematics, find :*

(a) *how many passed in both the subjects;*

(b) *how many passed in English only;*

(c) *how many failed in Mathematics.*

Sol. Let ξ be the set of all the candidates who took the test, *A* the set of candidates who passed in English and *B* of those who passed in Mathematics. Then

Given : $n(\xi) = 100, n(A \cup B) = 80, n(A) = 60, n(B) = 65$

(a) $n(A \cap B) = n(A) + n(B) - n(A \cup B) = 60 + 65 - 80 = 45$

∴   Number of candidates who passed in both the subjects = **45**.

(b) Number of candidates who passed only in English = $n(A - B) = n(A) - n(A \cap B) = 60 - 45 = \mathbf{15}$.

(c) Number of candidates who failed in Mathematics = $n(B') = n(\xi) - n(B) = 100 - 65 = \mathbf{35}$.

The Venn diagram is as shown :

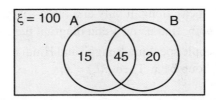

EXERCISE 1 (g)

1. If $n(\xi) = 80$, $n(A) = 48$, $n(B) = 40$ and $n(A \cap B) = 25$, draw a Venn diagram to find :

   (a) $n(A \cup B)$ (b) $n(A \cup B)'$ (c) $n(A - B)$ (d) $n(B - A)$ (e) $n(A \cap B')$ (f) $n(A' \cap B)$

2. If $\xi = \{x \mid x \in N, x < 10\}$,

   $A = \{x \mid x$ is a prime number, $x < 10\}$ $B = \{x \mid x$ is an even number, $x < 10\}$

   draw a Venn diagram to find :

   (a) $n(A \cup B)$ (b) $n(A \cap B)$ (c) $n(A \cup B)'$ (d) $n(A \cap B')$ (e) $n(A' \cap B)$.

3. Given $n(\xi) = 40$, $n(A') = 12$, $n(B) = 15$ and $B \subset A$

   Draw a Venn diagram to illustrate this information. Hence find $n(A - B)$.

4. The Venn diagram shows :

   ξ = {pupils in class 8}

   A = {pupils who play cricket}

   B = {pupils who play basketball}

   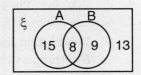

   How many pupils :

   (a) are in class 8 ?   (b) play cricket   (c) play basketball ?

   (d) play both cricket and basketball ?   (e) play neither cricket nor basketball ?

5. In the Venn diagram

   ξ = {people at a function}

   A = {those who asked for tea}

   B = {those who watched the ballet}

   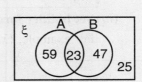

Write down the number who :

(a) asked for tea
(b) asked for tea and watched the ballet
(c) neither aksed for tea nor watched the ballet
(d) attened the function.

6. In a group of 30 people, 18 play squash and 19 play tennis. How many play both games, provided everyone plays at least one game ?

7. **In a class of 50 students 22 like History, 25 like Geography and 10 like both subjects. Draw a Venn diagram and find the number of students who**

   (a) do not like History
   (b) do not like Geography
   (c) like neither History nor Geography.

8. 2000 candidates appear in a written test in Mathematics and General awareness for a Government job. 1800 passed in at least one subject. If 1200 passed in Mathematics and 1500 in General Awareness, find:

   (a) how many passed in both the subjects,
   (b) how many passed in Mathematics only,
   (c) how many failed in General Awareness?

9. In a group of 80 people, 40 like Indian food, 36 like Chinese food and 27 do not like any kind of these foods. Draw Venn diagram to find :

   (a) how many like both kind of food;
   (b) how many like only the Indian food;
   (c) how many like only the Chinese food.

   [**Hint :** Let A and B be the sets of those people who like Indian and Chinese food respectively. Then, we have $n(A) = 40$, $n(B) = 36$, $n(A \cup B) = 80 - 27 = 53$]

10. In a group of people, two-seventh speak Bengali only and three-seventh speak Hindi only. If 20 people speak none of these languages and 80 speak both, find using Venn diagram the total number of people in the group.

    [**Hint :** Let A and B be the sets of people speaking Bengali and Hindi respectively.
    Let the number of people in the group be x. Then $n(\xi) = x$]

    $$\left[\therefore \ \frac{2x}{7} + \frac{3x}{7} + 80 + 20 = x \right]$$

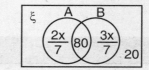

LOOKING BACK
Summary of Key Facts

1. A **set** is a well defined collection of objects.

2. Each thing in a set is called a **member** or an **element** of the set.

3. The symbol '$\in$' is used to denote **'is a member of'** or **'belongs to'**. Thus, if x is a member of set A, we write $x \in A$.

4. If x does not belong to set A, we write $x \notin A$.

5. Sets are specified by any of the following methods :

   (i) **Description method** : By writing the description in braces, *viz.* A = {months of year}, B = {primary colours}

   (ii) **Roster method :** By listing the names of the elements in braces,

   For example, the set of letters in the word 'NAINITAL' is written as A = {N, A, I, T, L}

Repetition is not done while listing the elements.

   (iii) **Set builder form.** A set is specified in the form {x | statement of property which x satisfies }

   For example, {x | x is a multiple of 4, $x \le 20$}

6. A set containing only one element is called a **singleton set**.

7. Two sets are called **overlapping sets**, if they have at least one element in common. Thus, A and B are overlapping sets if $A = \{0, 2, 3, 5, 7, 9\}$, $B = \{0, 3, 6, 9, 12, 15\}$

8. If two sets have no elements in common, they are called **disjoint sets**. For example, if $A = \{$letters of 'CAT'$\}$, $B = \{$letters of 'SUN'$\}$, then A and B are disjoint sets.

9. A set which contains a definite number of objects i.e, in which the counting comes to an end is called a **finite set**, e.g. $A = \{$people on Earth$\}$ is a finite set.

   If the process of counting the elements of a set cannot come to an end, it is an **infinite set.** The set of integers is an infinite set.

10. A set that has no members is called the **empty set** or the **null set**. It is denoted by the symbol $\{\ \}$ or ϕ.

11. The number of members in a set is called the **cardinal number** of the set. The cardinal number of a set A is denoted by $n(A)$.

    For example, if $A = \{p, q, r\}$, then $n(A) = 3$.

    > The cardinal number of an infinite set is not defined.
    > The cardinal number of the empty set is zero, i.e., $n(\phi) = 0$.

12. Sets containing equal number of elements are called **equivalent sets**. Sets containing the same elements are called **equal sets**.

    For example, if $A = \{$letters of 'TALE'$\}$, $B = \{$letters of 'MAIL'$\}$, $C = \{$letters of 'LATE'$\}$, then A and C are equal sets, while A and B, B and C are equivalent sets.

    > All equal sets are equivalent sets while all equivalent sets are not equal sets.

13. If every member of a set A is also a member of a second set B, then the set A is called a **subset** of set B. This is expressed by writing $A \subseteq B$. If a set E is a part of a set F, then the set E is called a **proper subset** of set F. This is expressed by writing $A \subset B$.

    For example, if $A = \{1, 2, 3, 4, 5, 6, 7\}$, $B = \{2, 3, 5, 7\}$, $C = \{3, 5\}$, $D = \{x \mid x \in N, x \le 7\}$, then $B \subset A$, $C \subset A$, $C \subset B$, $A \subseteq D$ and $D \subseteq A$. A and D are equal sets.

    The symbol $\nsubseteq$ is used to denote **'is not a subset of'** and $\not\subset$ to denote **'not a proper subset of'**.

    > 1. Every set is a subset of itself, i.e. $A \subseteq A$
    > 2. The null set is a subset of every set, i.e. $\phi \subset A$, where A is any set.
    > 3. The empty set is a proper subset of every set except itself, i.e. **the empty set has no proper subsets.**

14. The set of all possible subsets of a set A is called the **power set** of A. It is denoted by $P(A)$.

    For example, if $A = \{m, a, t\}$, then $P\{A\} = \{\phi, \{m\}, \{a\}, \{t\}, \{m, a\}\ \{a, t\}, \{m, t\}, \{m, a, t\}\}$.

15. The total number of subsets of a set containing n elements is 2^n. The total number of proper subsets is $2^n - 1$.

    For example, if $A = \{x \mid x \in Z, -3 \le x < 4\}$, then $A = \{-3, -2, -1, 0, 1, 2, 3\}$ and A has 2^7, i.e., 128 subsets. The number of proper subsets is $2^7 - 1$, i.e. $128 - 1$, i.e. 127.

16. A **universal set** is the set of elements from which elements may be chosen for a particular discussion. It is denoted by the symbol 'ξ'

17. If A is a subset of a universal set x, then the set of all those elements of x which do not belong to A is called the **complement** of A and is denoted by A' or $\overline{A}$ or A^c.

    For example, if $\xi = \{$digits of the whole number system$\}$
    A = set of digits in the number '203786' then
    $A' = \{1, 4, 5, 9\}$ Also, $n(\xi) = 10$, $n(A) = 6$, $n(A') = 4 = n(\xi) - n(A)$

    > $(A')' = A$
    > $\xi' = \phi$
    > $\phi' = \xi$

18. The **union of two sets** A and B denoted by $A \cup B$, is a set C formed by combining the elements of A and B. If A and B are overlapping sets, then the elements that are common to both A and B are listed only once in set C.
    $A \cup B = \{x \mid x \in A \text{ or } x \in B \text{ or } x \in \text{ both } A \text{ and } B\}$.

For example, if $A = \{2, 4, 6, 8, 10\}$, $B = \{5, 7, 9\}$, $C = \{0, 1, 2, 3, 4\}$ then
$A \cup B = \{2, 4, 5, 6, 7, 8, 9, 10\}$, $A \cup C = \{0, 1, 2, 3, 4, 6, 8, 10\}$,
$B \cup C = \{0, 1, 2, 3, 4, 5, 7, 9\}$

$A \cup \phi = A$
$A \cup \xi = \xi$
$A \cup A = A$
$A \cap A' = \xi$
If $A \subseteq B$, then $A \cup B = B$
$A \subseteq A \cup B, B \subseteq A \cup B$

19. The **intersection of two sets** A and B, denoted by $A \cap B$, is the set of elements common to A and B

$$A \cap B = \{x \mid x \in A, x \in B\}$$

For example, (i) if $A = \{x \mid x \in N, x \le 10\}$,
$B = \{x \mid x \text{ is an even number}, x \le 10\}$ then
$A \cap B = \{2, 4, 6, 8, 10\}$

(ii) If $A = \{\text{letters of 'MOUSE'}\}$,
$B = \{\text{letters of 'CALL'}\}$, then $A \cap B = \phi$.

$A \cap \xi = A$, $A \cap A = A$
$A \cap \phi = \phi$, $A \cap A' = \phi$
$A \cap B \subseteq A$, $A \cap B \subseteq B$

20. Difference of two sets. Let A and B be two sets, then '$A - B$' is the set of elements which belong to A but do not belong to B.

Thus, $A - B = \{x \mid x \in A \text{ and } x \notin B\}$.
Similarly, $B - A = \{x \mid x \in B \text{ and } x \notin A\}$

For example, (i) If $A = \{m, o, u, s, e\}$, $B = \{h, o, p, e\}$, then
$A - B = \{m, u, s\}$, $B - A = \{h, p\}$
(ii) $A = \{a, b, c, d, e, f\}$, $B = \{b, c, e,\}$, then
$A - B = \{a, d, f\}$, $B - A = \phi$

21. Venn diagrams are diagrams to express various ideas about sets and relationships between them. Usually a universal set is represented by a rectangle and its subsets by closed figures such as circles or ovals.

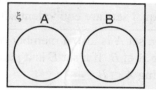 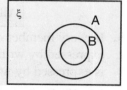

MENTAL MATHS – 1

Answer true or false (in Q. 1 to 14) :

1. {A pack of playing cards} is a set.
2. {Interesting novels in the library} is a set.
3. $\{1, 3, 5\} = \{5, 1, 3\}$.
4. $\{x \mid x \in N, x + 7 = 8\}$ is a singleton set.
5. If $A = \{x \mid x \text{ is a letter of the word 'TERROR'}\}$ then $n(A) = 6$.
6. $\{x \mid x \in N, 4 < x < 5\}$ is a finite set.
7. $\{x \mid x \in Z, 2x - 1 = 0\} = \phi$.
8. $\left\{\dfrac{1}{3}, \dfrac{1}{5}, \dfrac{1}{8}, \dfrac{1}{9}, \dfrac{1}{11}\right\}$ and $\left\{x \mid x \in N \text{ and } 4\dfrac{5}{8} < x < 10\right\}$ are equivalent sets.
9. If $P = \{\text{letter in the word 'READ'}\}$, $Q = \{\text{letter in the word 'DEAR'}\}$, then $P = Q$.
10. If $n(A) = n(B)$, then $A = B$.
11. If $A = \{3, 0, 1\}$, then
  (i) $0 \in A$ (ii) $3 \subseteq A$
  (iii) $\phi \subset A$ (iv) $\{0\} \subset A$

  (v) $\phi \in A$ (vi) $\{3, 1\} \subset A$
  (vii) A has 8 subsets and 7 proper subsets
  (viii) $A = B$, if $B = $ set of digits in the number '103'.
  (ix) $n(A) = 3$
  (x) A and B are equivalent sets if $B = $ set of letters in the work 'BOOK'.
12. $A = \{\text{vowels in the word 'PALMOLIVE}\}$
  $B = \{\text{vowels in the word TEMPTATION}\}$,
  then $A = B$.
13. $A = \{\text{first 5 natural numbers}\}$
  $B = \{\text{first 5 prime numbers}\}$ then A and B are overlapping sets.
14. Let $E = \{\text{letters of SON}\}$
  $F = \{\text{letters of MAMMAL}\}$, then
  (i) E and F are disjoint sets (ii) $n(E) = n(F)$
15. Let $P = \{\text{letters of QUEEN}\}$, find
  (i) P (ii) $n(P)$
  (iii) number of subsets of P
  (iv) number of proper subsets of P.

16. If $A = \{1, 3, 5, 7\}$, $B = \{2, 4, 6, 8\}$ $C = \{3, 5, 6\}$,
  find
  (i) $A \cap B$ (ii) $A \cup B$
  (iii) $A \cap C$ (iv) $A \cup C$
  (v) $B \cap C$ (vi) $A \cup B \cup C$
  (vii) $A \cap B \cap C$.

17. Fill in the blanks :
  (i) $A \cup A = $ ....   (ii) $A \cap A = $ ....
  (iii) $A \cup \phi = $ ....   (iv) $A \cap \phi = $ ....

18. If $n(\xi) = 18$ and $n(A') = 10$, find $n(A)$.

19. If $n(A) = 20$, $n(B) = 14$ and $n(A \cap B) = 7$, find $n(A \cup B)$.

20. Answer true or false.
  (i) $\xi \cap \phi' = \xi$
  (ii) If $A \subset B$ and $C \subset B$, then $A \subset C$.

UNIT REVIEW–1

1. Write each of the following sets in Roster form :
  (a) $A = $ set of all factors of 30
  (b) $B = $ set of letters in the word *AEROPLANE*
  (c) $C = \{x \mid x$ is an integer, $-4 \le x \le 4\}$
  (d) $D = \{x \mid x$ is a prime number, $x < 20\}$

2. Write each of the following sets in set builder form :
  (a) $A = \{0, 1, 2, 3, 4, 5, 6, 7\}$
  (b) $B = \{..., -4, -3, -2, -1, 0, 1, 2\}$
  (c) $C = \{0, 1, 8, 27, 64, 125, 216\}$

3. Which of the following are the empty set ?
  (a) $A = \{x \mid x + 7 = 7, x \in N\}$
  (b) $B = \{x \mid 2x + 9 = 1, x \in Z\}$
  (c) $C = \{x \mid x + 1 = x, x \in N\}$
  (d) $D = \{x \mid x$ is an even prime$\}$

4. State which of the following sets are finite and which are infinite :
  (a) Set of planets in the solar system
  (b) set of points on a line segment
  (c) $\{x \mid x \in N, x > 8000\}$
  (d) $\{x \mid x \in W, x < $ one million$\}$

5. (a) Find all possible subsets of the set $A = \{5, 7, 9\}$.   (b) Write the power set of A.

6. Let $A = \{$letters of *KALKA*$\}$ and $B = \{$letters of *KOLKATA*$\}$. State whether each of the following statements is true or false for the above sets :
  (i) $A \subseteq B$ (ii) $B \subseteq A$ (iii) $A \cap B = A$ (iv) $A \cup B = B$ (v) $B - A = \{O, T\}$

7. Let $A = \{x : x = 3p, p < 7\}$, find A when
  (a) $\xi = N$ (b) $\xi = W$ (c) $\xi = Z$

8. If $\xi = \{$digits of our number system$\}$
  $A = \{$Prime numbers between 1 and 10$\}$, $B = \{$multiples of 3 between 0 and 10$\}$, find :
  (a) $A \cup B$ (b) $A \cap B$ (c) A' (d) B'
  (e) $(A \cup B)'$ (f) $A' \cap B'$ (g) $A - B$ (h) $B - A$

9. Let $\xi = \{x \mid x \in N, 5 \le x < 21\}$ and A, B, C be subsets of ξ given by
  $A = \{x \mid x$ is a multiple 2$\}$, $B = \{x \mid x$ is a multiple 3$\}$ and $C = \{x \mid x \in W, x < 13\}$, then verify the following :
  (a) $(A \cup B)' = (A' \cap B')$ (b) $(A \cap B)' = (A' \cup B')$ (c) $A - B \ne B - A$
  (d) $A - B = A \cap B'$ (e) $n(A \cup B) = n(A) + n(B) - n(A \cap B)$ (f) $n(A) + n(A') = n(\xi)$
  (g) $n(B) + n(B') = n(\xi)$

10. If $n(\xi) = 45$, $n(A) = 22$, $n(B') = 18$ and $n(A \cup B) = 38$, find $n(B)$ and $n(A \cap B)$.

11. Use capital letters and the concept of is a subset of' to describe what each Venn diagram below illustrates.

(a)    (b)    (c)

12. From the adjoining Venn diagram, find the following sets

    (a) ξ

    (b) $A \cap B$

    (c) $A \cap B \cap C$

    (d) C'

    (e) $A - C$

    (f) $B - C$

    (g) $C - B$

    (h) $(A \cup B)'$

    (i) $(A \cup B \cup C)'$

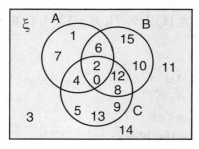

ANSWERS

EXERCISE 1 (a)

1. (a), (c), (e) and (g) are sets 2. (a) $3 \in N$ (b) $-5 \notin N$ 3. (a) $\notin$ (b) $\in$ (c) $\notin$ (d) $\in$
   (e) $\notin$ (f) $\notin$ 4. (a) True (b) False (c) True (d) False
5. (a) {2, 3, 5, 7} (b) {s, a, t, e, l, i} (c) φ 6. (a) Set of natural numbers greater than 14.
   (b) The set of positive integers that are multiples of 5. (c) Set of even whole numbers
   (d) Set of negative integers between 0 and –6.
7. (a) $A = \{x : x = 4n, n \in N\}$ (b) $B = \{x \mid x = n^2, n \in N, n > 1\}$ (c) $C = \{x \mid x \le 0, x \in Z\}$
   (d) $D = \left\{x \mid x = \dfrac{n}{n+1}, n \in N\right\}$ (e) $\{x \mid x = x + 1, x \in N\}$. Answers may vary.
8. (a) {1, 2, 3, 4, 5} (b) {5, 3, 4, 7, 2} (c) {2, 5, 8, 11, ...} (d) {16, 25, 36, 49, 64, 81, 100}
   (e) $\left\{\dfrac{1}{3}, \dfrac{2}{5}, \dfrac{3}{7}, \dfrac{4}{9}, \dfrac{5}{11}, \dfrac{6}{13}, \dfrac{7}{15}\right\}$

EXERCISE 1 (b)

1. (a) Finite (b) Finite (c) Finite (d) Infinite (e) φ, finite (f) Infinite (g) Finite (h) Infinite
   (i) Infinite (j) Finite 2. (a) and (c) are singleton sets. 3. a, c and d are empty sets.
4. (a) 8 (b) 21 (c) 3 (d) 0 (e) 2 (f) 10
5. (a) and (c) are equivalent. 6. (a) and (b) are equal 7. (a) Overlapping (b) Disjoint
   (c) Overlapping (d) Disjoint

EXERCISE 1 (c)

1. (a) Yes (b) Yes (c) No (d) Yes (The emply set is a subset of every set)
2. (a) φ, {0} (b) φ, {1}, {2}, {1, 2} (c) φ, {a}, {b}, {c}, {a, b}, {b, c}, {c, a}, {a, b, c} (d) φ
3. (a) φ (b) φ, {p}, {q} (c) φ, {c}, {a}, {b}, {c, a}, {a, b}, {c, b} (d) None
4. (a) 32 (b) 128
5. (a) 63 (b) 255 6. (a) False (b) True (c) False (d) True (e) True (f) True
7. (a) $P(A) = \{\phi, \{9\}, \{8\}, \{9, 8\}\}$ (b) $P(B) = \{\phi, \{K\}, \{I\}, \{D\}, \{K, I\}, \{I, D\}, \{K, D\}, \{K, I, D\}\}$
8. (a) F (b) F (c) T (d) F

EXERCISE 1 (d)

1. (a) {State capitals of India} (b) {Rivers of India} (c) {continents} (d) {Planets of our solar system}
   (e) $\{x \mid x = 5p, p \in W, 0 \le p \le 5\}$ or {Multiples of 5 between 0 and 25 including 0 and 25}
2. (a) {–3} (b) φ (c) {0, 1, 2, 3, 4} (d) {10, 11, 12, ...} (e) {2, 3, 5, 7, 11}
3. (a) {vowels} (b) {2002, 2006} (c) {U,S}
4. (a) $A' = \{2, 3\}$, $B' = \{2, 4\}$ (b) $A' = \{0, 9, 16, 49\}$, $B' = \{4, 25, 36, 49\}$
   (c) A' = {Monday, Tuesday, Thursday, Friday, Saturday}, B' = {Sunday, Monday, Wednesday, Thursday, Saturday}
5. $n(A') = 37$, $n(B') = 30$.

EXERCISE 1 (e)

1. (a) {1, 2, 3, 4, 6, 8} (b) {2, 3, 4, 6, 7, 8} (c) {2, 3, 6, 7, 9} (d) {3, 6, 9} (e) {1, 2, 3, 4, 6, 9}
   (f) {2, 3, 4, 6, 8, 9} (g) {5, 6, 7, 8, 9} (h) {1, 3, 5, 7, 9} (i) {1, 3, 5, 6, 7, 8, 9}
   (j) {5, 7, 9}
2. $A \cup (B \cup C) = \{1, 2, 3, 4, 6, 7, 8\}$, $(A \cup B) \cup C = \{1, 2, 3, 4, 6, 7, 8\}$ 3. {1, 2, 3, 4, 6, 8, 12, 16, 24}
4. (i) {c, r, i, k, e, t, a, p, l} (ii) {c, a, t, e, r, i, p, l, k} (iii) {c, r, i, k, e, t, a}

5. (a) {3, 5, 7, 11}　(b) {flightless birds}　(c) {c, h, n, a, i}　(d) {violet, green}　(e) φ　(f) {2}

(g) φ　(h) {1, 2, 3, 4, 6, 12}　6. $A \cup B = \{4, 6, 9, 15, 20, 21, 23\}$, $A \cap B = \{6, 15, 20\}$

8. (a) $A - B = \{b, c, d\}$, $B - A = \{g, h\}$　(b) $A - B = \{h\}$, $B - A = \{r, a, e\}$　(c) $A - B = \{8\}$, $B - A = \{3, 6, 12\}$

(d) $A - B = \{7, 9, 11, 13\}$, $B - A = φ$　(e) $A - B = \{e, t\}$, $B - A = \{a, i\}$

EXERCISE –1 (f)

1. 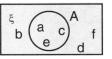　　2. (a) 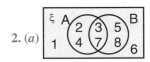　　(b) 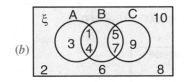　　(c)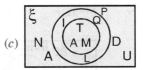

(d) 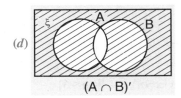　　(e)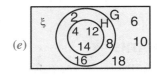

3. (i) $A \cap B$　　(ii) $A \cup B$　　(iii) $A \cup B$　　(iv) B　　(v) $A \cap B \cap C$　　(vi) $(A \cup B \cup C)'$

4. (a) 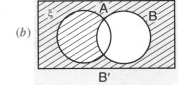　　(b) 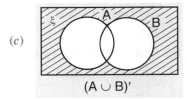　　(c)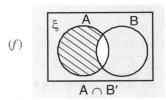

A′　　　　　　　　　　B′　　　　　　　　　(A ∪ B)′

(d) 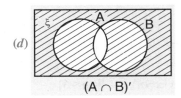　　(e) 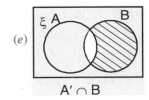　　(f)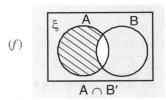

(A ∩ B)′　　　　　　　A′ ∩ B　　　　　　　A ∩ B′

5. (a)　(i) {d, c}　　　　　(ii) {a, b, c, d, e, f}　　(iii) {e, f, g, h, i}　　(iv) {a, b, g, h, i}

(v) {a, b}　　　(vi) {a, b, e, f, g, h, i}　(vii) {g, h, i}

(b)　(i) {1, 3, 5}　　(ii) {0, 1, 2, 3, 4, 5, 7}　(iii) {6, 8, 9}　　(iv) {0, 2, 4, 6, 7, 8, 9}

(v) {0, 2, 4, 7}　(vi) {0, 2, 4, 6, 7, 8, 9}　(vii) {6, 8, 9}

6. (a) {0, 1, 2, 3, ..., 8, 9}　(b) {0, 1, 2, 3, 4, 8}　(c) {3, 4, 8}　(d) {6, 8, 9}　(e) {8}

(f) {0, 1, 2, 3, 4, 6, 8, 9}　(g) {0, 1, 2, 3, 4, 5, 6, 7, 9}　(h) {0, 1, 2}　(i) {3, 4}　(j) {0, 1, 2, 5, 7}

EXERCISE –1 (g)

1. 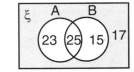　　(a) 63　　(b) 17　　(c) 23　　(d) 15　　(e) 23　　(f) 15

2. 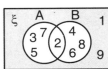　　(a) 7　　(b) 1　　(c) 2　　(d) 8　　(e) 3

3. 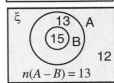　　4. (a) 45　(b) 23　(c) 17　(d) 8　(e) 13

5.   (a) 82   (b) 70   (c) 25   (d) 154

6.   7   7.   (i) 28   (ii) 25   (iii) 13

8.   (i) 900   (ii) 300   (iii) 500

9.   (i) 23   (ii) 17   (iii) 13   10. 350

MENTAL MATHS – 1

1. True   2. False   3. True   4. True   5. False   6. False   7. True   8. True

9. True   10. False

11. (i) True   (ii) False   (iii) True   (iv) True   (v) False   (vi) True   (vii) True   (viii) True

     (ix) True   (x) True

12. False   13. True   14. (i) True (ii) True   15. (i) {Q, U, E, N}   (ii) 4   (iii) 16   (iv) 15

16. (i) ϕ (ii) {1, 2, 3, 4, 5, 6, 7, 8}   (iii) {3, 5}   (iv) {1, 3, 5, 6, 7}   (v) {6}

     (vi) {1, 2, 3, 4, 5, 6, 7, 8}   (vii) ϕ

17. (i) A   (ii) A   (iii) A   (iv) ϕ 18. 8   19. 27   20. (i) True   (ii) False

UNIT REVIEW-1

1. (a) {1, 2, 3, 5, 6, 10, 15, 30}   (b) {a, e, r, o, p, l, n}   (c) {–4, –3, –2, –1, 0, 1, 2, 3, 4}

     (d) {2, 3, 5, 7, 11, 13, 17, 19}

2. (a) $A = \{x \mid x \in W, x < 8\}$ (b) $B = \{x \mid x \in Z, x \le 2\}$ (c) $C = \{x \mid x = n^3, n \in W, n \le 6\}$

3. (a) and (c)   4. (a), (d) are finite sets, (b), (c) are infinite sets

5. (i) ϕ, {5}, {7}, {9}, {5, 7}, {5, 9}, {7, 9}, {5, 7, 9}   (ii) {ϕ, {5}, {7}, {9}, {5, 7}, {5, 9}, {7, 9}, {5, 7, 9}}

6. (i) True   (ii) False   (iii) True   (iv) True   (v) True

7. (a) {3, 6, 9, 12, 15, 18}   (b) {0, 3, 6, 9, 12, 15, 18}   (c) {..., –9, –6, –3, 0, 3, 6, 9, 12, 15, 18}

8. (a) {0, 2, 3, 5, 6, 7, 9}   (b) {3}   (c) {0, 1, 4, 6, 8, 9}   (d) {1, 2, 4, 5, 7, 8}

     (e) {1, 4, 8}   (f) {1, 4, 8}   (g) {2, 5, 7}   (h) {0, 6, 9}

10. $n(B) = 27; n(A \cap B) = 11$ 11. (a) $N \subset M$ (b) $D \subset C; E \subset C; E \cap D = \phi$ (c) $Z \subset Y \subset X$

12. (a) $\xi = \{0, 1, 2, ..., 15\}$ (b) $A \cap B = \{6, 2, 0\}$ (c) $A \cap B \cap C = \{2, 0\}$ (d) $C' = \{1, 3, 6, 7, 10, 11, 14, 15\}$

     (e) $A - C = \{1, 6, 7\}$ (f) $B - C = \{6, 10, 15\}$ (g) $C - B = \{4, 5, 9, 13\}$

     (h) $(A \cup B)' = \{3, 5, 9, 11, 13, 14\}$ (i) $(A \cup B \cup C)' = \{3, 11, 14\}$

2. Number System

2.1 Revision

(Whole numbers, Integers and Rational numbers)

From your study in the earlier classes, you know that as a result of our wish to find a suitable numbers system, we extended the number system several times. We first considered the system of **natural numbers** or **counting numbers** (positive or non-negative integers) :

$$N = \{1, 2, 3, 4, 5, ...\}$$

To this we added zero and designated the new system as the system of whole numbers :

$$W = \{0, 1, 2, 3, 4, 5, ...\}$$

Then we extended this system to include the negative of each positive integer and obtained the complete system of integers :

$$I \text{ or } Z = \{... -3, -2, -1, 0, 1, 2, 3, ...\}$$

The positive integers are 1, 2, 3, ...

The negative integers are $-1, -2, -3, ...$

Zero is neither positive nor negative.

Next fractions were considered and we developed the system of rational numbers :

$$Q = \{\text{Numbers which can be expressed in the form } \frac{p}{q}, \text{ where } p \text{ and } q \text{ are integers and } q \neq 0\}.$$

All these are rational numbers : $-7, \frac{8}{4}, 0, 73\%, 3.84, \sqrt{25}, \sqrt[3]{-8}$

But a number like $\frac{5}{0}$ or $-\frac{6}{0}$ is not defined and hence is not a rational number.

2.2 Properties of Operations on Rational Numbers

The operations of addition and multiplication obey all the laws in rational numbers (Q) that they obey in integers (Z). In addition, they have the inverse property of multiplication in Q which they don't possess in Z.

The table below lists the properties that hold for any rational numbers a, b, c.

Addition	Multiplication
1. Closure	**1. Closure**
$a + b$ is a unique rational number.	$a . b$ is a unique rational number.
Ex. $\frac{3}{4} + \frac{5}{7} = \frac{41}{28}$, which is a rational number.	**Ex.** $\frac{3}{4} \times \frac{5}{7} = \frac{15}{28}$, which is a rational number.
2. Commutative	**2. Commutative**
$a + b = b + a$	$a \times b = b \times a$
Ex. $\frac{1}{2} + \frac{3}{5} = \frac{3}{5} + \frac{1}{2} = \frac{11}{10}$.	**Ex.** $\frac{1}{2} \times \frac{3}{5} = \frac{3}{5} \times \frac{1}{2} = \frac{3}{10}$.

3. **Associative**	3. **Associative**
$(a + b) + c = a + (b + c)$	$(a \times b) \times c = a \times (b \times c)$
Ex. $\left(\frac{1}{2}+\frac{1}{3}\right)+\frac{1}{4}=\frac{1}{2}+\left(\frac{1}{3}+\frac{1}{4}\right)=\frac{13}{12}.$	**Ex.** $\left(\frac{1}{2}\times\frac{1}{3}\right)\times\frac{1}{4}=\frac{1}{2}\times\left(\frac{1}{3}\times\frac{1}{4}\right)=\frac{1}{24}.$
4. **Identity**	4. **Identity**
There is a rational number 0 such that	There is a rational number 1 such that
$a + 0 = 0 + a = a$	$a \times 1 = 1 \times a = a$
Ex. $\frac{7}{15}+0=0+\frac{7}{15}=\frac{7}{15}.$	$\frac{7}{15}\times1=1\times\frac{7}{15}=\frac{7}{15}.$
5. **Additive Inverse**	5. **Multiplicative Inverse**
For every 'a' there is the rational number '−a' such that $a + (-a) = 0$	For every 'a' except 0 there is a rational number $\frac{1}{a}$ such that $\frac{1}{a}=1$
Ex. Since $\frac{2}{5}+\left(-\frac{2}{5}\right)=0,$ therefore $-\frac{2}{5}$ is the additive inverse of $\frac{2}{5}.$	Since $\frac{5}{7}\times\frac{7}{5}=1,$ therefore, $\frac{7}{5}$ is the multiplicative inverse of $\frac{5}{7}.$

6. **Distributive :** $a(b + c) = (a \times b) + (a \times c)$

$$\frac{2}{3}\times\left(\frac{1}{5}+\frac{1}{7}\right)=\left(\frac{2}{3}\times\frac{1}{5}\right)+\left(\frac{2}{3}\times\frac{1}{7}\right)=\frac{8}{35}.$$

2.3 Density Property of Rational Numbers

Between any two different rational numbers, there are infinitely many rational numbers.

To find many rational numbers between two given distinct rational numbers.

Method :

Let the given rational number be a and b. Then $q_1 = \frac{1}{2}(a+b),$ $q_2 = \frac{1}{2}(q_1+b),$ $q_3 = \frac{1}{2}(q_2+b),$ $q_4 = \frac{1}{2}(q_3+b),$ and so on.

In this manner we can find as many rational numbers as we please between two given distinct rational numbers.

Ex. 5. *Find three rational numbers between $\frac{1}{5}$ and $\frac{1}{3}.$*

Sol. Let q_1, q_2, q_3 be the three required rational numbers. Then

$$q_1 = \frac{1}{2}\left(\frac{1}{5}+\frac{1}{3}\right)=\frac{1}{2}\left(\frac{3+5}{15}\right)=\frac{1}{2}\times\frac{8}{15}=\frac{4}{15}.$$

$$q_2 = \frac{1}{2}\left(\frac{4}{15}+\frac{1}{3}\right)=\frac{1}{2}\left(\frac{4+5}{15}\right)=\frac{1}{2}\times\frac{9}{15}=\frac{3}{10}.$$

$$q_3 = \frac{1}{2}\left(\frac{3}{10}+\frac{1}{3}\right) = \frac{1}{2}\left(\frac{9+10}{30}\right) = \frac{1}{2} \times \frac{19}{30} = \frac{19}{60}.$$

$$\frac{1}{5} < \frac{4}{15} < \frac{3}{10} < \frac{19}{60} < \frac{1}{3}.$$

Hence, three rational numbers between $\frac{1}{5}$ and $\frac{1}{3}$ are $\frac{4}{15}$, $\frac{3}{10}$ and $\frac{19}{60}$.

2.4 Presentation of a Rational Number on a Number Line

Every rational number has a corresponding point representing it on the number line.

We have already learnt that integers can be represented by taking positive integers to the right of the point 0 and negative integers to the left of the point 0. Let us consider the length between two successive integers to be unit length. As we know integers are also rational numbers with denominator 1.

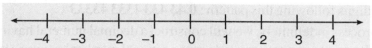

- *To represent a rational number of the form $\frac{p}{q}$ where $p < q$.*

Ex. 1. *Represent $\frac{2}{5}$ and $-\frac{2}{5}$ on the number line.*

Sol.

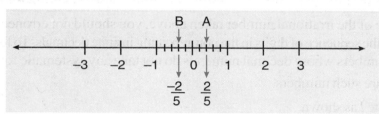

To represent $\frac{2}{5}$ on the number line we divide the unit length between 0 and 1 into 5 equal parts and take 2 out of the 5 parts. Then *A* represents $\frac{2}{5}$.

Similarly $-\frac{2}{5}$ can be represented by taking the unit length between 0 and -1.

- *To represent a rational number of the form $\frac{p}{q}$ where $p > q$.*

Ex. 2. *Represent $\frac{14}{3}$ and $-\frac{14}{3}$ on the number line.*

Sol. $\frac{14}{3} = 4\frac{2}{3}$ and $-\frac{14}{3} = -4\frac{2}{3}$.

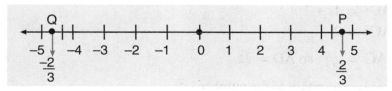

To represent $\frac{14}{3}$ or $4\frac{2}{3}$,

start from 0 and take 4 full units. Divide the unit length between 4 and 5 into 3 equal parts. Take two out 3

parts. Then the point P represents $\frac{14}{3}$ or $\left(4+\frac{2}{3}\right)$. Similarly point Q represents $-\frac{14}{3}$ or $-\left(4+\frac{2}{3}\right)$ on the left side of 0.

2.5 Irrational Numbers

You have learnt that one of the chief properties of the system of rational numbers is that every such number can be represented as a repeating or a terminating decimal. Certainly, it is possible to construct a decimal numeral that is *non-repeating* **and** *non-terminating,* **i.e., which is a** *non-repeating infinite* decimal.

- (*i*)   Start with **0.43**
- (*ii*)   Annex the digits **433,** making **0.43 433**
- (*iii*)   Annex the digits **4333** making **0.43 433 4333**
- (*iv*)   Continue annexing digits following this pattern : **0.43 433 4333 43333**

If we continue the process indefinitely, we will construct a decimal numeral having an endless succession of **different** blocks of digits. The number so constructed is not a rational number because a rational number can always be expressed as a repeating or a terminating decimal. We call such non-repeating decimals **irrational numbers**. Notice that the word "irrational" is formed by attaching the prefix *ir-*, which means "not" to the word "rational". Thus, an irrational number is not a rational number. **The word 'rational' is derived from the word 'ratio'.**

Irrational numbers are represented by non-terminating non-repeating decimals.

From the example of the irrational number taken above, you should not erroneously conclude that there is always some set pattern in the sequence of digits in the non-repeating infinite decimals. To fortify our point, we will now tell you about irrational numbers whose decimal numerals do not take any systematic form. As you will see, square roots such as $\sqrt{2}, \sqrt{3}, \sqrt{5}$, are such numbers.

- (*i*)   Draw a number line *l* as shown.
- (*ii*)   At *B*, draw a ray *m* perpendicular to *l*.
- (*iii*)   On *m* draw a line segment *BC*, one unit long.
- (*iv*)   Draw segment *AC*.
- (*v*)   With *A* as centre and radius *AC*, draw circular arc which intersects *l*. Call the point of intersection *D*.

Now two questions arise :

- (1)   To what number (if any) does the point *D* correspond?
- (2)   Is this number a rational number?

Consider the first question, "*To what number does the point D correspond?*"

$$AB = BC = 1$$
$$(AC)^2 = (AB)^2 + (BC)^2 \qquad \text{[Pythagoras' Theorem.]}$$
$$AC^2 = 1^2 + 1^2.$$
$$\Rightarrow \qquad AC^2 = 2.$$
$$\Rightarrow \qquad AC = \sqrt{2}, \text{ so } AD = \sqrt{2}$$

Therefore, the point D corresponds to the number $\sqrt{2}$.

If you find the square root of 2 by the division method (you will learn this in the next chapter), you will find that $\sqrt{2}$ can be represented by the non-repeating decimal 1.41421356237 ... and so it is irrational.

Similarly, $\sqrt{3}$ = 1.732050807 ... is an irrational number.

$\sqrt{17}$ = 4.12310562561766 ... is an irrational number.

$\sqrt{119}$ = 10.908712114635 ... is an irrational number.

$\sqrt[3]{5}$ = 1.709975947 ... is an irrational number.

> Check from your calculator

Irrational numbers occur as the square roots of certain numbers. They also result from many other mathematical processes. For example, the ratio of the circumference of any circle to its diameter is the irrational number π.

π = 3.14159 2653589 7932 384626433832 7950 2884 19716 939 9375 1058 2097494 ...

2.6 The Wheel of Theodorus

Theodorus of Cyrene, who lived around 425 B.C., was a philosopher of ancient Greece. It is said that he discovered the construction below, which is therefore called 'the wheel of Theodorus."

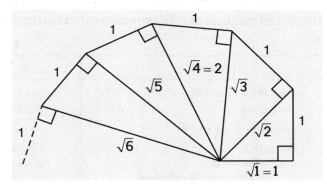

2.7 The Real Numbers

If we combine the rational numbers and the irrational numbers, we get real numbers which we denote by **R**.

The following diagram shows the relationships among the different kinds of numbers of the real number system.

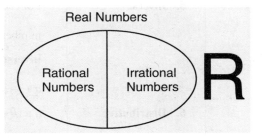

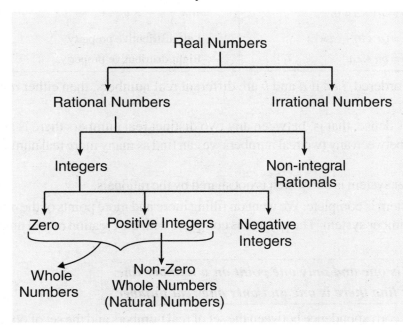

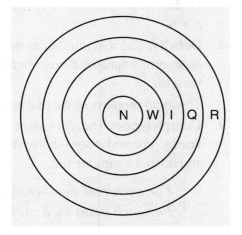

In the diagram, note the following relationships among the sets of numbers.

1. **A real number** is either a rational number or an irrational number. Thus, the real number 2 is a rational number while the real number $\sqrt{2}$ is irrational.

2. **A rational number** is either an integer or a non-integer. Thus, the rational number $\frac{3}{1}$ is an integer while the rational number $\frac{3}{4}$ is a non-integer.

3. **An integer** is either positive, negative, or zero. Thus, the integer 3 is positive, the integer -3 is negative, and the integer 0 **is neither positive nor negative**.

4. **A whole number** is either a natural number or zero. Thus, the whole number 3 is a natural number while the whole number 0 is not.

5. **A natural number** is a non-zero whole number. Thus, the natural number 2 is a non-zero whole number.

2.8 Properties of the Real Number System

All the properties of the system of rational numbers may be proved to extend to the system of real numbers. These may be summarized as under.

Property	Addition	Multiplication
1. Closure	$a + b$ is a real number.	$a \times b$ is a real number.
2. Commutative	$a + b = b + a$.	$a \times b = b \times a$.
3. Associative	$(a + b) + c = a + (b + c)$.	$(a \times b) \times c = a \times (b \times c)$.
4. Identity	For each a $a + 0 = 0 + a = a$. i.e. zero is the **identity element** for the operation of addition.	For each a $a \times 1 = 1 \times a = a$. i.e., one is the **identity element** for the operation of multiplication.
5. Inverse	For each a, there is a unique real number $(-a)$, called the **additive inverse** of a, such that $a + (-a) = (-a) + a = 0$.	For each $a \neq 0$, there is a real number $\frac{1}{a}$, called the **multiplicative inverse** of a, such that $a \times \frac{1}{a} = \frac{1}{a} \times a = 1$.
6. Distributive	$a \times (b + c) = (a \times b) + (a \times c)$ $(b + c) \times a = ba + ca$.	Left distributive property. Right distributive property.

7. **Order.** The real number system is ordered, *i.e.*, if a and b are different real numbers, then either $a < b$ or $a > b$.

8. **Density.** The real number system is dense, that is, between any two distinct real numbers there is always another real number. Consequently, between any two real numbers we can find as many more real numbers as we wish.

    The ninth property of the real number system is one which is not shared by the rationals.

9. **Completeness.** The real number system is complete. We went on filling more and more points of the number line by repeated extensions of the number system. The process is complete with the creation of real numbers and no more gaps are left.

> *For each real number there is one and only one point on a number line.*
> *For each point on a number line there is one and only one real number.*

In other words, there is a one-to-one correspondence between the set of real numbers and the set of points on a number line. The number line is complete. Together, the two statements above are called the **completeness property** of the set of real numbers.

Because of the completeness property, we can shade parts of number lines to represent the fact that every point in the shaded part is the graph of a real number. It would be inappropriate to suggest, for example, that the graph shown at the right is the

graph of a set of rational numbers, because there are infinitely many points in the shaded portion that do not have rational coordinates.

Ex. 1. *Graph the given set on a number line.*

    (a) *The set of all positive real numbers x for which* $x \geq 3$.

    (b) *The set of all real numbers x for which* $x > 3$.

Sol. Notice in Fig. Ex. 1(a) that the graph of 3 is shown as a shaded or solid circle to indicate that this point is included in the graph and the graph of 0 is shown as an unshaded or open circle to indicate that this point is not included. In Fig. Ex. 1(b) the shading indicates that the graph continues indefinitely to the right.

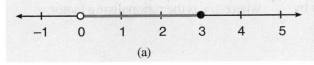 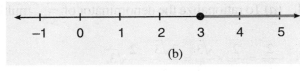

         (a)   (b)

      GRAPH of $x \leq 3$, $x \in R$.   GRAPH of $x \geq 3$, $x \in R$.

Ex. 2. **Specify the set of real numbers with the given graph :**

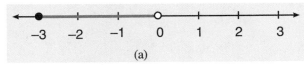 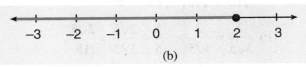

         (a)   (b)

Sol. (*i*) The set of negative real numbers greater than or equal to – 3.

Note that '0' is no included in the graph because it is not negative.

(*ii*) The set of all real numbers less than or equal to 2, *i.e.*, $x \leq 2$, *x* is a real number.

Note :

> **1.** $\sqrt{5} + \sqrt{7} \neq \sqrt{12}$, $\sqrt{7} - \sqrt{3} \neq \sqrt{7-3} = \sqrt{4}$
>
> **2.** $\sqrt{2} + \sqrt{2} \neq \sqrt{4}$. This is equal to $2\sqrt{2}$.
>
> $4\sqrt{3} + 3\sqrt{3} = (4+3)\sqrt{3} = 7\sqrt{3}$; $6\sqrt{5} - \sqrt{5} = (6-1)\sqrt{5} = 5\sqrt{5}$.
>
> **3.** If a and b are two rational numbers, then
>
> $\sqrt{ab} = \sqrt{a}.\sqrt{b}$ and $\sqrt{\dfrac{a}{b}} = \dfrac{\sqrt{a}}{\sqrt{b}}$ *i.e.*, $\sqrt{10} = \sqrt{2 \times 5} = \sqrt{2} \times \sqrt{5}$, $\sqrt{27} = \sqrt{3 \times 3 \times 3} = 3\sqrt{3}$
>
> $\dfrac{3}{\sqrt{3}} = \dfrac{\sqrt{3} \times \sqrt{3}}{\sqrt{3}} = \sqrt{3}$ and $\dfrac{\sqrt{10}}{\sqrt{2}} = \dfrac{\sqrt{5 \times 2}}{\sqrt{2}} = \dfrac{\sqrt{5} \times \sqrt{2}}{\sqrt{2}} = \sqrt{5}$.

2.9 Rationalisation

    The process of multiplying an irrational number by its *rationalising factor* is called *rationalisation*. What is a rationalising factor? *If the product of two irrational numbers is a rational number, then each number is called the rationalising factor of the other number.*

For example :

    (*i*) $\sqrt{7} \times \sqrt{7} = 7$, $\therefore$ $\sqrt{7}$ is a rationalising factor of $\sqrt{7}$.

    (*i*) $\left(2 - \sqrt{5}\right)\left(2 + \sqrt{5}\right) = 2^2 - \left(\sqrt{5}\right)^2 = 4 - 5 = 1$ $\therefore$ $2 - \sqrt{5}$ and $2 + \sqrt{5}$ are rationalising factors of each other.

(iii) $\left(\sqrt{11}+\sqrt{3}\right)\left(\sqrt{11}-\sqrt{3}\right)=\left(\sqrt{11}\right)^2-\left(\sqrt{3}\right)^2=11-3=8,$

$\boxed{(a+b)(a-b)=a^2-b^2}$

$\therefore$ $\sqrt{11}+\sqrt{3}$ and $\sqrt{11}-\sqrt{3}$ are rationalising factors of each other.

Rationalising the denominator

Rule : Multiply and divide the denominator of the irrational number by the rationalising factor of the denominator and then simplify if necessary.

Type 1.

Ex. 1. *Simplify by rationalizing the denominator of each irrational number.*

(a) $\dfrac{4}{\sqrt{3}}$ (b) $\dfrac{\sqrt{3}}{\sqrt{10}}$ (c) $\dfrac{2}{3\sqrt{5}}$ (d) $\dfrac{3+\sqrt{2}}{\sqrt{2}}$

Sol. *(a)* To rationalize the denominator of $\dfrac{2}{\sqrt{3}}$, multiply by $\dfrac{\sqrt{3}}{\sqrt{3}}$, where $\sqrt{3}$ is the rationalising factor.

$\therefore$ $\dfrac{2}{\sqrt{3}}=\dfrac{2}{\sqrt{3}}\times\dfrac{\sqrt{3}}{\sqrt{3}}=\dfrac{2\sqrt{3}}{3}=\dfrac{2}{3}\sqrt{3}.$

(b) $\dfrac{\sqrt{3}}{\sqrt{10}}=\dfrac{\sqrt{3}}{\sqrt{10}}\times\dfrac{\sqrt{10}}{\sqrt{10}}=\dfrac{\sqrt{30}}{10}.$

(c) $\dfrac{2}{3\sqrt{5}}=\dfrac{2}{3\sqrt{5}}\times\dfrac{\sqrt{5}}{\sqrt{5}}=\dfrac{2\sqrt{5}}{3\times5}=\dfrac{2\sqrt{5}}{15}.$

(d) $\dfrac{3+\sqrt{2}}{\sqrt{2}}=\dfrac{3+\sqrt{2}}{\sqrt{2}}\times\dfrac{\sqrt{2}}{\sqrt{2}}=\dfrac{\sqrt{2}\left(3+\sqrt{2}\right)}{2}=\dfrac{3\sqrt{2}+2}{2}.$

Type 2.

Ex. 2. *Simplify by rationalizing the denominator :*

(a) $\dfrac{1}{4-\sqrt{3}}$ (b) $\dfrac{\sqrt{6}}{\sqrt{2}+\sqrt{5}}$

Sol. *(a)* $\dfrac{1}{4-\sqrt{3}}=\dfrac{1}{4-\sqrt{3}}\times\dfrac{4+\sqrt{3}}{4+\sqrt{3}}=\dfrac{4+\sqrt{3}}{4^2-\left(\sqrt{3}\right)^2}=\dfrac{4+\sqrt{3}}{16-3}=\dfrac{4+\sqrt{3}}{13}.$

$\boxed{\because\quad\text{rationalising factor is }4+\sqrt{3}}$

(b) $\dfrac{\sqrt{6}}{\sqrt{2}+\sqrt{5}}=\dfrac{\sqrt{6}}{\sqrt{2}+\sqrt{5}}\times\dfrac{\sqrt{2}-\sqrt{5}}{\sqrt{2}-\sqrt{5}}=\dfrac{\sqrt{6}\left(\sqrt{2}-\sqrt{5}\right)}{\left(\sqrt{2}\right)^2-\left(\sqrt{5}\right)^2}=\dfrac{\sqrt{12}-\sqrt{30}}{2-5}=-\dfrac{1}{3}\left(\sqrt{12}-\sqrt{30}\right).$

EXERCISE 2

1. **Find three rational numbers between**

(a) $\dfrac{3}{5}$ and $\dfrac{3}{4}$ (b) $-\dfrac{3}{4}$ and $-1.$

2. Find four ratonal numbers between -1 and $-\dfrac{1}{2}.$

3. **Given the following real numbers :**

$-5, 0, \sqrt{3}, \dfrac{3}{5}, \sqrt{8}, 6.37, \pi, 4, \dfrac{-2}{7}, 0.03$

Tell,

(a) Which are rational?   (b) Which are irrational?   (c) Which are positive integers?

(d) Which are negative integers?   (e) Which number is neither positive nor negative?

4. **Write True or False to describe each sentence :**

(a) All rational numbers are real numbers.   (b) All real numbers are rational numbers.

(c) Some real numbers are rational numbers.   (d) All integers are rational numbers.

(e) No rational number is also an irrational number.

(f) There exists a whole number that is not a natural number.

5. Name a multiplication property that holds for the rational numbers, but not for the integers.

6. **Tell whether each decimal numeral represents a rational or an irrational number :**

(a) 0.578   (b) 0.573 333 ...   (c) 0.688 434 445 4 ...   (d) 0.724 374 75 ...

(e) 0.638 754 71 ...   (f) 0.471 717 1 ...   (g) 283   (h) 289.387 000 ...

(i) $5.\overline{93}$ (j) 2.309 87   (k) 0.585 885 888 ...

7. **State True (T) or False (F) :**

(a) $\sqrt{3}+\sqrt{11}=\sqrt{14}$ (b) $4\sqrt{3}-2\sqrt{3}=2\sqrt{3}$ (c) $2\sqrt{4}+3\sqrt{9}=5\sqrt{13}$ (d) $\sqrt{5}-\sqrt{3}=\sqrt{2}$

8. **State the rationalising factors of :**

(a) $\sqrt{6}$ (b) $2\sqrt{5}$ (c) $3+\sqrt{7}$ (d) $4-2\sqrt{3}$

9. **Simplify by rationalising the denominator :**

(a) $\dfrac{1}{\sqrt{3}}$ (b) $\dfrac{4}{\sqrt{7}}$ (c) $\dfrac{8}{3\sqrt{2}}$ (d) $\dfrac{3+\sqrt{2}}{\sqrt{5}}$ (e) $\dfrac{7-\sqrt{3}}{\sqrt{11}}$

10. **Simplify by rationalising the denominator :**

(a) $\dfrac{3}{\sqrt{2}-1}$ (b) $\dfrac{8}{\sqrt{7}+1}$ (c) $\dfrac{7}{\sqrt{3}+\sqrt{5}}$ (d) $\dfrac{2\sqrt{6}}{3+\sqrt{3}}$ (e) $\dfrac{6}{\sqrt{7}-\sqrt{2}}$

11. **Given a number line are the following sentences true or false ?**

(a) For every point on the line, there is a rational number.

(b) For every point on the number line, there is a real number.

LOOKING BACK

Summary of Key Facts

1. Numbers which can be expressed in the form of terminating or repeating decimals are called **rational numbers.**

   e.g., $\dfrac{7}{64}=0.109375$, $\dfrac{5}{12}=0.41\overline{6}$ are rational numbers.

2. Numbers which when converted into decimals are expressible neither as terminating nor as repeating decimals are called **irrational numbers.**

   e.g., $\sqrt{2}=1.41421356237\ldots$ is an irrational number.

3. An irrational number cannot be expressed in the form $\dfrac{p}{q}$ where $q\neq0$ and its exact root cannot be found.

4. The totality of all rational and all irrational numbers is called real numbers which we denote by **R**.

5. The natural numbers, whole numbers, integers, non-integral rationals $\left(\dfrac{5}{7}, -\dfrac{8}{9}\right)$ etc. are all contained in the set of real numbers.

6. Notations :

Natural numbers : $N = \{1, 2, 3, ...\}$

Whole numbers : $W = \{0, 1, 2, 3, ...\}$

Integers : Z or $I = \{..., -3, -2, -1, 0, 1, 2, 3, ...\}$

Rational numbers : $Q = \{$Numbers like $-\dfrac{7}{8}, \dfrac{11}{3}, -5, 7, ...\}$

which are expressible in the form $\dfrac{p}{q} (q \neq 0)$.

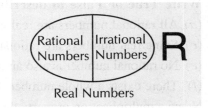

ANSWERS

EXERCISE 2

1. (a) $\dfrac{51}{80}, \dfrac{27}{40}, \dfrac{57}{80}$ (b) $\dfrac{-13}{16}, \dfrac{-7}{8}, \dfrac{-15}{16}$ 2. $-\dfrac{15}{16}, \dfrac{-7}{8}, \dfrac{-3}{4}, \dfrac{-5}{8}$

3. (a) $-5, 0, \dfrac{3}{5}, -\sqrt{9}, 6.37, 4, \dfrac{-2}{7}, 0.03$ (b) $\sqrt{3}, \sqrt{8}, \pi$ (c) 4   (d) $-5, -\sqrt{9}$ (e) 0.

4. (a) T   (b) F   (c) T   (d) T   (e) T   (f) T

5. Multiplicative inverse

6. (a) Rational   (b) Rational   (c) Irrational   (d) Irrational   (e) Irrational   (f) Rational   (g) Rational
    (h) Rational   (i) Rational   (j) Rational   (k) Irrational

7. (a) F   (b) T   (c) F   (d) F

8. (a) $\sqrt{6}$ (b) $\sqrt{5}$ (c) $3 - \sqrt{7}$ (d) $4 + 2\sqrt{3}$

9. (a) $\dfrac{\sqrt{3}}{3}$ (b) $\dfrac{4}{7}\sqrt{7}$ (c) $\dfrac{4}{3}\sqrt{2}$ (d) $\dfrac{3\sqrt{5}+\sqrt{10}}{5}$ (e) $\dfrac{7\sqrt{11}-\sqrt{33}}{11}$

10. (a) $3\sqrt{2}+3$ (b) $\dfrac{4}{3}\left(\sqrt{7}-1\right)$ (c) $\dfrac{7}{2}\left(\sqrt{5}-\sqrt{3}\right)$ (d) $\sqrt{6}-\sqrt{2}$ (e) $\dfrac{6}{5}\left(\sqrt{7}+\sqrt{2}\right)$

11. (a) F   (b) T

3. Factors and Multiples

3.1 Factors and Multiples

1. **Exact divisors** of a number are called its **factors**. Numbers obtained on multiplying a given number by whole numbers are called its **multiples**.

   For example, If we consider the mathematical sentence, $3 \times 7 = 21$

   then 3 and 7 are the factors of 21 and 21 is the multiple of 3 as well as 7.

   Note :

   - The **number 1 is** the **factor** of **every number**.
   - 1, 2, 3, 4, 6, 8, 12 and 24 are all the possible **factors** of 24.
   - The **multiples** of 3 are 0, 3, 6, 12, 15, 18, etc. 3, 6, 12, 15, 18 etc. are the **non-zero multiples** of 3. In the book, unless otherwise stated, when we talk of the mulitiples of a given number, we will mean the non-zero multiples.
   - 24 is a multiple of any of the numbers 1, 2, 3, 4, 6, 8, 12 and 24.

2. **Prime and Composite Numbers**

   - 2, 3, 5, 11, 13, 17, etc. are **Prime numbers**. A prime number has exactly *two* factors, itself and 1. It is not divisible by any number other than itself and 1. Note that 1 is not a prime number as it has only one factor.
   - The other natural numbers which are not prime numbers are called **composite numbers**. These numbers have more than two factors e.g., 4, 6, 8, 9, 10, 12, 14, etc. are all composite numbers. It should be noted that **1 is neither a prime number, nor a composite number.**
   - **Co-primes :** Every pair of two natural numbers having no common factor, other than 1, is called a pair of coprimes. e.g., (3, 5) (5, 6) (6, 11) (11, 17) etc.
   - **Twin Primes :** Prime numbers differing by two are called twin primes.
     e.g., (5, 7), (3, 5), (11, 13) etc. are twin primes.
   - **Prime Triplet :** The set {3, 5, 7} of three consecutive primes is called a prime triplet.

3. **Even and Odd Numbers**

   - 2, 4, 6, 8, etc. are exactly divisible by 2 and are called **even numbers**.
   - 1, 3, 5, 7, 9, 11, 13, 15, 17, 19, 21, etc. are called **odd numbers** as they are not exactly divisible by 2.
   - Note that zero is neither even nor odd.

4. **Prime Factors**

   A factor which is a prime number is called a **Prime Factor**. All factors of 36 are 1, 2, 3, 4, 6, 9, 12, 18, 36. Of these 2 and 3 are prime numbers. These are called prime factors.

   Rewriting 36 as a product of prime factors, we have $36 = 2 \times 2 \times 3 \times 3 = 2^2 \times 3^2$. We write 2^2 instead of 2×2.

The prime factors of 630 are obtained as follows :

$$
\begin{array}{r|l}
2 & 630 \\
\hline
3 & 315 \\
\hline
3 & 105 \\
\hline
5 & 35 \\
\hline
7 & 7 \\
\hline
& 1
\end{array}
$$

$$630 = 2 \times 3 \times 3 \times 5 \times 7$$
$$= 2 \times 3^2 \times 5 \times 7.$$

To express a natural number as a product of its prime factors is called **prime factorisation**. The prime factorisation of a natural number can also be expressed in the exponential form.

For example :

$$56 = 2 \times 2 \times 2 \times 7 = 2^3 \times 7$$
$$450 = 2 \times 3 \times 3 \times 5 \times 5 = 2 \times 3^2 \times 5^2.$$

3.2 Divisibility Tests

A number is divisible by 2 if the last digit is even or 0, *e.g.*, 612, 370, 948.

A number is divisible by 3 if the sum of its digits is divisible by 3, *e.g.*,927 is divisible by 3 as the sum of the digits = 9 + 2 + 7 = 18 which is divisible by 3.

A number is divisible by 9 if the sum of its digits is divisible by 9, *e.g.*, 657 is divisible by 9 as the sum of its digits = 6 + 5 + 7 = 18 which is divisible by 9.

A number is divisible by 5 if its last digit is 5 or 0, *e.g.*, 835, 290 can be divided exactly by 5.

A number is divisible by 11 if the difference between the sum of the digits in odd places and the sum of the digits in even places starting from the units place is 0 or divisible by 11 *e.g.*, in 1210, the sum of the digits in odd places is 0 + 2 = 2, and the sum of the digits in even places is 1 + 1 = 2. The difference between the sums is 2 – 2 = 0. Hence it is divisible by 11.

In 41679 sum of the digits in odd places is 9 + 6 + 4 = 19. Sum of the digits in even places is 7 + 1 = 8. Difference between the sums is 19 – 8 = 11. This is divisible by 11. Hence 41679 is divisible by 11.

A number is divisible by 6 if it is even and divisible by 3. The number 8034 is even and divisible by 3. It is divisible by 6 also.

Remark : If a number is divisible by two coprimes, then it is also divisible by their product.

e.g. the number 30162 is divisible both 2 and 3. It is divisible by their product 6 also.

Ex. 1. *Find the smallest number which must be added to 6313 to make it divisible by 3.*

Sol. For a number to be divisible by 3, the sum of its digits should be divisible by 3. The sum of the digits is 6 + 3 + 1 + 3 = 13. ∴ If we divide 13 by 3 the remainder is 1.

∴ The least number to be added is 3 – 1 = 2.

On adding 2 to the given number, the number becomes 6315, which is divisible by 3.

EXERCISE 3 (a)

1. (*a*) Pick out the prime and composite numbers from the following numbers.

    4, 17, 20, 9, 31, 64, 934, 87, 37, 19, 2, 5, 36, 13, 119, 3

    (*b*) Identify the even and odd numbers among the numbers given in (a) above.

2. Do you think there are 18 prime numbers less than 50 ? Find out.

3. **In each set, one number is not prime. Name it.**
   (a) {2, 5, 9, 11},   (b) {13, 15, 17, 19}   (c) {23, 29, 33, 37}
4. **Name each product as a product of its prime factors.**
   (a) 48   (b) 72   (c) 168   (d) 330   (e) 516
5. **The first pair of twin primes is (3, 5). Find three other pairs.**
6. **Make this sentence true :**
   With the exception of the number 2, prime numbers are .... numbers.
7. **Which of the following numbers are divisible by 3?**
   (a) 705   (b) 1433   (c) 2655   (d) 4737
8. **Which of the following numbers are divisible by 11?**
   (a) 3671   (b) 814   (c) 8060   (d) 4576
9. **Which of the following numbers are divisible by 6 ?**
   (a) 744   (b) 543   (c) 9258   (d) 52234
10. **Which of the following numbers are divisible by 9 ?**
    (a) 432   (b) 6021   (c) 6060   (d) 8427   (e) 5427
11. **Find the smallest number which must be added to 80234 to make it divisible by 9.**
12. **Replace the letter x in 48x 9 by the smallest digit so that it is divisible by 11.**

3.3 Highest Common Factor (H.C.F) or Greatest Common Divisor (G.C.D)

   The greatest factor that any two or more numbers have in common is their Highest Common Factor (abbreviated as H.C.F.) or Greatest Common Divisor (G.C.D.).

   For example : If we find the factors of 24 and 36, then we see that :

   Factors of 24 = 1, 2, 3, 4, 6, 8, 12, 24

   Factors of 36 = 1, 2, 3, 4, 6, 9, 12, 18, 36

   The common factors of 24 and 36 are 1, 2, 3, 4, 6, 12 of these 12 is the highest.

   ∴ The highest common factor (H.C.F.) is 12.

   There are two methods to find the H.C.F. We shall illustrate each of them by an example.

   ■ **Method 1 : Prime Factorisation Method**

Ex. 1. *Find the H.C.F of 72, 120 and 384.*

Sol.   Resolving each of them into prime factors :

2	72
2	36
2	18
3	9
3	3
	1

2	120
2	60
2	30
3	15
5	5
	1

2	384
2	192
2	96
2	48
2	24
2	12
2	6
3	3
	1

∴
$$72 = 2 \times 2 \times 2 \times 3 \times 3 = 2^3 \times 3^2$$
$$120 = 2 \times 2 \times 2 \times 3 \times 5 = 2^3 \times 3 \times 5$$
$$384 = 2 \times 2 \times 2 \times 2 \times 2 \times 2 \times 2 \times 3 = 2^7 \times 3$$

If you observe closely, you will find that out of 2^3, 2^3 and 2^7, the least power is 2^3 and out of 3^2 and 3, the least power is 3.

∴ H.C.F of 72, 120 and 384 = Product of the least powers of common prime factors

$$= 2^3 \times 3 = 8 \times 3 = \textbf{24}.$$

■ **Method 2 : Long Division Method**

Ex. 2. *Find the H.C.F of 910, 1442 and 7245.*

Sol. When the numbers are large, we use the long division or continued division method.

First we find the H.C.F of any two of the given numbers. Let us take 910 and 1442.

```
910) 1442 (1
     910
     ————
     532) 910 (1
          532
          ————
          378) 532 (1
               378
               ————
               154) 378 (2
                    308
                    ————
                    70) 154 (2
                        140
                        ————
                        14) 70 (5
                            70
∴ H.C.F of 910 and 1442 is 14.
                            0
```

Now we find the H.C.F of 14 and 7245

```
14) 7245 (517
    70
    ——
    24
    14
    ——
    105
     98
    ———
     7) 14 (2
        14
        ——
        0
∴ H.C.F of 14 and 7245 is 7
```

Hence, H.C.F of 910, 1442 and 7245 is **7**.

3.4 Least Common Multiple (L.C.M.)

The **L.C.M of two or more numbers is the smallest number into which each of the numbers will divide without a remainder.**

Consider the numbers 4, 12 and 18.

The multiples of 4 are 4, 8, 12, 16, 20, 24, 28, 32, ⃝36, 40, ...

The multiples of 12 are 12, 24, ⃝36, 48, ...

The multiples of 18 are 18, ⃝36, 54, ...

The least common multiple (L.C.M.) is **36**.

3.5 To Find the L.C.M.

To find the L.C.M also we have two methods.

■ **Method 1 : By Prime Factorisation**

Ex. 3. *Find the L.C.M of 36, 63 and 77.*

Sol. Prime factorising each of the numbers 36, 63 and 77

2	36
2	18
3	9
3	3
	1

3	63
3	21
7	7
	1

7	77
11	11
	1

$36 = 2 \times 2 \times 3 \times 3 = 2^2 \times 3^2$, $\qquad 63 = 3 \times 3 \times 7 = 3^2 \times 7$, $\quad 77 = 7 \times 11$

∴ L.C.M of 36, 63 and 77 = Product of the terms containing highest powers of all factors.

= $2^2 \times 3^2 \times 7 \times 11 =$ **2772.**

■ **Method 2 : Common Division Method**

Ex. 4. *Find the L.C.M of 21, 45, 63, 81.*

Sol. ∴   L.C.M of 21, 45, 63 and 81

= Product of divisors and undivided numbers.

= $3 \times 3 \times 7 \times 5 \times 9 =$ **2835.**

3	21,	45,	63,	81
3	7,	15,	21,	27
7	7,	5,	7,	9
	1,	5,	1,	9

3.6 Relation Between H.C.F. and L.C.M. of Two Natural Numbers

Product of two given numbers = Product of their H.C.F and L.C.M.

Note : 1.   If two given numbers are co-prime i.e., their H.C.F is 1, then product of the two given numbers = Their L.C.M

2.   The H.C.F of two numbers always divides their L.C.M exactly (*i.e.* leaving zero remainder.)

3.7 Miscellaneous Examples

Ex. 5. *Find the largest number which divides 1624, 1730 and 261 leaving remainders 4, 5 and 6 respectively.*

Sol.   When 1624 is divided, the remainder 4 is left, so 1624–4, *i.e.*, 1620 will be exactly divisible. Similarly, for other numbers. Hence, we subtract 4, 5 and 6 from 1624, 1730 and 261 respectively and find the H.C.F of the numbers thus obtained.

1624 – 4 = 1620, 1730 – 5 = 1725 and 261 – 6 = 255

∴   The required number is the H.C.F of 1620, 1725 and 255.

Let us first find the H.C.F of 1620 and 1725.

$$
\begin{array}{r}
1620)\ \overline{1725}\ (1 \\
1620 \\
\hline
105)\ 1620\ (15 \\
105 \\
\hline
570 \\
525 \\
\hline
45)\ 105\ (2 \\
90 \\
\hline
15)\ 45\ (3 \\
45 \\
\hline
0
\end{array}
$$

∴ H.C.F of 1620 and 1725 is 15.

Now we find the H.C.F of 15 and 255

$$
\begin{array}{r}
15)\ \overline{255}\ (17 \\
15 \\
\hline
105 \\
105 \\
\hline
0
\end{array}
$$

H.C.F of 15 and 255 is 15

⇒   H.C.F of 1620, 1725 and 255 is 15.

⇒   The required number is **15.**

Ex. 6. *Three tankers contain 585 litres, 819 litres and 702 litres of milk respectively. Find the maximum capacity of a container which can measure the milk in either of the three tankers exact number of times.*

Sol. The required capacity is the H.C.F. of 585, 819 and 702.

Taking 585 and 819 first.   Now we find the H.C.F. of 117 and 702

$$
\begin{array}{r}
585)\overline{819}(1 \\
585 \\
\hline
234)\overline{585}(2 \\
468 \\
\hline
117)\overline{234}(2 \\
234 \\
\hline
0
\end{array}
\qquad
\begin{array}{r}
117)\overline{702}(6 \\
702 \\
\hline
0
\end{array}
$$

H.C.F of 585 and 819 is 117.   H.C.F of 117 and 702 = 117.

$\therefore$ H.C.F of 585, 819 and 702 is 117.

Hence maximum capacity of the container is **117 litres.**

Ex. 7. *Find the least number of five digits exactly divisible by 16, 28, 36 and 42.*

Sol. First we find L.C.M. of 16, 28, 36, 42

2	16,	28,	36,	42
2	8,	14,	18,	21
3	4,	7,	9,	21
7	4,	7,	3,	7
	4,	1,	3,	1

L.C.M $= 2 \times 2 \times 3 \times 7 \times 4 \times 3 = 1008.$

The least number of 5 digits is 10000.

$\therefore$ Dividing 10000 by 1008, we have

$$
\begin{array}{r}
1008)\overline{10000}(9 \\
9072 \\
\hline
928
\end{array}
$$

$\therefore$ Least number of five digits exactly divisible by 1008

$$= 10000 + (1008 - 928) = 10000 + 80 = \textbf{10080.}$$

Ex. 8. *Find the L.C.M of two numbers, if their product is 8064 and their H.C.F is 12.*

Sol. Product of the two numbers = Product of their H.C.F and L.C.M

$$12 \times \text{L.C.M.} = 8064 \implies \text{L.C.M.} = \frac{8064}{12} = \textbf{672.}$$

Ex.9. *The L.C.M of two numbers is 11 times their H.C.F. The difference of H.C.F and L.C.M is 240. If one of the numbers is 66, find the other.*

Sol. Let the H.C.F. be $x \implies$ L.C.M. $= 11x$

Given $11x - x = 240 \implies 10x = 240 \implies x = \dfrac{240}{10} = 24$

$\therefore$ H.C.F. = 24 and L.C.M. = $11 \times 24 = 264$

$\because$ Product of the two numbers = product of their H.C.F. and L.C.M.

Given, one number = 66 $\therefore$ Other number = $\dfrac{\text{H.C.F.} \times \text{L.C.M.}}{\text{One number}} = \dfrac{24 \times 264}{66} = \textbf{96.}$

Ex.10. *Find the least number which when divided by 8, 12, 18 and 32 leaves a remainder of 3 in each case.*

Sol. Required number = (L.C .M of 8, 12, 18 and 32) + 3

2	8,	12,	18,	32
2	4,	6,	9,	16
2	2,	3,	9,	8
3	1,	3,	9,	4
	1,	1,	3,	4

∴ L.C.M of 8, 12, 18, 32
$= 2 \times 2 \times 2 \times 3 \times 3 \times 4 = 288$
∴ Required number = 288 + 3 = **291.**

3.8 H.C.F and L.C.M of Fractions

$$\text{H.C.F of given fractions} = \frac{\text{H.C.F of numerators}}{\text{L.C.M of denominators}}$$

$$\text{L.C.M of given fractions} = \frac{\text{L.C.M of numerators}}{\text{H.C.F of denominators}}$$

Ex.11. *Find the H.C.F and L.C.M of $\frac{6}{7}$, $\frac{24}{35}$ and $\frac{42}{49}$.*

Sol. H.C.F of the given fractions $= \dfrac{\text{H.C.F of numerators}}{\text{L.C.M of denominators}}$

H.C.F of 6, 24 and 42 = 6

L.C.M of 7, 35, 49 $= 7 \times 5 \times 7 = 245$

7	7,	35,	49
	1,	5,	7

∴ Required H.C.F $= \dfrac{6}{245}$.

L.C.M of the given fractions $= \dfrac{\text{L.C.M of numerators}}{\text{H.C.F of denominators}}$

L.C.M of 6, 24 and 42 $= 2 \times 3 \times 4 \times 7 = 168$

H.C.F of 7, 35 and 49 = 7.

2	6,	24,	42
3	3,	12,	21
	1,	4,	7

∴ Required L.C.M $= \dfrac{168}{7}$.

EXERCISE 3 (b)

1. **Write down in prime factors the H.C.F and L.C.M of :**
   (a) $2^3 \times 3^2$, $2^2 \times 3^4$
   (b) $2^4 \times 3^2 \times 5^2$, $2^2 \times 3^3 \times 7^2$
   (c) $2^2 \times 3^3 \times 5$, $2^3 \times 3^2 \times 5^2$, $2 \times 3^2 \times 5 \times 7$
   (d) $2^2 \times 3 \times 7$, $2^2 \times 3^2 \times 5$, $2^3 \times 3 \times 11$

2. **Find the H.C.F of the following by prime factorisation method :**
   (a) 225 and 135
   (b) 65, 78, 104
   (c) 440, 715, 935
   (d) 84, 144, 360, 420

3. **Find the H.C.F of the following by long division method:**
   (a) 703, 1387
   (b) 966, 2940 and 2660
   (c) 4030, 2470 and 2198
   (d) 12028 and 12772

4. **Find the L.C.M of :**
   (a) 33, 84, 77, 28, 56
   (b) 25, 50, 75, 100
   (c) 39, 117, 169
   (d) 36, 38, 57, 114, 19

5. Find the largest number which is a factor of 63, 483 and 777.

6. Find the smallest number which is a multiple of each of the numbers 91, 56 and 104.

7. Find the greatest number that will divide 1460 and 2780 leaving a remainder of 3 and 7 respectively.

8. Find the least number that is divided exactly by 15, 18 and 45 leaving a remainder of 5 in each case.

9. Find the greatest number of 5 digits that is exactly divisible by 14, 18, 28, 48 and 60.

10. Find the smallest number of 6 digits that is exactly divisible by 40, 35, 85, 119, 136.

11. Four children step off together while going to school. Their steps measure 25 cm, 30 cm , 35 cm and 45cm respectively. At what distance from the standing point will they step off together again ?

12. Find the size of the largest square tile needed to pave the floor of a room, given the length and breadth of the room are 8m and 6 m 40cm. Also find the least number of square tiles needed.

13. Find the smallest sum of money which can be divided into an exact number of shares either of 50p each or 75p each or Rs. 1 each or Rs 1.50 each.

14. A school teacher divided his students consisting of 224 boys and 336 girls, into largest possible equal classes, so that each class of boys should have the same number as each class of girls. Find also the number of classes.

15. The L.C.M and H.C.F of two numbers are 462 and 22 respectively. One of the numbers is 154, find the other.

16. The L.C.M of two co-prime numbers is 638. One number is 29, find the other.

17. The L.C.M of two numbers is 13 times their H.C.F. If the sum of the L.C.M and H.C.F is 560 and one of the numbers is 65, find the other.

18. **Find the H.C.F and L.C.M of :**

    (a) $\dfrac{2}{3}, \dfrac{8}{9}, \dfrac{10}{15}$ (b) $\dfrac{8}{11}, \dfrac{16}{33}, \dfrac{24}{55}$

19. Can two numbers have 45 as their H.C.F and 240 as the L.C.M ? Give reasons to support your answer.

20. Determine two numbers nearest to 3000 exactly divisible by 5, 7, 14, 15.

LOOKING BACK
Summary of Key Facts

1. A **factor of** a number is an exact divisor of that number .

2. 1 is a factor of every number.

3. A **multiple** of any natural number is obtained by multiplying this number by natural numbers 1, 2, 3,... .

4. A **prime number** is a whole number greater than 1 which is divisible only by 1 and by itself. A natural number greater than 1 which is not prime is called a **composite number**. The number 1 is neither prime nor composite.

5. Two natural numbers which do not have a common prime factor are called **co-primes**, *e.g.* (2, 3) (3, 4) (16, 25) etc.

6. Prime numbers that differ by 2 are called **twin primes**.

7. **Tests of divisibility** : A number is divisible by

    (i) 2, if the unit digit of the number is either 0 or an even number.

   (ii) 3, if the sum of the digits is divisible by 3.

  (iii) 4, if the number formed by its digits in tens and units places is divisible by 4.

  (iv) 5, if the unit's digit is either 0 or 5.

   (v) 6, if it is divisible by both 2 and 3, *i.e.,* if it is an even number, and the sum of its digits is divisible by 3.

  (vi) 8, if the number formed by its digits in hundred's, ten's and units place is divisible by 8.

 (vii) 9, if the sum of its digits is divisible by 9.

(viii) 10, if its unit's digit is 0.

(ix) 11, if the difference of the sum of its digits in odd places and in even places (starting from the unit's place) is divisible by 11.

8. The process of writing a composite number as the product of prime factors is called the **prime factorisation** of the given number.

9. The H.C.F of two or more numbers is the greatest number that divides each one of them exactly.

10. The L.C.M of two or more numbers is the least number that is divisible by all these numbers.

11. The product of two numbers is equal to the product of their H.C.F and L.C.M.

MENTAL MATHS – 2

1. Is 9229 divisible by 11?
2. What number should replace the star in 3 * 35 so that it may become divisible by 3 ?
3. Write the prime triplet known so far.
4. What is the H.C.F of 18 and 45?
5. What is the L.C.M of 8 and 15 ?
6. State the L.C.M of $2^2 \times 3^2 \times 5^2$, $2^3 \times 3 \times 5 \times 7$ as product of primes only.
7. State the prime factors of the smallest 3-digit number.
8. Two numbers are 15 and 45. Their H.C.F is 5. Find their L.C.M.
9. State the H.C.F. of $2^3 \times 5 \times 11$, $2^2 \times 3^2 \times 5^2$ and $2 \times 5^2 \times 3 \times 11$ as a product of primes only.

ANSWERS

EXERCISE 3 (a)

1. (a) 17, 31, 37, 19, 2, 5, 13 are prime numbers; 4, 20, 9, 64, 934, 87, 36, 119 are composite numbers
   (b) 17, 9, 31, 87, 37, 19, 5, 13, 119, 3 are odd numbers; 4, 20, 64, 934, 2, 36 are even numbers
2. No, there are 15. They are 2, 3, 5, 7, 11, 13, 17, 19, 23, 29, 31, 37, 41, 43, 47.
3. (a) 9   (b) 15   (c) 33
4. (a) $48 = 2 \times 2 \times 2 \times 2 \times 3$ (b) $72 = 2 \times 2 \times 2 \times 3 \times 3$ (c) $168 = 2 \times 2 \times 2 \times 3 \times 7$ (d) $330 = 2 \times 3 \times 5 \times 11$
   (e) $516 = 2 \times 2 \times 3 \times 43$
5. Any three correct pairs of twin primes, e.g. (11, 13), (17, 19), (29, 31), (41, 43), (59, 61) are acceptable   6. odd
7. (a), (c) and (d)   8. (b) and (d)   9. (a) and (c)   10. (a), (b) and (e)   11. 1   12. 2

EXERCISE 3 (b)

1. (a) H.C.F $= 2^2 \times 3^2$ (b) H.C.F $= 2^2 \times 3^2$ (c) H.C.F $= 2 \times 3^2 \times 5$ (d) H.C.F $= 2^2 \times 3$
   L.C.M. $= 2^3 \times 3^4$ L.C.M $= 2^4 \times 3^3 \times 5^2 \times 7^2$ L.C.M $= 2^3 \times 3^3 \times 5^2 \times 7$ L.C.M $= 2^3 \times 3^2 \times 5 \times 7 \times 11$
2. (a) 45   (b) 13   (c) 55   (d) 12   3. (a) 19   (b) 14   (c) 2   (d) 124
4. (a) 1848   (b) 300   (c) 1521   (d) 684   5. 21   6. 728   7. 47   8. 95
9. 95760   10. 104720   11. 3150 cm   12. 1 m 60 cm, 20 tiles   13. Rs 3 or 300p
14. 112 students each, 2 class for boy, 3 classes for girls.   15. 66.   16. 22   17. 320
18. (a) H.C.F $=$, $\frac{2}{45}$ L.C.M $= \frac{40}{3}$ (b) H.C.F $= \frac{8}{165}$, L.C.M $= \frac{48}{11}$ 19. No, H.C.F should divide L.C.M exactly
20. 2940, 3150.

MENTAL MATHS – 2

1. Yes   2. 1   3. (3,5,7)   4. 9   5. 120   6. $2^3 \times 3^2 \times 5^2 \times 7$ 7. $2^2 \times 5^2$
8. 135   9. 2×5

4. Fractions

4.1 What is a Fraction?

A fraction is a number that expresses part of a group. Fractions are written in the form $\frac{a}{b}$, where a and b are whole numbers and $b \neq 0$. The number a is called the **numerator** and the number b is called the **denominator**.

Ex. $\frac{1}{2}, \frac{3}{5}, \frac{6}{11}, \frac{4}{99}$ are all fractions.

4.2 Types of Fractions

1. **Proper Fractions :** Fractions having numerator less than the denominator are called proper fractions.

   Ex. $\frac{3}{7}, \frac{7}{13}, \frac{5}{21}, \frac{13}{121}$ are all proper fractions.

2. **Improper Fractions :** Fractions having numerators that are larger than or equal to their denominators are called improper fractions.

   Ex. $\frac{12}{5}, \frac{6}{6}, \frac{21}{11}, \frac{41}{20}$ are all improper fractions.

3. **Mixed Numbers :** Numbers having a whole number part and a fractional part are called mixed numbers. We denote a mixed number in the form $a\frac{b}{c}$.

   Ex. $4\frac{1}{3}, 2\frac{1}{5}, 7\frac{11}{20}, 19\frac{31}{60}$ are all mixed numbers.

> **Note :** Every mixed number can be written as an improper fraction and every improper fraction can be written as a mixed number.

   Example : (i) $2\frac{1}{7} = \frac{2 \times 7 + 1}{7} = \frac{15}{7}$ Mixed Number $\longrightarrow$ Improper Fraction

   (ii) $\frac{25}{8} = 25 \div 8 = 3\frac{1}{8}$ Improper Fraction $\longrightarrow$ Mixed Number.

   > Where 3 is the quotient and 1 is the remainder.

4. **Decimal Fractions :** Fractions having denominators as 10, 100 or 1000 or any other higher power of 10 are called decimal fractions.

   Ex. $\frac{4}{100}, \frac{35}{1000}, \frac{319}{10^4}, \frac{8734}{10^6}$, are all decimals.

5. **Vulgar Fractions :** Fractions having denominators as whole numbers other than any power of 10 are called vulgar fractions.

   Ex. $\frac{5}{31}, \frac{413}{99}, \frac{251}{600}, \frac{837}{8000}, \frac{937}{7180}$ etc., are all vulgar fractions.

6. **Simple Fractions :** Fractions having both the numerator and denominator as whole numbers are called simple fractions.

   Ex. $\dfrac{4}{5}, \dfrac{6}{95}, \dfrac{131}{421}$ etc.

7. **Complex Fractions :** Fractions having either or both the numerator and denominator as fractions or mixed numbers are called complex fractions.

   Ex. $\dfrac{\frac{2}{5}}{\frac{1}{3}}, \dfrac{1\frac{1}{3}}{3\frac{1}{5}}, \dfrac{7}{4\frac{1}{7}}$ etc. are all complex fractions.

   To simplify a complex fraction, we change the complex fraction into a division sum, i.e., divide the numerator by the denominator.

   Examples : (i) $\dfrac{\frac{2}{5}}{3} = 2 \div \dfrac{5}{3} = 2 \times \dfrac{3}{5} = \dfrac{6}{5}$.

   (ii) $\dfrac{2\frac{3}{4}}{6\frac{7}{11}} = 2\dfrac{3}{4} \div 6\dfrac{7}{11} = \dfrac{11}{4} \div \dfrac{73}{11} = \dfrac{11}{4} \times \dfrac{11}{73} = \dfrac{121}{292}$.

8. **Equivalent Fractions :** Fractions representing the same value are called equivalent fractions.

   Equivalent fractions can be found by multiplying or dividing the numerator and denominator of a fraction by the same non-zero number.

   We use equivalent fractions when adding or subtracting fractions and to compare the size of fractions.

   Examples :

   Equivalent fractions for $\dfrac{4}{5} = \dfrac{4 \times 3}{5 \times 3} = \dfrac{12}{15}, \dfrac{4}{5} = \dfrac{4 \times 5}{5 \times 5} = \dfrac{20}{25}$

   Equivalent fractions for $\dfrac{24}{36} = \dfrac{24 \div 3}{36 \div 3} = \dfrac{8}{12}, \dfrac{24}{36} = \dfrac{24 \div 12}{36 \div 12} = \dfrac{2}{3}$

9. **Like and Unlike Fractions :** Fractions having the same denominators are called like fractions, whereas fractions having different denominators are called unlike fractions.

   Examples :

   $\dfrac{4}{11}, \dfrac{6}{11}, \dfrac{2}{11}, \dfrac{7}{1}$ etc. are all like fractions.

   $\dfrac{3}{5}, \dfrac{4}{7}, \dfrac{11}{12}, \dfrac{19}{40}$ etc. are all unlike fractions.

   > **Note :** To **convert unlike fractions** to **like fractions**, we find the **L.C.M of the denominators** of the given fractions and convert each fraction into an equivalent like fraction with the L.C.M as the denominator.

   Ex. Convert $\dfrac{3}{5}$ and $\dfrac{4}{7}$ to like fractions

   L.C.M of 5 and 7 = 35

   $\therefore \dfrac{3}{5} = \dfrac{3 \times 7}{5 \times 7} = \dfrac{21}{35}$ and $\dfrac{4}{7} = \dfrac{4 \times 5}{7 \times 5} = \dfrac{20}{35}$

4.3 Reducing a Fraction to its Lowest Terms.

A fraction is in lowest terms when the H.C.F of its numerator and denominator is 1. There are two methods of reducing a fraction to its lowest terms.

Method 1 :

Divide the numerator and denominator by their H.C.F.

Ex. $\dfrac{24}{30} = \dfrac{24 \div 6}{30 \div 6} = \dfrac{4}{5}$

> H.C.F of 24 and 30 is 6

Method 2 :

Divide the numerator and denominator by any common factor. Keep dividing until there are no more common factors.

Ex. $\dfrac{24}{30} = \dfrac{24 \div 2}{30 \div 2} = \dfrac{12}{15} = \dfrac{12 \div 3}{15 \div 3} = \dfrac{4}{5}$

We show this process as: $\dfrac{\cancel{24}^{\,\cancel{12}^{\,4}}}{\cancel{30}_{\,\cancel{15}_{\,5}}} = \dfrac{4}{5}$

> First divide both the numerator and the denominator by the common factor 2 and then by 3.

4.4 Comparing Fractions

1. Like Fractions can be compared by comparing their numerators. The fraction with the greater numerator is greater.

   Ex. $\dfrac{11}{13} > \dfrac{9}{13} > \dfrac{5}{13}$

2. If two or more fractions have the same numerator, then the fraction with smaller denominator is greater.

   Ex. $\dfrac{41}{16} > \dfrac{41}{30} > \dfrac{41}{35}$

3. To compare fractions with different denominators, we take their cross product, *i.e.,* $\dfrac{a}{b}$ and $\dfrac{c}{d}$ can be compared

   by taking their cross product $\dfrac{a}{b} \diagdown\!\!\!\!\diagup \dfrac{c}{d}$, *i.e., ad* and *bc*.

   (i) If $ad > bc$ then $\dfrac{a}{b} > \dfrac{c}{d}$ *(ii)* If $ad = bc$ then $\dfrac{a}{b} = \dfrac{c}{d}$ *(iii)* If $ad < bc$ then $\dfrac{a}{d} < \dfrac{c}{d}$.

   Ex. To compare $\dfrac{3}{8}$ and $\dfrac{4}{7}$ and we take their cross products $\dfrac{3}{8} \diagdown\!\!\!\!\diagup \dfrac{4}{7}$ and have

   $3 \times 7 = 21$ $8 \times 4 = 32$ Since $21 < 32$, therefore $\dfrac{3}{8} < \dfrac{4}{7}$.

This method is generally used when we compare two fractions.

Ex. 1. *Arrange* $\dfrac{4}{5}, \dfrac{6}{15}$ *and* $\dfrac{7}{20}$ *in ascending order by*

         (a) *making denominators equals*   **(b)** *making numerators equal.*

Sol. *(a)* To make denominators equal we take the L.C.M of denominators 5, 15 and 20.

     L.C.M $= 5 \times 3 \times 4 = 60$

$\therefore \quad \dfrac{4}{5} = \dfrac{4 \times 12}{5 \times 12} = \dfrac{48}{60}, \ \dfrac{6}{15} = \dfrac{6 \times 4}{15 \times 4} = \dfrac{24}{60}, \ \dfrac{7}{20} = \dfrac{7 \times 3}{20 \times 3} = \dfrac{21}{60}$

5	5,	15,	20
	1,	3,	4

It can be clearly seen that $\dfrac{21}{60} < \dfrac{24}{60} < \dfrac{48}{60} \Rightarrow \dfrac{7}{20} < \dfrac{6}{15} < \dfrac{4}{5}$.

Hence the given fractions in ascending order are : $\dfrac{7}{20}, \dfrac{6}{15}, \dfrac{4}{5}$.

(b) To make numerators equal, we take the L.C.M of numerators, *i.e.*, 4, 6 and 7

L.C.M = $2 \times 2 \times 3 \times 7 = 84$

2	4,	6,	7
	2,	3,	7

$$\therefore \quad \frac{4}{5} = \frac{4 \times 21}{5 \times 21} = \frac{84}{105}, \quad \frac{6}{15} = \frac{6 \times 14}{15 \times 14} = \frac{84}{210}, \quad \frac{7}{20} = \frac{7 \times 12}{20 \times 12} = \frac{84}{240}$$

It can be clearly seen that on comparing denominators, $\frac{84}{240} < \frac{84}{210} < \frac{84}{105}$, *i.e.,* $\frac{7}{20} < \frac{6}{15} < \frac{4}{5}$

Hence the given numbers in ascending order are $\frac{7}{20}, \frac{6}{15}, \frac{4}{5}$.

Ex. 2. *Compare* $\frac{16}{21}$ *and* $\frac{20}{31}$.

Sol. Taking the cross product $\frac{16}{21} \diagtimes \frac{20}{31}$, we have $16 \times 31 = 496$ and $20 \times 21 = 420$

$$496 > 420 \Rightarrow \frac{16}{21} > \frac{20}{31}.$$

4.5 To Insert Fractions Between Two Given Fractions

If $\frac{a}{b}$ and $\frac{c}{d}$ are two given fractions then $\frac{a+c}{b+d}$ lies between $\frac{a}{b}$ and $\frac{c}{d}$.

Ex. 3. *Insert two fractions between* $\frac{2}{3}$ *and* $\frac{4}{5}$.

Sol. A fraction between $\frac{2}{3}$ and $\frac{4}{5} = \frac{2+4}{3+5} = \frac{6}{8} = \frac{3}{4}$ $\qquad \therefore \qquad \frac{2}{3} < \frac{3}{4} < \frac{4}{5}$

A fraction between $\frac{2}{3}$ and $\frac{3}{4}$ is $\frac{2+3}{3+4} = \frac{5}{7}$ $\qquad \therefore \qquad \frac{2}{3} < \frac{5}{7} < \frac{3}{4} < \frac{4}{5}$

$\therefore$ Two fractions between $\frac{2}{3}$ and $\frac{4}{5}$ are $\frac{5}{7}$ and $\frac{3}{4}$.

EXERCISE 4 (a)

1. Express each of the following mixed numbers as an improper fraction.

(a) $4\frac{14}{25}$ \qquad\qquad (b) $16\frac{4}{9}$ \qquad\qquad (c) $13\frac{2}{7}$ \qquad\qquad (d) $12\frac{7}{18}$

2. Express each of the following as a mixed number.

(a) $\frac{237}{17}$ \qquad\qquad (b) $\frac{725}{18}$ \qquad\qquad (c) $\frac{637}{25}$ \qquad\qquad (d) $\frac{585}{41}$

3. Reduce each of the following fractions to its lowest terms :

(a) $\frac{90}{135}$ \qquad\qquad (b) $\frac{98}{343}$ \qquad\qquad (c) $\frac{216}{243}$ \qquad\qquad (d) $\frac{144}{312}$

4. Compare the given fractions.

(a) $\frac{6}{25}$ and $\frac{10}{19}$ \qquad (b) $\frac{15}{26}$ and $\frac{11}{15}$ \qquad (c) $\frac{19}{14}$ and $\frac{17}{21}$ \qquad (d) $\frac{8}{27}$ and $\frac{13}{36}$

5. Arrange the following fractions in the ascending order of magnitude by making numerators equal.

(a) $\frac{2}{3}, \frac{4}{5}, \frac{3}{4}, \frac{5}{6}$ \qquad (b) $\frac{3}{5}, \frac{7}{8}, \frac{1}{11}, \frac{9}{13}$ \qquad (c) $\frac{5}{6}, \frac{10}{13}, \frac{6}{20}$

6. Arrange the following fractions in descending order of magnitude by making denominators equal.

(a) $\dfrac{3}{4}, \dfrac{7}{8}, \dfrac{11}{24}, \dfrac{13}{32}$ (b) $\dfrac{2}{11}, \dfrac{9}{22}, \dfrac{7}{33}, \dfrac{6}{55}$ (c) $\dfrac{3}{5}, \dfrac{7}{10}, \dfrac{6}{25}, \dfrac{11}{30}$

7. Insert three fractions between :

(a) $\dfrac{9}{11}$ and $\dfrac{13}{15}$ (b) $\dfrac{2}{3}$ and $\dfrac{7}{9}$ (c) $\dfrac{5}{8}$ and $\dfrac{17}{23}$

OPERATIONS ON FRACTIONS

4.6 Adding and Subtracting Fractions

I. The sum or difference of like fractions (*i.e.,* fractions with the same denominator) is the sum or difference of the numerators over the denominator.

(**Caution** : We do not add or subtract the denominators:)

Reduce the answer if necessary.

Examples : $\dfrac{3}{7} + \dfrac{6}{7} = \dfrac{3+6}{7} = \dfrac{9}{7} = 1\dfrac{\mathbf{2}}{\mathbf{7}}$, $\dfrac{8}{11} - \dfrac{2}{11} = \dfrac{8-2}{11} = \dfrac{\mathbf{6}}{\mathbf{11}}$.

II. The sum or difference of unlike fractions can be found by converting the unlike fractions to equivalent like fractions.

(1) First find the L.C.M of the denominators.

(2) Write equivalent fractions using this denominator and then add or subtract as in **I**.

Examples : $\dfrac{3}{5} + \dfrac{2}{3} = \dfrac{9}{15} + \dfrac{10}{15} = \dfrac{19}{15} = 1\dfrac{\mathbf{4}}{\mathbf{15}}$. $\boxed{\text{L.C.M of 3 and 5} = 15}$

$\dfrac{7}{10} - \dfrac{1}{2} = \dfrac{7}{10} - \dfrac{5}{10} = \dfrac{2}{10} = \dfrac{\mathbf{1}}{\mathbf{5}}$. $\boxed{\text{L.C.M of 2 and 10} = 10}$

Remark : To add or subtract mixed numbers, we simply convert them to improper fractions and then add or subtract as simple fractions.

4.7 Multiplication

If $\dfrac{a}{b}$ and $\dfrac{c}{d}$ are two fractions then $\dfrac{a}{b} \times \dfrac{c}{d} = \dfrac{a \times c}{b \times d}$.

Reduce the answer to the lowest terms or cancel out the common factor (if any) from the numerators and denominators of the given fractions.

For mixed numbers, first convert them to improper fractions and then proceed.

Examples :

$\dfrac{\overset{1}{\cancel{2}}}{\underset{3}{\cancel{15}}} \times \dfrac{\overset{2}{\cancel{10}}}{\underset{9}{\cancel{18}}} = \dfrac{1 \times 2}{3 \times 9} = \dfrac{2}{27}$ $\boxed{\text{Cancelling out by 2 and 5}}$

$4\dfrac{1}{5} \times 3\dfrac{4}{7} = \dfrac{\overset{3}{\cancel{21}}}{\underset{1}{\cancel{5}}} \times \dfrac{\overset{5}{\cancel{25}}}{\underset{1}{\cancel{7}}} = \mathbf{15}$. $\boxed{\text{Cancelling out by 5 and 7}}$

4.8 Reciprocal

The reciprocal of any non-zero fraction $\dfrac{a}{b}$, where a and $b \in N$ is $\dfrac{b}{a}$.

For a mixed number convert it into an improper fraction and then find the reciprocal.

> **Note :** The product of a fraction and its reciprocal is always 1.

Examples : Reciprocal of $\dfrac{16}{21}$ is $\dfrac{21}{16}$

Reciprocal of $4\dfrac{1}{5}$ = Reciprocal of $\dfrac{21}{5}$ = $\dfrac{5}{21}$.

4.9 Division of Fractions.

To divide a fraction by a fraction multiply the dividend by the reciprocal of the divisor.

If $\dfrac{a}{b}$ and $\dfrac{c}{d}$ are two non-zero fractions, then $\dfrac{a}{b} \div \dfrac{c}{d} = \dfrac{a}{b} \times \dfrac{d}{c}$.

In case of mixed numbers convert them to improper fractions and proceed as above.

Examples : $\dfrac{4}{5} \div \dfrac{8}{15} = \dfrac{\cancel{4}^{1}}{\cancel{5}_{1}} \times \dfrac{\cancel{15}^{3}}{\cancel{8}_{2}} = \dfrac{3}{2} = 1\dfrac{1}{2}$; $\quad 2\dfrac{1}{3} \div 4\dfrac{1}{5} = \dfrac{7}{3} \div \dfrac{21}{5} = \dfrac{\cancel{7}^{1}}{3} \times \dfrac{5}{\cancel{21}_{3}} = \dfrac{5}{9}$.

4.10 Use of 'OF'

'OF' Works like multiplication

Examples : $\dfrac{3}{4}$ of $24 = \dfrac{3}{\cancel{4}_{1}} \times \cancel{24}^{6} = 18$, $\quad \dfrac{11}{16}$ of $\dfrac{80}{77} = \dfrac{\cancel{11}^{1}}{\cancel{16}_{1}} \times \dfrac{\cancel{80}^{5}}{\cancel{77}_{7}} = \dfrac{5}{7}$.

4.11 Simplification

To simplify expressions involving fractions, the operations have to follow the rule of BODMAS *i.e.*, operations are performed in the order.

(*a*) *Brackets* (*b*) *Of* (*c*) *Division* (*d*) *Multiplication*

(*e*) *Addition* (*f*) *Subtraction*.

The brackets are removed in the order :

(*a*) _____; bar or veniculum (*b*) ( ); parenthesis

(*c*){ }; curly brackets (*d*) [ ]; square brackets

We also say **'innermost to outermost'** as these brackets appear in that order in an expressions.

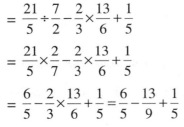

BODMAS

Ex. 1. *Simplify :* $4\dfrac{1}{5} \div 3\dfrac{1}{2} - \dfrac{2}{3} \times 2\dfrac{1}{6} + \dfrac{8}{25}$ *of* $\dfrac{15}{24}$.

Sol. Given expression = $\dfrac{21}{5} \div \dfrac{7}{2} - \dfrac{2}{3} \times \dfrac{13}{6} + \dfrac{\cancel{8}^{1}}{\cancel{25}_{5}}$ of $\dfrac{\cancel{15}^{\cancel{3}^{1}}}{\cancel{24}_{\cancel{3}_{1}}}$

> Operating of. Think that 'OF' means '×'

$= \dfrac{21}{5} \div \dfrac{7}{2} - \dfrac{2}{3} \times \dfrac{13}{6} + \dfrac{1}{5}$

$= \dfrac{21}{5} \times \dfrac{2}{7} - \dfrac{2}{3} \times \dfrac{13}{6} + \dfrac{1}{5}$

> operating ÷

$= \dfrac{6}{5} - \dfrac{2}{3} \times \dfrac{13}{6} + \dfrac{1}{5} = \dfrac{6}{5} - \dfrac{13}{9} + \dfrac{1}{5}$

> operating ×

$$= \frac{54-65+9}{45} = \frac{63-65}{45} = \frac{-2}{45}$$

Ex. 2 : *Simplify :* $4\frac{1}{2} - \frac{2}{3} \div \frac{5}{6}$ *of* $\frac{12}{15} + 3\frac{1}{5} - \frac{3}{4}\left(\frac{5}{6} - \overline{\frac{1}{3} - \frac{1}{4}}\right)$.

1.	Converting mixed numbers to improper fractions
2.	Operating '—'

Given expression $= \frac{9}{2} - \frac{2}{3} \div \frac{5}{6}$ of $\frac{12}{15} + \frac{16}{5} - \frac{3}{4}\left(\frac{5}{6} - \overline{\frac{4-3}{12}}\right) \longleftarrow$

$$= \frac{9}{2} - \frac{2}{3} \div \frac{5}{6} \text{ of } \frac{12}{15} + \frac{16}{5} - \frac{3}{4}\left(\frac{5}{6} - \frac{1}{12}\right) = \frac{9}{2} - \frac{2}{3} \div \frac{5}{6} \text{ of } \frac{12}{15} + \frac{16}{5} - \frac{3}{4}\left(\frac{10-1}{12}\right)$$

$$= \frac{9}{2} - \frac{2}{3} \div \frac{\cancel{5}^1}{\cancel{6}_1} \text{ of } \frac{\cancel{12}^2}{\cancel{15}_3} + \frac{16}{5} - \frac{\cancel{3}^1}{4} \times \frac{9}{\cancel{12}_4}$$

Operationg ( )

$$= \frac{9}{2} - \frac{2}{3} \div \frac{2}{3} + \frac{16}{5} - \frac{9}{16}$$

Operating 'of' and ×

$$= \frac{9}{2} - \frac{2}{3} \times \frac{3}{2} + \frac{16}{5} - \frac{9}{16}$$

Operating division

$$= \frac{9}{2} - 1 + \frac{16}{5} - \frac{9}{16}$$

Operating multiplication

$$= \frac{9 \times 40 - 1 \times 80 + 16 \times 16 - 9 \times 5}{80} = \frac{360 - 80 + 256 - 45}{80}$$

$$= \frac{616 - 125}{80} = \frac{491}{80} = 6\frac{11}{80}.$$

4.12 Word Problems on Fractions

Ex. 1. *If* $\frac{7}{11}$ *of the worth of a computer be Rs 35112, then what is the worth of the computer ?*

Sol. $\frac{7}{11}$ of worth of the computer = Rs 35112

∴ Worth of the computer $= \frac{11}{7}$ of Rs 35112 $= \frac{\cancel{35112}^{5016} \times 11}{\cancel{7}_1}$ = Rs (5016 × 11) = Rs 55, 176

∴ The total worth of the computer is **Rs 55, 176.**

Ex. 2. *If* $\frac{1}{5}$ *of a number is subtracted from* $\frac{1}{3}$ *of the number, the result is 25 greater than one twentieth of the number. Find the number.*

Sol. Let the number be x.

Then $\quad \frac{1}{3}x - \frac{1}{5}x = \frac{1}{20}x + 25 \qquad \Rightarrow \quad \frac{x}{3} - \frac{x}{5} - \frac{x}{20} = 25 \qquad \Rightarrow \quad \frac{20x - 12x - 3x}{60} = 25$

$\Rightarrow \quad \frac{5x}{60} = 25 \qquad \Rightarrow \quad x = \frac{25 \times 60}{5} = 300$

Hence, the required number is **300**.

Ex. 3. *A sum of money is divided between A and B. A receives* $\frac{2}{3}$ *of the total sum and B receives* $\frac{3}{11}$ *of the remainder. If the difference between the shares of A and B is Rs 570, what was the total sum?*

Sol. Let the sum be Rs x.

A's share $= \frac{2}{3}x$. Remaining sum $= x - \frac{2}{3}x = \frac{1}{3}x \qquad$ ∴ $\quad$ B' share $= \frac{3}{11}$ of $\frac{1}{3}x = \frac{3}{11} \times \frac{1}{3}x = \frac{1}{11}x$

A's share – B's share = Rs 570 $\Rightarrow$ $\dfrac{2}{3}x - \dfrac{1}{11}x = 570$ $\Rightarrow$ $\dfrac{22x - 3x}{33} = 570$

$\Rightarrow \dfrac{19x}{33} = 570$ $\Rightarrow x = \dfrac{570 \times 33}{19} = 990$ $\therefore$ The total sum of money was **Rs 990.**

Alternatively : Instead of taking the money as Rs x, you could have taken it as Re 1. Then,

A's share = $\dfrac{2}{3}$ of Re 1 = Re $\dfrac{2}{3}$, remainder = Re $\left(1 - \dfrac{2}{3}\right)$ = Re $\dfrac{1}{3}$ $\therefore$ B's share = $\dfrac{3}{11}$ of Re $\dfrac{1}{3}$ = Re $\dfrac{1}{11}$.

Difference of A's and B's share = Re $\left(\dfrac{2}{3} - \dfrac{1}{11}\right)$ = Re $\dfrac{19}{33}$.

When the difference is Re $\dfrac{19}{133}$, total sum = Re 1

When the difference is Rs 570, total sum = Rs 570 $\times \dfrac{33}{19}$ = Rs 990.

Ex. 4. *A man spends $\dfrac{1}{3}$ of his total money, loses $\dfrac{1}{4}$ of the remaining and then gives away in charity $\dfrac{3}{5}$ of what is left. If he still has Rs 100 left, what did he originally have?*

Sol. Let the total sum of money he has be Rs x.

He spends $\dfrac{1}{3}$ of x, i.e., Rs $\dfrac{x}{3}$ $\qquad \therefore$ Remaining amount = $x - \dfrac{x}{3} = \dfrac{3x - x}{3} = $ Rs $\dfrac{2x}{3}$

He loses $\dfrac{1}{4}$ of the remaining, i.e., $\dfrac{1}{4}$ of $\dfrac{2x}{3} = \dfrac{1}{4} \times \dfrac{2x}{3} = $ Rs $\dfrac{x}{6}$

$\therefore$ Remaining Amount = $\dfrac{2x}{3} - \dfrac{x}{6} = \dfrac{4x - x}{6} = \dfrac{3x}{6} = $ Rs $\dfrac{x}{2}$

He gives $\dfrac{3}{5}$ of the remaining amount in charity.

$\therefore$ Amount given in charity = $\dfrac{3}{5}$ of $\dfrac{x}{2} = \dfrac{3}{5} \times \dfrac{x}{2} = $ Rs $\dfrac{3x}{10}$

$\therefore$ Remaining amount = $\dfrac{x}{2} - \dfrac{3x}{10} = \dfrac{5x - 3x}{10} = \dfrac{2x}{10} = $ Rs $\dfrac{1}{5}x$

$\therefore \dfrac{x}{5} = 100 \Rightarrow x = 100 \times 5 = 500$. Therefore he originally had **Rs 500.**

Note : You could have taken the total sum of money he has as Re 1 and then worked out as in Ex. 3 above.

EXERCISE 4 (b)

1. Add the following :

(a) $\dfrac{5}{9} + \dfrac{11}{15} + \dfrac{3}{10}$ (b) $\dfrac{11}{13} + \dfrac{23}{26} + \dfrac{11}{39}$ (c) $2\dfrac{1}{2} + 3\dfrac{1}{3} + 4\dfrac{1}{4} + \dfrac{5}{6}$ (d) $3\dfrac{1}{11} + 2\dfrac{6}{22} + \dfrac{17}{44}$

2. Subtract :

(a) $\dfrac{11}{12} - \dfrac{5}{16}$ (b) $\dfrac{11}{57} - \dfrac{3}{38}$ (c) $6\dfrac{1}{8} - 2\dfrac{3}{16}$ (d) $3\dfrac{3}{14} - \dfrac{17}{35}$

3. Simplify :

(a) $\dfrac{8}{9} - \dfrac{1}{5} + \dfrac{3}{5} + \dfrac{1}{6} - \dfrac{3}{4}$

(b) $1\dfrac{3}{4} + 2\dfrac{5}{6} - 3\dfrac{1}{2} - \dfrac{5}{12}$

(c) $2\dfrac{3}{4} + 4\dfrac{4}{11} - 3\dfrac{1}{5}$

(d) $10\dfrac{1}{2} - \dfrac{25}{4} + \dfrac{11}{16} - 3\dfrac{3}{8}$

4. Multiply :

(a) $\dfrac{11}{42} \times \dfrac{28}{55}$

(b) $3\dfrac{3}{4} \times 7\dfrac{11}{12}$

(c) $9\dfrac{3}{5} \times \dfrac{15}{54}$

(d) $\dfrac{4}{3} \times 3\dfrac{1}{7} \times \dfrac{15}{22}$

5. Evaluate :

(a) $\dfrac{6}{7}$ of 12

(b) $\dfrac{7}{11}$ of $\dfrac{44}{35}$

(c) $3\dfrac{1}{4}$ of $4\dfrac{1}{5}$

(d) $6\dfrac{1}{2}$ of $\dfrac{20}{39}$

6. Divide :

(a) $3\dfrac{1}{7} \div 11$

(b) $\dfrac{32}{75} \div \dfrac{4}{15}$

(c) $4\dfrac{7}{12} \div 6\dfrac{3}{16}$

(d) $\dfrac{9}{11} \div 4\dfrac{2}{7}$

Simplify :

7. $\left(2\dfrac{2}{3} \text{ of } 3\dfrac{3}{4}\right) \div \left(2\dfrac{2}{3} + 3\dfrac{3}{4}\right)$

8. $\dfrac{3}{5} \div \dfrac{8}{9} - \dfrac{5}{8} + 7\dfrac{1}{2} \text{ of } \dfrac{11}{12}$

9. $2\dfrac{1}{12} \div 5\dfrac{5}{8} + 1\dfrac{7}{11} \text{ of } 2\dfrac{4}{9} - 2\dfrac{1}{2} \times 1\dfrac{3}{25}$.

10. $\left[7\dfrac{1}{4} - \left\{\dfrac{11}{17} \text{ of } 2\dfrac{2}{33} + \left(3\dfrac{1}{4} \text{ of } \dfrac{12}{39}\right)\right\}\right]$

11. $6\dfrac{4}{7} - \left\{7\dfrac{2}{3} - \left(\dfrac{5}{8} \div \overline{\dfrac{1}{2} - \dfrac{1}{4}}\right)\right\}$

12. $\dfrac{1}{2 + \dfrac{3}{4\frac{1}{5}}} \div \dfrac{3}{3 + \dfrac{1}{4\frac{5}{6}}}$

13. $1 + \dfrac{3}{2 + \dfrac{1}{4 + \dfrac{5}{7}}}$

14. $\dfrac{1 + \dfrac{\frac{1}{2} + \frac{1}{3}}{\frac{1}{3} - \frac{1}{6}}}{2 - \dfrac{\frac{4}{5} \text{ of } \frac{5}{6}}{\frac{2}{3}}}$

15. By how much does the sum of $12\dfrac{1}{4}$ and $6\dfrac{3}{5}$ exceed the difference between $2\dfrac{4}{25}$ and $\dfrac{3}{4}$?

16. If $\dfrac{3}{8}$ of an estate be worth Rs 10848, then find the value of $\dfrac{11}{16}$ of it.

17. If in $1\dfrac{1}{7}$ hours, a train travels $106\dfrac{5}{7}$ kilometres, what is its speed in km/hr ?

18. If a quarter of a number be added to one third of the number, the result is 20 greater than one half of the number. Find the number.

19. Find a fraction which is as much greater than $\dfrac{3}{11}$ as it is less than $\dfrac{11}{3}$.

20. In a village there are 693 children, $\dfrac{4}{7}$ of the total are boys and of these boys $\dfrac{8}{11}$ go to school. Of the boys at school, $\dfrac{2}{9}$ are at primary school. How many boys are there who go to primary school.

21. A man spends $\frac{1}{2}$ of his money in one shop, $\frac{2}{3}$ of the remainder in another shop and $\frac{4}{5}$ of what is left he gives away. If he has Rs 10 still left, how much did he have at first.

22. Of the leaves of a tree, one fourth fall in the first week of October, one third of the remainder in the next week and two fifth of those still remaining fall in the third week. There are then 1350 leaves left. How many were there at first ?

23. A bakery makes 1350 loaves of bread on one night shift. $\frac{7}{10}$ of these are white, $\frac{4}{25}$ are brown and the rest are wheat meal. Find how many of each type of loaf they have baked ?

24. In setting up a post, $\frac{1}{3}$ of its length is buried in the ground and $\frac{1}{5}$ of the remainder is tarred, the rest being painted green. What fraction of (*i*) the whole (*ii*) the part above the ground is green?

25. The highest scores in an innings was $\frac{2}{9}$ of the total and the next highest was $\frac{2}{9}$ of the remainder. These scores differ by 8 runs. What was the total ?

LOOKING BACK
Summary of Key Facts

1. Numbers of the form $\frac{a}{b}$ where $b \neq 0$ are called **fractions.**

2. **Improper Fractions** are those in which the numerator is greater than the denominator.

3. A **mixed number** has a whole number part and a fractional part.

4. **Equivalent fractions** represent the same value.

5. Multiplying or dividing the numerator and denominator by the same number does not change the value of the fraction.

6. A fraction can be changed to its simplest form by dividing both the numerator and denominator by their H.C.F.

7. **Comparison of the fractions** can be done in three ways.

(*i*) Changing them into equivalent fractions having same denominator by finding the L.C.M of the denominators and then comparing the numerators. Greater the numerator, greater the fraction.

(*ii*) Changing them into equivalent fractions having same numerator by finding the L.C.M of the numerators and then comparing denominators. Small the denominator, greater the fraction.

(*iii*) Finding cross product of $\frac{a}{b}$ and $\frac{c}{d}$ (two unlike fractions)

(*a*) If $ad > bc$ then $\frac{a}{b} > \frac{c}{d}$ (*b*) If $ad < bc$ then $\frac{a}{b} < \frac{c}{d}$ (*c*) If $ad = bc$ then $\frac{a}{b} = \frac{c}{d}$.

8. To **add** or **subtract** find equivalent fractions that have the same denominator.

9. To **multiply :** $\frac{a}{b} \times \frac{c}{d} = \frac{a \times c}{b \times d}$ then simplify.   **Ex.** $\frac{5}{7} \times \frac{3}{8} = \frac{5 \times 3}{7 \times 8} = \frac{15}{56}$.

10. **Reciprocal** of a fraction $\frac{a}{b}$ $(a \neq 0, b \neq 0) = \frac{b}{a}$.

11. To divide $= \frac{a}{b} \div \frac{c}{d} = \frac{a}{b} \times \frac{d}{c} = \frac{a \times d}{b \times c}$ (Reciprocal)   **Ex.** $\frac{8}{25} \div \frac{4}{15} = \frac{8}{25} \times \frac{15}{4} = \frac{6}{5} = 1\frac{1}{5}$.

12. If $\frac{a}{b}$ and $\frac{c}{d}$ $(a \in N, b \in N, c \in N, d \in N)$, are two fractions, the $\frac{a+b}{c+d}$ is a fraction between $\frac{a}{b}$ and $\frac{c}{d}$.

13. BODMAS is followed while simplifying a numerical expression having fractions.

MENTAL MATHS – 3

1. Which is greater $\dfrac{16}{21}$ or $\dfrac{10}{9}$?

2. What fraction is 25 days of 5 weeks ?

3. Find the value of $\dfrac{5}{6} - \dfrac{7}{11}$.

4. Write in increasing order : $\dfrac{1}{7}, \dfrac{1}{9}, \dfrac{1}{3}, \dfrac{1}{10}$ and $\dfrac{1}{4}$.

5. Simplify : $\dfrac{1}{4} \div \dfrac{1}{8} \times \dfrac{1}{2}$.

6. Find a fraction between $\dfrac{6}{11}$ and $\dfrac{5}{13}$.

7. Sixteen students went to eat pizza. There was a special offer "Eat one, get a half free". They all took advantage of the offer. How many pizzas did they eat ?

8. Find $\dfrac{3}{4}$ of $5\dfrac{1}{3}$.

9. **Simplify :** (a) $\dfrac{1}{9} \div \dfrac{8}{9} - \dfrac{2}{7} \times \dfrac{7}{16}$; (b) $\dfrac{\frac{2}{3} \text{ of } 24}{\frac{32}{3}}$.

10. Find the reciprocal of $45 \div \dfrac{3}{2}$.

ANSWERS

EXERCISE 4 (a)

1. (a) $\dfrac{114}{25}$ (b) $\dfrac{148}{9}$ (c) $\dfrac{93}{7}$ (d) $\dfrac{223}{18}$ 2. (a) $13\dfrac{16}{17}$ (b) $40\dfrac{5}{18}$ (c) $25\dfrac{12}{25}$ (d) $14\dfrac{11}{41}$

3. (a) $\dfrac{2}{3}$ (b) $\dfrac{2}{7}$ (c) $\dfrac{8}{9}$ (d) $\dfrac{6}{13}$ 4. (a) $\dfrac{6}{25} < \dfrac{10}{19}$ (b) $\dfrac{15}{26} < \dfrac{11}{15}$ (c) $\dfrac{19}{14} > \dfrac{17}{21}$ (d) $\dfrac{8}{27} < \dfrac{13}{36}$

5. (a) $\dfrac{2}{3}, \dfrac{3}{4}, \dfrac{4}{5}, \dfrac{5}{6}$ (b) $\dfrac{1}{11}, \dfrac{3}{5}, \dfrac{9}{13}, \dfrac{7}{8}$ (c) $\dfrac{6}{20}, \dfrac{10}{13}, \dfrac{5}{6}$ 6. (a) $\dfrac{7}{8}, \dfrac{3}{4}, \dfrac{11}{24}, \dfrac{13}{32}$ (b) $\dfrac{9}{22}, \dfrac{7}{33}, \dfrac{2}{11}, \dfrac{6}{55}$

(c) $\dfrac{7}{10}, \dfrac{3}{5}, \dfrac{11}{30}, \dfrac{6}{25}$ 7. (a) $\dfrac{5}{6}, \dfrac{11}{13}, \dfrac{6}{7}$ (b) $\dfrac{5}{7}, \dfrac{3}{4}, \dfrac{10}{13}$ (c) $\dfrac{9}{13}, \dfrac{22}{31}, \dfrac{13}{18}$

EXERCISE 4 (b)

1. (a) $\dfrac{143}{90}$ (b) $\dfrac{157}{78}$ (c) $10\dfrac{11}{12}$ (d) $5\dfrac{33}{44}$ 2. (a) $\dfrac{29}{48}$ (b) $\dfrac{13}{114}$ (c) $3\dfrac{15}{16}$ (d) $2\dfrac{51}{70}$

3. (a) $\dfrac{127}{180}$ (b) $\dfrac{2}{3}$ (c) $3\dfrac{201}{220}$ (d) $1\dfrac{9}{16}$ 4. (a) $\dfrac{2}{15}$ (b) $29\dfrac{11}{16}$ (c) $2\dfrac{2}{3}$ (d) $2\dfrac{6}{7}$

5. (a) $10\dfrac{2}{7}$ (b) $\dfrac{4}{5}$ (c) $13\dfrac{13}{20}$ (d) $3\dfrac{1}{3}$ 6. (a) $\dfrac{2}{7}$ (b) $1\dfrac{3}{5}$ (c) $\dfrac{20}{27}$ (d) $\dfrac{21}{110}$

7. $1\dfrac{43}{77}$ 8. $6\dfrac{37}{40}$ 9. $\dfrac{212}{135}$ 10. $4\dfrac{11}{12}$ 11. $\dfrac{59}{42}$ 12. $\dfrac{217}{551}$ 13. $2\dfrac{26}{73}$ 14. 6.

15. $17\dfrac{11}{25}$ 16. Rs 19888 17. $93\dfrac{3}{8}$ km/hr 18. 240 19. $\dfrac{65}{33}$ 20. 64

21. Rs. 300. 22. 4500 leaves 23. White = 945, Brown = 216, Wheat meal = 189 24. $\dfrac{8}{15}, \dfrac{4}{5}$ 25. 162 runs.

MENTAL MATHS – 3

1. $\dfrac{10}{9}$ 2. $\dfrac{5}{7}$ 3. $\dfrac{13}{66}$ 4. $\dfrac{1}{10}, \dfrac{1}{9}, \dfrac{1}{7}, \dfrac{1}{4}, \dfrac{1}{3}$ 5. 1 6. $\dfrac{11}{24}$ 7. 24

8. 4 9. (a) 0 (b) $\dfrac{3}{2}$ 10. $\dfrac{1}{30}$

5. Decimals

5.1 Decimal Numbers

Numbers like 15.1, 2.05 or 3.782 are used in situations where more accuracy or precision is required than what whole numbers can provide. These numbers are called Decimal numbers.

A decimal number has two parts separated by the decimal point. The part to the **left** of the decimal point is called the **whole number part** and that to the **right** of the decimal point is called the **decimal part**, which is **less than one**.

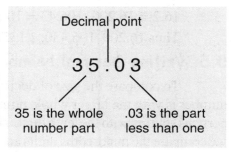

Decimal point

35.03

35 is the whole   .03 is the part
number part   less than one

5.2 Place Value

As with whole numbers, a digit in a decimal number has a place value which depends on the place of the digit. The places to the left of the decimal point are units, tens, hundreds and so on as with whole numbers and to the right are tenths, hundredths, thousandths and so on.

This place value diagram will help you to understand what 35.03 means :

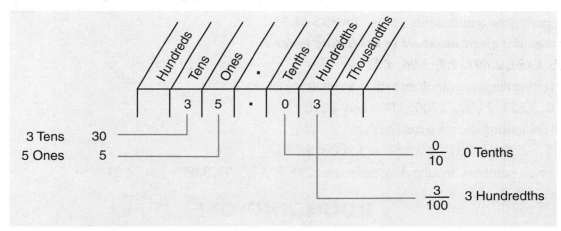

Thus the given number in the expanded form can be written as

$$35.03 = 30 + 5 + 0.0 + 0.03 = 30 + 5 + \frac{0}{10} + \frac{3}{100}$$
$$= 3 \text{ tens} + 5 \text{ ones} + 0 \text{ tenths} + 3 \text{ hundredths}.$$

An important property of decimals is that **adding extra zeros to the right of a decimal number does not change its value**

i.e., $4.7 = 4.70 = 4.700 = 4.7000 \ldots$ and so on.

5.3 Like Decimals

Decimals having the same number of decimal places are called **like decimals**.

Ex. 7.353, 47.851, 137.030, 2051.893 all have three decimal places, so are like decimals.

5.4 Unlike Decimals

Decimals having different number of decimal places are called unlike decimals.

Ex. 4.3, 67.32, 901.045 are all unlike decimals.

We can convert unlike decimals to like decimals by adding zeros to the right of decimal number and making the decimal places in all the numbers same.

Ex.1. *Convert 16.2, 106.43, 2.135, 40.05 to a set of like decimals.*

Since the maximum number of decimal places is 3, so adding zeros, we write

16.2 = 16.200, 106.43 = 106.430, 2.135 = 2.135 and 40.05 = 40.050

Thus 16.200, 106.430, 2.135 and 40.050 are all like decimals.

5.5 Writing Decimal Numbers in Order of their Size

To compare the size of decimal numbers, we compare their whole number parts first. The larger decimal number is with the larger whole number part. If the whole number parts are equal, then we compare the decimal portions starting with the tenth digit. The number with larger tenth digit is bigger. If the tenths digits are also equal then we compare the hundredths digits and so on.

Ex. 2. *Compare* **(a)** *47.635 and 573.03* **(b)** *68.35 and 68.53.*

Sol. (*a*) Making them like decimals we have 47.635 and 573.030.

Comparing whole number parts we can see that 573 > 47

$\therefore$ 573.030 > 47.635.

(*b*) For 68.35 and 68.53, we can clearly see that the whole number parts are equal.

Comparing the tenths digits 5 > 3 $\therefore$ 68.53 > 68.35.

Whole number parts are equal

68.35　　68.53

Compare the tenth parts 5 > 3

Ex. 3. *Arrange the given numbers in ascending order :*

2.91, 3.853, 2.091, 2.7, 3.96, 4.21

Sol. Converting the given numbers to like decimals we have

2.910, 3.853, 2.091, 2.700, 3.960 and 4.210

Now comparing them we can see that

2.091 < 2.700 < 2.910 < 3.853 < 3.960 < 4.210

$\Rightarrow$ The given numbers in ascending order are : 2.091, 2.7, 2.91, 3.853, 3.96, 4.21

ROUNDING OFF

5.6 Rounding off Decimal Numbers to Desired Decimal Places

To round off a given number to the required number of decimal places we follow the given steps :

Step 1. *We retain the digit up to one place more than the required number of decimal places.*

Step 2. *If the extra digit retained is 5 or more than 5, then we add 1 to the digit just before it, else we leave the digit before it as such.*

Step 3. *The extra digit is then omitted.*

Ex. 4. *Round off :*

　　　　(a) *12.45 to the nearest whole number.* 　　**(b)** *18.354 to one d.p.* 　　**(c)** *6.0589 to two d.p.*

Sol. (*a*) Retaining one digit after the decimal point we have 12.4 $\because$ 4 < 5.

$\therefore$ 12.4 is rounded off as 12 after omitting the extra digit i.e., 4.

Hence 12.45 to the nearest whole number = **12**

(*b*) Since we have to round off to one d.p we retain 2 digits after the decimal point, *i.e.*, number = 18.35.

∴ the extra digit is equal to 5. ∴ We add 1 to the digit preceding it, and omit one extra digit.

∴ The number rounded off to one d.p is **18.4**.

(c) Since we have to round off to 2 d.p, we retain 3 digits after the decimal point, *i.e.,*

number = 6.058.

∵ the third or extra digit = 8 > 5 ∴ we add 1 to the digit preceding it and omit the extra digit.

∴ The number rounded off to 2 d.p is **6.06**.

5.7 Significant Figures or Digits

The total number of digits present in the number except the zeros preceding the first numeral are called significant digits.

> **Note : 1.** The zeros between the numerals and also after the last numeral are counted as significant digits.
>
> **2.** The zero before the first numeral is not counted and the position of the decimal point is immaterial.

Ex. 5. *Find the number of significant digits in :*

     (a) *6203*   **(b)** *2.07080*   **(c)** *0.0034*   **(d)** *0.003400*

Sol. (a) 6203 has 4 significant digits.   (b) 2.07080 has 6 significant digits

     (c) 0.0034 has 2 significant digits.   (d) 0.003400 has 4 significant digits.

Rounding to desired significant digits is done in the same way as for decimal places.

Ex. 6. *Round off :*

     (a) *25.935 correct to 3 s.f*   **(b)** *18.406 correct to 4 s.f*

     (c) *0.00835 correct to 1 s.f*   **(d)** *7.193 correct to 2 s.f*

Sol. (a) 25.935 = 25.9 correct to 3 s.f   (b) 18.406 = 18.41 correct to 4 s.f

     (c) 0.00835 = 0.008 correct to 1 s.f   (d) 7.193 = 7.2 correct to 2 s.f

EXERCISE 5 (a)

1. Write the following decimals in the expanded form :

(a) 930.683   (b) 9.207   (c) 0.053   (d) 18.006

2. Round off the following decimals :

(a) 0.53 to the nearest whole number   (b) 35.062 to one d.p   (c) 6.3513 to 2 d.p

(d) 0.31478 to 3 d.p   (e) 78.35 to 3 s.f   (f) 0.008540 to 1 s.f   (g) 1.00791 to 4 s.f

(h) 163.4500 to 4 s.f

3. Arrange the following sets of decimals in ascending order :

(a) 4, 6.8, 4.08, 6.354, 6.324, 4.19   (b) 12.5, 12.05, 12.51, 17.083, 17.089, 17.983

4. Arrange the following sets of decimals in descending order :

(a) 5.935, 6.04, 5.94, 5.093, 6.35   (b) 17, 9.84, 24.19, 24.32, 9.09

OPERATIONS ON DECIMALS

5.8 Adding and Subtracting Decimals

To add or subtract decimals, line up the decimal points and then follow the rules for adding or subtracting whole numbers placing the decimal point in the same vertical line.

When one number has more decimal places than the other, add 0's after the last numeral to make the same number of decimal places.

Ex. 1. *Add* **(a)** *56.69 + 21.37*   **(b)** *356.053 + 4.3*

Sol.

(a) Line up the decimal points and add.	(b) Make number of decimals places same after adding zeros, line up the decimal points and add.
$$\begin{array}{r} 56.69 \\ +\ 21.37 \\ \hline 78.06 \end{array}$$ **Ans.**	$$\begin{array}{r} 356.053 \\ +\ \ \ \ 4.300 \\ \hline 360.353 \end{array}$$ **Ans.**

Ex. 2. *Subtract* **(a)** *24.358 from 36.053*   **(b)** *6.008 from 18.2*

Sol.

(a) Line up the decimal points and subtract	(b) Add extra zeros to make number of decimal places same, line up the decimal points and subtract
$$\begin{array}{r} 36.053 \\ -\ 24.358 \\ \hline 11.695 \end{array}$$ **Ans.**	$$\begin{array}{r} 18.200 \\ -\ 6.008 \\ \hline 12.192 \end{array}$$ **Ans.**

5.9 Multiplication

Case 1. *Multiplication by 10 or any other power of 10.*

Multiplying a decimal number by 10^n moves the decimal point n places to the right :

Examples :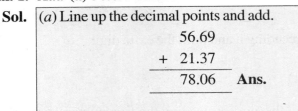

$64.321 \times 10 = 643.21$	Move decimal point 1 place to the right
$4.035 \times 100 = 403.5$	Move decimal point 2 places to the right
$0.0356 \times 1000 = 35.6$	Move decimal points 3 places to the right

Case 2. *Multiplication of a Decimal Number by a Whole number or a Decimal number.*

Multiply as if there were no decimal points at all and fix the position by the rule that there are as many decimal places in the product as there are in the multiplier and multiplicand put together.

Ex. 3. *Multiply :*

(a) *82.03 by 8*   **(b)** *48.35 by 0.027*

Sol.

(a) Multiplying both numbers without decimal points :	(b) Multiplying both numbers without taking decimal points	
$8203 \times 8 = 65624$	$4835 \times 27 = 130545$	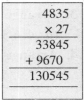
$\because$ Total number of decimal places in both $= 2$	Total number of decimal places $= 5$	
$\therefore 82.03 \times 8 = \mathbf{656.24}.$	$\therefore 48.35 \times 0.027 = \mathbf{1.30545}.$	

5.10   Division

Case 1. Dividing a whole number or decimal number by 10 or any higher power of 10.

Dividing a whole number or decimal number by 10^n moves the decimal point n places to the left.

Ex. $53 \div 10 = 5.3$ | Move one decimal place to the left |

$164.5 \div 100 = 1.645$ | Move 2 decimal places to the left |

$0.1536 \div 1000 = 0.0001536$ | Here we add 3 zeros to get the reqd. number of d.p. |

Case 2. Dividing a decimal number by a whole number

When dividing a decimal by a whole number, put the decimal point in the answer above the decimal point in the number being divided.

Ex. 4. *Dividing (a) 39.95 by 17*   *(b) 0.12052 ÷ 23*

Sol. *(a)*

```
          2.35
   17) 39.95
        34
       ──
        59
        51
       ──
        85
        85
       ──
         0
```

$\therefore 39.95 \div 17 = \mathbf{2.35}$. **Ans.**

(b)

```
          0.524
   23) 0.12052
        115
       ───
         55
         46
       ───
         92
         92
       ───
          0
```

$0.12.052 \div 23 = \mathbf{0.524}$. **Ans.**

Case 3. Dividing a Decimal by Decimal

To divide by a decimal, multiply the divisor by a power of 10 great enough to obtain a whole number. Multiply the dividend by that same power of 10. Then proceed as in case 2.

Ex. 5. *Divide (a) 16.416 ÷ 3.6*   *(b) 11.385 ÷ 0.45*

Sol. *(a)* $\dfrac{16.416}{3.6} = \dfrac{16.416 \times 10}{3.6 \times 10} = \dfrac{164.16}{36}$

↑ Make the divisor a whole number

```
          4.56
   36) 164.16
       144
       ───
        201
        180
       ───
        216
        216
       ───
          0
```

$\therefore 16.416 \div 3.6 = \mathbf{4.56}$. **Ans.**

(b) $\dfrac{11.385}{0.45} = \dfrac{11.385 \times 100}{0.45 \times 100} = \dfrac{1138.5}{45}$

↑ Make the divisor a whole number

```
          25.3
   45) 1138.5
        90
       ────
        238
        225
       ────
        135
        135
       ────
          0
```

$\therefore 11.385 \div 0.45 = \mathbf{25.3}$. **Ans.**

5.11 Simplification

Type 1. Using BODMAS

Ex. 6. *Simplify : 4.8 + 5.6 ÷ 1.4 − 1.2 × 0.2 + 3.6 ÷ 0.6 of 2.*

Sol. $4.8 + 5.6 \div 1.4 - 1.2 \times 0.2 + 3.6 \div 0.6$ of 2

$= 4.8 + 5.6 \div 1.4 - 1.2 \times 0.2 + 3.6 \div 1.2$ [(Simplifying of) **Think :** 0.6 of $2 = 0.6 \times 2 = 1.2$]

$= 4.8 + 4 - 1.2 \times 0.2 + 3$ [(Simplifying $\div$) **Think :** $5.6 \div 1.4 = 56 \div 14 = 4$, $3.6 \div 1.2 = 36 \div 12 = 3$]

$= 4.8 + 4 - 0.24 + 3$ [(Simplifying $\times$) **Think :** $12 \times 2 = 24 \Rightarrow 1.2 \times 0.2 = 0.24$]

$= 11.8 - 0.24$ (Simplifying +)

$= \textbf{11.56}.$ [**Think :** $11.8 - 0.24 = 11.80 - 0.24$]

Type 2. Using Identities

$$(a + b)^2 = a^2 + 2ab + b^2, \quad (a - b)^2 = a^2 - 2ab + b^2, \quad (a + b)(a - b) = a^2 - b^2$$

Ex. 7. *Simplify :* $\dfrac{(9.7)^2 - (8.2)^2}{(9.7 + 8.2)}$.

Sol. Take $x = 9.7$ and $y = 8.2$. Then $\dfrac{(9.7)^2 - (8.2)^2}{(9.7 + 8.2)} = \dfrac{x^2 - y^2}{x + y} = \dfrac{(x + y)(x - y)}{(x + y)} = x - y = 9.7 - 8.2 = \textbf{1.5}.$

Ex. 8 *Simplify :* $\dfrac{(4.69)^2 - (2.34)^2}{4.69 \times 4.69 - 2 \times 4.69 \times 2.34 + 2.34 \times 2.34}.$

Sol. Take $x = 4.69$ and $y = 2.34$.

Then $\dfrac{(4.69)^2 - (2.34)^2}{4.69 \times 4.69 - 2 \times 4.69 \times 2.34 + 2.34 \times 2.34}$

$= \dfrac{x^2 - y^2}{x^2 - 2xy + y^2} = \dfrac{(x + y)(x - y)}{(x - y)^2} = \dfrac{x + y}{x - y}$

$= \dfrac{4.69 + 2.34}{4.69 - 2.34} = \dfrac{7.03}{2.35} = \dfrac{703}{235} = \textbf{2.99}$ (approx.)

```
           2.991
235) 7 0 3.000
     4 7 0
     2 3 3 0
     2 1 1 5
       2 1 5 0
       2 1 1 5
         3 5 0
         2 3 5
         1 5
```

EXERCISE 5 (b)

1. Add :

 (*a*) $12.362 + 4.06 + 234.5 + 112.045$ (*b*) $27.418 + 0.97 + 25 + 1.967$

2. Subtract :

 (*a*) 4.503 from 18   (*b*) 0.0691 from 5.48   (*c*) 3.8 from 12.45   (*d*) 0.735 from 0.8005

3. Evaluate :

 (*a*) $7.21 - 4.48 - 12.57 + 37.91 + 86.03 - 54.835$ (*b*) $23.65 - 8.045 + 4.01 + 12 - 11.33 - 0.989$

4. Evaluate :

 (*a*) 0.045×10 (*b*) 8.2463×100 (*c*) 0.00028×1000 (*d*) 0.008×10

5. Multiply :

 (*a*) 64.89 by 3.6   (*b*) 1.235 by 2.45   (*c*) 0.00489 by 0.027   (*d*) 0.76×0.38

 (*e*) $0.08 \times 800 \times 0.008 \times 0.001$

6. Evaluate :

 (*a*) $289 \div 100$ (*b*) $827.34 \div 1000$ (*c*) $0.0625 \div 10$ (*d*) $0.0038 \div 100$ (*e*) $14.04 \div 600$

7. Divide :

 (*a*) 107.52 by 24   (*b*) 609.96 by 2.6   (*c*) $0.11436 \div 0.012$ (*d*) 11.56 by 2.72   (*e*) 37.44 by 3.12

Simplify :

8. $6.4 \div 8 + 1.6$ of $5 - 2.4 \div 0.4$ **9.** $12.5 - 3.5 \div 7 \times 1.5 - 1.2$ of 0.3

10.	$0.81 \div 0.3$ of $3 + 4.5 - 0.36 \div 0.04$	**11.**	$40.8 + 2.5$ of $1.5 - 8.19 \div 0.3$
12.	$\dfrac{6.2 \times 6.2 - 3.8 \times 3.8}{6.2 - 3.8}$	**13.**	$\dfrac{11.4 \times 11.4 - 3.6 \times 3.6}{11.4 \times 11.4 + 2 \times 11.4 \times 3.6 + 3.6 \times 3.6}$
14.	$\dfrac{4.3 \times 4.3 - 2 \times 4.3 \times 2.8 + 2.8 \times 2.8}{7.6 \times 7.6 + 2 \times 7.6 \times 2.4 + 2.4 \times 2.4}$	**15.**	$\dfrac{11.9 \times 11.9 - 6.9 \times 6.9}{11.9 - 6.9}$

5.12 Converting Fractions to Decimals

To convert fractions to decimal numbers divide the numerator by the denominator.

Thus $\dfrac{6}{7} = 6 \div 7$

This is illustrated by the following example.

Ex.1. *Convert each of the following to decimal.*

    (a) $\dfrac{3}{8}$ **(b)** $\dfrac{2}{11}$

Sol.   (*a*) $\dfrac{3}{8} = 3 \div 8$

```
       0.375
   8) 3.000
      24
      ——
       60
       56
       ——
        40
        40
        ——
         0
```

(We add zeros after the decimal point so as to complete the division and give an exact answer)

$\therefore \quad \dfrac{3}{8} = \textbf{0.375.}$

In the division of $\dfrac{3}{8}$, the quotient 0.375 is called a **terminating decimal** because the division process ends when a remainder of 0 is reached.

(*b*) $\dfrac{2}{11} = 2 \div 11$

```
        0.1818
   11) 2.0000
       11
       ——
        90
        88
        ——
         20
         11
         ——
          90
          88
          ——
           2
```

$\therefore \quad \dfrac{2}{11} = \textbf{0.1818...}$

In the division of 2 by 11, the quotient 0.1818... is a **non terminating repeating decimal**. The process of division never terminates as a remainder of zero is not reached and the same block of digits repeats itself without end. Here the block of digit is 18. The decimal representation of $\dfrac{2}{11} = 0.\overline{18}$ where bar is used to indicate the repeating block of digits.

Maths Alert : Only that fraction in simplest form, that has a denominator having prime factor only 2, only 5 or both 2 and 5 can be represented by a terminating decimal.

For example, $\frac{3}{50}$ represents terminating decimal as $50 = 2 \times 5^2$, while $\frac{7}{15}$ does not represent a terminating decimal as $15 = 5 \times 3$.

> **Note :** Every terminating or a non terminating-repeating decimal represents a rational member.

5.13 Changing Decimals into Fractions

Case 1. **When the decimals are terminating.**

You can write a terminating decimal as a rational number with a denominator that is a power of 10.

Thus (*a*) $0.5 = \frac{5}{10} = \frac{1}{2}$ ←——Rewrite the rational number in lowest terms.

(*b*) $0.47 = \frac{47}{100}$　　　(*c*) $3.4 = 3\frac{4}{10} = 3\frac{2}{5}$.　　　(*d*) $5.032 = \frac{5032}{1000} = \frac{629}{125}$.

> **Method :**
> 1. Remove the decimal point and write the resulting number in the numerator.
> 2. Write 1 in the denominator and annex as many zeros as the number of digits after the decimal point in the given decimal number.

Ex. 1. *Convert the following decimals into fractions.*

(a) *5.84*　　　　(b) *7.6385*　　　　(d) *4.00076*　　　　(e) *19.000048*

Sol. (*a*) $5.84 = \frac{584}{100} = \frac{146}{25}$.

2 digits after decimal point 　— 2 zeros after one

(*b*) $7.6385 = \frac{76385}{10000} = \frac{15277}{2000}$

4 digits after decimal point 　— 4 zeros after one

(*c*) $4.00076 = \frac{400076}{100000} = \frac{100019}{25000}$.

5 digits after decimal point 　— 5 zeros after one

(*d*) $19.000048 = \frac{19000048}{1000000} = \frac{1187503}{62500}$

6 digits after decimal point 　— 6 zeros after one

Case 2. **When the decimals are repeating.**

Defintions :

1. **Pure recurring decimals :** *A decimal in which all the figures after the decimal point are repeated is known as a pure recurring decimal.*

   e.g. $0.\overline{5}$, $0.\overline{28}$, $0.\overline{34798}$ etc., are pure recurring decimals.

2. **Mixed recurring decimal :** A decimal in which at least one figure after the decimal point is not repeated and then some figure or figures are repeated is known as a mixed recurring decimal.

   e.g., $0.3\overline{8}$, $0.23\overline{76}$, $0.5987\overline{426}$ etc., are mixed recurring decimals.

Type 1 : **Pure recurring decimals.**

Ex. 2. *Express each decimal as a fraction in simplest form.*

(a) $0.\overline{8}$　　　　(b) $1.\overline{27}$　　　　(c) $0.\overline{407}$

Sol. (*a*) Let 　　$n = 0.\overline{8} = 0.888$ 　　　...(*i*)

　　　　$10n = 10 \times 0.888 = 8.888$ 　　　...(*ii*)

> **Think**
> Since there is one digit in the repetend 8 we multiply both members, of $n = 0.\overline{8}$ by 10. This shifts the repeating digit one place to the left. The subtraction produces a terminating decimal numeral.

Subtracting (i) from (ii), we get

$$9n = 8$$

or $\qquad 9 \times 0.\overline{8} = 8$

$\therefore \qquad\qquad 0.\overline{8} = \dfrac{8}{9}.$

(b) Let $\qquad\qquad n = 1.\overline{27} = 1.2727 \ldots$

Multiply : $\qquad 100n = 127.\overline{27}$

Subtract : $\qquad \dfrac{n = 1.\overline{27}}{99n = 126}$

Divide : $\qquad n = \dfrac{126}{99} = \dfrac{14}{11}.$

> **Think**
> Since there are two digits in the repetend 27, we multiply both members, of $n = 1.\overline{27}$ by 10^2, or 100. This shifts the repeating block of digits two places to the left. The subtraction produces a terminating decimal numeral.

(c) Let $\qquad\qquad n = 0.\overline{407}$

Multiply : $\qquad 1000n = 407.\overline{407}$

Subtract : $\qquad \dfrac{n = 0.\overline{407}}{999n = 407}$

$\therefore \qquad\qquad n = \dfrac{407}{999} = \dfrac{11}{27}.$

> Since the block of repeating digits contains 3 digits, we multiply by 10^3, or 1000.

> **Rule.** *Write the repeated figure only once in the numerator and write as many nines in the denominator as is the number of repeated digits.*

Applying this rule to the above examples, we get

$$0.\overline{6} = \frac{6}{9} = \frac{2}{3}, \; 0.\overline{71} = \frac{71}{99}, \; 1.\overline{48} = 1 + \frac{48}{99} = 1 + \frac{16}{33} = \frac{49}{33}; \; 0.\overline{927} = \frac{927}{999} = \frac{103}{111}.$$

Type 2 : **Mixed recurring decimals.**

Ex. 3. *Convert* (a) $3.21\overline{6}$, (b) $4.23\overline{48}$ *into fractions in the simplest form.*

Sol. (a) Let $\qquad\qquad n = 3.21\overline{6} \qquad\qquad \ldots(i)$

Multiply : $\qquad 10n = 32.16\overline{6} \qquad\qquad \ldots(ii)$

Subtracting (i) from (ii), we get

> Note that here we have taken the case in which the first digit of the sequence of repeating digits is not immediately to the right of the decimal.

$$9n = 28.95 = \frac{2895}{100}$$

$\therefore \qquad\qquad n = \dfrac{2895}{900} = \dfrac{193}{60}.$

(b) Let $\qquad\qquad n = 4.23\overline{48} \qquad\qquad\qquad \ldots(i)$

Multiply : $\qquad 100n = 423.48\overline{48} \qquad\qquad \ldots(ii)$

Subtracting (i) from (ii), we get

$$99n = 419.25$$

$$n = \frac{419.25}{99} = \frac{41925}{9900} = \frac{559}{132}.$$

> **Rule.** Consider the decimal part. Subtract the non-repeating part from the whole and divide by (as many nines as are the repeating digits × as many tens as are non-repeating digits.)

Thus,

$$3.21\overline{6} = 3 + \frac{216 - 21}{900}$$

$$= 3 + \frac{195}{900} = 3 + \frac{13}{60} = \mathbf{\frac{193}{60}}.$$

$$4.23\overline{48} = 4 + \frac{2348 - 23}{9900}$$

$$= 4 + \frac{2325}{9900}$$

$$= 4 + \frac{31}{132} = \mathbf{\frac{559}{132}}.$$

$$5.1\overline{926} = 5 + \frac{1926 - 1}{9990}$$

$$= 5 + \frac{1925}{9990} = 5 + \frac{385}{1998} = \mathbf{\frac{10375}{1998}}.$$

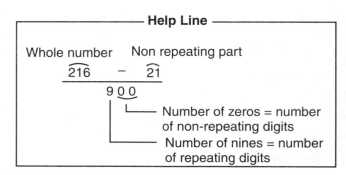

— Help Line —

Whole number   Non repeating part

$$\overset{\frown}{216} \quad - \quad \overset{\frown}{21}$$

$$9\,0\,0$$

└── Number of zeros = number of non-repeating digits

Number of nines = number of repeating digits

5.14 H.C.F and L.C.M of Decimals

To find the H.C.F and L.C.M of decimals, we convert the given decimals to like decimals. Now we find the H.C.F and L.C.M of the numbers without taking the decimal point into consideration (*i.e.,* treating them as whole numbers.) Then mark the decimal point in the answer equal to the number of decimal places in the given numbers.

Ex. 1. *Find the H.C.F and L.C.M of 3.6, 0.24 and 1.2*

Sol. Converting them to like decimals we have 3.60, 0.24, 1.20. Treating them as whole numbers i.e. without decimal points, the numbers are 360, 24, 120.

$$24 = 2^3 \times 3, \quad 120 = 2^3 \times 3 \times 5, \quad 360 = 2^3 \times 3^2 \times 5$$

2	24
2	12
2	6
	3

2	120
2	60
2	30
3	15
	5

2	360
2	180
2	90
3	45
3	15
	5

∴ H.C.F of 24, 120 and 360 = $2^3 \times 3$ = 24

L.C.M of 24, 120 and 360 = $2^3 \times 3^2 \times 5$ = 360

⇒ H.C.F of 0.24, 1.20 and 3.60 is **0.24**.

L.C.M of 0.24, 1.20 and 3.60 is **3.60**.

∵ All of them have two places of decimal.

> There are 2 d.p in the given numbers, so, we put decimal point after 2 places is 24 and 360.

EXERCISE 5 (c)

1. Which of the following fractions have a terminating decimal representation ?

$$\frac{1}{4}, \frac{3}{8}, \frac{5}{6}, \frac{2}{3}, \frac{1}{12}, \frac{14}{32}, \frac{137}{25}, \frac{19}{150}, \frac{251}{1280}, \frac{25}{22}$$

2. Which of the following fractions have a non-terminating repeating decimal representation?

$$\frac{3}{5}, \frac{5}{7}, \frac{1}{9}, \frac{13}{200}, \frac{17}{30}, \frac{5}{28}, \frac{413}{625}$$

3. Express each of the following fractions as a decimal.

(a) $\dfrac{1}{4}$ (b) $\dfrac{1}{8}$ (c) $\dfrac{4}{5}$ (d) $\dfrac{5}{4}$ (e) $\dfrac{27}{800}$

(f) $\dfrac{2157}{625}$ (g) $\dfrac{9}{40}$ (h) $\dfrac{35}{16}$ (i) $\dfrac{718}{200}$ (j) $\dfrac{57}{80}$

4. Find the decimal representation of each of the following fractions.

(a) $\dfrac{1}{3}$ (b) $\dfrac{25}{6}$ (c) $\dfrac{5}{9}$ (d) $\dfrac{11}{8}$ (e) $2\dfrac{4}{11}$

(f) $4\dfrac{3}{7}$ (g) $\dfrac{88}{7}$ (h) $\dfrac{5}{74}$ (i) $\dfrac{22}{7}$ (j) $\dfrac{49}{75}$

Express each rational number as a fraction in simplest form.

5. (a) 0.84   (b) 0.015   (c) 52.54   (d) 129.6   (e) 0.0008

6. (a) $0.\overline{4}$ (b) $0.\overline{25}$ (c) $0.\overline{585}$ (d) $5.\overline{2}$ (e) $2.\overline{31}$ (f) $5.\overline{160}$ (g) $23.\overline{43}$

7. (a) $0.1\overline{7}$ (b) $0.4\overline{92}$ (c) $0.12\overline{3}$ (d) $0.003\overline{52}$ (e) $15.7\overline{12}$ (f) $2.25\overline{45}$ (g) $0.125\overline{4}$

Find the H.C.F and L.C.M of :

8. 1.5, 0.1, 0.25   **9.** 0.64, 2.16, 7.2, 4.8   **10.** 0.18, 0.27, 8.1, 0.9

LOOKING BACK

Summary of Key Facts

1. A fraction whose denominator is 10^n where n is a positive integer is called a decimal fraction.
2. A decimal number has two parts, whole number part to the left of decimal point and decimal part to the right of the decimal point.
3. **To add or subtract decimals :**
   (i) Line up the decimal points
   (ii) add or subtract
   (iii) Put the point in the answer.

4. To multiply decimals by 10^n where n is a positive integer move the decimal point n places to the right whereas to divide decimals by 10^n where n is a positive integer move the decimal point n places to the left.
5. To multiply decimal with whole numbers or decimals mulitply the number without taking the decimal point. Then the product has the same number of decimal places as there are in the multiplier and the multiplicand put together.
6. When dividing a decimal by a whole number put the decimal point in the answer above the decimal point in the number being divided.
7. To round a decimal number to given decimal places (or significant figures).
   (i) Take one digit extra than the required decimal places.
   (ii) If it is 5 or more then add 1 to the previous digit and if it is less than 5 leave the previous digit as such and omit the extra digit.
8. To change fractions to decimals divide the numerator by denominator.
9. A fraction $\dfrac{p}{q}$ is a terminating decimal if in its lowest form the denominator has factors as 2 or 5 or both 2 and 5.
10. A fraction $\dfrac{p}{q}$ is a non-terminating repeating or recurring decimal if a digit or a block of digits are repeated in the decimal part.

MENTAL MATHS – 4

Work out :

1. $6.5 + 2.63 + 4.5 - 1.63$
2. 3 kg of Sugar costs Rs 66.60. Find the cost of 5kg of sugar.
3. Write the place value of the digit 9 is 0.394.
4. Find 0.357×100
5. Convert $\dfrac{4}{5}$ to a decimal number.

6. Which is larger 6.43 or 6.34 ?
7. Divide 4.57 by 1000.
8. Round off 42.0256 correct 2 d.p.
9. Write the number 17.504 correct to 3 s.f.
10. Express 0.72 as a fraction.
11. Write $0.1\overline{7}$ correct to 3 s.f.

ANSWERS

EXERCISE 5 (a)

1. (a) $9\times100+3\times10+0\times1+6\times\dfrac{1}{10}+8\times\dfrac{1}{100}+3\times\dfrac{1}{1000}$ (b) $9\times1+2\times\dfrac{1}{10}+0\times\dfrac{1}{100}+7\times\dfrac{1}{1000}$

(c) $5\times\dfrac{1}{100}+3\times\dfrac{1}{1000}$ (d) $1\times10+8\times1+0\times\dfrac{1}{10}+0\times\dfrac{1}{100}+6\times\dfrac{1}{1000}$

2. (a) 1   (b) 35.1   (c) 6.35   (d) 0.315   (e) 78.4   (f) 0.009
   (g) 1.008   (h) 163.5
3. (a) 4, 4.08, 4.19, 6.324, 6.354, 6.8   (b) 12.05, 12.5, 12.51, 17.083, 17.089, 17.983
4. (a) 6.35, 6.04, 5.94, 5.935, 5.093   (b) 24.32, 24.19, 17, 9.84, 9.09

EXERCISE 5 (b)

1. (a) 362.967   (b) 55.355   2. (a) 13.497   (b) 5.4109   (c) 8.65   (d) 0.0655
3. (a) 59.265   (b) 19.296   4. (a) 0.45   (b) 824.63   (c) 0.28   (d) 0.08
5. (a) 233.604   (b) 3.02575   (c) 0.00013203   (d) 0.2888   (e) 0.000512
6. (a) 2.89   (b) 0.82734   (c) 0.00625   (d) 0.000038   (e) 0.0234
7. (a) 4.48   (b) 234.6   (c) 9.53   (d) 4.25   (e) 12   8. 2.8   9. 11.39
10. –3.6   11. 17.25   12. 10   13. 0.52   14. 0.0225   15. 18.8

EXERCISE 5 (c)

1. $\dfrac{1}{4}, \dfrac{3}{8}, \dfrac{14}{32}, \dfrac{137}{25}, \dfrac{251}{1280}$ 2. $\dfrac{5}{7}, \dfrac{1}{9}, \dfrac{17}{30}, \dfrac{5}{28}$ 3. (a) 0.25   (b) 0.125   (c) 0.8   (d) 1.25   (e) 0.03375

(f) 3.4512   (g) 0.225   (h) 2.1875   (i) 3.59   (j) 0.7125

4. (a) $0.\overline{3}$ (b) $4.1\overline{6}$ (c) $0.\overline{5}$ (d) 1.375   (e) $2.\overline{36}$ (f) $4.\overline{428571}$

(g) $12.\overline{571428}$ (h) $0.06\overline{75}$ (i) $3.\overline{142857}$ (j) $0.65\overline{3}$ 5. (a) $\dfrac{21}{25}$ (b) $\dfrac{3}{200}$

(c) $\dfrac{2627}{50}$ (d) $\dfrac{648}{5}$ (e) $\dfrac{1}{1250}$ 6. (a) $\dfrac{4}{9}$ (b) $\dfrac{25}{99}$ (c) $\dfrac{585}{999}$

(d) $\dfrac{47}{9}$ (e) $\dfrac{229}{99}$ (f) $\dfrac{5155}{999}$ (g) $\dfrac{2320}{99}$

7. (a) $\dfrac{8}{45}$ (b) $\dfrac{244}{495}$ (c) $\dfrac{37}{300}$ (d) $\dfrac{349}{99000}$ (e) $15\dfrac{47}{66}$ or $\dfrac{1037}{66}$ (f) $2\dfrac{14}{55}$ or $\dfrac{124}{55}$ (g) $\dfrac{69}{550}$
8. H.C.F = 0.05, L.C.M = 1.5   9. H.C.F = 0.08, L.C.M = 86.4   10. H.C.F = 0.09, L.C.M = 8.1

MENTAL MATHS – 4

1. 12   2. Rs 111   3. $\dfrac{9}{100}$ 4. 35.7   5. 0.8   6. 6.43

7. 0.00457   8. 42.03.   9. 17.5   10. $\dfrac{18}{25}$ 11. 0.178

6. Squares and Square Roots

6.1 Squares

If a number is multiplied by itself, the product so obtained is called the square of that number.

For example :

$3 \times 3 = 3^2 = 9$ We say that 9 is the square of 3.

$16 \times 16 = 16^2 = 256$ We say that 256 is the square of 16 .

$0.7 \times 0.7 = (0.7)^2 = 0.49$ We say that 0.49 is the square of 0.7.

$\dfrac{4}{5} \times \dfrac{4}{5} = \left(\dfrac{4}{5}\right)^2 = \dfrac{16}{25}$ We say that $\dfrac{16}{25}$ is the square of $\dfrac{4}{5}$.

> The square of a number is a number raised to the power of 2.

6.2 Perfect Square

The numbers 1, 4, 9, 16, 25, 36 are the squares of natural numbers 1, 2, 3, 4, 5, 6 respectively and are called perfect squares or square numbers.

> A natural number is called a **perfect square** or a square number if it is the square of some natural number.
>
> **Test :** *A given number is a perfect square if its prime factors can be expressed in pairs of equal factors.*

Ex.1. *Is 900 a perfect square ? If so , find the number whose square is 900.*

Sol. Resolving into prime factors, we find that :

$900 = \underline{2 \times 2} \times \underline{3 \times 3} \times \underline{5 \times 5}$

Since, 900 can be grouped into pairs of equal factors, therefore 900 is a perfect square.

Also $900 = (2 \times 3 \times 5) \times (2 \times 3 \times 5) = 30 \times 30 = (30)^2$

∴ 900 is a square of 30.

2	900
2	450
3	225
3	75
5	25
5	5
	1

Ex. 2. *Show that 3675 is not a perfect square.*

Sol. Resolving into prime factors, we see that

$3675 = 3 \times \underline{5 \times 5} \times \underline{7 \times 7}$

Grouping the factors into pairs of equal factors we find that 3 does not form a pair.

∴ 3675 is not a perfect square.

Remark : If we multiply or divide 3675 by the unpaired factor, *i.e.*, 3, the product or the quotient becomes a perfect square.

Thus $3675 \times 3 = \underline{3 \times 3} \times \underline{5 \times 5} \times \underline{7 \times 7}$

$\qquad\qquad = (3 \times 5 \times 7) \times (3 \times 5 \times 7) = 105 \times 105 = (105)^2.$

$3675 \div 3 = \underline{5 \times 5} \times \underline{7 \times 7} = (5 \times 7) \times (5 \times 7) = 35 \times 35 = (35)^2.$

3	3675
5	1225
5	245
7	49
7	7
	1

6.3 Properties of Square Numbers

1. A perfect square is never negative.
2. A square number never ends in 2, 3, 7 or 8.
3. The number of zeros at the end of a perfect square is always even. *e.g.* $300 \times 300 = 90000$
   4-even
4. The square of an even number is always even, e.g. $(12)^2 = 12 \times 12 = 144$.
5. The square of an odd number is always odd. *e.g.* $(15)^2 = 15 \times 15 = 225$.

Ex. 1. *The following numbers are not perfect squares. Give reason.*

   (a) *1057*   (b) *23453*   (c) *7928*   (d) *222222*   (e) *64000*   (f) *505050*

Sol. (*a*) to (*d*) : We know that the natural numbers ending in the digits 2, 3, 7 or 8 are not perfect squares. Therefore, 1057, 23453, 7928 and 222222 are not perfect squares.

   (*e*) and (*f*) : We know that the numbers ending in an odd number of consecutive zeros are not perfect squares. Therefore, 64000 and 505050 are not perfect squares.

EXERCISE 6 (a)

1. Using prime factorization method, show that the following numbers are perfect squares. Also find the number in each case whose square is the given number.
   (*a*) 100   (*b*) 784   (*c*) 3600   (*d*) 4225

2. Using prime factorization, find which of the following numbers are not perfect squares.
   (*a*) 400   (*b*) 768   (*c*) 6300   (*d*) 1296   (*e*) 8000   (*f*) 9025

3. Find the squares of :

   (*a*) 14   (*b*) 97   (*c*) $\dfrac{6}{7}$ (*d*) 0.8   (*e*) 0.011   (*f*) 1.7

4. Find the smallest number by which the given number must be multiplied as that the product is a perfect square. Also find the perfect square obtained.
   (*a*) 512   (*b*) 700   (*c*) 1323   (*d*) 35280

5. Find the smallest number by which each of the given numbers should be divided so that the result is a perfect square. Also find the perfect square obtained.
   (*a*) 180   (*b*) 1575   (*c*) 6912   (*d*) 19200

6. Determine whether square of the following numbers will be even or odd. (Do not find the square)
   (*a*) 537   (*b*) 31298   (*c*) 900265   (*d*) 7000132

   (**Hint :** See properties (4) and (5) of perfect squares given above.)

SQUARE ROOTS

6.4 Meaning of Square Root

The square root of a number *n* is that number which when multiplied by itself gives *n* as the product.

For example : $5 \times 5 = 25$, so 5 is the square root of 25. We write $\sqrt{25} = 5$.

The symbol $\sqrt{}$ is used to indicate square root.

$11 \times 11 = 121$, so $\sqrt{121} = 11$, $17 \times 17 = 289$ so $\sqrt{289} = 17$.

$0.7 \times 0.7 = 0.49$ so $\sqrt{0.49} = 0.7$, $0.25 \times 0.25 = 0.0625$ so $\sqrt{0.0625} = 0.25$

$\dfrac{3}{8} \times \dfrac{3}{8} = \dfrac{9}{64}$ so $\sqrt{\dfrac{9}{64}} = \dfrac{3}{8}$, $\dfrac{10}{19} \times \dfrac{10}{19} = \dfrac{100}{361}$ so $\sqrt{\dfrac{100}{361}} = \dfrac{10}{19}$.

6.5 Finding Square Root of a Perfect Square

Method 1. *By Prime Factorization*

> **Step 1 :** *Resolve the given number into prime factors.*
> **Step 2 :** *Form pairs of like factors.*
> **Step 3 :** *From each pair, pick out one prime factor.*
> **Step 4 :** *Multiply the factors so picked.*

Note. (*i*) We may also write the product of prime factors in exponential form and for finding the square root, we take half of the index value of each factor and then multiply.

(*ii*) Square root of a fraction, *i.e.*, $\sqrt{\dfrac{p}{q}} = \dfrac{\sqrt{p}}{\sqrt{q}} = \dfrac{\text{Square root of the numerator}}{\text{Square root of the denominator}}$, *e.g.*, $\sqrt{\dfrac{121}{49}} = \dfrac{\sqrt{121}}{\sqrt{49}} = \dfrac{11}{7}$.

(*iii*) Square root of a decimal number = Square root of the corresponding decimal fraction.

e.g., $\sqrt{0.25} = \sqrt{\dfrac{25}{100}} = \dfrac{\sqrt{25}}{\sqrt{100}} = \dfrac{5}{10} = 0.5$.

Ex. 1. *Find the square root of :* (a) *7225* (b) $10\dfrac{6}{25}$ (c) *0.0196*

Sol. (*a*) **Step 1.** Resolving into prime factors and forming pairs of like factors.

$7225 = \underline{5 \times 5} \times \underline{17 \times 17}$

Step 2. From each pair pick out one prime factor, *i.e.*,

1st pair	2nd pair
(5×5)	(17×17)
↑	↑
pick out 5	pick out 17

5	7225
5	1445
17	289
17	17
	1

Step 3. Multiply the factors so picked : $5 \times 17 = 85$.

The product is the square root of the given number.   ∴ $\sqrt{7225} = 5 \times 17 = \mathbf{85}$.

Alternatively, $7225 = 5^2 \times 17^2$.

Taking $\dfrac{1}{2}$ of the index values of each fraction $\sqrt{7225} = 5 \times 17 = 85$

(*b*) $10\dfrac{6}{25} = \dfrac{256}{25}$

∴ $\sqrt{\dfrac{256}{25}} = \dfrac{\sqrt{256}}{\sqrt{25}}$

$= \dfrac{\sqrt{2^8}}{\sqrt{5^2}} = \dfrac{2^4}{5} = \dfrac{\mathbf{16}}{\mathbf{5}}$.

2	256
2	128
2	64
2	32
2	16
2	8
2	4
	2

(*c*) $0.0196 = \dfrac{196}{10000}$

$\sqrt{0.0196} = \sqrt{\dfrac{196}{10000}} = \dfrac{\sqrt{196}}{\sqrt{10000}}$

$= \dfrac{\sqrt{2^2 \times 7^2}}{\sqrt{10^4}} = \dfrac{2 \times 7}{10^2} = \dfrac{14}{100} = \mathbf{0.14}.$

2	196
2	98
7	49
	7

> **Note :** It would help you find out square roots quickly if you memorise squares of numbers at least up to 30.

Ex. 2. *Find the square root of 396900.*

Sol. By prime factorization, we get

$396900 = (2 \times 2) \times (3 \times 3) \times (3 \times 3) \times (5 \times 5) \times (7 \times 7)$

$\therefore \quad \sqrt{396900} = 2 \times 3 \times 3 \times 5 \times 7 = \mathbf{630.}$

2	396900
2	198450
3	99225
3	33075
3	11025
3	3675
5	1225
5	245
7	49
7	7
	1

Ex. 3. *Find the square root of 0.00003136.*

Sol. $0.00003136 = 0.00000001 \times 3136$

$= 0.01 \times 0.01 \times 0.01 \times 0.01 \times 2^6 \times 7^2.$

$\therefore \quad \sqrt{0.00003136} = 0.01 \times 0.01 \times 2^3 \times 7 = 0.0001 \times 56 = \mathbf{0.0056}$

Alternatively, the following working may appear easier to you.

$\sqrt{0.00003136} = \sqrt{\dfrac{3136}{100000000}} = \sqrt{\dfrac{2^6 \times 7^2}{10^8}} = \dfrac{2^3 \times 7}{10^4} = \dfrac{56}{10000} = \mathbf{0.0056}.$

2	3136
2	1568
2	784
2	392
2	196
2	98
7	49
7	7
	1

Ex. 4. *What factor will turn 98 into a perfect square?*

Sol. $98 = 2 \times 7 \times 7 = 2 \times (7 \times 7)$

You require one more 2 to make a pair (2×2). So required factor is 2.

If we multiply by 2, then $98 \times 2 = (2 \times 2) \times (7 \times 7) = 196$

which is a perfect square.

2	98
7	49
7	7
	1

Ex. 5. *Simplify :* $\sqrt{900} + \sqrt{0.09} + \sqrt{0.000009}$

Sol. If p and q are natural number then $\sqrt{pq} = \sqrt{p} \times \sqrt{q}$

$\sqrt{900} = \sqrt{9 \times 100} = \sqrt{9} \times \sqrt{100} = 3 \times 10 = 30$

$\sqrt{0.09} = \sqrt{0.3 \times 0.3} = 0.3$

$\sqrt{0.000009} = \sqrt{0.003 \times 0.003} = 0.003$

$\therefore \quad \sqrt{900} + \sqrt{0.09} + \sqrt{0.000009}$

$= 30 + 0.3 + 0.003 = \mathbf{30.303.}$

Method 2 : *By Long Division Method*

       Sometimes it is not easy or convenient to write the factors of a number. In such cases, we use the method of long division to find the square root.

Ex. 1. *Find the square root of 17424.*

Sol.

Therefore, $\sqrt{17424} = \mathbf{132.}$

> **Think**
>
> Square root of 9 is 3. Also, 0.09 contains 2 decimal places so one of its equal factors will contain one decimal place.
>
> 0.000009 contains 6 decimal places so one of its equal factors will contain 3 decimal places.

Mark off the digits in pairs from right to left

Step 1. $1^2 = 1$

Step 2. Twice $1 = 2$

Step 3. 2 goes into 7 three times. Put 3 on top and in the divisor as shown $23 \times 3 = 69$

Step 4. Double 13. You get 26. First digit of 26 which is 2, goes into the first digit of 524 which is 5, 2 times. Place 2 on top and in the divisor as shown. $2 \times 262 = 524.$

Step 5. Subtract. The remainder is 0.

Ex. 2. *Find the square root of 543169.*

Sol. **Step 1.** Begin on the right. Mark off the digits in pairs from right to left. ($\longleftarrow$)

Step 2. Take the first pair of digits, and find the nearest perfect square. The largest perfect square less than 54 is 49, the square of 7. Write 7 on top in the answer and also in the divisor. Subtract $7 \times 7 = 49$ from the first period. The remainder is 5.

Step 3. Bring down the next pair, 31. Double 7, the number on top, and place its double, 14, on the outside as shown, Divide 14 into 53 to obtain 3. Write 3 on top to the right of 7 in the answer and to the right of 4 in the divisor. Multiply 143 by 3 and place under 531. Subtract. The remainder is 102.

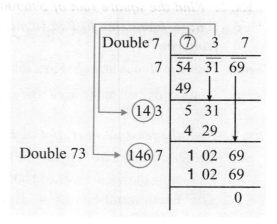

Step 4. Bring down the next pair 69. Double 73, the number on top, and place its double, 146, on to to the outside. Divide 14 into 102 to obtain 7. Write 7 on to the right of 3 in the answer and to the right of 6 in 146 in the divisor. Multiply 1467 by 7 and place under 10269. Subtract.

The remainder is 0. Therefore, 737 is the exact square root of 543169.

Ex. 3. *Find the square root of* $56\dfrac{569}{1225}$.

Sol. $56\dfrac{569}{1225} = \dfrac{69169}{1225}$ $\quad \therefore \quad \sqrt{56\dfrac{569}{1225}} = \sqrt{\dfrac{69169}{1225}} = \dfrac{\sqrt{69169}}{\sqrt{1225}}$ $\quad \left[\text{Using } \sqrt{\dfrac{a}{b}} = \dfrac{\sqrt{a}}{\sqrt{b}} \right]$

We find the square roots of 69169 and 1225 separately.

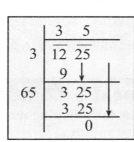

Thus $\sqrt{69169} = 263$, $\sqrt{1225} = 35$

$\therefore \quad \dfrac{\sqrt{69169}}{\sqrt{1225}} = \dfrac{263}{35}$

Hence, $\sqrt{56\dfrac{569}{1225}} = \dfrac{263}{35} = 7\dfrac{18}{35}$.

6.6 Simple Problems on Square Roots

Ex. 4. *Find the least number which must be subtracted from 2361 to make it a perfect square.*

Sol. From the working shown, we find that if 57 be subtracted from the given number, the square root of the remainder (2361 − 57 = 2304) will be 48.

Hence the required number is **57.**

$$
\begin{array}{r|rr}
 & 4\;\;8 \\
\hline
4 & 23\;\;61 \\
 & 16 \\
\hline
88 & 761 \\
 & 704 \\
\hline
 & 57
\end{array}
$$

Ex. 5. *Find the least number which must be added to 4931 to make it a perfect square.*

Sol. We observe that the given number is greater than $(70)^2$ but less than $(71)^2$.

The number to be added $= (71)^2 - 4931 = 5041 - 4931 = \textbf{110.}$

$$
\begin{array}{r|rr}
 & 7\;\;0 \\
\hline
7 & 49\;\;31 \\
 & 49 \\
\hline
 & 31
\end{array}
$$

Ex. 6. *A General wishing to draw up his 64019 men in the form of a solid square, found that he had 10 men over. Find the number of men in the front row.*

Sol. Number of men arranged in a solid square = 64019 – 10 = 64009.

∴ Number of men in the front row = $\sqrt{64009}$ = **253.**

```
          2 5 3
    2 | 6̄ 4̄0̄ 0̄9̄
      |  4
   45 | 240
      | 225
  503 | 1509
      | 1509
      |    0
```

Ex. 7. *Find the least number of 4 digits which is a perfect square.*

Sol. The least number of 4 digits = 1000

Extracting the square root of 1000, we find that $(31)^2 < 1000 < (32)^2$.

∴ The least number of 4 digits, which is a perfect square is $(32)^2 =$ **1024.**

```
         3 1
    3 | 1̄0̄ 0̄0̄
      |  9
   61 | 100
      |  61
      |  39
```

Ex. 8. *Find the greatest number of 4 digits, which is a perfect square.*

Sol. The greatest number of four digits = 9999.

Extracting the square root of 9999, we find that $(99)^2$ is less than 9999 by 198.

Hence, the required number = 9999 – 198 = **9801.**

```
         9 9
    9 | 9̄9̄ 9̄9̄
      | 81
  189 | 1899
      | 1701
      |  198
```

Ex. 9. *Find the least number which is a perfect square and which is also divisible by 16, 18 and 45.*

Sol. L.C.M of 16, 18 and 45 = 2 × 9 × 8 × 5
= $2^2 × 3^2 × 2^2 × 5 = 720$

```
    2 | 16,  18,  45
    9 |  8,   9,  45
      |  8,   1,   5
```

∴ In order to get the required number, we should multiply 720 by 5. Hence, the required number is 720 × 5 or **3600.**

EXERCISE 6 (b)

1. Find by prime factorization the square root of the the following numbers.

(*a*) 144   (*b*) 2500   (*c*) 256   (*d*) 1936   (*e*) 2916   (*f*) 7056

(*g*) 9025   (*h*) 11664

2. Find the square root of the following fractions

(*a*) $\dfrac{196}{484}$ (*b*) $\dfrac{1225}{2025}$ (*c*) $1\dfrac{396}{9604}$ (*d*) 0.01   (*e*) 0.0009   (*f*) 0.00000144

Simplify :

3. $\sqrt{\left(5^2 - 4^2\right)}$ **4.** $\sqrt{\left(5^2 + 12^2\right)}$ **5.** $(-8)^2 - \sqrt{64}$ **6.** $\left(-\sqrt{\dfrac{4}{9}}\right)\left(-\sqrt{\dfrac{81}{100}}\right)$

7. $\sqrt{400} + \sqrt{0.04} + \sqrt{0.000004}$

8. Find the square root of each of the following numbers by long division method

(*a*) 15129   (*b*) 75625   (*c*) 166464   (*d*) 39790864   (*e*) 9548100

(*f*) 64432729   (*g*) 17749369   (*h*) $9\dfrac{15120}{18769}$

9. 3600 soldiers are asked to stand in different rows. Every row has as many soldiers as there are rows. Find the number of rows.

10. Find the perimeter of a square whose area is 71824 m².
11. A society collected Rs 53361, each member contributing as many rupees as there were members. Find the number of members of the society.
12. In a basket there are 1250 flowers. A man goes for worship and puts as many flowers as there are temples in the city. Thus he needs 8 baskets of flowers. Find the number of temples in the city.
13. What should be subtracted from 16,160 to get a perfect square number? What is this perfect square number? Also, find its square root.
14. What should be added to 2582415 to make the sum a perfect square?
15. Find the least number which must be subtracted from 18,265 to make it a perfect square.
16. (*i*) Find the least number of six digits which is a perfect square.
    (*ii*) Find the greatest number of six digits which is a perfect square.
17. A General arranges his soldiers in rows to form a perfect square. He finds that in doing so, 60 soldiers are left out. If the total number of soldiers be 8160, find the number of soldiers in each row.
18. A gardener arranges his plants in rows to form a perfect square. He finds that in doing so, 4 plants are left out. If the total number of plants be 3604, find the number of plants in each row.

6.7 Finding Square Root of Perfect Square Decimal Numbers by Division Method

There is a slight variation in method when it is required to find the square root of a decimal.

While finding the square root of a natural number, say, 46656, we make pairs by counting from *right to left* and if in the last, one digit is left, we leave it by itself. For example, while finding the square root of 276676 and 46656, we form periods as under :

$$\overleftarrow{27} \ \overleftarrow{66} \ \overleftarrow{76} \qquad\qquad 4 \ \overleftarrow{66} \ \overleftarrow{56}$$

> *In case of a decimal number, we count to the right for the decimals and to the left for the whole numbers.*

If the last period of the decimal number contains only one figure we may add zero to it. This is because two digits are necessary to make up a period. The addition of a zero at the right of a decimal figure does not change its value.

For example, while finding the square roots of 0.00 00 2601, 492.84, 998.56, 252.70729 the periods will be formed as under :

$$0.\overrightarrow{00} \ \overrightarrow{00} \ \overrightarrow{26} \ \overrightarrow{00}, \qquad 4\overleftarrow{92}.\overrightarrow{84}, \qquad 9\overleftarrow{88}.\overrightarrow{56}, \qquad 2\overleftarrow{52}.\overrightarrow{70} \ \overrightarrow{72} \ \overrightarrow{90} \qquad \text{(one zero is added)}$$

The square root of a decimal will contain as many decimal places as there are periods, or half as many decimal places as the given number.

The operations in obtaining the square root of a decimal number are the same as for whole numbers. Follow the steps in the following example :

Ex.1. *Find the square root of 1227.8016.*

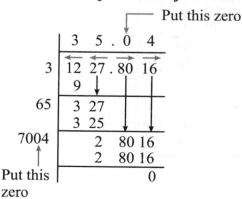

Step 1.	Beginning at the decimal point, mark off points to left and right.	
Step 2.	3 is the largest whole-number square root that is contained in 12, which constitutes the first period.	
Step 3.	Double 3 and place on the outside. Bring down the next pair to get 327. Divide 6 into 32 to obtain 5. Write 5 on top as well as in the divisor. Multiply 65 by 5 and place it under 327. Subtract. The remainder is 2.	
Step 4.	Place decimal point in the root after the 5 because the root of the next period has a decimal value.	
Step 5.	Bring down 80 which is next to 27, making 280 the new dividend. Since 70 does not divide 28, put a zero both in the root and the divisor and bring down the next pair 16 also.	
Step 6.	Since the given number is a perfect square, the remainder is zero.	

$$\therefore \quad \sqrt{1227.8016} = 35.04.$$

Note : *As is done in step 5 above, in working square root example, when a divisor is larger than the corresponding dividend, write zero in the trial divisor and bring down the next root period.*

Ex.2. **Find the square root of 0.00002601.**

Sol.

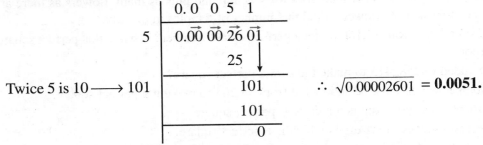

∴ $\sqrt{0.00002601}$ = **0.0051.**

Ex. 3. **Find the value of $\sqrt{23104}$ and use it to find the value of $\sqrt{231.04}$ and $\sqrt{2.3104}$.**

Sol.

```
        1 5 2
   1  | 2 31 04
      | 1
  25  | 131
      | 125
 302  | 604
      | 604
      |   0
```

∴ $\sqrt{23104} = 152$

Now $\sqrt{231.04} + \sqrt{2.3104} = \sqrt{\dfrac{23104}{100}} + \sqrt{\dfrac{23104}{10000}}$

$= \dfrac{\sqrt{23104}}{\sqrt{100}} + \dfrac{\sqrt{23104}}{\sqrt{10000}} = \dfrac{152}{10} + \dfrac{152}{100}$

$= 15.2 + 1.52 = $ **16.72.**

6.8 Square Root of Natural Numbers Which are not Perfect Squares.

Now we will see how to find the square root of numbers which are not perfect squares. In such cases, add zeros after the decimal point, or after the last figure if the original number is already in decimal form and carry out the answer to the desired number of places.

Ex.1. **Find the square root of 1869 to 2 decimal places.**

Sol. Since the square root is to be found to 2dp, add 6 zeros to form 3 pairs.

$\sqrt{1869}$ = 43.231 to 3 dp

= **43.23** to 2 dp.

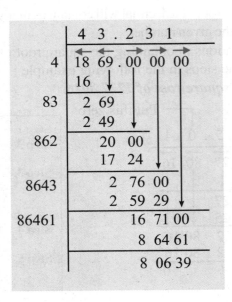

Ex. 2. *Find the square root of (a) 7 to three decimal places (b) 11 to four decimal places.*

Sol.

(a)

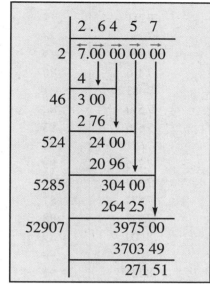

```
          2 . 6 4 5 7
    2  | 7.00 00 00 00
       | 4
   46  | 3 00
       | 2 76
  524  | 24 00
       | 20 96
 5285  | 304 00
       | 264 25
52907  | 3975 00
       | 3703 49
       |  271 51
```

(b)

```
           3. 3  1  6  6  2
     3  | 11.00 00 00 00 00
        |  9
    63  | 200
        | 189
   661  | 11 00
        |  6 61
  6626  | 4 39 00
        | 3 97 56
 66326  | 41 44 00
        | 39 79 56
663322  | 1 64 44 00
        | 1 32 66 44
        |   31 77 56
```

∴ $\sqrt{7}$ = 2.6457 to 4 dp. = **2.646** to 3 dp.

$\sqrt{11}$ = 3.31662 to 5 d.p = **3.3166** to 4 d.p.

EXERCISE 6 (c)

1. Find the square root of each of the following numbers :

(a) 235.3156   (b) 81.5409   (c) 794.6761

(d) 291.7264   (e) 64.144081   (f) 0.000004

(g) 0.00001369   (h) 0.00037636

2. Find the value of $\sqrt{15625}$ and from this value, evaluate $\sqrt{156.25} + \sqrt{1.5625}$.

3. Find the square roots of 2304 and 1764 and hence find the value of $\dfrac{\sqrt{0.2304} + \sqrt{0.1764}}{\sqrt{0.2304} - \sqrt{0.1764}}$.

4. The area of a square playground is 477.4225 square metres. Find the length of one side of the playground.

Find the square root of each of the following numbers to 3 decimal places.

5. 789   **6.** 478   **7.** 6153   **8.** 66

9. 3   **10.** 2   **11.** 17

6.9 Square Roots by Using Tables

A table containing square roots of all natural numbers from 1 to 100 approximating to 3 dp, has been given here. Besides using this table to find out square roots of natural numbers less than 100, you can use this to find square roots of other numbers also. This is illustrated in the examples given after the table.

n	$\sqrt{n}$	n	$\sqrt{n}$	n	$\sqrt{n}$	n	$\sqrt{n}$
1	1.000	26	5.099	51	7.141	76	8.718
2	1.414	27	5.198	52	7.211	77	8.775
3	1.732	28	5.292	53	7.280	78	8.832
4	2.000	29	5.385	54	7.348	79	8.888
5	2.236	30	5.477	55	7.416	80	8.944
6	2.449	31	5.568	56	7.483	81	9.000
7	2.646	32	5.657	57	7.550	82	9.055
8	2.828	33	5.745	58	7.616	83	9.110
9	3.000	34	5.831	59	7.681	84	9.165
10	3.162	35	5.916	60	7.746	85	9.220
11	3.317	36	6.000	61	7.810	86	9.274
12	3.464	37	6.083	62	7.874	87	9.327
13	3.606	38	6.164	63	7.937	88	9.381
14	3.742	39	6.245	64	8.000	89	9.434
15	3.873	40	6.325	65	8.062	90	9.487
16	4.000	41	6.403	66	8.124	91	9.539
17	4.123	42	6.481	67	8.185	92	9.591
18	4.243	43	6.557	68	8.246	93	9.644
19	4.359	44	6.633	69	8.307	94	9.695
20	4.472	45	6.708	70	8.367	95	9.747
21	4.583	46	6.782	71	8.426	96	9.798
22	4.690	47	6.856	72	8.485	97	9.849
23	4.796	48	6.928	73	8.544	98	9.899
24	4.899	49	7.000	74	8.602	99	9.950
25	5.000	50	7.071	75	8.660	100	10.000

Ex. 1. *Using the square root tables, find the values of :*

    (a) $\sqrt{11}$ **(b)** $\sqrt{87}$ **(c)** $\sqrt{75}$ **(d)** $\sqrt{464}$.

Sol. *(a)* $\sqrt{11}$ = **3.317.**(From the table of square roots)

    (b) $\sqrt{87}$ = **9.327.**(From the table of square roots)

    (c) $\sqrt{75} = \sqrt{5\times5\times3} = 5\times\sqrt{3}$ = 5 × 1.732 = **8.660.**

    (d) $\sqrt{464} = \sqrt{4\times4\times29} = 4\times\sqrt{29}$ = 4× 5.385 = **21.54.**

Ex. 2. *By using the square root table, find the value of* **2300**.

Sol. $\sqrt{2300} = \sqrt{100\times23} = \sqrt{100}\times\sqrt{23} = 10\sqrt{23}$

    = 10 × 4.796 = **47.96**.

Ex. 3. *Using square root table, find the value of :*

    (a) $\sqrt{110}$ **(b)** $\sqrt{1.1}$ **(c)** $\sqrt{663}$

Sol. *(a)* $\sqrt{110} = \sqrt{11\times10} = \sqrt{11}\times\sqrt{10}$

                 = 3.317 × 3.162 = 10.488354 = 10.488 (to 3 dp)

```
        3317
        3162
       6634
      19902
     3317
     9951
   10488354
```

(b) $\sqrt{1.1} = \sqrt{\dfrac{11}{10}} = \sqrt{\dfrac{110}{100}} = \dfrac{\sqrt{110}}{10} = \dfrac{10.488}{10} = \mathbf{1.0488.}$

(c) $\sqrt{663} = \sqrt{3 \times 13 \times 17} = \sqrt{3} \times \sqrt{13} \times \sqrt{17}$

$\qquad = 1.732 \times 3.606 \times 4.123$

$\qquad = 25.750575816 = \mathbf{25.751}$ (to 3 dp).

```
        1 7 3 2                    6 2 4 5 5 9 2
      × 3 6 0 6                  ×         4 1 2 3
      _____                _____
        1 0 3 9 2                1 8 7 3 6 7 7 6
    1 0 3 9 2 0                1 2 4 9 1 1 8 4
    5 1 9 6                    6 2 4 5 5 9 2
    _____              2 4 9 8 2 3 6 8
    6 2 4 5 5 9 2            _____
                            2 5 7 5 0 5 7 5 8 1 6
```

Put decimal point after 9 places from the right.

Ex.4. *By using the square root table, find the value of* $\sqrt{\dfrac{11}{25}}$.

Sol. $\sqrt{\dfrac{11}{25}} = \dfrac{\sqrt{11}}{\sqrt{25}} = \dfrac{\sqrt{11}}{5} = \dfrac{3.317}{5} = \mathbf{0.6634.}$

EXERCISE 6 (d)

Using square root table, find the square roots of the following numbers :

1. $\sqrt{19}$ 2. $\sqrt{47}$ 3. $\sqrt{1100}$ 4. $\sqrt{150}$ 5. $\sqrt{810}$ 6. $\sqrt{410}$

7. $\sqrt{828}$ 8. $\sqrt{425}$ 9. $\sqrt{\dfrac{13}{16}}$ 10. $\sqrt{\dfrac{148}{169}}$

LOOKING BACK

Summary of Key Facts

1. If a number is multiplied by itself, the product so obtained in called the **square** of that number. It is a number raised to the power 2.

   Thus, $7 \times 7 = 7^2 = 49$ 49 is the square of 7

   The number 7 is called the **square root** of 49.

2. The square of a natural number is called a perfect square.

3. **Properties of Squares**

   (i) A perfect square is never negative.

   (ii) A square number never ends in 2, 3, 7 or 8.

   (iii) The number of zeros at the end of a perfect square is always even.

   (iv) The square of an even number is even.

   (v) The square of an odd number is odd.

(*vi*) For any natural number n,

n^2 = sum of the first n odd natural numbers   (**Ex.** $4^2 = 1 + 3 + 5 + 7$)

4. Properties of Square Root

(*i*) If a number ends in an odd number of zeros, then it does not have a square root.

(*ii*) The square root of an even square number is even and square root of an odd square number is odd.

(*iii*) If p and q are perfect squares ($q \neq 0$), then

(*a*) $\sqrt{p \times q} = \sqrt{p} \times \sqrt{q}$ (*b*) $\sqrt{\dfrac{p}{q}} = \dfrac{\sqrt{p}}{\sqrt{q}}$

5. Finding the square root :

(*i*) The square root of a perfect square number can be obtained by finding the prime factorisation of the square number, pairing equal factors and picking out one prime factor out of each pair.

Thus, $900 = \underline{2 \times 2} \times \underline{3 \times 3} \times \underline{5 \times 5}$ and $\sqrt{900} = 2 \times 3 \times 5 = 30$.

(*ii*) The square root of a number may also be found by division method.

(*iii*) The pairing of numbers in the division method starts from the decimal point. For the integral part, it goes from right to left ($\leftarrow$) and for the decimal part, it goes from left to right ($\rightarrow$) as shown below.

$1\overset{\leftarrow}{66}\overset{\leftarrow}{41}$ $\overset{\leftarrow}{59}\overset{\leftarrow}{37}\overset{\leftarrow}{28}.\overset{\rightarrow}{97}$ $.\overset{\rightarrow}{00}\overset{\rightarrow}{37}\overset{\rightarrow}{48}\overset{\rightarrow}{00}$ $593.721 \Rightarrow 5\overset{\leftarrow}{93}.\overset{\rightarrow}{72}\overset{\rightarrow}{10}$

(*iv*) If a positive number is not a perfect square, then an approximate value of its square may be obtained by the division method.

(*v*) If n is not a perfect square, then $\sqrt{n}$ is not a rational number *e.g.* $\sqrt{2}, \sqrt{3}, \sqrt{7}$ are not rational numbers.

MENTAL MATHS – 5

1. Square of 4 = ...   **2.** Square of 6 = ...   **3.** Square of 8 = ...   **4.** Square of $\dfrac{5}{9}$ = ...

5. Square of 0.3 is ...   **6.** Square of 0.12 is ...   **7.** $15^2 - 14^2$ = ...   **8.** $99^2 - 98^2$ = ...

9. Square of 0.07 = ...   **10.** Without adding, find the sum of $1 + 3 + 5 + 7 + 9 + 11 + 13 + 15 + 17$

11. $\sqrt{0.0081}$ = ...   **12.** Find the square root of 10000000000.

13. Why is each of the following numbers not a perfect square?

(*a*) 372,   (*b*) 59307

(*c*) 71298   (*d*) 39000

14. Find the least number which should be subtracted from 18 to make it a perfect square.

ANSWERS

EXERCISE 6 (a)

1. (*a*) 10   (*b*) 28   (*c*) 60   (*d*) 65   **2.** (*b*), (*c*) and (*e*)

3. (*a*) 196   (*b*) 9409   (*c*) $\dfrac{36}{49}$ (*d*) 0.64   (*e*) 0.000121   (*f*) 2.89

4. (*a*) 2; 1024   (*b*) 7; 4900   (*c*) 3; 3969   (*d*) 5; 176400   **5.** (*a*) 5; 36   (*b*) 7; 225

    (*c*) 3; 2304   (*d*) 3; 6400   **6.** (*a*) & (*c*) will be odd; (*b*) & (*d*) will be even.

EXERCISE 6 (b)

1. (*a*) 12   (*b*) 50   (*c*) 16   (*d*) 44   (*e*) 54   (*f*) 84

    (*g*) 95   (*h*) 108   **2.** (*a*) $\dfrac{7}{11}$ (*b*) $\dfrac{7}{9}$ (*c*) $1\dfrac{1}{49}$ (*d*) 0.1   (*e*) 0.03

(*f*) 0.0012   3. 3   4. 13   5. 56   6. $\frac{3}{5}$ 7. 20.202   8. (*a*) 123

(*b*) 275   (*c*) 408   (*d*) 6308   (*e*) 3090   (*f*) 8027   (*g*) 4213   (*h*) $3\frac{18}{137}$

9. 60   10. 1072 m   11. 231   12. 100   13. 31; 16129; 127   14. 34

15. 40   16. (*i*) 100489   (*ii*) 998001 (**Hint :** Same type on solved examples 7 and 8)

17. 90   18. 60

EXERCISE 6 (c)

1. (*a*) 15.34   (*b*) 9.03   (*c*) 28.19   (*d*) 17.08   (*e*) 8.009   (*f*) 0.002   (*g*) 0.0037

(*h*) 0.0194   9. 125 ; 13.75   10. 48 ; 42 ; 15   11. 21.85m   12. 28.089   13. 21.863   14. 78.441

15. 8.124   16. 1.732   17. 1.414   18. 4.123

EXERCISE 6 (d)

1. 4.359   2. 6.856   3. 33.17   4. 12.25   5. 28.458 (to 3 d.p)   6. 20.246

7. 28.776   8. 20.615 (to 3 dp)   9. 0.9015   10. 0.936 (to 3 d.p)

MENTAL MATHS – 5

1. 16   2. 36   3. 64   4. $\frac{25}{81}$ 5. 0.09   6. 0.0144

7. 29   8. 197   9. 0.0049   10. 81 (**Hint :** The sum of first *n* odd numbers = n^2)

11. 0.09   12. 100000

13. (*i*) ends in 2   (*ii*) ends in 7   (*iii*) ends in 8   (*iv*) The odd no. of zeros at the end   14. 2

7. Cubes and Cube Roots

7.1 Cubes

The cube of a number is the number raised to the power 3. Thus

$$\text{cube of } 2 = 2^3 = 2 \times 2 \times 2 = 8, \text{ cube of } 5 = 5^3 = 5 \times 5 \times 5 = 125.$$

7.2 Perfect Cube

We know that $2^3 = 8$, $3^3 = 27$, $6^3 = 216$, $7^3 = 343$, $10^3 = 1000$.

The numbers 8, 27, 216, 343, 1000, ... are called perfect cubes. A natural number is said to be a perfect cube, if it is the cube of some natural number. That is,

A natural number n is a perfect cube if there exists a natural number m such that $m \times m \times m = n$, i.e., $m^3 = n$.

> **Test.** A given natural number is a perfect cube if in its prime factorization; every prime occurs three times or a multiple of three times, *i.e.*, if it is expressible as the product of **triples** of the same prime factors.

The cubes of first 20 natural numbers are given below. You may learn them by heart.

Number	Cube	Number	Cube	Number	Cube	Number	Cube
1	1	6	216	11	1331	16	4096
2	8	7	343	12	1728	17	4913
3	27	8	512	13	2197	18	5832
4	64	9	729	14	2744	19	6859
5	125	10	1000	15	3375	20	8000

Ex. 1. *Show that 74088 is a perfect cube.*

Sol. Resolving 74088 into prime factors, we have

$74088 = \underline{2 \times 2 \times 2} \times \underline{3 \times 3 \times 3} \times \underline{7 \times 7 \times 7}$

Here, we find that the prime factors 2, 3 and 7 of the given number can be grouped into triplets of equal factors and no factor is left out. Hence, 74088 is a perfect cube

Also, 74088 is the cube of $2 \times 3 \times 7$, *i.e.* **$74088 = (42)^3$.**

2	74088
2	37044
2	18522
3	9261
3	3087
3	1029
7	343
7	49
7	7
	1

Ex. 2. *What is the smallest number by which 1323 may be multiplied so that the product is a perfect cube?*

Sol. Resolving 1323 into prime factors, we have

$1323 = \underline{3 \times 3 \times 3} \times 7 \times 7$

Since one more 7 is required to make a triplet of 7, the smallest number by which 1323 should be multiplied to make it a perfect cube is 7.

3	1323
3	441
3	147
7	49
7	7
	1

Ex. 3. *What is the smallest number by which 1375 should be divided so that the quotient may be a perfect cube?*

Sol. Resolving 1375 into prime factors, we have

$1375 = \underline{5 \times 5 \times 5} \times 11$.

The factor 5 makes a triplet, and 11 is left out. So, clearly 1375 should be divided by 11 to make it a perfect cube.

5	1375
5	275
5	55
11	11
	1

7.3 Properties of Cubes

From the table of cubes given above it is easy to observe that

1. Cubes of all odd natural numbers are odd. Thus $3^3 = 27$, $5^3 = 125$, $7^3 = 343$, $9^3 = 729$ etc.
2. Cubes of all even natural numbers are even. Thus $2^3 = 8$, $4^3 = 64$, $6^3 = 216$, $8^3 = 512$ etc.
3. Cubes of negative integers are negative
   Thus $(-1)^3 = (-1) \times (-1) \times (-1) = -1$.

7.4 Cube Root

The cube root of a number a is that number which when multiplied by itself three times gives a, i.e.,

If $a \times a \times a = a^3$ then $\sqrt[3]{a^3} = a$.

> **Note :**
>
> 1. Cube root is denoted by the symbol $\sqrt[3]{}$.
>
> 2. Cube root of a negative number is negative $\sqrt[3]{-a^3} = -a$.
>
> 3. If a and b are two whole numbers, then $\sqrt[3]{a.b} = \sqrt[3]{a}.\sqrt[3]{b}$.
>
> 4. If a and b are two whole numbers, $(b \neq 0)$, then $\sqrt[3]{\dfrac{a}{b}} = \dfrac{\sqrt[3]{a}}{\sqrt[3]{b}}$.

7.5 Finding the Cube Root

Method 1 : Prime Factorisation Method

Step 1 : *Resolve the given number into prime factors.*

Step 2 : *Form groups of threes of like factors.*

Step 3 : *Take out one factor from each group and multiply.*

3	9261
3	3087
3	1029
7	343
7	49
7	7
	1

Ex.1. *Find the cube root of*

(a) *9261*　　　**(b)** $4\dfrac{12}{125}$　　　**(c)** *0.729*

Sol. (a) Resolving into prime factors

$9261 \quad = \quad \underline{3 \times 3 \times 3} \quad \times \quad \underline{7 \times 7 \times 7}$

$\sqrt[3]{9261} = \qquad 3 \qquad \times \qquad 7$

$\qquad\qquad = \quad \mathbf{21}$

(b) $4\dfrac{12}{125} = \dfrac{512}{125} = \dfrac{2^9}{5^3}$ $\qquad \therefore \quad \sqrt[3]{4\dfrac{12}{125}} = \sqrt[3]{\dfrac{512}{125}} = \dfrac{\sqrt[3]{512}}{\sqrt[3]{125}} = \dfrac{2^3}{5} = \dfrac{8}{5}$.

(c) $0.729 = \dfrac{729}{1000} = \dfrac{3^6}{10^3}$ $\qquad \sqrt[3]{\dfrac{729}{1000}} = \dfrac{\sqrt[3]{729}}{\sqrt[3]{1000}} = \dfrac{3^2}{10} = \dfrac{9}{10} = \mathbf{0.9}$.

2	512
2	256
2	128
2	64
2	32
2	16
2	8
2	4
	2

3	729
3	243
3	81
3	27
3	9
	3

For cube root take one third of the power of both numerator and denominator.

Ex.2. *Find the value of* $\sqrt[3]{968} \times \sqrt[3]{1375}$.

Sol. $\sqrt[3]{968} \times \sqrt[3]{1375} = \sqrt[3]{968 \times 1375}$

Resolving 968 and 6125 into prime factors, we have

2	968
2	484
2	242
11	121
11	11
	1

5	1375
5	275
5	55
11	11
	1

∴ $968 \times 1375 = 2 \times 2 \times 2 \times 11 \times 11 \times 5 \times 5 \times 5 \times 11$

$= (2 \times 2 \times 2) \times (11 \times 11 \times 11) \times (5 \times 5 \times 5)$

∴ $\sqrt[3]{968 \times 1375} = 2 \times 11 \times 5 = \mathbf{110}.$

EXERCISE 7 (a)

Find the cubes of the following numbers :

1. (*a*) 8   (*b*) 13   (*c*) 400   2. (*a*) $\dfrac{3}{5}$ (*b*) $\dfrac{-4}{9}$ (*c*) $2\dfrac{5}{7}$

3. (*a*) 0.3   (*b*) − 2.4   (*c*) 0.001

4. **Which of the following numbers are perfect cubes?**

   64, 125, 243, 729, 1331, 864, 4096,

   (**Hint.** Resolve into prime factors and see if you can group these factors into triplets of equal numbers)

5. What is the smallest number by which 675 should be multiplied so that the product is a perfect cube?

6. What is the smallest number by which 2916 should be divided so that the quotient is a perfect cube?

Find the cube root by prime factorisation method of the following numbers :

7. 4096   8. 91125   9. $\dfrac{125}{343}$ 10. $-\dfrac{2744}{5832}$ 11. $5\dfrac{23}{64}$ 12. 0.216

13. 4.096   14. Show that $\sqrt[3]{27} \times \sqrt[3]{125} = \sqrt[3]{27 \times 125}$ 15. Find the value of $\sqrt[3]{392} \times \sqrt[3]{448}$

16. Find the smallest number by which 47916 must be multiplied so that the product is a perfect cube. Also, find the cube root of the product.

17. Find the smallest number by which 120393 should be divided so that the quotient is a perfect cube. Also find the cube root of the quotient.

7.6 Cube Root Tables

As you have seen cube roots of some numbers can be found by factors. The cube root of other numbers can be found from tables. Here, we give a table containing $\sqrt[3]{n}$, $\sqrt[3]{10n}$ and $\sqrt[3]{100n}$, where *n* is natural number from 1 to 100.

Using this table, we may find the cube root of any given number. The examples given after the table will help you to understand the method.

TABLE OF CUBE ROOTS

n	$\sqrt[3]{n}$	$\sqrt[3]{10n}$	$\sqrt[3]{100n}$	n	$\sqrt[3]{n}$	$\sqrt[3]{10n}$	$\sqrt[3]{100n}$
1	1.000	2.154	4.642	51	3.708	7.990	17.21
2	1.260	2.714	5.848	52	3.733	8.041	17.32
3	1.442	3.107	6.694	53	3.756	8.093	17.44
4	1.587	3.420	7.368	54	3.780	8.143	17.54
5	1.710	3.684	7.937	55	3.803	8.193	17.65
6	1.817	3.915	8.434	56	3.826	8.243	17.76
7	1.913	4.121	8.879	57	3.849	8.291	17.86
8	2.000	4.309	9.283	58	3.871	8.340	17.97
9	2.080	4.481	9.655	59	3.893	8.387	18.07
10	2.154	4.642	10.00	60	3.915	8.434	18.17
11	2.224	4.791	10.32	61	3.936	8.481	18.27
12	2.289	4.932	10.63	62	3.958	8.527	18.37
13	2.351	5.066	10.91	63	2.979	8.573	18.47
14	2.410	5.192	11.19	64	4.000	8.618	18.57
15	2.466	5.313	11.45	65	4.021	8.662	18.66
16	2.520	5.429	11.70	66	4.041	8.707	18.76
17	2.571	5.540	11.93	67	4.062	8.750	18.85
18	2.621	5.646	12.16	68	4.082	8.794	18.95
19	2.668	5.749	12.39	69	4.102	8.837	19.04
20	2.714	5.848	12.60	70	4.121	8.879	19.13
21	2.759	5.944	12.81	71	4.141	8.921	19.22
22	2.802	6.037	13.01	72	4.160	8.963	19.31
23	2.844	6.127	13.20	73	4.179	9.004	19.40
24	2.884	6.214	13.39	74	4.198	9.045	19.49
25	2.924	6.300	13.57	75	4.217	9.086	19.57
26	2.962	6.383	13.75	76	4.236	9.126	19.66
27	3.000	6.463	13.92	77	4.254	9.166	19.75
28	3.037	6.542	14.09	78	4.273	9.205	19.83
29	3.072	6.619	14.26	79	4.291	9.244	19.92
30	3.107	6.694	14.42	80	4.309	9.283	20.00
31	3.141	6.768	14.58	81	4.327	9.322	20.08
32	3.175	6.840	14.74	82	4.344	9.360	20.17
33	3.208	6.910	14.89	83	4.362	9.398	20.25
34	3.240	6.980	15.04	84	4.380	9.435	20.33
35	3.271	7.047	15.18	85	4.397	9.473	20.41
36	3.302	7.114	15.33	86	4.414	9.510	20.49
37	3.332	7.179	15.47	87	4.431	9.546	20.57
38	3.362	7.243	15.60	88	4.448	9.583	20.65
39	3.391	7.306	15.74	89	4.465	9.619	20.72
40	3.420	7.368	15.87	90	4.481	9.655	20.80
41	3.448	7.429	16.01	91	4.498	9.691	20.88
42	3.476	7.489	16.13	92	4.514	9.726	20.95
43	3.503	7.548	16.26	93	4.531	9.761	21.03
44	3.530	7.606	16.39	94	4.547	9.796	21.10
45	3.557	7.663	16.51	95	4.563	9.830	21.18
46	3.583	7.719	16.63	96	4.579	9.865	21.25
47	3.609	7.775	16.75	97	4.595	9.899	21.33
48	3.634	7.830	16.87	98	4.610	9.933	21.40
49	3.659	7.884	16.98	99	4.626	9.967	21.47
50	3.684	7.937	17.10				

Ex.1. *Evaluate*

     (a) $\sqrt[3]{38}$ **(b)** $\sqrt[3]{380}$ **(c)** $\sqrt[3]{3800}$ **(d)** $\sqrt[3]{3.8}$

Sol. *(a)* $\sqrt[3]{38} = 3.362$ (From table) | See against 38 in the column for $\sqrt[3]{n}$ |

      (b) $\sqrt[3]{380} = \sqrt[3]{10 \times 38} = 7.243$ (From table) | See against 38 in the column for $\sqrt[3]{10n}$ |

      (c) $\sqrt[3]{3800} = 15.60$ (From table) | See against 38 in the column for $\sqrt[3]{100n}$ |

      (d) $\sqrt[3]{3.8} = \sqrt[3]{\dfrac{38}{10}} = \sqrt[3]{\dfrac{3800}{1000}} = \dfrac{1}{10}\sqrt[3]{3800} = \dfrac{1}{10} \times 15.60 = \mathbf{1.560}.$

Ex. 2. *Find the cube of*   **(a)** *47000*   **(b)** *470000.*

Sol. *(a)* $\sqrt[3]{47000} = \sqrt[3]{47 \times 1000} = \sqrt[3]{47} \times \sqrt[3]{1000} = 3.609 \times 10 = \mathbf{36.09}.$

      (b) $\sqrt[3]{470000} = \sqrt[3]{47 \times 1000 \times 10} = 10 \times \sqrt[3]{47 \times 10} = 10 \times \sqrt[3]{470}$ | See against 47 in the column for $\sqrt[3]{10n}$ |

               $= 10 \times 7.775 = \mathbf{77.75}.$

Ex. 3. *Find the cube root of 57.84.*

Sol. The number 57.84 lies between 57 and 58.

    From the table, we have

         $\sqrt[3]{57} = 3.849$ and $\sqrt[3]{58} = 3.871$

         $\sqrt[3]{58} - \sqrt[3]{57} = 3.871 - 3.849 = 0.022$

Now, apply unitary method.

When the difference in value is 1, difference in cube root is 0.022.

∴   When the difference in value is 0.84, difference in cube root is $\dfrac{0.022}{1} \times 0.84 = 0.018$

∴ $\sqrt[3]{57.84} = 3.849 + 0.018 = \mathbf{3.867}.$

EXERCISE 7 (b)

Using table find the cube roots of the following numbers :

1. 35   **2.** 59   **3.** 74   **4.** 540   **5.** 780   **6.** 690

7. 7.8   **8.** 7600   **9.** 9.8   **10.** 3.2

LOOKING BACK

Summary of Key Facts

1. The cube of a number is the number raised to the power 3, *e.g.*, cube of $7 = 7^3$

                                           $= 7 \times 7 \times 7 = 343.$

2. A number n is a perfect cube if it can be expressed as $n = m^3$ for some natural number m, *e.g.*, 8 is a perfect cube as 8 can be expressed as $8 = 2^3$.

3. *(i)* The cube of an even number is even, *e.g.*, $4^3 = 64$.

   (ii) The cube of an odd number is odd, *e.g.*, $5^3 = 125$.

4. The cube root of a number n is the number whose cube is n. It is denoted by $\sqrt[3]{n}$, *e.g.*, since $6^3 = 6 \times 6 \times 6 = 216$, therefore, cube root of $216 = \sqrt[3]{216} = 6$.

5. The cube root of a number can be found by resolving the number into prime factors, making groups of 3 equal factors, picking out one of the equal factors from each group and multiplying the factors so picked.

6. e.g., $1728 = \underline{2 \times 2 \times 2} \times \underline{2 \times 2 \times 2} \times \underline{3 \times 3 \times 3}$ so $\sqrt[3]{1728} = 2 \times 2 \times 3 = 12$.

7. The cube root of a negative perfect cube is negative e.g., $\sqrt[3]{-8} = -2$.

8. For any integer a and b, we have

(i) $\sqrt[3]{ab} = \sqrt[3]{a} \times \sqrt[3]{b}$ (ii) $\sqrt[3]{\dfrac{a}{b}} = \dfrac{\sqrt[3]{a}}{\sqrt[3]{b}}$

e.g. (i) $\sqrt[3]{4} \times \sqrt[3]{54} = \sqrt[3]{4 \times 54} = \sqrt[3]{2 \times 2 \times 2 \times 3 \times 3 \times 3} = 2 \times 3 = 6$.

(ii) $\sqrt[3]{\dfrac{8}{27}} = \dfrac{\sqrt[3]{8}}{\sqrt[3]{27}} = \dfrac{2}{3}$.

MENTAL MATHS – 6

1. Is 8000 a perfect cube? Yes/No

2. Write the cubes of first five natural numbers.

3. What is the smallest number by which 4 should be multiplied to make it a perfect cube.

4. What is the smallest number by which 81 should be divided to make it a perfect square?

5. Find the cube root of $\dfrac{27}{64}$.

6. Find the cube root of 0.008.

7. Find the cube root of -27000.

8. Identify the perfect cubes in the following 27, 64, 125, 98, 100, -9000.

9. Simplify $(10)^2 - 4^3$.

10. $\sqrt[3]{0.001} \times 10$.

UNIT REVIEW – 2

1. Fill in the blanks

  (a) 0.979797...names a _____ number.

  (b) Nonterminating, non-repeating decimal numerals represent ——numbers.

  (c) Each repeating and terminating decimal names a unique _____number.

  (d) 0.667666776666777... names a(n) _____ number.

2. Find all the possible values of the missing digits in the given questions.

  (a) 60 * 18 is divisible by 3 (b) 83 * is divisible by 4 (c) 919 * 8 is divisible by 11

3. Find the H.C.F of : (a) 426, 994 (b) 1007, 2279

4. What is the shortest distance that can be measured exactly both by a 5 m pole and by a walking stick 3m 50cm long.

5. If 150, 190 and 260 are each divided by a certain number, the remainders are 3, 1 and 8 respectively. What is the greatest value of the divisor.

6. Find the H.C.F and L.C.M of $\dfrac{4}{5}, \dfrac{12}{25}, \dfrac{16}{35}, \dfrac{8}{15}$ **7. Simplify :** (a) $\dfrac{1}{1\frac{2}{5}} \div \dfrac{1}{1\frac{3}{4}} - \dfrac{1}{1\frac{3}{5}}$ (b) $\dfrac{1 - \dfrac{1}{2 - \dfrac{1}{3}}}{1 + \dfrac{1}{2 + \dfrac{1}{3}}}$

8. Express as fractions in their lowest terms : (a) 62.68 (b) 0.3636.... (c) $0.5\overline{36}$

9. Express as decimal (a) $\dfrac{17}{9}$ (b) $\dfrac{127}{11}$

10. Evaluate :   (a) $0.06 + 0.04 - 0.05 - 0.005 + 5$ (b) $1.1 \times 0.01 \times 0.03 \times 700 \times 0.004$

    (c) $3.6 \div 0.012 + 1.2$ of $0.5 - 0.02$ (d) $\dfrac{3.2\{(1.5)^2 - (0.5)^2\}}{0.128\{(1.5 + 0.5)\}}$

11. Find the H.C.F and L.C.M of 21, 7, 56, 14.
12. Find the square root of 6.0025 by long division method.
13. Find the largest number of 5 digits that is a perfect square.
14. Find the square root of 27 correct to 3 s.f.
15. Find the cube root of 1280 using cube root tables correct to 3 d.p.
16. Find the cube root of 5400 using tables correct to 3 d.p.

17. Arrange $\dfrac{1}{5}, \dfrac{13}{20}$, 0.45 and 0.63 in ascending order of magnitude.

    (**Hint :** Convert the fractions to decimal form and arrange)

18. Insert 2 rational numbers between $-\dfrac{2}{3}$ and $\dfrac{7}{8}$.

19. Arrange $\dfrac{2}{3}, \dfrac{4}{7}, \dfrac{6}{11}, \dfrac{3}{13}$ in ascending order of magnitude by making numerators equal.

20. A man spends $\dfrac{7}{15}$ of his income at home, $\dfrac{1}{6}$ of his income on holidays and saves the rest. If he saves Rs 22000 in a year, what is his income ?

ANSWERS

EXERCISE 7 (a)

1. (a) 512   (b) 2197   (c) 64000000   2. (a) $\dfrac{27}{125}$ (b) $-\dfrac{64}{729}$ (c) $\dfrac{6859}{343}$

3. (a) 0.027   (b) −13.824   (c) 0.000000001. 4. 64, 125, 729, 1331, 4096,   5. 5   6. 4

7. 16   8. 45   9. $\dfrac{5}{7}$ 10. $\dfrac{-14}{18}$ 11. $1\dfrac{3}{4}$ 12. 0.6   13. 1.6

15. 56   16. 6; 66   17. 13; 21

EXERCISE 7 (b)

1. 3.271   2. 3.893   3. 4.198   4. 8.143   5. 9.205   6. 8.837   7. 1.983
8. 19.66   9. 2.140   10. 1.471

MENTAL MATHS – 6

1. Yes   2. 1, 8, 27, 64, 125   3. 2   4. 3   5. $\dfrac{3}{4}$

6. 0.2   7. −30   8. 27, 64, 125   9. 36   10. 1

UNIT REVIEW – 2

1. (a) rational   (b) irrational   (c) rational   (d) irrational   2. (a) 0, 3, 6, 9   (b) 2, 6   (c) 3

3. (a) 142   (b) 53   4. 35 m   5. 21   6. H.C.F. = $\dfrac{4}{525}$, L.C.M. = $\dfrac{48}{5}$.

7. (a) $\dfrac{5}{8}$ (b) $\dfrac{7}{25}$ 8. (a) $\dfrac{1567}{25}$ (b) $\dfrac{4}{11}$ (c) $\dfrac{59}{110}$ 9. (a) $1.\overline{8}$ (b) $11.\overline{54}$

10. (*a*) 5.045   (*b*) 0.00924   (*c*) 300.58   (*d*) 25   **11.** H.C.F = 7, L.C.M = 168.

12. 2.45   **13.** 99856   **14.** 5.20   **15.** 10.856   **16.** 17.54   **17.** $\dfrac{1}{5}$, 0.45, 0.63, $\dfrac{13}{20}$

18. $\dfrac{5}{48}, \dfrac{47}{96}$ **19.** $\dfrac{3}{13}, \dfrac{6}{11}, \dfrac{4}{7}, \dfrac{2}{3}$ **20.** Rs 60000.

HISTORICAL NOTE
Aryabhata - 1

1. **Aryabhata - 1** was the first Indian to have given a scientific basis to Astronomy. He was also a great mathematician. He was born on March 21, 476 - a little over 1,515 years ago at Kusumapura, near Pataliputra (Modern Patna). He recorded all his thoughts, theories and calculations in his book 'Aryabhatiya' which he wrote when he was only 23 years of age. He made important contributions to Astonomy and all branches of mathematics- Algebra, Geometry and Arithmetic.

2. He was the first to propound the theory that the earth was spherical and that it revolved round the sun.

3. He could calculate 1500 years ago that the length of one day and one night was 23 hours, 56 minutes and 4.1 seconds. Modern scientists have calculated the same period to be 23 hours, 56 minutes and 4.091 seconds.

4. He gave an accurate value of π(Pi).

Aryabhata wrote

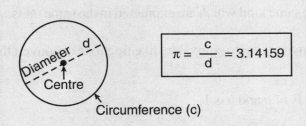

$$\pi = \frac{c}{d} = 3.14159$$

100 + 4 multiply by 8 add to 62,000. This is approximately the measure of the circumference of a circle whose diameter is 20,000, which mathematically can be written as :

$$\frac{62832}{20000} = 3.1416.$$

Note that Aryabhata-I added this ratio was approximate. It is even today that with the help of computers an exact value has not been found.

5. India's first artificial satellite was named after him. Its launching coincided with his 1500th birth anniversary.

UNIT – 3 : COMMERCIAL MATHEMATICS

8. Ratio and Proportion

8.1 Introduction

You have already studied ratio and proportion in earlier classes. Here we will take up more problems to strengthen your understanding of this important topic.

8.2 Ratio (Quick Review)

Ratio compares quantities of the same kind in the same units. *Ratio between two quantities a and b, (of same kind and same unit) is written as **a : b*** (read as : **a is to b**) *and is expressed as a fraction* $\frac{a}{b}$.

a and *b* are called the **terms** of the ratio.

a is called the **antecedent** and *b* is called the **consequent**.

> **Note :**
> 1. In a ratio, order of terms is very important.
> 2. Since ratio is a fraction, the ratio will remain unchanged if each term of the ratio is multiplied or divided by the same non-zero number.
>
> $$\frac{a}{b} = \frac{ma}{mb} = \frac{a \div m}{b \div m} \qquad m \neq 0$$
>
> 3. Ratio always exists between quantities of the same kind which are expressed in the same units.
> 4. Ratio has no unit.
> 5. To compare two or more ratios, we either convert them to equivalent like fractions or convert them to the decimal form.
> 6. A ratio $a : b = \frac{a}{b}$ is in its lowest term if H.C.F. of *a* and *b* is 1.
> 7. If a quantity increases or decreases in the ratio *a : b,* then
>
> new quantity $= \frac{a}{b}$ of the original quanity. $\frac{b}{a}$ is called the multiplying ratio.

8.3 Solved Examples

Ex.1. *Express the following ratios in simplest forms.*

    (a) 560 to 7200   **(b) 40 cm to** $2\frac{4}{5}$ **m**   **(c) 2.4 mm to 1.6 cm**

Sol. (*a*) $560 : 7200 = \frac{560}{7200} = \frac{7}{90} = \mathbf{7 : 90.}$

(*b*) First we convert $2\frac{4}{5}$ m to cm. We have $2\frac{4}{5}$ m $= \frac{14}{5}$ m $= \left(\frac{14}{5} \times 100\right)$ cm $= 280$ cm

Then, 40 cm : $2\frac{4}{5}$ m $= 40$ cm : 280 cm $= \frac{40}{280} = \frac{1}{7} = \mathbf{1 : 7.}$

(c) $2.4 \text{ mm} = \frac{24}{10} \text{ mm} = \frac{24}{10} \times \frac{1}{10} \text{ cm} = \frac{24}{100} \text{ cm} = 0.24 \text{ cm}$

> **Think directly**
> that 2 dp in the numerator, 1 dp in the denominator. So to convert to fraction, we multiply the denominator by 10

$\therefore \quad 2.4 \text{ mm} : 1.6 \text{ cm} = 0.24 \text{ cm} : 1.6 \text{ cm} = \dfrac{0.24}{1.6} = \dfrac{\frac{24}{100}}{\frac{16}{10}} = \dfrac{24}{100} \times \dfrac{10}{16} = \dfrac{24}{160} = \dfrac{3}{20} = \mathbf{3 : 20.}$

Ex. 2. *Simplify the following ratios :*

$\quad$ **(a)** $6\frac{3}{4} : 3\frac{3}{5}$ $\qquad\qquad$ **(b)** $3\frac{1}{2} : 4.2$ $\qquad\qquad$ **(c)** $\frac{5}{3} : \frac{3}{4} : \frac{1}{6}$

Sol. (a) $6\frac{3}{4} : 3\frac{3}{5} = \dfrac{27}{4} : \dfrac{18}{5} = \dfrac{27}{4} \div \dfrac{18}{5} = \dfrac{27}{4} \times \dfrac{5}{18} = \dfrac{15}{8} = \mathbf{15 : 8.}$

$\quad$ (b) $3\frac{1}{2} : 4.2 = \dfrac{7}{2} : \dfrac{42}{10} = \dfrac{7}{2} \div \dfrac{42}{10} = \dfrac{7}{2} \times \dfrac{10}{42} = \dfrac{5}{6} = \mathbf{5 : 6.}$

$\quad$ (c) $\dfrac{5}{3} : \dfrac{3}{4} : \dfrac{1}{6} = \dfrac{5}{3} \times 12 : \dfrac{3}{4} \times 12 : \dfrac{1}{6} \times 12 = \mathbf{20 : 9 : 2.}$

> Multiplying each term by the L.C.M of the denominators *i.e.*, 12.

Ex. 3. *Write the following ratios in descending order :*

$\quad$ *1 : 3,$\quad$ 2 : 5,$\quad$ 7 : 15,$\quad$ 5 : 6*

Sol. Convert the given ratios, *i.e.*, $\dfrac{1}{3}, \dfrac{2}{5}, \dfrac{7}{15}$ and $\dfrac{5}{6}$ into equivalent like fractions.

$\quad$ L.C.M. of the denominators 3, 5, 15, 6 = $3 \times 5 \times 2 = \mathbf{30}$

3	3,	5,	15,	6
5	1,	5,	5,	2
	1,	1,	1,	2

$\therefore \quad \dfrac{1}{3} = \dfrac{1 \times 10}{3 \times 10} = \dfrac{10}{30}, \dfrac{2}{5} = \dfrac{2 \times 6}{5 \times 6} = \dfrac{12}{30}, \dfrac{7}{15} = \dfrac{7 \times 2}{15 \times 2} = \dfrac{14}{30}, \dfrac{5}{6} = \dfrac{5 \times 5}{6 \times 5} = \dfrac{25}{30}$

$\because \quad 25 > 14 > 12 > 10$

$\therefore \quad \dfrac{25}{30} > \dfrac{14}{30} > \dfrac{12}{30} > \dfrac{10}{30} \Rightarrow \dfrac{5}{6} > \dfrac{7}{15} > \dfrac{2}{5} > \dfrac{1}{3}$

$\quad$ Hence the given ratios in descending order are **5 : 6, 7 : 15, 2 : 5, 1 : 3.**

Ex. 4. *Divide Rs 2240 between A, B and C in the ratio* **12 : 13 : 15.**

Sol. Sum of terms of the ratio = 12 + 13 + 15 = 40

$\quad \therefore$ A's share = Rs $\left(\dfrac{12}{40} \times 2240\right)$ = **Rs 672**, B's share = Rs $\left(\dfrac{13}{40} \times 2240\right)$ = **Rs 728.**

$\quad$ C's share = Rs $\left(\dfrac{15}{40} \times 2240\right)$ = **Rs 840.**

Ex.5. *Divide Rs 1218 among Roma, Ankit and Resham in the ratio* $\dfrac{1}{2} : \dfrac{3}{5} : \dfrac{5}{6}$.

Sol. Given ratio $\quad = \dfrac{1}{2} : \dfrac{3}{5} : \dfrac{5}{6} = \dfrac{1}{2} \times 30 : \dfrac{3}{5} \times 30 : \dfrac{5}{6} \times 30$

> Multiply each term by the L.C.M of denominators = $2 \times 5 \times 3 = 30$

$\qquad\qquad\qquad = 15 : 18 : 25$

$\quad \therefore$ Sum of terms of the ratio = 15 + 18 + 25 = 58

$\quad \therefore \qquad$ Roma's share = Rs $\left(\dfrac{15}{58} \times 1218\right)$ = **Rs 315,**

Ankit's share = Rs $\left(\dfrac{18}{58} \times 1218\right)$ = **Rs 378,**

Resham's share = Rs $\left(\dfrac{25}{58} \times 1218\right)$ = **Rs 525.**

EXERCISE 8 (a)

1. **Express each of the following ratios in the simplest form.**

    (a) 65 cm : 2 m 60 cm   (b) 90 secs : 1 minute 15 secs   (c) 800 m : $2\dfrac{2}{5}$ km

    (d) 4 scores : 20 dozen   (e) 250 gm : 2 kg 50 gm   (f) 2 days : 88 hours

2. **Simplify the following ratios :**

    (a) $4\dfrac{2}{3} : 3\dfrac{1}{5} : 2\dfrac{2}{9}$ (b) $4\dfrac{2}{3} : 5.6$ (c) $\dfrac{3}{7} : \dfrac{11}{14} : \dfrac{2}{3}$ (d) 1.2 : 1.6 : 0.8

3. **Which ratio is greater ?**

    (a) (6 : 7) or (3 : 5)   (b) $\left(2\dfrac{1}{2} : 3\dfrac{1}{4}\right)$ or $\left(1\dfrac{1}{2} : 2\dfrac{1}{3}\right)$ (c) $\left(\dfrac{1}{2} : \dfrac{1}{5}\right)$ or $\left(\dfrac{1}{7} : \dfrac{1}{8}\right)$ (d) $\left(\dfrac{2}{5} : \dfrac{4}{10}\right)$ or (0.6 : 0.7)

4. **Arrange the following ratios in ascending order of magnitude**
    (a) 6 : 7, 2 : 5 and 11 : 15   (b) 19 : 21, 11 : 28, 5 : 7 and 13 : 14

5. Divide Rs 390 among A, B and C in the ratio 3 : 5 : 7.

6. Divide Rs 744 among Anuj, Asha and Ashu in the ratio $\dfrac{1}{4} : \dfrac{2}{3} : \dfrac{3}{8}$.

7. Divide Rs 4970 among A, B and C such that A gets $\dfrac{1}{5}$ of what B gets and the ratio of the shares of B and C is 6 : 7.

8. Divide the number 3870 into three parts A, B and C such that 2 times the first is equal to 7 times the second is equal to 8 times the third.
    (**Hint :** $2A = 7B = 8C$)

9. Divide Rs 312 among Kanchi, Rohan and Sana such that $\dfrac{1}{3}$ of Kanchi's share = $\dfrac{1}{4}$ of Rohan's share = $\dfrac{1}{5}$ of Sana's share.

10. Divide 840 into two parts, one of which is $\dfrac{10}{11}$ of the other.

8.4 More Examples

Ex. 6. *If A : B = 6 : 7 and B : C = 9 : 11 find A : B : C.*

Sol.   Given $\dfrac{A}{B} = \dfrac{6}{7}$ and $\dfrac{B}{C} = \dfrac{9}{11}$

To find A : B : C, we have to make B equal in both the ratios.

∴ L.C.M. of 7 and 9 = 7 × 9 = 63

A : B = 6 : 7 = $\dfrac{6}{7} = \dfrac{6 \times 9}{7 \times 9} = \dfrac{54}{63} = 54 : 63$

and B : C = 9 : 11 = $\dfrac{9}{11} = \dfrac{9 \times 7}{11 \times 7} = \dfrac{63}{77} = 63 : 77$

∴ **A : B : C = 54 : 63 : 77.**

Ex. 7. *If A : B = 5 : 7 and A : C = 3 : 4, find B : C and A : B : C.*

Sol. $A : B = 5 : 7 \Rightarrow \dfrac{A}{B} = \dfrac{5}{7} \Rightarrow \dfrac{B}{A} = \dfrac{7}{5}$, $A : C = 3 : 4 = \dfrac{A}{C} = \dfrac{3}{4}$

∴ $B : C = \dfrac{B}{C} = \dfrac{B}{A} \times \dfrac{A}{C} = \dfrac{7}{5} \times \dfrac{3}{4} = \dfrac{21}{20} = 21 : 20$

A : B = 5 : 7 and B : C = 21 : 20

L.C.M. of the two values of B = 21

∴ $A : B = 5 : 7 = \dfrac{5}{7} = \dfrac{5 \times 3}{7 \times 3} = \dfrac{15}{21} = 15 : 21$ and $B : C = 21 : 20$ $\Rightarrow$ **A : B : C = 15 : 21 : 20.**

> Note : You can work out as under :
>
> When B is 21, C is 20 ∴ When B is 7, C is $\dfrac{20}{21} \times 7 = \dfrac{20}{3}$
>
> ∴ $A : B : C = 5 : 7 : \dfrac{20}{3} = 15 : 21 : 20.$

Ex. 8. *If 3A = 4B = 9C then find A : B : C*

Sol. Let $3A = 4B = 9C = x$ $\Rightarrow A : B : C = \dfrac{x}{3} : \dfrac{x}{4} : \dfrac{x}{9} = \dfrac{1}{3} : \dfrac{1}{4} : \dfrac{1}{9}$

$= \dfrac{1}{3} \times 36 : \dfrac{1}{4} \times 36 : \dfrac{1}{9} \times 36 = 12 : 9 : 4$ ∴ **A : B : C = 12 : 9 : 4**

> Multiplying each term of the ratio by L.C.M. of denominators i.e. $3 \times 4 \times 3 = 36$

Ex. 9. *Divide Rs 5830 into three parts such that the first is $\dfrac{1}{4}$ of the second and the ratio between the second and third part is 5 : 7.*

Sol. Since the ratio between the second and third part is 5 : 7, so let the second and third parts be $5x$ and $7x$ respectively.

Now first part $= \dfrac{1}{4}$ of second part $= \dfrac{1}{4}$ of $5x = \dfrac{5x}{4}$

(Given, sum of the three parts = 5830   ∴ $\dfrac{5x}{4} + 5x + 7x = 5830$

$\Rightarrow \dfrac{5x + 20x + 28x}{4} = 5830$ $\Rightarrow \dfrac{53x}{4} = 5830 \Rightarrow x = \dfrac{5830 \times 4}{53} = 440$

∴ First part $= Rs \left(\dfrac{5}{4} \times 440 \right) =$ **Rs 550**, Second part $= Rs \left(5 \times 440 \right) =$ **Rs 2200**,

Third part = Rs (7 × 440) = **Rs 3080.**

Ex.10. *A bag contains Rs 885 in the form of 1 rupee, 50 paise and 20 paise coins in the ratio 2 : 5 : 7. Find the number of each type of coins.*

Sol. Since the ratio of 1 rupee, 50 paise and 20 paise coins is 2 : 5 : 7, let the number of three coins be $2x$, $5x$ and $7x$ respectively.

∴ Value of 1 rupee coins $= Rs (1 \times 2x) = Rs\ 2x$, Value of 50 paise coins $= Rs \left(\dfrac{50}{100} \times 5x \right) = Rs\ \dfrac{5x}{2}$

Value of 20 paise coins = Rs $\left(\dfrac{20}{100} \times 7x\right)$ = Rs $\dfrac{7x}{5}$

Given $2x + \dfrac{5x}{2} + \dfrac{7x}{5} = 885 \implies \dfrac{20x + 25x + 14x}{10} = 885$

$\implies \dfrac{59x}{10} = 885 \implies x = \dfrac{885 \times 10}{59} = \mathbf{150}.$

$\therefore$ Number of 1 rupee coin = $2 \times 150 = \mathbf{300}$,   Number of 50 paise coins = $5 \times 150 = \mathbf{750}$,
Number of 20 paise coins = $7 \times 150 = \mathbf{1050}$.

Ex. 11. *Two numbers are in the ratio 11 : 13. If their sum is 192, find the numbers.*

Sol. Let the two numbers be $11x$ and $13x$

Given $11x + 13x = 192 \implies 24x = 192 \implies x = \dfrac{192}{24} = 8$

$\therefore$ The numbers are $11 \times 8 = \mathbf{88}$ and $13 \times 8 = \mathbf{104}$.

Alternatively, Sum of the terms of the ratio = $11 + 13 = 24$

$\therefore$ The numbers are $\dfrac{11}{1\overline{24}} \times \overline{192}^{\,8}$ and $\dfrac{13}{1\overline{24}} \times \overline{192}^{\,8}$, *i.e.,* 88 and 104.

Ex.12. *A sum of money is divided among A and B in the ratio 5 : 13. If B's share Rs 780, find A's share and the sum of money.*

Sol. Let A's share = Rs $5x$ and B's share = Rs $13x$, Then total amount = Rs $(5x + 13x)$ = Rs $18x$

Given B's share = Rs 780 $\implies$ $13x = 780$ $\implies$ $x = \dfrac{780}{13} = 60$

$\therefore$ A's share = Rs (5×60) = **Rs 300** and total amount = Rs (18×60) = **Rs 1080**.

Alternatively, you may work out as under :

Given, $A : B = 5 : 13$

So, when B's share is Rs 13, A's share is Rs 5

$\therefore$ When B's share is Rs 780, A's share = Rs $\dfrac{5}{1\overline{13}} \times \overline{780}^{\,60} = $ Rs 300.

Ex.13. *Two numbers are in the ratio 2 : 3. When 4 is added to both the terms, the ratio becomes 3 : 4, find the numbers.*

Sol. Let the numbers be $2x$ and $3x$.

When 4 is added to both the numbers the ratio becomes 3 : 4

$\implies \quad \dfrac{2x+4}{3x+4} = \dfrac{3}{4} \implies 4(2x + 4) = 3(3x + 4) \implies 8x + 16 = 9x + 12$

$\implies \quad 9x - 8x = 16 - 12 \implies x = 4$ $\therefore$ The numbers are $2 \times 4 = \mathbf{8}$ and $3 \times 4 = \mathbf{12}$.

Ex. 14. *The salary of Radha increased in the ratio 6 : 7. If the original salary was Rs 21600, find her new salary.*

Sol. New salary = $\dfrac{7}{6}$ of original salary = $\dfrac{7}{6} \times 21600 = $ Rs 25200

$\therefore$ The new salary is Rs **25200**.

Ex. 15. *Decrease the number 325 in the ratio 5 : 4*

Sol. Required number = $\dfrac{4}{5}$ of $325 = \dfrac{4}{5} \times 325 = \mathbf{260}$.

EXERCISE 8 (b)

1. Two numbers are in the ratio 9 : 13. If the large number is 390, find the smaller.
2. A sum of money is divided among three people in the ratio 4 : 5 : 7. If the second person gets Rs 245, what is the sum and how much do the first and third get.
3. Shreya's height increases in the ratio 4 : 5. Her height was 144 cm. What is her new height.
4. The consumption of rice of a family decreases in the ratio 11 : 9. Their original consumption was 12.1 kg. What is their consumption now.
5. A, B and C play cricket such that A's runs : B's runs = 3 : 2 and B's runs : C's runs = 6 : 11. If the total runs scored are 234, find how much did each score.
6. Find A : B : C if

   (a) A : B = 3 : 7 and B : C = 5 : 8   (b) A : B = $\frac{2}{3} : \frac{3}{4}$ and B : C = $\frac{5}{6} : \frac{3}{10}$

7. If A : B = 4 : 7 and A : C = 11 : 15, find B : C and A : B : C.
8. If A : C = 1 : 3 and B : C = 5 : 7, find A : B and A : B : C.
9. If A : B : C = 4 : 5 : 7 and C = 42, find A and B.
10. If 4A = 5B = 12C, find A : B : C.
11. A bag contains Rs 372 in the form of 50 paise, 25 paise and 20 paise coins in the ratio 4 : 5 : 7. Find the number of each type of coin.
12. The number of teachers in a school is 124. If the number of male teachers is 93, find the ratio of female teachers to the total number of teachers in the school.
13. The ratio between two numbers is 4 : 7. If 8 is added to each number, the ratio becomes 3 : 5. Find the numbers.
14. Two numbers are in the ratio 5 : 6. If 5 is subtracted from each number, the ratio becomes 4 : 5. Find the numbers.
15. A class is making a model of the school building and the ratio of the lengths of the model to the lengths of the actual building is 1 : 20. The gym is 6 m high. How high, in centimetres, should the model of the gym be ?
16. The perimeter of a triangle is 60 cm and lengths of the sides are in the ratio 2 : 3 : 5. Find the lengths of the three sides.

8.5 Proportion (Quick Review)

1. Two equal ratios form a proportion

   Thus $\frac{2}{3} = \frac{8}{12}$ form a proportion and this is expressed as 2 : 3 : : 8 : 12 read as '2 is to 3 as 8 is to 12'. For working we generally use the fractional form only.

   In general terms, if **four numbers a, b, c, d are in proportion,** *i.e.,* **a : b : : c : d** then $\frac{a}{b} = \frac{c}{d}$.

   a and **d** are called **extremes** and **b** and **c** are called the **means**.

   In a proportion $\frac{a}{b} = \frac{c}{d} \Rightarrow ad = bc$

   i.e., **Product of extremes = Product of means**

2. In the proportion *a : b : : c : d*, *d* is called the **fourth proportional.**
3. Three quantities *a, b* and *c* (of the same kind) are said to be in **continued proportion** if *a : b : : b : c,* *i.e.,* $\frac{a}{b} = \frac{b}{c}$. Here *a* is called the **first proportional**, *c* is called the **third proportional** and *b* the **mean proportional**.

From $\dfrac{a}{b} = \dfrac{b}{c}$, we get $b^2 = ac \Rightarrow b = \sqrt{ac}$.

Thus, the mean proportional between a and c is $\sqrt{ac}$.

8.6 Solved Examples

Ex. 1. *Are 2.8, 3.5, 1.6, 2.0 in proportion ?*

Sol. For the given quantities to be proportion, product of extremes = product of means

Here extremes are 2.8 and 2.0 $\therefore$ Product of extremes = $2.8 \times 2 = 5.6$

Means are 3.5 and 1.6 $\therefore$ Product of means = $3.5 \times 1.6 = 5.60 = 5.6$

$\because$ **Product of extremes = Product of means** $\therefore$ 2.8, 1.5, 1.6 and 2.0 are proportion.

Ex. 2. *Find the value of x if*

     (a) $8 : 2.4 :: 0.3 : x$ **(b) $2\dfrac{1}{2} : x :: 3\dfrac{1}{4} : 1\dfrac{2}{5}$**

Sol. *(a)* Given $8 : 2.4 :: 0.3 : x$

The four numbers are in proportion if product of extremes = product of means

i.e., $8 \times x = 2.4 \times 0.3$, $x = \dfrac{2.4 \times 0.3}{8} = \dfrac{24}{10} \times \dfrac{3}{10} \times \dfrac{1}{8} = \dfrac{9}{100} = \mathbf{0.09}$.

(b) The given proportion can be written as $\dfrac{5}{2} : x :: \dfrac{13}{4} : \dfrac{7}{5}$

The four numbers are in proportion if product of extremes = product of means

i.e., $\dfrac{5}{2} \times \dfrac{7}{5} = x \times \dfrac{13}{4}$ $\Rightarrow$ $\dfrac{13x}{4} = \dfrac{7}{2}$ $\Rightarrow$ $x = \dfrac{7}{2} \times \dfrac{4}{13} = \dfrac{14}{13} = \mathbf{1\dfrac{1}{13}}$.

Ex. 3. *Find the fourth proportional to :*

     (a) $3.6, 6.4$ and 1.8   **(b) $\dfrac{1}{2}, \dfrac{1}{5}$ and $\dfrac{2}{7}$**

Sol. *(a)* Let the fourth proportional to 3.6, 6.4 and 1.8 be x. Then $3.6 : 6.4 :: 1.8 : x$

$\Rightarrow$ $3.6 \times x = 6.4 \times 1.8 \Rightarrow x = \dfrac{6.4 \times 1.8}{3.6} = \mathbf{3.2}$.

> Products of extremes
> = Product of means

(b) Let the fourth proportional to $\dfrac{1}{2}, \dfrac{1}{5}$ and $\dfrac{2}{7}$ be x

Then $\dfrac{1}{2} : \dfrac{1}{5} :: \dfrac{2}{7} : x$ $\Rightarrow$ $\dfrac{1}{2} \times x = \dfrac{1}{5} \times \dfrac{2}{7}$, $x = \dfrac{2}{35} \div \dfrac{1}{2} = \dfrac{2}{35} \times \dfrac{2}{1} = \dfrac{\mathbf{4}}{\mathbf{35}}$.

Ex. 4. *Find the mean proportional between :*

     (a) 64 and 4   **(b) 0.25 and 400**   **(c) $\dfrac{1}{4}$ and $\dfrac{1}{49}$.**

Sol. *(a)* Let x be the mean proportional between 64 and 4. Then

     $x^2 = 64 \times 4 \Rightarrow x = \sqrt{64 \times 4} = 8 \times 2 = \mathbf{16}$.

> $b^2 = ac$

(b) Let x be the mean proportional between 0.25 and 400. Then

     $x^2 = 0.25 \times 400$ $\Rightarrow$ $x = \sqrt{0.25 \times 400} = 0.5 \times 20 = \mathbf{10}$.

(c) Mean proportional between $\frac{1}{4}$ and $\frac{1}{49}$ = $\sqrt{\frac{1}{4} \times \frac{1}{49}}$ = $\frac{1}{2} \times \frac{1}{7}$ = $\frac{1}{14}$.

$$\boxed{b = \sqrt{ac}}$$

Ex. 5. *Find the third proportional to **6, 18**.*

Sol. Let the third proportional to 6, 18 be x. Then $6 : 18 :: 18 : x$

$$\Rightarrow 6 \times x = 18 \times 18 \Rightarrow x = \frac{18 \times 18}{6} = \mathbf{54}.$$

Ex. 6. *If 8, x and 72 are in continued proportion, find the value of x.*

Sol. $8, x,$ and 72 are in continued proportion

$$\Rightarrow \quad 8 : x :: x : 72 \quad \Rightarrow \quad \frac{8}{x} = \frac{x}{72} \quad \Rightarrow \quad x^2 = 8 \times 72$$

$$\Rightarrow \quad x = \sqrt{8 \times 72} = \sqrt{4 \times 2 \times 2 \times 36} = 2 \times 2 \times 6 = \mathbf{24}.$$

EXERCISE 8 (c)

1. Examine whether the following numbers are in proportion or not ?

(a) $\frac{3}{5}, \frac{12}{25}, \frac{1}{3}, \frac{4}{15}$

(b) $5.1, 3.8, 0.09, 0.06$

(c) $6\frac{1}{4}, 4\frac{2}{7}, 1\frac{1}{6}, \frac{4}{5}$

(d) $25, 18, 6, 12$

2. Find the value of x in the following proportions :

(a) $4.5 : 0.09 :: x : 1.8$ (b) $\frac{3}{4} : x :: \frac{1}{5} : \frac{2}{3}$ (c) $42 : 1.2 :: 5.6 : x$ (d) $x : 7\frac{1}{2} :: 5\frac{1}{3} : 2\frac{1}{3}$

3. Find the fourth proportional to :

(a) $31, 124, 0.12$ (b) $\frac{3}{5}, \frac{2}{3}, 2\frac{1}{7}$ (c) 43 kg, 64.5 kg, 13 kg   (d) 80 paise , Rs 4, 60 paise

4. Find the mean proportional between :

(a) 4 and 9 (b) 0.25 and 0.36 (c) $\frac{1}{96}$ and $\frac{1}{24}$ (d) $5\frac{1}{7}$ and 175 (e) 12.8 and $\frac{1}{5}$

5. Find the third proportional to :

(a) 8 and 12 (b) $2.6, 5.2$ (c) $3\frac{1}{8}, 11\frac{1}{4}$ (d) $0.17, 5.1$ (e) $\frac{7}{6}, \frac{14}{15}$

6. Check whether $1.25, 1.5, 1.8$ are in continued proportion or not.

7. If 45 is the third proportional to 20 and x, find x.

8. The weights of A and B are in the ratio 3 : 5. If B's weight is 85.5 kg. What is A's weight ?

9. The cost of a litre of milk and cold drink are in the ratio 5 : 9. If the cost of a litre of milk is Rs 20, what is the cost of a litre of cold drink ?

10. From the numbers 4, 10, 15, 6 form a proportion.

DIRECT AND INDIRECT PORPORTION

8.7 Direct Proportion or Variation

When two quantities are so related that an increase (decrease) in one causes an increase (decrease) in the other, the two quantities are said to vary directly.

Examples :

1. The cost of articles varies directly as the number of articles.

   More (less) number of articles $\Rightarrow$ More (less) cost

   Ratio of number of articles = Ratio of their costs

2. The distance covered by a moving object varies directly as the speed (time remaining same)

3. The work done varies directly as the number of men at work.

   More men $\Rightarrow$ More work done, Less men $\Rightarrow$ Less work done.

8.8 Indirect Proportion or Variation

When two quantities are so related than increase (decrease) in one cause a decrease (increase) in the other, the two quantities are said to vary inversely.

Examples :

1. Speed varies inversely as time, (provided distance covered remains same)

   More speed $\Rightarrow$ less time; less speed $\Rightarrow$ more time

   Ratio of speed = inverse Ratio of time

2. Number of men at work varies inversely as time. More men at work $\Rightarrow$ less time taken;

   less men at work $\Rightarrow$ more time taken

   Ratio of the number of men at work = Inverse ratio of time taken

8.9 Rule of Three

The method of finding the fourth term of a proportion when other three are known is called the rule of three.

Method :

1. *Let the unknown quantity be x and take it as the fourth term.*
2. *Take the third term as the quantity which has the same unit as x.*
3. *If it is a case of direct proportion, take the direct ratio as the first two terms of the proportion.*
4. *If it is case of indirect proportion, take the inverse ratio of the first two terms.*
5. *Now find x.*

8.10 Solved Examples

Ex. 1. *7 fountain pens cost Rs 57.40. What do a score of fountain pens cost ?*

Sol. 1 score = 20

Let the cost of 20 fountain pens be Rs x

More fountain pens $\Rightarrow$ more cost $\Rightarrow$ It is a case of direct proportion.

$\therefore$ Ratio of the number of pens : : Ratio of the costs *i.e.,* $7 : 20 : : 57.40 : x$

$\Rightarrow$ $7 \times x = 20 \times 57.40$ $\Rightarrow x = \dfrac{20 \times 57.40}{7} = \mathbf{160}$

$\therefore$ 20 fountain pens cost **Rs 160.**

Ex. 2. *153 rails placed end to end in a straight line stretch to 680 m. How far will 135 rails stretch?*

Sol. Let 135 rails stretch to a distance of x m

Less number of rails $\Rightarrow$ less distance covered $\Rightarrow$ A case of direct proportion

$\therefore$ Ratio of number of rails : : Ratio of distance covered *i.e.,* $153 : 135 : : 680 : x$

$\Rightarrow$ $153 \times x = 135 \times 680$ $\Rightarrow x = \dfrac{135 \times 680}{153} = \textbf{600}$

$\therefore$ 135 rails stretch to a distance of **600 m.**

Ex. 3. *15 men can repair a road in 28 days; how long will 35 men take to do so?*

Sol. Let 35 men take x days to repair the road.

More men $\Rightarrow$ Less days $\Rightarrow$ A case of indirect proportion

$\therefore$ Inverse ratio of number of men : : ratio of number of days *i.e.,* $35 : 15 : : 28 : x$

$\Rightarrow$ $15 \times 28 = x \times 35$ $\Rightarrow x = \dfrac{15 \times 28}{35} = \textbf{12}$

$\therefore$ 35 men take **12 days** to repair the road.

Ex. 4. *When a certain sum of money is divided equally among 25 people each receives Rs 42; how much would each person receive if the same sum had been equally divided among 30 people.*

Sol. Let each of the 30 people receive Rs x.

More people $\Rightarrow$ less money received (total sum remaining same)

$\Rightarrow$ A case of indirect proportion

$\therefore$ Inverse ratio of the number of people : : ratio of sum received *i.e.,* $30 : 25 : : 42 : x$

$\Rightarrow$ $30 \times x = 42 \times 25$ $\Rightarrow x = \dfrac{42 \times 25}{30} = \textbf{35}$

$\therefore$ When the same sum is divided among 30 people each receives **Rs 35.**

EXERCISE 8 (d)

1. Radha takes 3 hours in walking a distance of 18 km. What distance would she cover in 5 hours?
2. If 13 burners consume 91 cubic metre of gas in 2 hours, how much will 7 burners consume in the same time?
3. The railway charges Rs 2112 to carry a certain amount of luggage, 416 km. What should the charge be to carry the same amount of luggage, 572 km.
4. 89 litres of oil cost Rs 2091.50. What is the cost of 15 litres?
5. 56 packets weigh 1 kg 232 gms. What will be weight of 90 packets?
6. A car can do a certain journey in 12 hours if it travels at 65 km/hr. How much time will it take if it travels at 78 km/hr?
7. A work force of 350 men with a contractor can finish a work in 12 months. How many more men should be employed so that the work is completed in 7 months?
8. It is found that a book will contain 540 pages if 28 lines are allowed in a page. How many lines should be allowed in a page if the book has to contain 360 pages?
9. 32 men can do a certain work in 8 hours 36 minutes; how long will it take 48 men to do it ?
10. If 27 men can reap a field in 32 days, how long will 48 men take ?
11. 12 pipes through which water flows at the same rate can fill a tank in 32 minutes. If 4 pipes go out of order, how long will the remaining pipes take to fill the tank?
12. In a hostel of 65 girls, there are food provisions for 48 days. If 13 more girls join the hostel, how long will the provisions last?

LOOKING BACK
Summary of Key Facts

1. Ratio compares two quantities of the same kind and in the same units using division.

2. $a : b = \dfrac{a}{b}$ where a is antecedent and b is the consequent.

3. A ratio $a : b$ is in its simplest form if H.C.F. of a and b is 1.

4. Ratios can be compared in the same ways as the fractions are compared.

5. If $a : b = c : d$ then a, b, c, d are in proportion, which is written as $a : b : : c : d$. a, d are called **extremes**; b, c are called **means**.

6. $a : b = c : d$ when $\dfrac{a}{b} = \dfrac{c}{d} \Rightarrow ad = bc$ i.e., **product of extremes = product of means**.

7. In $a : b : : c : x$, x is the **fourth proportional** to a, b, c.

8. In $a : b : : b : c$ (i) b is the **mean proportional** to a, c (ii) c is the **third proportional** to a, b.

9. Mean proportional between a and $c = \sqrt{ac}$.

MENTAL MATHS – 7

1. Divide Rs 1200 in the ratio 3 : 4 : 5
2. Express the ratio 450 gm to 5 kg in the simplest form.
3. Find the value of x when

   (a) $x : 36 = 4 : 9$ (b) $\dfrac{1}{3} : x = \dfrac{1}{2} : \dfrac{1}{5}$
4. A journey of 850 km is covered partly by train and partly by bus, the respective distances being in the ratio 14 : 3. Work out the distance covered by train.

5. In a certain textile factory 20 machines are used to complete a work in 28 days. If 6 machines break down how long will it take to complete the work.
6. If the cost of 15 books is Rs 450, what will be the cost of 8 such books.
7. Are 8 : 9 : : 4 : 12 in proportiion.
8. Find the mean proportional between 9 and 16

ANSWERS

EXERCISE 8 (a)

1. (a) 1 : 4   (b) 6 : 5   (c) 1 : 3   (d) 1 : 3   (e) 5 : 41   (f) 6 : 11

2. (a) 105 : 72 : 50   (b) 5 : 6   (c) 18 : 33 : 28   (d) 6 : 8 : 4

3. (a) (6 : 7)   (b) $\left(2\dfrac{1}{2} : 3\dfrac{1}{4}\right)$ (c) $\left(\dfrac{1}{2} : \dfrac{1}{5}\right)$ (d) $\left(\dfrac{2}{5} : \dfrac{4}{10}\right)$ 4. (a) 2 : 5, 11 : 15, 6 : 7   (b) 11 : 28; 5 : 7; 19 : 21; 13 : 14

5. Rs 78, Rs 130, Rs 182   6. Rs 144, Rs 384, Rs 216   7. Rs 420, Rs 2100, Rs 2450

8. 2520, 720, 630   9. 78, 104, 130   10. 400, 440

EXERCISE 8 (b)

1. 270   2. Sum = Rs 784 : first gets Rs 196 : Third gets Rs 343   3. 180 cm

4. 9.9 kg   5. A → 81, B → 54, C → 99   6. (a) 15 : 35 : 56   (b) 200 : 225 : 81

7. B : C = 77 : 60; A : B : C = 44 : 77 : 60   8. A : B = 7 : 15; A : B : C = 7 : 15 : 21   9. A = 24, B = 30   10. 15 : 12 : 5

11. 320, 400, 560   12. 1 : 4   13. 64 and 112   14. 25 and 30   15. 30 cm   16. 12 cm, 18 cm, 30 cm

EXERCISE 8 (c)

1. (*a*) Yes   (*b*) No   (*c*) Yes   (*d*) No

2. (*a*) 90   (*b*) $\dfrac{5}{2}$ (*c*) 0.16   (*d*) $17\dfrac{1}{7}$

3. (*a*) 0.48   (*b*) $2\dfrac{8}{21}$ (*c*) 19.5 kg   (*d*) Rs 3

4. (*a*) 6   (*b*) 0.3   (*c*) $\dfrac{1}{48}$ (*d*) 30   (*e*) 1.6

5. (*a*) 18   (*b*) 10.4   (*c*) $40\dfrac{1}{2}$ (*d*) 153   (*e*) $\dfrac{56}{75}$

6. Yes   7. $x = 30$ 8. 51.3 kg   9. Rs 36   10. $10 : 4 : : 15 : 6$

EXERCISE 8 (d)

1. 30 km   2. 49 m^3 3. Rs 2904   4. Rs 352.50   5. 1 kg 980 gms   6. 10 hours   7. 250 more men
8. 42 lines   9. 5 hours 44 mins   10. 18 days   11. 48 minutes   12. 40 days

MENTAL MATHS – 7

1. Rs 300, Rs 400, Rs 500   2. $9 : 100$ 3. (*a*) 16   (*b*) $\dfrac{2}{15}$ 4. 700 km   5. 40 days
6. Rs 240   7. No   8. 12

HISTORICAL NOTE

THE GREAT INDIAN MATHEMATICIAN BHASKARA

There are two persons by the name Bhaskaracharya. The elder one lived in 6th century and was disciple of Aryabhata. He wrote a Commentary on Aryabhata's work. Not much is known about him except his Commentary on Aryabhata.

Bhaskara II was one of the most famous mathematicians that India has produced. He was born in 1114 A.D in Biddur (Bijapur, Karnataka) and died in 1185 A.D. in Ujjain. He had knowledge of number system, 0, and negative numbers and was the first to declare confidently that any term divided by zero is infinity and the sum of any term and infinity is infinity. His most famous work is the solution of the Diophantine equation $nx^2 + 1 = y^2$, using elementary mathematics.

The Western mathematicians later, took the credit on themselves for him.

Bhaskaracharya is also famous for his book on mathematics called **Lilawati**. It is full of interesting problems. At one time there was even a popular saying, "Whoever is well versed with **Lilavati** can tell the exact number of leaves in a tree".

He was an astronomer of repute and wrote books on astronomy, one of which was **Karna Kutuhala**, a manual of astronomical calculations.

9. Percentage

9.1 Introduction

The phrase per cent is often heard about in our daily life in the form of reduction in prices during 'sales', examination result of a student, increase in wages and discounts etc.

The words '**per cent**', symbolically written as **%** mean '**in every hundred**' or **per hundred**. Thus 40% means '40 in every hundred.'

9.2 Percentages, Fractions and Decimals

Percentages, Fractions and Decimals are linked to each other, 20% can be written as the fraction $\frac{20}{100}$ or as the decimal 0.2.

- **To change a percentage to a fraction,** *write it as a fraction with a denominator 100 and simplify if possible.*

- **To change it to a decimal,** *change the fraction so obtained to a decimal.*

Ex. $\quad 30\% = \frac{30}{100} = \frac{3}{10} \quad = 0.3 \qquad 225\% = \frac{225}{100} = \frac{9}{4} \quad = 2.25$

$\qquad\qquad\qquad\quad\uparrow\qquad\qquad\uparrow\qquad\qquad\qquad\qquad\quad\uparrow\qquad\qquad\uparrow$

$\qquad\qquad\qquad\text{Fraction}\quad\text{Decimal}\qquad\qquad\qquad\qquad\text{Fraction}\quad\text{Decimal}$

- **To change fractions and decimals to percentages,** *multiply by 100.*

Ex. $\quad 0.64 = 0.64 \times 100\,\% = 64\%, \quad \frac{3}{20} = \frac{3}{20} \times 100\% = 15\%.$

- **To find a percentage of a quantity,** *change the percentage to a fraction or a decimal and multiply it by the quantity.*

$$25\% \text{ of Rs } 80 = \frac{25}{100} \times \text{Rs } 80 = \textbf{Rs 20.}$$

9.3 Percentage Increase and Decrease

- **To increase a quantity by a percentage,** *find the percentage of the quantity and add it to the original quantity.*

Ex. 1. *Increase 320 by 20%.*

Sol. $\quad 20\% \text{ of } 320 = \frac{20}{100} \times 320 = 64, \qquad \therefore \quad$ Increased amount = Rs 320 + Rs 64 = **Rs 384.**

- **To decrease a quantity by a percentage,** *find the percentage of the quantity and subtract it from the original quantity.*

Ex.2. *Decrease Rs 120 by $12\frac{1}{2}\%$.*

Sol. $\quad 12\frac{1}{2}\% \text{ of } 120 = \text{Rs } \frac{12.5}{100} \text{ of } 120 = \text{Rs } \frac{125}{10 \times 100} \times 120 = \text{Rs } 15$

$\therefore$ Decreased amount = Rs 120 – Rs 15 = **Rs 105.**

9.4 To Find One Quantity as a Percentage of the Other

Method   **1.** *Write the two quantities as a fraction.*

         2. *Multiply by 100%*

Ex. 3. ***Express 30 cm as a per cent of 2 m 40 cm.***

Sol. Required % $= \dfrac{30}{240} \times 100\% = \mathbf{12.5\%}$.

> First express in the same units
> 2 m 40 cm = 200 cm + 40 cm = 240 cm

9.5. Percentage Change

$$\text{Percentage change} = \left(\frac{\text{Actual change (Increase or Decrease)}}{\text{Original quantity}} \times 100 \right)\%$$

$$\text{Percentage error} = \left(\frac{\text{error}}{\text{actual value}} \times 100 \right)\%$$

Ex. 4. ***Rita's weight decreased from 80 kg to 60 kg. Find the percentage decrease.***

Sol. Decrease in weight = (80 – 60) kg = 20 kg.

∴   % decrease $= \dfrac{20}{80} \times 100\% = \mathbf{25\%}$.

Ex. 5. ***The distance between two places was 200 km. It was measured as 280km. Find the percentage error.***

Sol. Error = 280 km – 200 km = 80 km.

∴   % error $= \dfrac{\text{error}}{\text{actual value}} \times 100\% = \dfrac{80}{200} \times 100 = \mathbf{40\%}$.

9.6 Finding the Original Amount Before a Percentage Change

Ex. 6. ***The cost of a train ticket from New Delhi to Dehradun has risen by 20% to Rs 600. What was the original price of the ticket?***

Sol. Let the original price be Rs 100.

∴   Increase in price = 20% = Rs 20.

∴   Increased price = original price + increase in price = Rs 120.

    Given, new cost of the ticket = Rs 600.

> **Think :** when new price is Rs 120, original price = Rs 100
> ∴ When new price is Rs 600, original price = Rs $\dfrac{100}{120} \times 600$

∴   Original price = Rs $\dfrac{100}{120} \times 600 = \mathbf{Rs\ 500}$.

∴   Original price was **Rs 500**.

EXERCISE 9 (a)

1. **Write these percentages as fractions and decimals :**

(*a*) 60%   (*b*) 240%   (*c*) $12\dfrac{1}{2}\%$ (*d*) $54\dfrac{2}{3}\%$

2. **Write these numbers as percentages :**

(*a*) $\dfrac{3}{4}$ (*b*) $\dfrac{21}{40}$ (*c*) 0.008   (*d*) 0.375   (*e*) 1.07

3. **Express the following percentage as ratios:**

(*a*) 200%   (*b*) $6\dfrac{2}{3}\%$ (*c*) 75%   (*d*) $33\dfrac{1}{3}\%$

4. Express the following ratios as percentage:

   (a) $1 : 2$ (b) $7 : 10$ (c) $21 : 25$ (d) $5 : 12$

5. Evaluate :

   (a) 19% of Rs 4200   (b) 75% of 440 kg   (c) 30% of 20 g   (d) 2.5% of 350 m

6. Express the first quantity as a percentage of the second :

   (a) 20 g of 4 kg   (b) 200 ml of 5 litres   (c) 48 cm of 1m   (d) $\dfrac{2}{3}$ of $\dfrac{1}{2}$

7. (a) If 14% of a certain number is 63, find the number.

   (b) If $12\dfrac{1}{2}\%$ of a certain amount is Rs 62.50, find the amount.

8. There were 4800 people at a concert and 1600 of these were female. What percentage were male?

9. The cost of a theatre ticket is increased by 40% for a special movie. What is the new price if the normal price was Rs 160.

10. A motorcycle originally cost Rs 40,000. Its value has decreased by 22%. What is its value now?

11. The price of a garment has been reduced by 15% in a sale to Rs 306. Find its original price.

12. A piece of elastic was stretched by 24% to a length of 31 cm. Find its unstretched original length.

9.7 Some More Solved Examples

Ex. 7. *In a class, 80 students passed and the rest failed. If 80% of the students failed, find the number of students in the class.*

Sol. 80% of the students failed $\Rightarrow$ 20% of the students passed.

20% of total number of students $= 80 \quad \Rightarrow \quad \dfrac{20}{100}$ of total number $= 80$

$\therefore$ Total number of students $= 80 \times \dfrac{100}{20} = \textbf{400}$.

Ex. 8. *Two candidates A and B contest an election. A gets 46% of the valid votes and is defeated by 1600 votes. Find the total number of valid votes cast in the election.*

Sol. A gets 46% of the valid votes $\Rightarrow$ B gets $(100 - 46)\% = 54\%$ of the valid votes.

$\therefore$ % difference of the votes by which A is defeated $= 54\% - 46\% = 8\%$.

$\therefore$ 8% of total number of valid votes cast $= 1600$.

$\Rightarrow \dfrac{8}{100}$ of total votes $= 1600 \Rightarrow$ Total number of valid votes cast $= 1600 \times \dfrac{100}{8} = \textbf{20,000}$.

Ex. 9. *My income was increased by 10% and later decreased by 10%. What is the total change in per cent in my income.*

Sol. Let my income be Rs 100.

10% increase means that my income becomes Rs 110.

Decreased income $=$ Rs $110 - $ Rs $\dfrac{10}{100} \times 110 =$ Rs $110 - $ Rs $11 = $ Rs 99.

$\therefore$ % change in income $= \dfrac{\text{change in income}}{\text{original income}} \times 100\% = \dfrac{\text{Rs } 100 - \text{Rs } 99}{\text{Rs } 100} \times 100\% = \textbf{1\%}.$

Ex. 10. *A gets 20% more salary than B. By what per cent is B's salary less than A's salary?*

Sol. Let B's salary be Rs 100.

Then A's salary is 20% more than that of B ∴ A's salary = Rs 120.

∴ B's salary is Rs 20 less than A's salary

∴ % of B's salary less than A's salary = $\frac{20}{120} \times 100 = 16\frac{2}{3}\%$.

∴ B's salary is less than A's salary by $16\frac{2}{3}\%$.

Ex. 11. *B's salary is 25% less than A's salary. By what per cent is A's salary more than B's salary?*

Sol. Let A's salary be Rs 100.

∵ B's salary is 25% less than A's salary

∴ B's salary = Rs **75**   ∴ A's salary is Rs 25 more than B's salary.

∴ % of A's salary more than B's salary = $\frac{25}{75} \times 100\% = \frac{100}{3}\% = 33\frac{1}{3}\%$.

Ex. 12. *A man gives 40% of his money to his children and 20% of the remaining to a trust. If he is still left with Rs 9600, what did he originally have?*

Sol. Let the original amount of money with him be Rs 100

∵ 40% of the original money is given to children, ∴ Remaining money = Rs (100 − 40) = Rs 60

Money given to trust = 20% of remaining = $\frac{20}{100}$ of Rs 60 = Rs 12

∴ Remaining money = Rs (60 − 12) = Rs 48

It is given that remaining money = Rs 9600.

When the remaining amount is Rs 48, original amount = Rs 100

∴ When the remaining amount is Rs 9600, original amount = Rs $\frac{100}{1\cancel{48}} \times \cancel{9600}^{200}$ = Rs 20,000

∴ The man originally had Rs **20,000.**

Ex.13. *In an examination, a candidate A scores 30% and fails by 40 marks, while another candidate B scores 40% and gets 20 marks more than the minimum pass marks. Find the maximum marks and minimum pass marks.*

Sol. Let the maximum marks be x.

∴ Pass marks for A = 30% of x + 40 = $\frac{30x}{100} + 40$

Pass marks for B = 40% of x − 20 = $\frac{40x}{100} - 20$

∵ Pass marks for both the cases are same

∴ $\frac{30x}{100} + 40 = \frac{40x}{100} - 20 \Rightarrow \frac{40x}{100} - \frac{30x}{100} = 40 + 20 \Rightarrow \frac{10x}{100} = 60 \Rightarrow x = 600$

∴ Maximum marks = 600 and Pass marks = $\frac{30}{100} \times 600 + 40$ = **220 marks.**

(We can find pass marks using any of the statements *i.e.* for A or for B.)

Ex.14. *Raj has some apples. He sold 40% more than he ate. If he sold 70 apples, how many did he eat?*

Sol. Let x be the number of apples he ate.

∴ He sold 40% more than he ate means he sold $x + \frac{40}{100}x$ apples = $x + \frac{2}{5}x = \frac{7x}{5}$ apples.

Given : Apples sold = 70 $\therefore \dfrac{7x}{5} = 70 \Rightarrow x = \dfrac{70 \times 5}{7} = \textbf{50}.$

$\therefore$ Hence he ate **50 apples.**

Ex.15. *In an examination, there were 2000 candidates out of which 900 candidates were boys and the rest were girls. If 32% of the boys and 38% of the girls failed, then find the total percentage of passed candidates.*

Sol.   Total number of candidates = 2000,
Number of boys = 900 $\therefore$ Number of girls = 2000 − 900 = 1100

32% of the boys failed $\Rightarrow$ 68% of the boys passed $\therefore$ Number of boys passed = $\dfrac{68}{100} \times 900 = 612$

38% of the girl failed $\Rightarrow$ 62% of the girls passed $\therefore$ Number of girls passed = $\dfrac{62}{100} \times 1100 = 682$

$\therefore$ Number of candidates passed = 612 + 682 = 1294

$\Rightarrow$ percentage of candidates who passed = $\dfrac{1294}{2000} \times 100 = \textbf{64.7\%}.$

EXERCISE 9 (b)

1. Divide 90 into two parts such that one part is 20% of the other.
2. If 70% of the students in a school are boys and the number of girls is 540, find the number of boys in the school.
3. The cost of a meal in a restaurant has increased from Rs 120 to Rs 150. Find the percentage increase in the cost of the meal.
4. What per cent of votes are in favour of a candidate if 25 persons vote for him and 45 persons vote against him.
5. Manoj's income increased by 20% and then decreased by 20%. What is the total percentage change in Manoj's income.
6. A's income is 25% more than B's income. By what per cent is B's income less than A's income.
7. A man spends 45% of his income and saves Rs 2640 in a month. What is his monthly income?
8. In an examination, a candidate has to secure 40% marks to pass. The candidate gets 212 marks and fails by 28 marks. Find the maximum marks of the examination.
9. A candidate scored 25% marks in an examination and failed by 30 marks while another candidate who scored 50% marks got 20 marks more than the minimum pass marks. Find the maximum marks and the minimum pass marks.
10. After deducting 10% from a sum and then 20% from the remainder, Rs 3600 are left. Find the original amount.
11. If 15% of 40 is greater than 25% of a number by 2, find the number.
12. Calculations show that an angle is $37\dfrac{1}{2}^{\circ}$. The size obtained by drawing and measurement is 35^{0}. Find the error per cent.
13. At an election there were two candidates. One of them got 62% of the valid votes and won by a majority of 7200 votes. Find the total number of valid votes cast.
14. The sides of a rectangle are 20 cm and 15 cm. If each side of the rectangle is increased by 20%, find the percentage increase in the area.
15. In an examination 2500 students appeared out of which 1100 were girls. 50% of the boys and 40% of the girls passed the examination. What percentage of candidates failed in the examination.
16. An electric supply company raises its charges by 20% and a year later increases the new charges by 20%. If the total increase had been made all at once, to what percentage would it have been equivalent.
17. The price of a pair of shoes is Rs 960. The tax levied on it is 12%. Find the price which a consumer has to pay for the pair of shoes.
18. An article costing Rs 1500 is sold for Rs 1650 after adding tax to it. Calculate the % of tax on the product.

LOOKING BACK
Summary of Key Facts

1. Per cent means per hundred.

2. A percentage can be converted to a fraction by writing the % number in the numerator and 100 in the denominator and dropping % sign e.g. $79\% = \frac{79}{100}$, $75\% = \frac{75}{100} = \frac{3}{4}$.

3. To change percentage to decimal, divide by 100 e.g. $25\% = \frac{25}{100} = \frac{1}{4} = 0.25$.

4. To change percentage to ratio, write it as fraction with denominator 100 and reduce to lowest terms if possible *e.g.* $60\% = \frac{60}{100} = \frac{3}{5} = 3 : 5$.

5. To change a fraction or decimal or ratio to percentage multiply by 100.

6. To work out a percentage of an amount :
   (*i*) Write percentage as a fraction.

   (*ii*) Multiply the fraction by that amount e.g. 40% of Rs 720 = Rs $\frac{40}{100} \times 720$ = Rs 288.

7. To find the new value after percentage change :
   (*i*) If there is increase, work out the increase and add it to the original amount.
   (*ii*) If there is decrease, work out the decrease and subtract it from the original amount.

8. Percentage change or error = $\dfrac{\text{Actual change or error}}{\text{Original value}} \times 100$

9. To express one quantity as a percentage of the other :
   (*i*) Write one quantity as the fraction of the other.

   (*ii*) Multiply by 100 e.g. 73 days as a per cent of a year = $\frac{73}{365} \times 100\% = \frac{1}{5} \times 100\% = 20\%$.

10. Original value = $\dfrac{100}{100 + R} \times$ New value when increased by R%. = $\dfrac{100}{100 - R} \times$ New value when decreased by R%.

    e.g., original price of a book which has increased by 10% to Rs 220 = Rs $\frac{100}{100 + 10} \times 220$ = Rs $\frac{100}{110} \times 220$ = Rs 200.

MENTAL MATHS – 8

1. Find 8% of Rs 500.

2. Convert 35% to (*i*) a fraction (*ii*) a decimal (*iii*) a ratio.

3. Find the number whose 15% is 60.

4. What percentage of 240m is 12m.

5. A school has 300 students. 40% of the students are girls. Find the number of boys.
   [**Think :** 60% are boys]

6. The weight of the box by mistake was written as 21 kg, while it was 25 kg. What is the error %.

7. A pudding is made of 100 gm sugar, 200gm eggs, 150gm flour and 50gm dry fruits. What is the per cent of sugar present in the whole pudding ?

8. The % of total quantity represented by 90° sector in a pie chart is _____.

9. Increase 200 by 4%

10. A boy remains awake for 16 hrs a day. For what percentage of the time does he sleep.

ANSWERS

EXERCISE 9 (a)

1. (a) $\frac{3}{5}$; 0.6   (b) $\frac{12}{5}$; 2.4   (c) $\frac{1}{8}$, 0.125   (d) $\frac{41}{75}$; 0.547 (approx)

2. (a) 75%   (b) $52\frac{1}{2}\%$ (c) 0.8%   (d) 37.5%   (e) 107%

3. (a) 2 : 1   (b) 1 : 15   (c) 3 : 4   (d) 1 : 3

4. (a) 50%   (b) 70%   (c) 84%   (d) $41\frac{2}{3}\%$

5. (a) Rs 798   (b) 330 kg   (c) 6 g   (d) 8.75 m

6. (a) 0.5%   (b) 4%   (c) 48%   (d) $33\frac{1}{3}\%$ 7. (a) 450   (b) Rs 500

8. $66\frac{2}{3}\%$ 9. Rs 224   10. Rs 31200   11. Rs 360   12. 25 cm

EXERCISE 9 (b)

1. 75, 15   2. 1260   3. 25%   4. $35\frac{5}{7}\%$ 5. 4%   6. 20%

7. Rs 4800   8. 600   9. Max marks = 200, min. pass marks = 80   10. Rs 5000

11. 16   12. $6\frac{2}{3}\%$ 13. 30,000 votes.   14. 44%   15. 54.4%   16. 44%

17. Rs 1075.20   18. 10%

MENTAL MATHS – 8

1. Rs 40   2. (i) $\frac{7}{20}$ (ii) 0.35   (iii) 7 : 20   3. 400   4. 5%

5. 180   6. 16%   7. 20%   8. 25%   9. 208   10. $66\frac{2}{3}\%$

10. Profit and Loss and Discount

10.1 Introduction

In earlier classes, you have learnt about percentage and its application in problems related to profit and loss. In this chapter we will take up more problems on profit and loss and discount.

10.2 Quick Review

1. Cost price (C.P.) is the amount at which a shopkeeper buys his goods.
2. Selling price (S.P.) is the amount at which a shopkeeper sells his goods.
3. Profit or gain = S.P. – C.P.

   A loss is made when the selling price is less than the cost price.

   Loss = C.P. – S.P.
4. Profit or loss per cent is calculated on cost price and not on selling price.
5. $\text{Gain}\% = \left(\dfrac{\text{Gain} \times 100}{\text{C.P.}}\right)$, $\text{Loss}\% = \left(\dfrac{\text{Loss} \times 100}{\text{C.P.}}\right)$
6. $\text{S.P.} = \left(\dfrac{100 + \text{Gain}\%}{100}\right) \times \text{C.P.}$, $\text{S.P.} = \left(\dfrac{100 - \text{Loss}\%}{100}\right) \times \text{C.P.}$
7. $\text{C.P.} = \left(\dfrac{100}{100 + \text{Gain}\%}\right) \times \text{S.P.}$, $\text{C.P.} = \left(\dfrac{100}{100 - \text{Loss}\%}\right) \times \text{S.P.}$
8. If an article is sold at a gain of 10%, then S.P. = 110% of C.P.

   If an article is sold at a loss of 10%, then S.P. = 90% of C.P.

10.3 Solved Examples

Ex.1. *An article was bought for Rs 1500 and sold for 2000. Find the gain and gain %.*

Sol. C.P. = Rs 1500, S.P. = Rs 2000 ∵ C.P. < S.P. ∴ it is a gain

Gain = S.P. – C.P. = Rs (2000 – 1500) = **Rs 500**

$\text{Gain} \% = \dfrac{\text{Gain}}{\text{C.P.}} \times 100 = \dfrac{500}{1500} \times 100 = 33\dfrac{1}{3}\%$.

Ex. 2. *Asha bought a cycle for Rs 720 and sold it for Rs 698.40 find the loss%.*

Sol. C.P. = Rs 720, S.P. = Rs 698.40   ∵ C.P. > S.P.   ∴ it is a loss

Loss = C.P. – S.P. = Rs (720 – 698.40) = Rs 21.60

∴ $\text{Loss}\% = \left(\dfrac{\text{Loss}}{\text{C.P.}} \times 100\right)\% = \dfrac{21.60}{720} \times 100 = \mathbf{3\%}.$

Ex. 3. *If the C.P. of 10 articles is equal to the S.P. of 12 articles. Find the gain or loss %.*

Sol. Let the C.P. of 1 article = Rs 1,   ∴ C.P. of 12 articles = Rs 12

S.P. of 12 articles = C.P. of 10 articles = Rs 10

∵ S.P. < C.P., it is a loss

Loss = C.P. – S.P. = Rs 12 – Rs 10 = Rs 2

∴ Loss % = $\left(\dfrac{\text{Loss}}{\text{C.P}} \times 100\right) = \dfrac{2}{12} \times 100 = 16\dfrac{1}{3}\%$.

Ex.4. *If a person sells an article for Rs 400 gaining $\dfrac{1}{4}$ of its C.P., find the gain per cent.*

Sol. Let the C.P. of the article be Rs x. Then Gain = $\dfrac{1}{4}$ of C.P. = Rs $\dfrac{x}{4}$

∴ **Gain** % = $\dfrac{\text{Gain}}{\text{C.P}} \times 100 = \left(\dfrac{\frac{x}{4}}{x} \times 100\right)\% = \left(\dfrac{1}{4} \times 100\right)\% = \mathbf{25\%}$.

Ex. 5. *12 bananas are bought for Rs 10 and 10 bananas are sold for Rs 12. Find the gain % or loss %.*

Sol. C.P. of 12 bananas = Rs 10, ∴ C.P. of 1 banana = Rs $\dfrac{10}{12}$

S.P. of 10 bananas = Rs 12, ∴ S.P. of 1 banana = Rs $\dfrac{12}{10}$

∵ S.P. of 1 banana > C.P. of 1 banana, ∴ it is a gain

Gain = S.P. – C.P. = Rs $\left(\dfrac{12}{10} - \dfrac{10}{12}\right)$ = Rs $\left(\dfrac{144-100}{120}\right)$ = Rs $\dfrac{44}{120}$

∴ **Gain** % = $\left(\dfrac{\text{Gain}}{\text{C.P}} \times 100\right)\% = \left(\dfrac{\frac{44}{120}}{\frac{10}{12}} \times 100\right)\% = \left(\dfrac{44}{120} \times \dfrac{12}{10} \times 100\right)\% = \mathbf{44\%}$.

Ex. 6. *Toffees are bought at the rate of 7 for a rupee and sold at the rate of 5 for a rupee. Find the gain per cent?*

Sol. (L.C.M of 7 and 5) = 35. Suppose there are 35 toffees which are bought at rate of 7 for a rupee and sold at the rate of 5 for rupee.

∴ C.P. of 35 toffees = Rs $\dfrac{35}{7}$ = Rs 5, S.P. of 35 toffees = Rs $\dfrac{35}{5}$ = Rs 7

∵ S.P. > C.P., it is a gain and **Gain** = S.P. – C.P. = Rs 2

∴ **Gain**% = $\left(\dfrac{\text{Gain}}{\text{C.P.}} \times 100\right)\% = \left(\dfrac{2}{5} \times 100\right)\% = \mathbf{40\%}$.

Ex. 7. *What is the cost price of an article which is sold at a loss of 25% for Rs 150?*

Sol. Let the C.P. Rs 100, Then S.P. = Rs 75.

When the S.P. is Rs 75, C.P. = Rs 100

∴ When the S.P. is Rs 150, C.P. = Rs $\dfrac{100}{75} \times 150$ = **Rs 200**.

Ex. 8. *By selling a washing machine for Rs 11400, a dealer losses 5%. For how much should he sell this machine to gain 5%?*

Sol. First we find the C.P. If the S.P. is Rs 95 then C.P. is Rs 100

∴ If the S.P. is Rs 11,400, then C.P. is Rs $\frac{100}{95} \times 11,400$ = Rs 12000

Now, if the C.P. is Rs 100, then S.P. is Rs 105

∴ If the C.P. is Rs 12000, then S.P. is Rs $\frac{105}{100} \times 12,000$ = Rs 12,600

Therefore, to gain 5% he should sell the machine for **Rs 12,600**.

Ex. 9. *A man sold two articles for Rs 2970 each, gaining 10% on one and losing 10% on the other. Find his gain (or) loss per cent on the whole transaction.*

Sol.

Ist article	IInd article
S.P. = Rs 2970, Gain% = 10%	S.P. = Rs 2970, Loss % = 10%
C.P. = $\frac{S.P \times 100}{100 + gain\%}$ = Rs $\left(\frac{2970 \times 100}{110}\right)$	C.P. = $\frac{S.P \times 100}{100 - loss\%}$ = Rs $\left(\frac{2970 \times 100}{90}\right)$
= Rs 2700	= Rs 3300

Total S.P. of both the articles = Rs (2 × 2970) = Rs 5940

Total C.P. of both the articles = Rs 2700 + Rs 3300 = Rs 6000

∵ C.P. > S.P., therefore it is a loss

Loss = C.P. – S.P. = Rs (6000 – 5940) = Rs 60

∴ Loss % = $\left(\frac{Loss}{C.P.} \times 100\right)\% = \left(\frac{60}{6000} \times 100\right)\% = \mathbf{1\%}$.

∴ It is a **loss of 1%** on the whole transaction.

Ex.10. *By selling 100 Diwali cards, a shopkeeper gains the S.P. of 40 cards. Find his gain per cent.*

Sol. Gain = (S.P. of 100 cards) – (C.P. of 100 cards)

⇒ S.P. of 40 cards = S.P. of 100 cards – C.P. of 100 cards.

⇒ S.P. of 60 cards = C.P. of 100 cards

Let C.P. of 1 card be Re 1, then S.P. of 60 cards = Rs 100

∴ Gain = S.P. of 40 cards = Rs $\frac{100}{60} \times 40$ = Rs $\frac{200}{3}$

This gain is on C.P. of 100 cards which is Rs 100 ∴ Gain% = $\frac{200}{3}\% = \mathbf{66\frac{2}{3}\%}$.

Ex.11. *Prem sells an article to Dinesh at a gain of 20% and Dinesh sells it to Sudhir at a gain of 10% and Sudhir sells it to Prashant at a gain of $12\frac{1}{2}\%$. If Prashant pays Rs 14850, find the cost price of Prem.*

Sol. Let Prem's C.P. be Rs 100, then C.P. of Dinesh = Rs 120

C.P. of Sudhir = 110 % of Rs 120 = Rs $\frac{110}{100} \times 120$ = Rs 132

C.P. of Prashant = $112\frac{1}{2}\%$ of Rs 132 = Rs $\frac{225}{2 \times 100} \times 132$ = Rs $\frac{297}{2}$

When C.P. of Prashant is Rs $\frac{297}{2}$, C.P. of Prem = Rs 100

When C.P. of Prashant is Rs 14850, C.P. of Prem = Rs $100 \times \frac{2}{297} \times 14850$ = **Rs 10,000**.

Ex.12. *A dinner set is sold at a gain of 16%. Had it been sold for Rs 200 more, the gain would have been 20%. Find the C.P. of the dinner set.*

Sol. Let C.P. of the dinner set = Rs 100

First gain = 16% ∴ First S.P. = Rs (100 + 16) = Rs 116

Second gain = 20% ∴ Second S.P. = Rs (100 + 20) = Rs120

Difference between the two S.P.'s is = Rs 120 – Rs 116 = Rs 4

If the difference is Rs 4, then C.P. = Rs 100

If the difference is Re 1, then C.P. = Rs $\dfrac{100}{4}$

If the difference is Rs 200, then C.P. = Rs $\dfrac{100}{4} \times 200$ = **Rs 5000.**

Hence C.P. of the dinner set = **Rs 5000.**

Ex.13. *Irshad bought 100 hens for Rs 8000 and sold 20 of these at a gain of 5%. At what gain per cent must he sell the remaining hens so as to gain 20% on the whole?*

Sol. C.P. of 100 hens = Rs 8000, Gain = 20%

S.P.. of 100 hens = $\dfrac{100 + \text{Profit\%}}{100} \times$ C.P. = Rs $\dfrac{100 + 20}{100} \times 8000$ = Rs $\dfrac{120}{100} \times 8000$ = Rs 9600

C.P. of 100 hens = Rs 8000

∴ C.P. of 20 hens = Rs $\dfrac{8000}{100} \times 20$ = Rs 1600.

Gain = 5% ∴ S.P. of 20 hens = $\dfrac{100 + 5}{100} \times 1600$ = Rs $\dfrac{105}{100} \times 1600$ = Rs 1680

∴ S.P. of 80 hens = S.P. of 100 hens – S.P. of 80 hens = Rs 9600 – Rs 1680 = Rs 7920.

C.P. of 80 hens = C.P. of 100 hens – C.P. of 20 hens = Rs 8000 – Rs 1600 = Rs 6400

∴ Gain = Rs 7920 – Rs 6400 = Rs 1520

∴ **Gain %** = $\dfrac{\text{Total gain}}{\text{C.P.}} \times 100$ = $\dfrac{1520}{6400} \times 100$ = $\dfrac{95}{4}\%$ = $23\dfrac{3}{4}\%$ = **23.75%.**

Hence, he should sell the remaining hens at a gain of **23.75%.**

Ex.14. *Some toffees are bought at the rate of 11 for Rs 10 and the same toffees at the rate of 9 for Rs 10. If the whole lot is sold at one rupee per toffee, find the gain or loss per cent in the whole transaction.*

Sol. Let the number of toffees bought of each kind

┌───── Note this figure
↓
= 99

| LCM of 11 and 9 = 99 |

∴ C.P. of 1st kind of toffees = Rs $\dfrac{10}{11} \times 99$ = Rs 90

C.P. of 2nd kind of toffees = Rs $\dfrac{10}{9} \times 99$ = Rs 110

Total C.P. = Rs 90 + Rs 110 = Rs 200.

Total number of toffees = (99 + 99) = 198

Total S.P. @ Re 1 per toffee = Rs (198 × 1) = Rs 198

Loss = Rs 200 – Rs 198 = Rs 2

∴ Loss per cent = $\left(\dfrac{\text{Loss}}{\text{C.P.}} \times 100\right)\%$ = $\dfrac{2}{200} \times 100$ = **1%.**

Ex.15. *Rekha bought 16 dozen ball pens and sold them at a loss equal to S.P. of 8 ball pens. Find (i) her loss per cent (ii) S.P. of 1 dozen ball pens, if she purchased these 16 dozen ball pens for Rs 576.*

Sol. C.P. – S.P. = Loss $\Rightarrow$ C.P. = S.P. + Loss

∴ C.P. of 16 dozen ball pens = S.P. of 16 dozen ball pens + S.P. of 8 ball pens

i.e., C.P. of 192 ball pens = S.P. of 192 ball pens + S.P. of 8 ball pens = S.P. of 200 ball pens

Now, C.P. of 192 ball pens = Rs 576

∴ S.P. of 200 ball pens = Rs 576

S.P. of 1 ball pen = Rs $\dfrac{576}{200}$ ∴ S.P. of 192 ball pens = Rs $\dfrac{576}{25 \, 200} \times 192^{24}$ = Rs $\dfrac{13824}{25}$

Loss = Rs 576 – Rs $\dfrac{13824}{25}$ = Rs $\dfrac{14400 - 13824}{25}$ = Rs $\dfrac{576}{25}$

∴ Loss % = $\dfrac{\text{Loss}}{\text{C.P}} \times 100\% = \dfrac{576}{25} \times \dfrac{1}{576} \times 100\%$ = **4%**.

Now, S.P. of 200 ball pens = Rs 576

S.P. of 1 ball pen = Rs $\dfrac{576}{200}$ ∴ S.P. of 12 ball pens = Rs $\dfrac{576}{200} \times 12$ = Rs $\dfrac{864}{25}$ = **Rs 34.56.**

Ex.16. *Bhawna bought two fans for Rs 3605. She sold one at a profit of 15% and the other at a loss of 9%. If Bhawana obtained the same amount for each fan, find the cost price of each fan.*

Sol. Let C.P. of first fan = Rs x

Then C.P. of second fan = Rs $(3605 - x)$, profit = 15%

∴ S.P. of first fan = $\dfrac{100 + \text{Profit}\%}{100} \times$ C.P. = Rs $\dfrac{100 + 15}{100} \times (x)$ = Rs $\dfrac{115x}{100}$

For the sale of second fan, loss = 9%

∴ S.P. of second fan = Rs $\dfrac{100 - \text{Loss}\%}{100} \times$ C.P. = Rs $\dfrac{100 - 9}{100} \times (3605 - x)$ = Rs $\dfrac{91(3605 - x)}{100}$

By the given condition, S.P. of first fan = S.P. of second fan

∴ $\dfrac{115x}{100} = \dfrac{91(3605 - x)}{100}$ $\Rightarrow$ $115\,x = 91\,(3605 - x) \Rightarrow 115\,x = 91 \times 3605 - 91x$

$\Rightarrow$ $115\,x + 91\,x = 91 \times 3605 \Rightarrow 206\,x = 91 \times 3605 \Rightarrow x = \dfrac{91 \times 3605}{206} = \dfrac{91 \times 35}{2} = \dfrac{3185}{2} = 1592.50$

∴ C.P. of first fan = Rs x = **Rs 1592.50**

and C.P. of second fan = Rs 3605 – Rs 1592.50 = **Rs 2012.50.**

EXERCISE 10 (a)

1. Ramesh bought a house for Rs 2, 75, 000. He spent Rs 25,000 on its repairs Then he sold it for Rs 3, 50, 000. Find his gain per cent.

2. A man buys a T.V for Rs 6800. For how much should he sell it so as to (i) gain 10%, (ii) lose 5% on it ?

3. By selling a radio for Rs 528, Mohit gains 10%. Find his cost price.

4. A watch sold for Rs 448 gives a profit of only 12%. Find the profit % if the selling price had been Rs 512.

5. Prem sold a transistor to Sudhir at a gain of 10% and Sudhir sold it to Hari at a gain of 15%. Prem had bought it for Rs 500, what did it cost to Hari?

6. A manufacturer sells an article to a wholesaler at a profit of 18%, the wholesaler sells it to a retailer at a profit of 20%. The retailer sells it to a customer at a profit of 25%. If the customer pays Rs 30.09 for it, find the cost of the manufacturer.

7. A shopkeeper sold an article at a gain of 5%. If he had sold it for Rs 16.50 less, he would have lost 5%. Find the cost price of the article.

8. By selling a stool for Rs 67.50, a carpenter losses 10%. How much per cent would he gain or lose by selling it for Rs 82.50?

9. If the cost price of 11 shirts is equal to the selling price of 10 shirts, find the percentage profit or loss.

10. A shopkeeper buys two T.V. sets of the same type. He sells one of them at a profit of 20% and the other at a loss of 5%. If the difference in selling prices is Rs 700, find the cost price of each T.V. set.

11. A publisher sells a book for Rs 168 at a profit of 20%. If his cost of production increases by 30%, what should be the increase in the price of the book so that his percentage profit remains the same?

12. The difference in prices when a commodity is sold at a profit of 4% and at a profit of 6% is Rs 3. Find the selling prices of the commodity in the two cases.

13. A man buys a plot of land at Rs 3,60,000. He sells one third of the plot at a loss of 20%. Again, he sells one - third of the plot left at a profit of 25%. At what price should he sell the remaining plot in order to get a profit of 10% on the whole?

14. A shopkeeper bought locks at the rate of 8 locks for Rs 34 and sold them at the rate of 12 locks for Rs 57. Calculate :

(_i_) his gain per cent, and (_ii_) the number of locks he should sell to earn a profit of Rs 45.

15. Sneha bought a purse for Rs 480. She sold it to Neha at a gain of $6\frac{1}{4}\%$ and Neha sold it to Devi at a gain of 10%. How much did Devi pay for it.

16. Dinesh sold his motor cycle to Navin at a loss of 28%. Navin spent Rs 1680 on its repairs and sold the motor cycle to Saran for Rs35,910 thereby making a profit of 12.5%. Find the cost of the motor cycle for Dinesh.

17. A shopkeeper sold two pairs of jeans for Rs 720 each, gaining 20% on one and losing 20% on the other. Find his gain or loss %.

18. Pens are bought at 12 for a rupee and sold at 9 for a rupee. Find the gain %.

19. By selling 100 mangoes a fruit seller gains the S.P. of 20 mangoes. Find his gain %.

20. The cost price of 25 articles is equal to the S.P. of 20 articles. Find the gain %.

DISCOUNT

10.4 Introduction

Sometimes to increase the sale or dispose off the old stock, a dealer offers his goods at reduced prices. The reduction in price offered by the dealer is called discount.

10.5 Definition

1. **Marked Price :** The printed price or the tagged price of an article is called the **marked price (M.P)**. It is also called the list price

2. **Discount :** The deduction allowed on the marked price is called **discount**. Discount is generally given as per cent of the marked price.

3. **Net Price :** The selling price at which the article is sold to the customer after deducting the discount from the marked price is called the **net price**.

Remember that discount is always calculated on the marked price of the article.

4. **Formulas** (*i*) S.P. = M.P. – Discount

(*ii*) Rate of discount = Discount% = $\dfrac{\text{Discount}}{\text{M.P.}} \times 100$.

(*iii*) S.P. = M.P $\times \left(\dfrac{100 - \text{Discount\%}}{100} \right)$ (*iv*) M.P. = $\dfrac{100 \times \text{S.P}}{100 - \text{Discount\%}}$.

10.6 Solved Examples

Ex. 1. *Find the S.P. when M.P. = Rs 550 and discount = 10%.*

Sol. Discount = 10% on M.P. = Rs $\dfrac{10}{100} \times 550 = $ Rs 55

∴   S.P. = M.P. – Discount = Rs 550 – Rs 55 = **Rs 495.**

Ex. 2. *Find the rate of discount when M.P = Rs 600 and S.P. = Rs 510.*

Sol. M.P = Rs 600, S.P. = Rs 510 ∴   Discount = M.P – S.P. = Rs 600 – Rs 510 = Rs 90

∴   Rate of discount, i.e. discount % = $\dfrac{\text{Discount}}{\text{M.P}} \times 100 = \dfrac{90}{600} \times 100\% = $ **15%.**

Ex. 3. *Find the M.P., when S.P. = Rs 9000 and discount = 10%.*

Sol. S.P. = Rs 9000, discount = 10%

Let the M.P. be Rs 100. Since discount = 10%, so S.P. = Rs 90

When S.P. is Rs 90, M.P. is Rs 100.

When S.P. is Re 1, M.P. is Rs $\dfrac{100}{90}$

When S.P. is Rs 9000, M.P is Rs $\dfrac{100}{90} \times 9000 = $ **Rs 10,000.**

Alternatively, M.P. = $\dfrac{100 \times \text{S.P}}{100 - \text{Discount\%}} = $ Rs $\dfrac{100 \times 9000}{100 - 10} = $ Rs $\dfrac{100 \times 9000}{90} = $ **Rs 10,000.**

Ex. 4. *A dealer prices an article at 20% more than the cost price and allows a discount of 10% on it. Find the gain per cent.*

Sol. Let C.P. be Rs 100. Then marked price = Rs 120.

Discount = 10% ∴ S.P. = 90% of Rs 120 = Rs 108.

∴   Gain = Rs 108 – Rs 100 = Rs 8 which is on Rs 100

∴   Gain per cent = 8%

Ex. 5. *Shirish purchased a watch at 20% discount on its marked price but sold it at the marked price. Find the gain per cent of Shirish on this transaction.*

Sol. Let marked price be Rs 100. Discount = 20%

∴   C.P. of watch for Shirish = Rs 100 – Rs 20 = Rs 80

Shirish sells the watch at marked price so S.P. for him = Rs 100

∴   Shirish's gain = S.P. – C.P. = Rs 100 – Rs 80 = Rs 20

This gain is on C.P. which is Rs 80   ∴ Gain % = $\dfrac{20}{80} \times 100 = $ **25%.**

Ex. 6. *A garment dealer allows his customer 10% discount on a marked price of the goods and still gets a profit of 25%. What is the cost price of a shirt if the marked price is Rs 1250 ?*

Sol.   M.P. = Rs 1250, Discount = 10%

When M.P. is Rs 100, S.P. is Rs 90

When M.P is Rs 1250, S.P. is Rs $\frac{90}{100} \times 1250$ = Rs 1125

> **Think :** that on a M.P of Rs 100, discount = Rs 10 and so S.P = Rs 90

Profit = 25% $\therefore$ C.P. = $\frac{100}{100 + \text{Profit}\%} \times$ S.P = Rs $\frac{100}{100 + 25} \times 1125$ = Rs $\frac{100}{125} \times 1125^9$

= Rs (100×9) = **Rs 900.**

Ex. 7. *What price should Kiran mark on a Sari which costs her Rs 3000, so as to gain 20% after allowing a discount of 10%?*

Sol.   C.P. = Rs 3000, gain = 20% $\therefore$ S.P. = $\frac{100 + \text{gain}\%}{100} \times$ C.P.

= Rs $\frac{100 + 20}{100} \times 3000$ = Rs $\frac{120}{100} \times 3000$ = Rs 3600

Discount = 10%. This means for a M.P. of Rs 100, S.P. = Rs 90

When S.P. is Rs 90, M.P. is Rs 100

When S.P. is Rs 3600, M.P. is Rs $\frac{100}{90} \times 3600$ = **Rs 4000.**

Hence, Kiran should mark a price of **Rs 4000** on the sari.

EXERCISE 10 (b)

1. Find the S.P. when M.P = Rs 1500 and discount = 12%

2. Find the discount and the amount actually paid if :

   (*a*) A shirt having a price tag of Rs 600 is sold at 15% discount.

   (*b*) A vacuum cleaner with a marked price of Rs 6000 is sold at a discount of 5% on immediate cash payment.

3. Find the rate of discount when :

   (*i*) M.P = Rs 300 and S.P = Rs 240   (*ii*) M.P. = Rs 2800 and S.P = Rs 2100

4. Find the M.P when :

   (*i*) S.P = Rs 1900 and discount = 5%   (*ii*) S.P = Rs 4200 and discount = 16%

5. A shopkeeper marks his goods 30% above the cost price and gives a discount of 15% on the marked price . What gain % does he make?

6. A watch dealer pays 10% custom duty on a watch which costs Rs 500 abroad. For how much should he mark it, if he desires to make a profit of 20% after giving a discount of 25% to the buyer.

7. A shopkeeper allows a cash discount of 12.5% on a machine. A customer pays an amount of Rs 437.50 for a machine. At what price is the machine listed?

8. A shopkeeper offers 10% off-season discount to the customers and still makes a profit of 28%. What is the cost price of a pair of shoes marked at Rs 1120?

9. A shopkeeper buys an article for Rs 400 and marks it for sale at a price that may give him 80% profit on his cost. He, however gives 15% discount on the marked price to his customer. Calculate :

   (*i*) the marked price of the article.   (*ii*) the discount in rupees given to the customer,

   (*iii*) the actual percentage profit made by the shopkeeper.

10. When a discount of 15% is allowed on the marked price of an article, it is sold for Rs 2975 :

    Calculate   (*i*) its marked price

    (*ii*) its cost price, given that the marked price is 40% above the cost price of the article

    (*iii*) the profit in rupees, made by the sale of the article.

11. A shopkeeper allows a discount of 20% on the marked price of an article, and sells it for Rs 896 :

    (*a*) Calculate the marked price of the article,

    (*b*) By selling the article, at the discounted price if he still gains 12% on his cost price, what was the cost price?

    (*c*) What would have been his profit percentage if he had sold the article at the marked price?

12. A firm dealing in furniture allows 4% discount on the marked prices of each item. What price must be marked on dining table which costs Rs 4000 to assemble, so as to make a profit of 20%.

13. A sells an old car priced at Rs 36,000. He gives a discount of 8% on the first Rs 20,000 and 5% on remaining Rs 16,000. B also sells a car of the same marked priced at Rs 36000. He gives a discount of 7% on the total price. Calculate the actual prices charged by A and B for the cars

---

LOOKING BACK

Summary of Key Facts

1. In case of profit (if S.P. > C.P.)

    (*i*) Profit = S.P. – C.P   (*ii*) S.P. = Profit + C.P

    (*iii*) C.P = S.P. – Profit   (*iv*) Profit % = $\dfrac{\text{Profit}}{\text{C.P}} \times 100$

    (*v*) Profit = $\dfrac{\text{C.P} \times \text{Profit \%}}{100}$ (*vi*) S.P. = $\text{C.P} \times \left(\dfrac{100 + \text{Profit\%}}{100} \right)$

    (*vii*) C.P = $\dfrac{100 \times \text{S.P}}{100 + \text{Profit\%}}$

2. In case of loss (if S.P. < C.P.)

    (*i*) Loss = C.P – S.P.   (*ii*) S.P. = C.P – Loss   (*iii*) C.P = Loss + S.P.

    (*iv*) Loss% = $\dfrac{\text{Loss}}{\text{C.P}} \times 100$ (*v*) Loss = $\dfrac{\text{C.P} \times \text{Loss\%}}{100}$ (*vi*) S.P. = $\text{C.P} \times \left(\dfrac{100 - \text{Loss\%}}{100} \right)$

    (*vii*) C.P = $\dfrac{100 \times \text{S.P}}{100 - \text{loss\%}}$

3. (*i*) Discount is usually expressed as a certain per cent of the M.P.

    (*ii*) Discount = M.P – S.P.   (*iii*) Rate of discount = Discount% = $\dfrac{\text{Discount}}{\text{M.P}} \times 100$

    (*iv*) S.P.. = $\text{M.P} \times \left(\dfrac{100 - \text{Discount\%}}{100} \right)$ (*v*) M.P = $\dfrac{100 \times \text{S.P}}{100 - \text{Discount\%}}$.

ANSWERS

EXERCISE 10 (a)

1. $16\dfrac{2}{3}\%$ 2. (*i*) Rs 7480   (*ii*) Rs 6460   3. Rs 480   4. 28%   5. Rs 632.50

6. Rs 17   7. Rs 165   8. Gain 10%   9. Profit 10%   10. Rs 2800   11. Rs 50.40

12. Rs 156, Rs 159   13. Rs 1,50,000   14. (*i*) $11\frac{13}{17}\%$ (*ii*) 90 locks   15. Rs 561   16. Rs 42000

17. 4%   18. $33\frac{1}{3}\%$ 19. 25%   20. 25%

EXERCISE 10 (b)

1. Rs 1320   2. (*a*) Rs 90, Rs 510   (*b*) Rs 300, Rs 5700   3. (*i*) 20%   (*ii*) 25%

4. (*i*) Rs 2000   (*ii*) Rs 5000   5. 10.5%   6. Rs 880   7. Rs 500   8. Rs 787.50

9. (*i*) Rs 720   (*ii*) Rs 108   (*iii*) 53%   10. (*i*) Rs 3500   (*ii*) Rs 2500   (*iii*) Rs 475

11. (*i*) Rs 1120   (*ii*) Rs 800   (*iii*) 40%   12. Rs 5000   13. Rs 33,600; Rs 33480

FUN WITH NUMBERS

1. By using each number and each sign can you reach a total of 42?

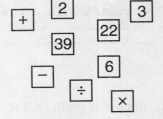

THE NUMBER 111

2.
$$111 = 3 \times 37$$
$$= 16 + 17 + 18 + 19 + 20 + 21$$

In cricket, a score of 111 is called 'The Nelson' and is considered unlucky. A 'Double Nelson' is 222. Numbers like 111 which are just written with ones are called **repunits**. See what happens when you square repunits. Here is part of the pattern which goes on for ever.

$$1^2 = 1$$
$$11^2 = 121$$
$$111^2 = 12321$$
$$1111^2 = 1234321$$
$$11111^2 = 123454321$$
$$111111^2 = 12345654321$$
$$1111111^2 = 1234567654321$$
$$11111111^2 = 123456787654321$$
$$111111111^2 = 12345678987654321$$

It has been proved that no repunits, however long can be square numbers.

Answer : 1. $39 \div 3 \times 2 + 22 - 6$

11. Simple and Compound Interest

11.1 Some Important Terms

1. **Principal (P)** : The money borrowed or lent.
2. **Interest (I)** : It is the additional money paid to the lender, for the use of the money borrowed.
3. **Rate (R)** : Interest for 1 year per Rs 100.
4. **Time (T)** : The time period for which the money is borrowed.
5. **Simple Interest or (S.I.)** : When the interest is paid to the lender regularly every year or every half year, we call the interest simple interest.
6. **Amount (A)** : Principal + Interest.

11.2 Formula Used

$(a)\ S.I. = \dfrac{P \times R \times T}{100}$ $\qquad (b)\ P = \dfrac{S.I. \times 100}{R \times T}$ $\qquad (c)\ R = \dfrac{S.I. \times 100}{P \times T}$ $\qquad (d)\ T = \dfrac{S.I. \times 100}{P \times R}$

$(e)\ A = P + S.I. = P + \dfrac{P \times R \times T}{100} = P\left(1 + \dfrac{R \times T}{100}\right)$

> **Note :**
> 1. (i) Rate 4% per annum means Rs 4 for every Rs 100 per year.
>   (ii) Rate 1.5% per month means Rs 1.50 for every Rs 100 per month.
>   = Rs 1.5 ◊ 12 = Rs 18 for every Rs 100 per year = 18% p.a.
> 2. (i) When time is given in days, we convert it to year by dividing it by 365.
>   (ii) When time is given in months, we convert it to year by dividing it by 12.
>   (iii) When dates are given, the day on which the sum is borrowed is not included but the day on which money is returned is included, while counting the number of days.

11.3 Solved Examples

Ex.1. *Find the interest and amount when*

(a) *Principal = Rs 1050, Rate = 7% p.a. and Time = $4\frac{1}{2}$ Years*

(b) *Principal = Rs 1560, Rate = 10% p.a. and Time = 3 years 4 months.*

(c) *Principal = Rs 6250, Rate 1% per month and Time = 73 days.*

Sol. $(a)\ P = $ Rs 1050, $R = 7\%$ p.a. , $T = \dfrac{9}{2}$ years

$\therefore\quad S.I. = \dfrac{P \times R \times T}{100} = $ Rs $\dfrac{1050 \times 7 \times 9}{100 \times 2} = $ **Rs 330.75**

$\therefore\quad$ Amount $= P + S.I. = $ Rs 1050 + Rs 330.75 = **Rs 1380.75**.

$(b)\ P = $ Rs 1560, $R = 10\%$ p.a., $T = 3$ years $+ \dfrac{4}{12}$ years $= 3 + \dfrac{1}{3}$ years $= \dfrac{10}{3}$ years

$$S.I. = \frac{P \times R \times T}{100} = \text{Rs} \frac{1560 \times 10 \times \frac{10}{3}}{100} = \text{Rs} \frac{1560 \times 10 \times 10}{3 \times 100} = \textbf{Rs 520.}$$

$\therefore$ Amount = P + S.I. = Rs 1560 + Rs 520 = **Rs 2080.**

(c) $P = \text{Rs } 6250$, $R = 1\%$ per month $= (1 \times 12)\%$ p.a. $= 12\%$ p.a., $T = 73$ days $= \frac{73}{365}$ year $= \frac{1}{5}$ year

$$S.I. = \frac{P \times R \times T}{100} = \text{Rs} \frac{6250 \times 12 \times \frac{1}{5}}{100} = \text{Rs} \frac{6250 \times 12 \times 1}{100 \times 5} = \textbf{Rs 150}$$

$\therefore$ Amount = S.I. + P = Rs 6250 + Rs 150 = **Rs 6400.**

Ex. 2. *Find the Simple interest on Rs 7300 from 11th May, 2005 to 14th September, 2005 at 6% per annum.*

Sol. P = Rs 7300, R = 6% p.a.

The numbers of days for which the money is borrowed are counted as

Month :	May	June	July	August	September
Days :	20	30	31	31	14

> May 11 is not counted, Sept 14 is counted.

$\therefore$ $T = (20 + 30 + 31 + 31 + 14)$days $= 126$ days $= \frac{126}{365}$ year $= \frac{2}{5}$ year

$$\therefore \quad S.I. = \frac{P \times R \times T}{100} = \text{Rs} \frac{7300 \times 6 \times \frac{2}{5}}{100} = \text{Rs} \frac{7300 \times 6 \times 2}{100 \times 5} = \text{Rs} \frac{876}{5} = \text{Rs } \textbf{175.20.}$$

11.4 Inverse Problems

> **To find Principal, Rate and Time when *S.I.* is given :**

Ex. 3. *What sum of money will yield an interest of Rs 138.75 at 8% per annum in 3 years and 1 month ?*

Sol. Here $P = ?$, $S.I. = \text{Rs } 138.75$, $R = 8\%$ p.a., $T = 3$ years $+ \frac{1}{12}$ year $= 3\frac{1}{12}$ years $= \frac{37}{12}$ years

$$\therefore \quad P = \frac{S.I. \times 100}{R \times T} = \text{Rs} \frac{138.75 \times 100}{8 \times \frac{37}{12}} = \text{Rs} \frac{138.75 \times 100 \times 12}{8 \times 37} = \textbf{Rs 562.50.}$$

Ex. 4. *In what time will a sum of money put at $6\frac{2}{3}\%$ simple interest becomes 4 times of itself.*

Sol. Let Principal = Rs P $\Rightarrow$ Amount = Rs $4P$

$\therefore$ $S.I. = \text{Amount} - \text{Principal} = \text{Rs } 4P - \text{Rs } P = \text{Rs } 3P$, $R = 6\frac{2}{3}\% = \frac{20}{3}\%$

$$T = \frac{S.I. \times 100}{P \times R} = \left(\frac{3P \times 100}{P \times \frac{20}{3}} \right) = \left(\frac{3P \times 100 \times 3}{P \times 20} \right) \text{ years} = \textbf{45 years.}$$

Alternatively, Let the Principal be Rs 100. Then amount = Rs 400

$\therefore$ $S.I. = \text{Rs } 400 - \text{Rs } 100 = \text{Rs } 300$

Rate $= 6\frac{2}{3}\%$ p.a. $= \frac{20}{3}\%$ p.a. Let the time be T years

$$T = \frac{S.I. \times 100}{P \times R} = \frac{300 \times 100}{100 \times \frac{20}{3}} = \frac{300 \times 3}{20} = \textbf{45 years.}$$

Ex. 5. *At what rate per cent per annum will Rs 5130 produce Rs 256.50 as simple interest in 2 years 8 months ?*

Sol. $P =$ Rs 5130, $S.I. =$ Rs 256.50, $T = 2$ years 8 months $= 2$ years $+ \dfrac{8}{12}$ year $= \dfrac{8}{3}$ years

$$R = \dfrac{S.I.\times 100}{P\times T} = \left(\dfrac{256.50\times 100}{5130\times \dfrac{8}{3}}\right)\% = \left(\dfrac{256.50\times 100\times 3}{5130\times 8}\right)\% = \dfrac{\dfrac{25650}{100}\times 100\times 3}{5130\times 8}$$

$$= \dfrac{25650\times 3}{5130\times 8} = \dfrac{5\times 3}{8} = \dfrac{15}{8} = 1.875 \therefore \text{ rate } = 1.9\% \text{ p.a. (to 1 dp)}$$

Ex. 6. *In what time will Rs 72 become Rs 81 at $6\dfrac{1}{4}\%$ p.a. simple interest ?*

Sol. $P =$ Rs 72, $A =$ Rs 81, $R = \dfrac{25}{4}\%$ $\therefore$ $S.I. = A - P =$ Rs 81 $-$ Rs 72 $=$ Rs 9

$$\therefore T = \dfrac{S.I.\times 100}{P\times R} = \left(\dfrac{9\times 100}{72\times \dfrac{25}{4}}\right) \text{ years } = \left(\dfrac{9\times 100\times 4}{72\times 25}\right) \text{ years } = \textbf{2 years.}$$

Ex. 7. *If Rs 1440 amounts to Rs 1584 in 3 years 4 months, what will Rs 920 amount to in 5 years at the same rate of interest per annum ?*

Sol. Given $P =$ Rs 1440, $A =$ Rs 1584, $T = 3$ years 4 months $= 3\dfrac{1}{3}$ years $= \dfrac{10}{3}$ years

$\therefore$ $S.I. = A - P =$ Rs 1584 $-$ Rs 1440 $=$ Rs 144

$$\therefore R = \dfrac{S.I.\times 100}{P\times T} = \left(\dfrac{144\times 100}{1440\times \dfrac{10}{3}}\right)\% = \left(\dfrac{144\times 100\times 3}{1440\times 10}\right)\% = \textbf{3\% p.a.}$$

Now if Rs 920 is invested at the same rate for 4 years, $P =$ Rs 920, $R = 3\%$, $T = 4$ years

$$\therefore S.I. = \dfrac{P\times R\times T}{100} = \text{Rs} \left(\dfrac{920\times 3\times 4}{100}\right) = \text{Rs } 110.40$$

$\therefore$ Amount $= P + S.I. =$ Rs 920 $+$ Rs 110.40 $= \textbf{Rs 1030.40.}$

Ex. 8. *What sum lent out at 6.25% p.a. produces the same simple interest in 5 years as Rs 1800 lent out at 4% produces in $2\dfrac{1}{2}$ years ?*

Sol. Let the required sum be Rs P

$\boxed{6.25\% = \dfrac{625}{100}\% = \dfrac{25}{4}\%}$

When this sum is lent out at 6.25% p.a. for 5 years

$$S.I. = \dfrac{P\times R\times T}{100} = \dfrac{P\times \dfrac{25}{4}\times 5}{100} = \dfrac{P\times 25\times 5}{4\times 100} = \text{Rs } \dfrac{5P}{16}$$

$\boxed{P = \text{Rs } P, R = 6.25\%, T = 5 \text{ years}}$

Now in the second case it is given that, $P =$ Rs 1800, $R = 4\%$, $T = 2\dfrac{1}{2}$ years $= 5\dfrac{1}{2}$ years

$$\therefore S.I. = \dfrac{P\times R\times T}{100} = \dfrac{1800\times 4\times 5}{100\times 2} = \text{Rs } 180.$$

It is given that interest in both cases is same $\therefore \dfrac{5P}{16} = 180 \Rightarrow P = \dfrac{180 \times 16}{5} = \mathbf{576}$

$\therefore$ **Required sum = Rs 576.**

Ex. 9. *The S.I. on a sum of money is $\dfrac{1}{9}$ th of the principal and the number of years is equal to rate per cent p.a. Find the rate %.*

Sol. Let the sum be Rs P then $\therefore$ S.I. = Rs $\dfrac{P}{9}$

$\because$ Let Time = x years $\Rightarrow$ Rate = $x\%$ | $\because$ Given : Time = Rate |

Then $S.I. = \dfrac{P \times R \times T}{100} \Rightarrow \dfrac{P}{9} = \dfrac{P \times x \times x}{100} \Rightarrow x^2 = \dfrac{100 \times P}{9 \times P} = \dfrac{100}{9}$

$\Rightarrow \qquad\qquad x = \sqrt{\dfrac{100}{9}} = \dfrac{10}{3}$.

$\therefore$ Rate % p.a. $= \dfrac{10}{3}\% = 3\dfrac{1}{3}\%$.

Ex. 10. *A and B borrowed Rs 3500 and Rs 4000 respectively at the same rate of interest for $2\dfrac{1}{2}$ years. If B paid Rs 150 more than A, find the rate of interest.*

Sol.

A	**B**
P = Rs 3500, $T = \dfrac{5}{2}$ years, $R = r\%$ p.a.	P = Rs 4000, $T = \dfrac{5}{2}$ years, $R = r\%$ p.a.
$S.I. = \dfrac{P \times R \times T}{100} = \dfrac{3500 \times 5 \times r}{2 \times 100}$	$S.I. = \dfrac{P \times R \times T}{100} = \dfrac{4000 \times 5 \times r}{2 \times 100}$
$= \text{Rs } \dfrac{175r}{2}$	$= \text{Rs } 100\,r$

Given : B paid Rs 150 more interest than A $\Rightarrow$ S.I. for B $-$ S.I. for A = Rs 150

$\Rightarrow 100\,r - \dfrac{175}{2}r = 150 \Rightarrow \dfrac{200r - 175r}{2} = 150$

$\Rightarrow \dfrac{25r}{2} = 180 \Rightarrow r = \dfrac{150 \times 2}{25} = 12\%$.

$\therefore$ Required rate = **12% p.a.**

Ex. 11. *Divide Rs 6600 into two parts so that the S.I. on the first part for 5 years at 6% per annum is equal to the S.I. on the second part for 3 years at 12% per annum.*

Sol. Let the two parts be Rs x and Rs $(6600 - x)$

For 1ˢᵗ part	For 2ⁿᵈ part
P = Rs x, R = 6% p.a., T = 5 years	P = Rs $(6600 - x)$, R = 12% p.a., T = 3 years
$S.I. = \dfrac{P \times R \times T}{100} = \text{Rs } \dfrac{x \times 6 \times 5}{100}$	$S.I. = \dfrac{P \times R \times T}{100} = \text{Rs } \dfrac{(6600 - x) \times 12 \times 3}{100}$
$= \text{Rs } \dfrac{30x}{100} = \text{Rs } \dfrac{3x}{10}$	$= \text{Rs } \dfrac{36(6600 - x)}{100}$

Given : The interests for the first part and second part are equal.

$$\therefore \quad \frac{3x}{10} = \frac{36(6600-x)}{100} \Rightarrow (6600-x) = \frac{3x \times 100}{36 \times 10} = \frac{10x}{12}$$

$$\Rightarrow 6600 = \frac{10x}{12} + x = \frac{10x+12x}{12} = \frac{22x}{12} \Rightarrow x = Rs \frac{6600 \times 12}{22} = Rs\ 3600 \quad \therefore\ 6600-x = 3000.$$

$\therefore$ The two parts are **Rs 3600** and **Rs 3000**.

Ex.12. *A certain sum of money amounts to Rs 1260 in 2 years and to Rs 1350 in 5 years. Find the sum and the rate of interest.*

Sol. $P + (S.I.$ for 5 years$) = Rs\ 1350,\ P + (S.I.$ for 2 years$) = Rs\ 1260$

Subtracting, S.I. for 3 years = Rs 1350 – Rs 1260 = Rs 90

$\therefore$ S.I. for 1 year = Rs $\frac{90}{3}$ = Rs 30, S.I. for 2 years = Rs 30 × 2 = Rs 60

$\therefore \quad P = Rs\ 1260 - Rs\ 60 = Rs\ 1200$

Now, $\quad P = Rs\ 1200,\ T = 2$ years, $S.I. = Rs\ 60$

$\therefore \quad$ Using $S.I. = \frac{P \times R \times T}{100},\ R = \frac{S.I. \times 100}{P \times T}\% = \frac{60 \times 100}{1200 \times 2}\% = \frac{5}{2}\% = \textbf{2.5\%}.$

EXERCISE 11 (a)

1. Find the simple interest and amount when

   (*a*) Principal = Rs 1050, Rate = 12% per annum and Time = $3\frac{1}{2}$ years.

   (*b*) Principal = Rs 860, Rate = $6\frac{3}{4}$% per annum and Time = 18 months.

   (*c*) Principal = Rs 1550, Rate = $3\frac{1}{5}$% per annum and Time = 146 days.

2. Find the simple interest on Rs 6400 at 10% p.a. from March 3, 2005 to July 27, 2005.

3. What sum will produce an interest of Rs 1320 for $2\frac{1}{2}$ years at $5\frac{1}{2}$% rate of interest per annum ?

4. What sum will amount to Rs 9520 at 9% p.a. in 4 years at simple interest ?

5. At what rate of interest will a sum become three times itself in $12\frac{1}{2}$ years?

6. S.I. on a certain sum is $\frac{16}{25}$ of the sum. Find the rate per cent and time, if they are both equal.

7. A certain sum of money lent out at a certain rate of interest per annum doubles itself in 15 years. In how many years will it treble itself.

8. Rahul borrowed a certain sum of money at 12% per annum for 3 years and Ranjana borrowed the same sum at 18% per annum for 6 years. Find the ratio of their amounts.

9. In how many years does a certain sum amount to 3 times the principal at the rate of $16\frac{2}{3}$% ?

10. Rita borrowed Rs 14600 from her friend at 12% per annum. After 2 years, she paid Rs 15304 and a watch to clear off the debt. What is the cost of the watch?

11. If Rs 480 amounts to Rs 640 in 5 years, what will Rs 7035 amount to in $3\frac{1}{2}$ years at the same rate per cent per annum?

12. Divide Rs 8000 into two parts such that the simple interest on one part lent out at 8% per annum for 5 years may be equal to the simple interest of the second part for 8 years at 3% per annum.

13. The simple interest on a certain sum for 5 years at 8% rate of interest p.a. is Rs 272 less than the simple interest on the same sum for 6 years at 12% per annum. Find the sum.

14. The simple interest on a certain sum for 5 years at 8% per annum is Rs 200 less than the simple interest on the same sum for 3 years and 4 months at 18% per annum. Find the sum.

15. A sum of money lent out at simple interest amounts to Rs 2800 in 4 years and to Rs 2200 in one year. Find the sum of money and the rate of interest.

16. A sum of money at simple interest amounts to Rs 2240 in 2 years and Rs 2600 in 5 years. Find the sum and the rate of interest.

COMPOUND INTEREST

11.5 Introduction

You already know how to calculate simple interest, but in normal business circles simple interest is very rarely used. Take for example a man who deposits Rs 1000 in a savings account at an interest rate of 5% per annum. At the end of one year he will get Rs 50 interest on his deposit. However, unless he takes out his Rs 50 in cash, it will be added to his original Rs 1000. Thus, if he leaves his money in his account, in the next year the bank will be paying him interest on his original Rs 1000 plus the Rs 50 interest, *i.e.* Rs 1050. In the third year the interest will once again be added to the new principal of Rs 1050, and so on for as long as the money is left in the account.

This kind of interest is known as **compound interest**. Some banks and other institutions pay interest yearly, others every six or even after every three months.

11.6 Solved Examples

Ex. 1. *Find the compound interest on Rs 8500 for 2 years at 8% per annum.*

Sol. **Step 1 :** Principal for the first year = Rs 8500

Interest for the first year = Rs $\frac{8500 \times 8 \times 1}{100}$ = Rs 680

$$\boxed{S.I. = \frac{P \times R \times T}{100}}$$

∴ Amount at the end of first year = Rs 8500 + Rs 680 = Rs 9180.

Step. 2 : Principal for the second year = Rs 9180

Interest for the second year = Rs $\frac{9180 \times 8 \times 1}{100}$ = Rs 734.40

∴ Amount at the end of second year = Rs 9180 + Rs 734.40 = Rs 9914.40

∴ Compound interest after 2 years = Rs 9914.40 ñ Rs 8500 = **Rs 1414.40.**

Ex. 2. *Find the compound interest when principal = Rs 50000, rate of interest = 10% p.a. and time = 3 years. Find the amount payable at the end of 3 years.*

Sol. **Step 1:** Principal for the first year = Rs 50,000, Rate = 10% p.a.

Interest for the first year = Rs $\frac{50000 \times 10 \times 1}{100}$ = Rs 5000

$$\boxed{S.I. = \frac{P \times R \times T}{100}}$$

∴ Amount at the end of the first year = Rs (50000 + 5000) = Rs 55000

Step. 2 : ∴ Principal for the second year = Rs 55000

Interest for the second year = Rs $\frac{55000 \times 10 \times 1}{100}$ = Rs 5500

∴ Amount at the end of second year = Rs (55000 + 5500) = Rs 60500

Step 3 : Principal for the third year = Rs 60500

∴ Interest for the third year = Rs $\dfrac{60500 \times 10 \times 1}{100}$ = Rs 6050

Amount payable at the end of third year = Rs (60500 + 6050) = **Rs 66550**.

∴ Compound Interest = Rs 66550 – Rs 50000 = **Rs 16550.**

EXERCISE 11 (b)

Find the compound interest on the following :

Principal	Rate % p.a.	Number of years		Principal	Rate % p.a.	Number of years
1. Rs 10000	12%	2		**4.** Rs 2000	20%	2
2. Rs 5000	10%	2		**5.** Rs 8000	15%	3
3. Rs 625	16%	2				

6. Find the amount and compound interest on a sum of Rs 15625 at 4% per annum for 3 years compounded annually.

7. To renovate his shop, Anurag obtained a loan of Rs 8000 from a bank. If the rate of interest at 5% per annum is compounded annually, calculate the compound interest that Anurag will have to pay after 3 years.

8. Maria invests Rs 93750 at 9.6% per annum for 3 years and the interest is compound annually, calculate

   (*a*) the amount standing to her credit at the end of the second year,

   (*b*) the interest for the 3rd year.

9. A sum of Rs 9,600 is invested for 3 years at 10% p.a. compound interest

   (*a*) What is the sum due at the end of the first year?   (*b*) What is the sum due at the end of the second year?

   (*c*) Find the compound interest earned in the first 2 years. (*d*) Find the amount at the end of 3 years?

10. Shankar takes a loan of Rs 10,000 at a compound interest rate of 10% per annum p.a.

   (*a*) Find the amount after one year

   (*b*) Find the compound interest for 2 years.

   (*c*) Find the sum of money required to clear the debt at the end of 2 years.

   (*d*) Find the difference between the compound interest and the simple interest at the same rate for 2 years.

LOOKING BACK
A Summary of Key Points

Let Principal = Rs *P*, Rate p.a.. = *R*%, Time = *T* years, Amount = *A* and Simple Interest = *S.I.*, then

1. $S.I. = \dfrac{P \times R \times T}{100}$ **2.** $P = \dfrac{S.I. \times 100}{R \times T}$,   **3.** $R = \dfrac{S.I. \times 100}{P \times T}$

4. $T = \dfrac{S.I. \times 100}{P \times R}$ **5.** $A = S.I. + P$ **6.** $A = P + \dfrac{P \times R \times T}{100}$

7. (*a*) Time in months is changed to years by dividing it by 12.

   (*b*) Time in days is changed to years by dividing it by 365.

   (*c*) In calculating the time, the day on which money is borrowed is not included and the day on which money is paid back is included.

8. Compound interest is calculated by taking the amount at the end of previous year as the principal for the next year.

MENTAL MATHS – 9

1. Find the *S.I.* on Rs 900 at 5% for 1 year
2. Find the *S.I.* on Rs 600 at 6% p.a. for 2 years.
3. Find the *S.I.* on Rs 1000 at 2% for 6 months
4. At what rate will a sum of money double itself in 20 years.
5. In what time shall Rs 500 amount to Rs 700 at 8% S.I. p.a.
6. Find the sum which yields a *S.I.* of Rs 240 at 12% p.a. in 5 years.

ANSWERS

EXERCISE 11 (a)

1. (*a*) Rs 441; Rs 1491   (*b*) Rs 87.075; Rs 947.075   (*c*) Rs 19.84; Rs 1569.84   2. Rs 256

3. Rs 9600   4. Rs 7000   5. 16% p.a.   6. 8% p.a., 8 years $\left(\textbf{Hint}: T = \dfrac{\frac{16}{25}P \times 100}{P \times T} \Rightarrow T^2 = 64 \Rightarrow T = 8\right)$

7. 30 years   8. 17 : 26   9. 12 years   10. Rs 2800   11. Rs 8676.50   12. Rs 3000, Rs 5000
13. Rs 850   14. Rs 1000   15. Rs 2000, 10%   16. Rs 2000, 6%

EXERCISE 11 (b)

1. Rs 2,544   2. Rs 1,050   3. Rs 216   4. Rs 880   5. Rs 4,167   6. Rs 17576; Rs 1951
7. Rs 1261   8. (*a*) Rs 112614   (*b*) Rs 10810.94   9. (*a*) Rs 10,560   (*b*) Rs 11,616   (*c*) Rs 2016
(*d*) Rs 12,777.60   10. (*a*) Rs 11000   (*b*) Rs 2100   (*c*) Rs 12100   (*d*) Rs 100.

MENTAL MATHS – 9

1. Rs 45   2. Rs 72   3. Rs 10   4. 5% p.a.   5. 5 years   6. Rs 400

ENRICHMENT
NAMES OF LARGE NUMBERS
(INDIAN NOMENCLATURE)

At the time of Mahabharata, the following number system was used :

Lakh = 10^5 : Ten Lakh = 10^6 Crore = 10^7 : Ten Crore = 10^8
Arab = 10^9 : Ten Arabs = 10^{10} Khrab = 10^{11} : Ten Khrab = 10^{12}
Neel = 10^{13} : Ten Neels = 10^{14} Padma = 10^{15} : Ten Padams = 10^{16}
Shankh = 10^{17} : Ten Shankhs = 10^{18}

Mahashankh = 10^{19}

There must have been a good reason that the ancients stopped at Mahashankh, as there is no mention of Ten Mahashanks. Is it that Mahashankh was the largest number that man ever encountered at that time? Incidentally chess has 64 squares, and 2^{64} is approximately equal to 1.845 Mahashankhs, *i.e.* 1.845×10^{19} or 1845×10^{16}. There are numbers still greater than 1845×10^{16}, namely "googol" and "googolplex", which are nowadays used in Physics and Astronomy. A "googol" is 10 raised to the 100th power or 1 followed by 100 zeros. A "googolplex" is 10 raised to the power of a googol or 1 followed by googol zeros $10^{10^{100}}$

Recently our politicians have started talking in terms of Arabs or Billions only. So far they were talking in terms of millions only. In the West not long ago the people had no need to count beyond a million (10^6) or a billion (10^9). Trillion (10^{12}) is comparatively a recent origin. Previously we talked of very wealthy people who were billionaires. Now, we have started talking of trillionaries. Centillion is 1 followed by 600 zeros.

12. Unitary Method and its Applications

12.1 Unitary Method

The method wherein we find the value of a given quantity by first finding the value of a unit quantity is called unitary method.

While solving problems based on unitary method, we come across two types of variations:

(*i*) Direct Variation   (*ii*) Inverse Variation

12.2 Direct Variation

When an increase (or decrease) in one quantity causes an increase (or decrease) in the other quantity, it is a case of direct variation.

Ex. 1. *26 iron rods of the same size weigh 312 kg. What will be weight of 42 such iron rods?*

Sol. ∵ The weight of 26 iron rods = 312 kg.

∴ The weight of 1 iron rod = $\dfrac{312}{26}$ kg

∴ The weight of 42 iron rods = $\left(\dfrac{312}{26} \times 42\right)$ = (12×42) kg = **504 kg.**

12.3 Inverse Variation

When an increase (or decrease) in one quantity causes a decrease (or) an increase in the other, then the two quantities vary inversely.

Ex. 2. *120 men had food provision for 210 days. After 10 days 40 men died due to an epidemic. How long will the remaining food last?*

Sol. After 10 days 40 men died   ∴   The remaining food is sufficient for 200 days for 120 men.

We have to find how long the remaining food will last for 80 men.

For 120 men, the food is sufficient for 200 days

∴ For 1 man, the food lasts (200×120) days   (less men, more days)

∴ For 80 men, the food lasts for $\dfrac{200 \times 120}{80}$ = **300 days**   (more men, less days)

12.4 Compound Variation

There are many problems involving more than one variation in which more than two different types of quantities are used.

Ex. 3. *15 chests of tea, each chest containing 20 kg cost Rs 350. What will be the price at this rate of 12 chests each containing 25 kg.*

Sol. 15 chests each containing 20 kg cost Rs 350.

∴   1 chest containing 20kg costs Rs $\frac{350}{15}$ (less no. of chests, less cost)

∴   1 chest containing 1 kg costs Rs $\left(\frac{350}{15 \times 20}\right)$ (less quantity, less cost)

∴   12 chests containing 1 kg cost Rs $\left(\frac{350}{15 \times 20} \times 12\right)$ (more no. of chests, more cost)

multiplication

∴   12 chests containing 25 kg cost Rs $= \left(\frac{350 \times 12 \times 25}{15 \times 20}\right) = $ **Rs 350**.   (more quantity, more cost)

Ex. 4. *25 horses eat 5 bags of corn in 12 days, how much will 10 horses eat in 18 days?*

Sol. In 12 days 25 horses eat 5 bags of corn

∴   In 1 day 25 horses eat $\frac{5}{12}$ bags of corn   (less days, less corn)

Division

In 1 day 1 horse eats $\frac{5}{12 \times 25}$ bags of corn   (less no. of horses, less corn)

In 1 day 10 horses will eat $\frac{5}{12 \times 25} \times 10$ bags.   (more horses, more corn)

In 18 days 10 horses will eat $\frac{5 \times 10 \times 18}{12 \times 25}$ bags of corn = **3 bags**.   (more days, more corn)

EXERCISE 12 (a)

1. If a man working for 56 hours earns Rs 1876, how much will he earn working for 27 hours ?

2. The interest on Rs 900 is Rs 45. What is the interest on Rs 1870 ?

3. How many days would it take 59 men to build a wall which 118 men can build in 3 weeks ?

4. Ram has enough money to buy 75 machines worth Rs 200 each. How many machines can he buy if he gets a discount of Rs 50 on each machine ?

5. 4 men can make 4 cupboards in 4 days ; how many cupboards can 14 men make in 14 days ?

6. In a hostel it costs Rs 1800 to keep 50 children for 8 weeks. For what length of time did the cost of keeping 90 children amount to Rs 21060 ?

7. In how many days of working 8 hours each day, can 12 men do the same work as 10 men working 9 hours a day do in 16 days?

8. If 10 men, working 7 hours a day dig a trench 147 m long, how many men working 8 hours a day will dig a trench 168 m long (of the same breadth and depth as the first in the same number of days)?

9. Three pumps working 8 hours a day can empty a tank in 2 days. How many hours a day must 4 pumps work to empty the tank in 1 day ?

10. If a man travels 65 km in 3 days by walking $7\frac{1}{2}$ hours a day, in how many days will he travel 156 km by walking 8 hours a day?

12.5 Time and Work

While solving problems on time and work, following points should be remembered :

1. A man's 1 day's work $= \dfrac{1}{\text{Total number of days required to finish the work}}$

    i.e., If A can complete a work in 12 days, then in 1 day he does $\frac{1}{12}$ of the work.

2. Total number of days to finish a work $= \dfrac{1}{\text{One day's work}}$

   i.e. If A can complete $\dfrac{1}{6}$ of a work in 1 day, then

   the total number of days required to complete the work $= \dfrac{1}{\frac{1}{6}} = 6$ days.

3. No. of days required to complete a work $= \dfrac{\text{Work to be completed}}{\text{One day's work}}$.

Ex. 1. *A can do a piece of work in 15 days and B can do it in 30 days. If both of them work at it together, in how many days will they be able to finish the work ?*

Sol. In 1 day A can do $\dfrac{1}{15}$ of the work. In 1 day B can do $\dfrac{1}{30}$ of the work

∴ In 1 day A and B can together do $\left(\dfrac{1}{15} + \dfrac{1}{30}\right)$; i.e., $\dfrac{2+1}{30} = \dfrac{3}{30}$ of the work

∴ A and B together can complete the work in $\left(1 \div \dfrac{3}{30}\right) = \dfrac{30}{3} = \textbf{10 days.}$

Ex. 2. *A can do a piece of work in 12 days, which A and B working together can do in 8 days. How long will B take working alone ?*

Sol. $(A + B)$'s 1 day's work $= \dfrac{1}{8}$, A's 1 day's work $= \dfrac{1}{12}$

∴ B's 1 day work $= (A + B)$'s 1 day's work $-$ A's 1 day's work $= \left(\dfrac{1}{8} - \dfrac{1}{12}\right) = \dfrac{3-2}{24} = \dfrac{1}{24}$

∴ B working alone will finish the work in **24 days**.

Ex. 3. *A can do $\dfrac{1}{6}$ of the work in 3 hours while B can do $\dfrac{1}{4}$ of the work in 9 hours. In how many days can both do it together?*

Sol. Since A can complete $\dfrac{1}{6}$ of the work in 3 hours

∴ To complete the work A takes $\left(3 \times \dfrac{6}{1}\right)$ hours $= 18$ hours

Since B can complete $\dfrac{1}{4}$ of the work in 9 hours

∴ To complete the work B takes $\left(9 \times \dfrac{4}{1}\right)$ hours $= 36$ hours

∴ A's 1 day's work $= \dfrac{1}{18}$, B's 1 day's work $= \dfrac{1}{36}$

$(A + B)$'s 1 day's work $= \dfrac{1}{18} + \dfrac{1}{36} = \dfrac{2+1}{36} = \dfrac{3}{36} = \dfrac{1}{12}$

∴ A and B together can complete the work in **12 hours**.

Ex. 4. *A can do a piece of work in 20 days and B in 25 days. They work together for 10 days and then A goes away. In how many days will B finish the remaining work ?*

Sol. A's 1 day's work = $\frac{1}{20}$, B's 1 day's work = $\frac{1}{25}$

(A and B)'s 1 day's work = $\frac{1}{20} + \frac{1}{25} = \frac{5+4}{100} = \frac{9}{100}$

$\therefore$ Working together for 10 days they complete = $10 \times \frac{9}{100} = \frac{9}{10}$ of the work.

Work remaining = $1 - \frac{9}{10} = \frac{1}{10}$. $\because$ B can complete this work in 25 days.

$\therefore$ B can complete the remaining portion in $\frac{1}{10} \times 25$ days = $2\frac{1}{2}$ **days.**

Ex. 5. *A and B can do a piece of work in 10 days, B and C can do it in 15 days and A and C together can do it in 12 days. How long will they take to do it together and each separately?*

Sol. (A + B)'s 1 day's work = $\frac{1}{10}$, (B + C)'s 1 day's work = $\frac{1}{15}$, (A + C)'s 1 day's work = $\frac{1}{12}$

Adding, we get, 2(A + B + C)'s 1 day's work = $\frac{1}{10} + \frac{1}{15} + \frac{1}{12} = \frac{6+4+5}{60} = \frac{15}{60}$

$\therefore$ (A + B + C)'s 1 day's work = $\frac{1}{2} \times \frac{15}{60} = \frac{1}{8}$

$\therefore$ Together A, B and C can finish the work in 8 days.

A's 1 day's work = (A + B + C)'s 1 day's work – (B + C)'s 1 day's work

$$= \frac{1}{8} - \frac{1}{15} = \frac{15-8}{120} = \frac{7}{120}$$

$\therefore$ A alone takes $\frac{120}{7}$ days to complete the work.

B's 1 day's work = (A + B + C)'s 1 day's work – (A + C)'s 1 day's work

$$= \frac{1}{8} - \frac{1}{12} = \frac{3-2}{24} = \frac{1}{24}$$

$\therefore$ B alone takes **24 days** to complete the work.

C's 1 day's work = (A + B + C)'s 1 day's work – (A + B)'s 1 day's work

$$= \frac{1}{8} - \frac{1}{10} = \frac{5-4}{40} = \frac{1}{40}$$

$\therefore$ C alone takes **40 days** to complete the work.

Ex. 6. *Vinod, Aslam and Karim can weave a carpet in 12 days, 15 days and 20 days respectively. If all the three work at it together and they are paid Rs 2640 for the whole work, how should the money be divided among them?*

Sol. Vinod's 1 day's work = $\frac{1}{12}$, Aslam's 1 day's work = $\frac{1}{15}$, Karim's 1 day's work = $\frac{1}{20}$

$\therefore$ Ratio of shares of Vinod, Aslam and Karim = Ratio of their 1 day's work

$= \frac{1}{12} : \frac{1}{15} : \frac{1}{20} = \frac{1}{12} \times 60 : \frac{1}{15} \times 60 : \frac{1}{20} \times 60 = 5 : 4 : 3$
    | Taking L.C.M. 12, 15, 20 |

$\therefore$ Sum of the ratios = 5 + 4 + 3 = 12
    | Multiplying each term of the ratio by the LCM of 12, 15, 16, i.e. 60 |

$\therefore$ Vinod's share = Rs $\left(2640 \times \frac{5}{12}\right)$ = **Rs 1100**

$$\text{Aslam's share} = \text{Rs}\left(2640\times\frac{4}{12}\right) = \textbf{Rs 880}, \text{Karim's share} = \text{Rs}\left(2640\times\frac{3}{12}\right) = \textbf{Rs 660}.$$

Ex. 7. _A and B together can complete a work in 15 days. If A is three times as good a workman as B, in how many days will A alone finish the work?_

Sol. ∵ A is three times as good workman as B.

A's one day work = B's 3 day's work ⇒ B's one day work = A's $\frac{1}{3}$ day's work

Given (A + B)'s 1 day's work = $\frac{1}{15}$ ⇒ A's 1 day's work + B's 1 day's work = $\frac{1}{15}$

⇒ A's 1 day's work + A's $\frac{1}{3}$ day's work = $\frac{1}{15}$

∴ A's $\left(1+\frac{1}{3}\right)$ day's work = $\frac{1}{15}$ _i.e._ A's $\frac{4}{3}$ day's work = $\frac{1}{15}$

∴ A's 1 day's work = $\frac{1}{15}\times\frac{3}{4}=\frac{1}{20}$ ∴ A alone can complete the work in **20 days.**

Ex. 8. _P can copy 80 pages in 20 hours, P and Q together can copy 135 pages in 27 hours. In what time can Q copy 48 pages?_

Sol. In 20 hours P can copy 80 pages   ∴ In 1 hour P can copy $\frac{80}{20}$ pages

In 27 hours (P + Q) can copy 135 pages.   ∴ In 1 hour (P + Q) can copy $\frac{135}{27}$ pages

⇒ In 1 hour Q can copy $\frac{135}{27}-\frac{80}{20}$ pages = $\frac{2700-2160}{540}=\frac{540}{540}=1$ page

∴ Q can copy 48 pages in **48 hours.**

Ex.9. _Working alone, A, B and C can do a piece of work in 11 days, 20 days and 55 days respectively. How soon can the work be done if A is assisted by B and C on alternate days ?_

Sol. A's 1 day's work = $\frac{1}{11}$, B's 1 day's work = $\frac{1}{20}$, C's 1 day's work = $\frac{1}{55}$

Since B and C assist A on alternate days

∴ Work done in 2 days = $\frac{1}{11}\times2+\frac{1}{20}\times1+\frac{1}{55}\times1=\frac{40+11+4}{220}=\frac{55}{220}=\frac{1}{4}$

⇒ $\frac{1}{4}$ of the work is done in 2 days   ∴ Complete work is done in $2\times\frac{4}{1}$ days = **8 days.**

12.6 Pipes and Cisterns

A cistern or a water tank is connected with two types of pipes -

(_i_) **Inlet** - A pipe that fills the cistern or water tank.

(_ii_) **Outlet**- A pipe that empties the cistern or water tank.

Points to Remember

1. _If an inlet fills up a cistern in n hours, then in 1 hour it will fill up $\frac{1}{n}$th part of the cistern._

2. _If an outlet empties a full cistern in m hours, then in 1 hour it will empty $\frac{1}{m}$th part of the cistern._

3. _The work done by an inlet is always **positive** whereas the work done by the outlet is always **negative**._

Ex.10. *One tap fills a tank in 12 minutes and the other in 15 minutes. The outlet can empty the tank in 10 minutes. In what time will the tank be filled if both the taps are turned on and the outlet has been left open accidentally.*

Sol. Tank filled by first tap in 1 min. $= \dfrac{1}{12}$; Tank filled by second tap in 1 min. $= \dfrac{1}{15}$;

Tank emptied by outlet in 1 min. $= \dfrac{1}{10}$

∴ Tank filled in 1 min. when both the taps and the outlet are open $= \dfrac{1}{12} + \dfrac{1}{15} - \dfrac{1}{10} = \dfrac{5+4-6}{60} = \dfrac{3}{60} = \dfrac{1}{20}$

∴ $\dfrac{1}{20}$ of the tank in filled in 1 min.   ∴ The tank will be full in **20 min.**

Ex. 11. *An outlet pipe can empty $\dfrac{5}{6}$ of the cistern in 20 minutes. In 9 minutes what part of the cistern will be emptied?*

Sol. In 20 minutes $\dfrac{5}{6}$ of the cistern is emptied,

∴ In 1 minute $\dfrac{5}{6} \times \dfrac{1}{20} = \dfrac{1}{24}$ of the cistern will be emptied,

∴ In 9 minutes $\dfrac{1}{24} \times 9 = \dfrac{3}{8}$ of the cistern will be emptied.

EXERCISE 12 (b)

1. A can do a piece of work in 30 days and B can do it in 6 days. How long will A and B take to do the work working together?

2. Two taps, running together can fill a bath in 4 minutes., which is filled by one of the taps by itself in 7 minutes. How long would it take, if the other pipe is running by itself ?

3. A and B can polish the floors of a building in 12 days. A alone can do $\dfrac{1}{5}$ of this job in 4 days. In how many days can B alone polish the floors ?

4. A can do $\dfrac{3}{4}$ of the work in 12 days. In how many days can he finish $\dfrac{1}{8}$ th of the work?

5. Asha and Reema can weave a certain number of baskets in 25 days and 30 days respectively. They work together for 5 days and then Asha leaves. In how many days will Reema finish the rest of the work?

6. A, B and C working together, take 30 min. to address a pile of envelopes. A and B together would take 40 min; A and C together would take 45 min. How long would each take working alone?

7. A and B can do a piece of work together in 15 days. They both start but after 6 days B falls ill and A takes 30 more days to finish the work by himself. How long will each take working alone?

8. A and B can do a piece of work in 6 days and 4 days respectively. A started the work; worked at it for 2 days and then was joined by B. Find the total time taken to complete the work.

9. Rs 720 are paid for a task which A can do in 3 days. B in 4 days and C in 6 days. If all work together, how much money should each receive ?

10. X works twice as fast as Y. If Y alone can complete a job in 18 days, find how many days will X and Y together take to complete the job.

11. A can do a job in 20 days, B in 30 days and C in 60 days. If A is helped by B and C on every third day, then in how many days will the job be finished ?

12. A can copy 150 pages in 30 hours, A and B together can copy 280 pages in 35 hours. In what time would B copy 200 pages?

13. A tap can fill a cistern in 25 minutes. and another can empty it in 50 minutes. Find in how many minutes the tank will be filled up?

14. Two taps can fill a cistern in 8 hours and 10 hours respectively. A third tap can empty it in 6 hours. How long will they take to fill the cistern if all the taps are opened?

15. A cistern can be filled by 3 taps A, B and C when turned on separately in 24 min, 10 min and 30 min. respectively. If all are turned on together for $2\frac{2}{3}$ minutes and if B and C are then turned off, how much time will A alone take to fill the cistern?

LOOKING BACK
Summary of Key Facts

1. If a person can finish a piece of work in n days, then the work done by the person in 1 day is $\frac{1}{n}$ th part of the work.

2. If a person completes $\frac{1}{n}$ th part of a work in 1 day, then the time taken by the person to finish the work is n days.

3. A cistern is filled with two pipes, one pipe to fill it, which is called an inlet and the other pipe to empty it, which is called an outlet.

4. If an inlet fills a tank in n hours, then it will fill $\frac{1}{n}$ th part of the tank in 1 hour, *i.e.*, the work done by it in 1 hour is $\frac{1}{n}$.

5. If an outlet empties a full tank in m hours, then it will empty $\frac{1}{m}$ th part of the tank in 1 hour, i.e; the work done by it in 1 hour is $-\frac{1}{m}$.

MENTAL MATHS – 10

1. The cost of 16 balls is Rs 144. What is the cost of 30 such balls?

2. Rakhi can complete a work in 10 days and Rekha in 5 days. How much time will both take to complete the work?

3. 7 men can complete a work in 28 days. In how many days will 14 men do the same work?

4. Rajat can complete a work in 24 days. How much work will he complete in 8 days?

5. A car covers a certain distance in 4 hrs if it moves at the rate of 70 km/hr. How much time will it take to cover the same distance at a rate of 56 km/hr?

ANSWERS

EXERCISE 12 (a)

1. Rs 904.50   2. Rs 93.50   3. 6 weeks   4. 100 machines   5. 49 cupboards   6. 52 weeks

7. 15 days   8. 10 men   9. 12 hours   10. $6\frac{3}{4}$ days.

EXERCISE 12 (b)

1. 5 days   2. 9 min. 20 seconds   3. 30 days   4. 2 days   5. 19 days

6. A → 72 mins. B → 90 mins. C → 2 hours

7. A → 50 days; B → $21\frac{3}{7}$ days

8. $3\frac{3}{5}$ days

9. A → Rs 320, B → Rs 240, C → Rs160

10. 6 days

11. 15 days (**Hint :** Type solved Ex. 10. Here work done in 3 days = $\frac{1}{20}\times3+\frac{1}{30}\times1+\frac{1}{60}+1$)

12. $66\frac{2}{3}$ hours (**Hint :** Type solved Ex. 9)

13. 50 mins.

14. $17\frac{1}{7}$ hours

15. 12 min. 48 seconds

[**Hint :** Work done by A, B, C is $2\frac{2}{3}$, *i.e.*, $\frac{8}{3}$ min. $=\frac{8}{3}\left(\frac{1}{24}+\frac{1}{10}+\frac{1}{30}\right)=\frac{7}{15}$

Remaining part $=\left(1-\frac{7}{15}\right)=\frac{8}{15}$

Now $\frac{1}{24}$ th part is filled by A is 1 min. So $\frac{8}{15}$ part will be filled in $\left(\frac{8}{15}\times\frac{24}{1}\right)$ min]

MENTAL MATHS – 10

1. Rs 270

2. $3\frac{1}{3}$ days

3. 14 days

4. $\frac{1}{3}$ of the work

5. 5 hours

NUMBER FACTS

1. **The number 1000.** *M* is an abbreviation for the Roman word mille, meaning a thousand. It, stood for 1000 in Roman numeration system. We have entered new millenium. A **millenium** is 1000 years and a millipede has 1000 legs as imagined by persons who named it so. A distance of one mile was originally 1000 paces. The Romans counted one pace as two steps.

   These days the letter *K* is used for 1000.

2. **A prefix** is a word element you add on in front of a word to change its meaning. A prefix makes the differences between a **kilometre** and a **centimetre** since **kilo** means **(thousand)** and **centi** means **1 hundredth.**

   Prefixes given in the table can be used to build words to have very large and very small measurements.

   The following facts will give you an idea of very large and very small numbers.

LARGE MEASUREMENTS		
tera	**giga**	**mega**
1 trillion	1 billion	1 million
SMALL MEASUREMENTS		
micro	**nano**	**pico**
1 millionth	1 billionth	1 trillionth

   1. A large power plant generates 300 megawatts of electricity. It is 30 crore watts (300,000,000 watts).

   2. The nucleus of an atom is less than one picometre wide. (it means less than one trillionth)

   $$10^{-12}\text{ metre} = \frac{1}{1,000,000,000,000}\text{ metre}$$

   3. Pluto orbits at a distance of almost 6 terametres from the sun. It is equal to 6 trillion $\left(6\times10^{12}\right)$ metres.

   4. Light can travel 30 cm in one nano second, *i.e*, one billionth

   $$10^{-9}\text{ second} = \frac{1}{1,000,000,000}\text{ second}$$

   5. All the power plants in a developed country can generate 560 gigawatts (= 560 billion watts).

   6. The speed of advanced computers is calculated in picoseconds *i.e*, Trillionths of a second.

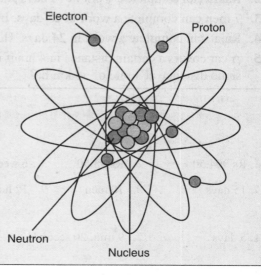

Electron

Proton

Neutron

Nucleus

13. Time and Distance

13.1 Speed

The speed of a moving object is the distance covered by it in unit time.

$$\text{Speed} = \frac{\text{distance travelled}}{\text{time taken}}$$

e.g. if we say that a man walks 10 km in 2 hrs. then his speed $= \frac{10}{2}$ km/hr $= 5$ km/hr.

$$\text{Average Speed} = \frac{\text{Total distance covered}}{\text{Total time taken}}$$

$$1 \text{ km/hr} = 1000 \times \frac{1}{60} \times \frac{1}{60} = \frac{\mathbf{5}}{\mathbf{18}} \text{ m/sec.} \quad e.g. \text{ to convert 36 km/hr to m/sec., we multiply by } \frac{5}{18}$$

$$36 \text{ km/hr} = \left(36 \times \frac{5}{18}\right) \text{ m/sec.} = \mathbf{10 \text{ m/sec.}}$$

$$1 \text{ m/sec.} = 1000 \times \frac{1}{60} \times \frac{1}{60} = \frac{\mathbf{18}}{\mathbf{5}} \text{ km/hr.} \quad e.g. \text{ to convert 40 m/sec. to km/hr, we multiply by } \frac{18}{5}$$

$$40 \text{ m/sec.} = \left(40 \times \frac{18}{5}\right) \text{ km/hr} = \mathbf{144 \text{ km/hr.}}$$

13.2 Problems on Trains

Note that

(*i*) While passing a stationary object like a signal post or a telegraph pole or a standing man, **a train travels a distance equal to its length**.

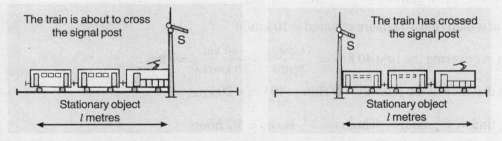

In crossing the lamp-post the train has travelled a distance equal to its length, *i.e.*, $= l$.

(*ii*) While passing a stationary object like a bridge or a tunnel or a platform, **a train travels a distance equal to the sum of its length and the object which it crosses.**

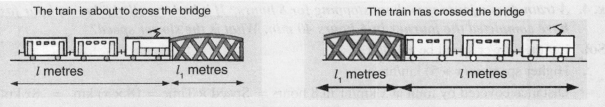

In crossing the bridge the train travels a distance equal to the sum of the lengths of the train and the bridge, *i.e.*, $= l + l_1$.

13.3 Solved Examples

Ex. 1. *A man walks 14.4 km in 4 hours. Calculate the speed of the man in km/hr as well as m/sec. Also, find how much distance will be covered by him in 6 hours.*

Sol. Distance Covered = 14.4 km, Time taken = 4 hours

$$\therefore \qquad \text{Speed} = \frac{\text{Distance}}{\text{Time}} = \frac{14.4\,\text{km}}{4\,\text{hr}} = 3.6 \text{ km/hr}$$

$$= \left(3.6 \times \frac{5}{18}\right) \text{m/sec} = 1 \text{ m/sec.}$$

> To convert km/hr to m/sec, multiply by 5/18

$\therefore$ Distance covered in 6 hours = speed × time = (3.6 km/hr) × 6 hours = **21.6 km.**

Ex. 2. *A car covers a distance of 80 km at a speed of 60 km/hr and another 140 km at a speed of 70 km/hr. Find the average speed of the car for the whole journey.*

Sol. Time taken to cover 80 km at 60 km/hr = $\dfrac{\text{Distance}}{\text{Speed}} = \left(\dfrac{80}{60}\right)\text{hrs} = \dfrac{4}{3}$ hrs

Time taken to cover 140 km at 70 km/hr = $\dfrac{\text{Distance}}{\text{Speed}} = \left(\dfrac{140}{70}\right)$ hrs = 2 hrs.

Total distance travelled = 80 km + 140 km = 220 km.

Total time taken for the whole journey = $\dfrac{4}{3}$ hrs + 2 hrs = $\dfrac{10}{3}$ hrs.

$\therefore$ Average speed = $\dfrac{\text{Total distance travelled}}{\text{Total time taken}} = \dfrac{220 \text{ km}}{\dfrac{10}{3}\text{ hrs}} = \left(\dfrac{220 \times 3}{10}\right)$ km/hr = **66 km/hr.**

Ex.3. *A cyclist covers a distance of 60 km in $6\dfrac{1}{2}$ hours. If he covers the first two third of the journey at 10 km/hr, find the speed of the cyclist for the rest of the journey.*

Sol. Total distance travelled by the cyclist = 60 km.

Distance of two - third journey = $\dfrac{2}{3} \times 60$ km. = 40 km.

The speed at which first 40 km are covered = 10 km/hr

$\therefore$ Time taken in covering the first 40 km = $\dfrac{\text{Distance}}{\text{Speed}} = \dfrac{40 \text{ km}}{10 \text{ km/hr}} = 4$ hr.

Remaining distance of the journey = 60 km − 40 km = 20 km.

Remaining time = $6\dfrac{1}{2}$ hours − 4 hours = $2\dfrac{1}{2}$ hours = 5/2 hours

$\therefore$ Speed for the rest of the journey = $\dfrac{\text{Distance}}{\text{Time}} = \dfrac{20 \text{ km}}{5/2 \text{ hours}} = $ **8 km/hr**

$\therefore$ Speed of the cyclist for the rest of the journey is **8 km/hr.**

Ex. 4. *A train does a journey without stopping for 8 hours. If it had travelled 5 km an hour faster, it would have completed the journey in 6 hours 40 min. What is the slower speed?*

Sol. Let the slower speed be x km/hr.

$\therefore$ Higher speed = $(x + 5)$ km/hr.

Distance covered by train at x km/hr in 8 hours = Speed × Time = $(8 \times x)$ km. = $8x$ km.

Distance covered by train at $(x + 5)$ km/hr in 6 hours 40 min. $\left(= 6\dfrac{40}{60} \text{ hours} = \dfrac{20}{3} \text{ hours} \right)$

$$= \text{Speed} \times \text{time} = \left((x+5) \times \dfrac{20}{3} \right) \text{km.} = \left(\dfrac{20x}{3} + \dfrac{100}{3} \right) \text{km.}$$

But both the distances are same $\therefore \ \dfrac{20x}{3} + \dfrac{100}{3} = 8x$

$\Rightarrow$ $\qquad 8x - \dfrac{20x}{3} = \dfrac{100}{3} \Rightarrow \dfrac{24x - 20x}{3} = \dfrac{100}{3} \Rightarrow 4x = 100 \Rightarrow x = \mathbf{25}$

$\therefore$ The slower speed is **25 km/hr.**

Ex. 5. *If a person walks from his house at a speed of 4 km/hr, he misses the train by 9 minutes. If he walks at a speed of 6 km/hr, he reaches the station 6 minutes before the departure of the train. What is the distance between his house and station?*

Sol. Let x km be the distance between his house and the station.

At a speed of 4 km/hr, time taken to cover a distance of x km $= \dfrac{\text{Distance}}{\text{Speed}} = \dfrac{x \text{ km}}{4 \text{ km/hr}} = \dfrac{x}{4}$ hours.

At a speed of 6 km/hr. the time taken to cover x km $= \dfrac{\text{Distance}}{\text{Speed}} = \dfrac{x \text{ km}}{6 \text{ km/hr}} = \dfrac{x}{6}$ hrs.

Difference in time taken $= \left(\dfrac{x}{4} - \dfrac{x}{6} \right)$ hours $= \left(\dfrac{3x - 2x}{12} \right)$ hours $= \dfrac{x}{12}$ hours $= \dfrac{x}{12} \times 60$ min. $= 5x$ min.

Actual difference in time $= (9 + 6)$ min. $= 15$ min.

$\therefore \qquad 5x = 15 \Rightarrow x = 3$

$\therefore$ Distance between his house and station $= \mathbf{3 \ km.}$

Ex. 6. *A car travels at a speed of 40 km/hr over a certain distance and then returns over the same distance at the speed of 60 km/hr. What is the average speed for the whole journey?*

Sol. Let the distance covered be x km.

$\therefore$ Time taken to cover x km at a speed of 40 km/hr $= \dfrac{\text{Distance}}{\text{Speed}} = \dfrac{x \text{ km}}{40 \text{ km/hr}} = \dfrac{x}{40}$ hours

Time taken to cover x km at a speed of 60 km/hr $= \dfrac{\text{Distance}}{\text{Speed}} = \dfrac{x \text{ km}}{60 \text{ km/hr}} = \dfrac{x}{60}$ hours.

$\therefore$ Total time taken $= \left(\dfrac{x}{40} + \dfrac{x}{60} \right)$ hours $= \left(\dfrac{3x + 2x}{120} \right)$ hours $= \dfrac{5x}{120}$ hours $= \dfrac{x}{24}$ hours

Total distance travelled $= x$ km $+ x$ km $= 2x$ km

$\therefore$ Average speed $= \dfrac{\text{Total distance travelled}}{\text{Total time taken}} = \dfrac{2x \text{ km}}{\dfrac{x}{24} \text{ hour}} = \left(\dfrac{2x}{x} \times 24 \right)$ km/hr $= \mathbf{48 \ km/hr.}$

Ex. 7. *Find the time taken by a train 180m long running at 72 km/hr in crossing an electric pole.*

Sol. Speed of the train $= 72$ km/hr $= \left(72 \times \dfrac{5}{18} \right)$ m/sec $= 20$ m/sec.

Distance covered in crossing a pole $=$ length of the train $= 180$ m

$\therefore$ Time taken to cross the electric pole $= \dfrac{\text{Distance}}{\text{Speed}} = \dfrac{180 \text{ m}}{20 \text{ m/sec}} = \mathbf{9 \ sec.}$

Ex.8. *A train is running at a speed of 54 km/hr. If it crosses a tree in 15 sec., find the length of the train.*

Sol. Speed of the train $= 54$ km/hr $= \left(54 \times \dfrac{5}{18}\right)$ m/sec. $= 15$ m/sec.

Time taken by the train to cross the tree $= 15$ sec.

Length of the train $=$ Distance covered by it in the time in which it crosses the tree

$\qquad = $ Speed $\times$ time

$\qquad = 15$ m/sec $\times 15$ sec $= 225$ m

$\therefore$ Length of the train $= $ **225 m.**

Ex. 9. *How much time will a train 181 m long, take to cross a bridge 219 m long, if it is running at a speed of 60km/hr ?*

Sol. Speed of the train $= 60$ km/hr $= 60 \times \dfrac{5}{18}$ m/sec. $= \dfrac{50}{3}$ m/sec.

Distance covered by the train in crossing the bridge

$\qquad = $ Length of the train $+$ length of the bridge

$\qquad = (181 + 219)$ m $= 400$ m

$\therefore$ Time taken to cross the bridge $= \dfrac{\text{Distance covered}}{\text{Speed}} = \dfrac{400\,\text{m}}{\dfrac{50}{3}\,\text{m/s}} = \dfrac{400 \times 3\,\text{sec}}{50} = $ **24 sec.**

Ex.10. *A 175 m long train crosses a 185 m long tunnel in 45 sec. Find speed of the train in km/hr.*

Sol. Length of the train $= 175$ m, Length of the tunnel $= 185$ m.

$\therefore$ Distance covered by train in crossing the tunnel $= 175$ m $+ 185$ m $= 360$ m

Time taken $= 45$ sec.

$\therefore$ Speed of the train $= \dfrac{\text{Distance covered}}{\text{Time taken}} = \dfrac{360\,\text{m}}{45\,\text{sec}} = 8$ m / sec

$\qquad = \left(8 \times \dfrac{18}{5}\right)$ km/hr $= \left(\dfrac{144}{5}\right)$ km/hr $= $ **28.8 km/hr** .

Hence, speed of the train in km/hr $= $ **28.8 km/hr.**

EXERCISE 13 (a)

1. A cyclist is travelling at a speed of 15 km/hr. How much distance will it cover in 1 hour 15 minutes?

2. A man covers 2.5 km in 5 minutes. Find the speed in km/hr.

3. Find the time taken by a boy to run around a rectangular field with length as 25 m and breadth as 15 m, if he runs at a speed of 7.2 km/hr.

(**Hint :** Total distance travelled by the boy $=$ Perimeter of the field.)

4. A boy runs at a speed 2 m/sec and another boy cycles at a speed of 8.5 km/hr. Who is faster?

5. An aeroplane flies from A to B, 1080 km apart, at a speed of 720 km/hr. Another aeroplane flies the same distance in 15 min. less time. At what speed does this plane fly?

6. It takes me 20 min. to go to my friend's farm if I go by car at steady speed of 40 km /hr. How long would it take me to cycle there if I averaged 15 km/hr?

7. A car does a journey without stopping for 7 hours. If it had travelled 10 km/hr faster, it would have completed the journey in 5 hours and 20 minutes. What is the slower speed?

8. A man cycles at 20 km/hr over a certain distance and then returns over the same distance at a speed of 15 km/hr. What is the average speed for the whole journey?

9. A man jogs 190 m in 48 sec and another 250 m in 62 sec. Find his average speed in km/hr.

10. A train covers 108 km in the first two hours, 36 km in the next half an hour and 90 km in the next one and a half hour. Find the average speed of train during the whole journey.

11. A car has to cover a distance of 100 km in 1 hour 50 min. If it travels for the first 36 km at 72 km/hr, at what speed must it travel for the rest of the distance in order to complete the journey in time ?

12. Sanjana goes to school at the rate of 4 km/ hr and reaches 5 min. late. If she goes at the speed of 6 km/hr, she reaches 10 min. earlier. What is the distance of the school from her home?

13. A man can walk at a speed of 6 km/hr and jog at a speed of 10 km/hr. He covered a distance of 9 km in one hour, partly by walking and partly by jogging .Find for how much time he walked and how much distance?

14. A train leaves station A toward station B, 24 km away and has to reach B in half an hour. If it travels at 45 km/hr for the first quarter of an hour, at what speed must it travel for the rest of the journey to complete it in time ?

15. How long will a train 330 m long travelling at 40 km/hr take to cross a platform 110 m long? How long will it take to pass a man sitting on the platform?

16. A 560 m long train travelling at uniform speed takes 1 min and 20 second to pass a telegraph pole. What its speed in km/hr?

17. A 500 m long train took 33 second to pass a bridge 160 m long. Find the speed of the train in km/hr.

18. A train crosses a telegraph post in 8 sec. and a bridge 200 m long in 24 sec. Find the speed of the train.

    (**Hint :** In 8 sec train covers distance = length of train.

    In 24 sec train covers distance = length of train + length of bridge.

    ⇒ In 16 sec distance covered =length of bridge = 200 m. Hence find speed)

19. Normally it takes 3 hours for a train to run from A to B. One day, due to a minor trouble, the train had to reduce the speed by 12 km/hr and so it took $\frac{3}{4}$ th of an hour more than the usual. What is the distance from A to B ?

20. A train running at a speed of 72 km/hr, passes an electric pole in 12 seconds. How much time will it take to cross a tunnel 80 m long ?

13.4 Relative Speeds

1. If two bodies are moving in opposite directions towards each other with speeds u km/hr and v km/hr respectively, then they approach each other or are coming nearer to each other with a speed of $(u + v)$ km/hr. This speed is called the relative speed.

2. If two bodies are moving in the same direction with speeds u km/hr and v km/hr respectively, such that $u > v$ then the faster body approaches the other body with a speed of $(u – v)$ km/hr. Their relative speed is $(u – v)$ km/hr.

3. **Fundamental Idea** The speed of A with u km/hr *relative* to the speed of B with v km/hr is found by making B *stationary* by giving it a speed of v km/hr in the direction opposite to the one it is moving in, and by giving the same speed v km/hr to A also in the same direction.

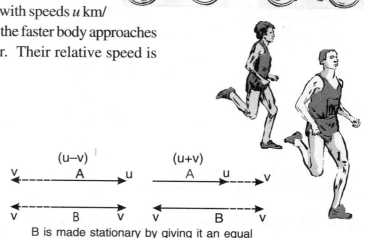

B is made stationary by giving it an equal velocity v in opposite direction

13.5 Relative Motion in Case of Two Trains

(A) *Two trains passing each other while moving in the opposite directions.*

Let two trains of length is l_1 metres and l_2 metres respectively be moving on two parallel tracks in the opposite directions with speeds u km/hr and v km/hr.

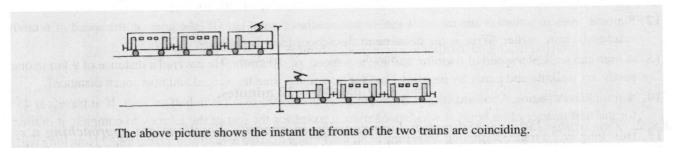

The above picture shows the instant the fronts of the two trains are coinciding.

It is clear that they will have passed each other when their rears coincide. They will pass each other with a relative speed of $(u + v)$ km/hr and cover a distance of $(l_1 + l_2)$ metres in doing so.

(B) *Two trains passing each other while moving in the same direction*

If $u > v$, then they will pass each other with a relative speed of $(u - v)$ km/hr and cover a distance of $(l_1 + l_2)$ metres as in case (A).

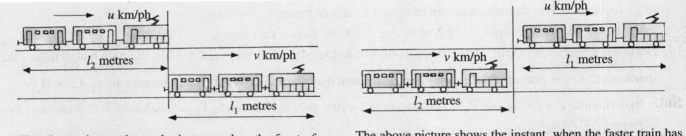

The above picture shows the instant when the front of the faster train coincides with the rear of the slower train.

The above picture shows the instant when the faster train has crossed the slower train. The rear of the faster train coincides with the front of the slower train.

The same concept will apply in case of a train passing a man running towards it and a train passing a man running in the same direction.

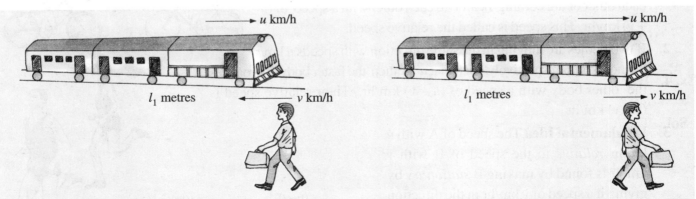

The train passes the man with a relative speed of $(u + v)$ km/hr and covers a distance of l_1 metres in doing so.

The train passes the man with a relative speed of $(u - v)$ km/hr and cover a distance of l_1 metres in doing so.

Ex. 1. *Two trains travel in the same direction at 50 km/h and 46 km/h respectively. If the lengths of the trains are 350 m and 450 m respectively, how long would it take to pass each other.*

Sol. As the two trains are moving in the same direction,

so the relative speed with which they pass each other = (50 – 46) km/hr = 4 km/hr and

distance covered in doing so = sum of the lengths of the trains.

$\therefore$ $$= (350 \text{ m} + 450 \text{ m}) = 800 \text{ m} = \frac{800}{1000} \text{ km} = \frac{4}{5} \text{ km}$$

$$\text{Time taken in passing each other} = \frac{\text{Distance}}{\text{Speed}} = \frac{\frac{4}{5}}{4} \text{ hour} = \frac{4}{5 \times 4} \text{ hr} = \frac{1}{5} \text{ hr}$$

$$= \frac{1}{5} \times 60 \text{ minutes} = \textbf{12 minutes.}$$

Ex. 2. *Two trains 250 and 350 metres long running in opposite directions are approaching a railway station at speeds of 40 km/hr and 20 km/hr respectively. How long would it take to pass each other?*

Sol. As the two trains are moving in opposite directions, so their relative speed at which they pass each other

= sum of their speeds = (40 + 20) km/h = 60 km/h.

Total distance covered = 250 m + 350 m = 600 m = $\frac{600}{1000}$ km = $\frac{3}{5}$ km

$\therefore$ Time taken to pass each other = $\frac{\text{Distance}}{\text{Speed}}$ = $\frac{\frac{3}{5}}{60}$ hr = $\frac{3}{5 \times 60} \times 3600$ sec. = **36 sec.**

Ex. 3. *A train leaves Dehra Dun railway station at 9 a.m. at a speed of 60 km/hr for Mumbai. Another train leaves Dehra Dun railway station at 11 a.m. and moves towards Mumbai at a speed of 80 km/hr. At what time will it catch the slower train?*

Sol. Speed of the first train = 60 km/hr

Distance travelled by it in 2 hours (9 a.m. to 11 a.m.) = (60 × 2) km = 120 km

Speed of second train = 80 km/hr

$\therefore$ Relative speed of the train = (80 – 60) km/h = 20 km/hr.

So in order to catch the first train, the second train will have to cover a distance of 120 km with a relative speed of 20 km/hr.

$\therefore$ Time taken by the second train to catch the first train = $\frac{\text{Distance}}{\text{Speed}}$ = $\left(\frac{120}{20}\right)$ hr = 6 hours.

Hence, the second train will catch the first train 6 hours after 11 a.m., i.e., at **5 p.m.**

Ex. 4. *When two trains were running in the same direction at 72 km/hr and 54 km/hr respectively, the faster train passed a man in the slower train in 70 seconds. Find the length of the faster train.*

Sol. The relative speed of the trains = (72 – 54) km/hr = 18 km/hr

$$\left(18 \times \frac{5}{18}\right) \text{m/sec} = 5 \text{ m/sec}$$

Given : Faster train passes a man in the slower train in 70 seconds.

Therefore, length of the faster train = distance covered by it with a speed of 5 m/sec in 70 seconds

$$= (5 \times 70) \text{ metres} = 350 \text{ metres}$$

$$\boxed{D = S \times T}$$

Hence, the length of the faster train is **350 metres.**

Ex. 5. *When two trains were running in the opposite directions at 50 km/hr and 40 km/hr respectively, the faster train passed a man in the slower train in 15 seconds. Find the length of the faster train.*

Sol. The relative speed of the train $= (50 + 40)$ km/hr $= 90$ km/hr $= \left(90 \times \dfrac{5}{18}\right)$ m/sec $= 25$ m/sec.

Given : Faster train passes a man in the slower train in 15 seconds.

So, length of the faster train = distance covered by it in 15 seconds

$\qquad\qquad = (25 \times 15)$ metres $= 375$ metres

$\boxed{D = S \times T}$

Hence, the length of the faster train is **375 metres**.

EXERCISE 13 (b)

1. Two trains, 250 metres and 350 metres in length are running towards each other on parallel tracks, one at the rate of 55 km/hr and the other at 35 km/hr. In what time will they pass each other from the moment they meet ?

2. How long will a train 160 m long, travelling at 60 km/hr, take to pass a train 190 m long travelling at 25 km/hr in the same direction?

3. Train A is 280 m in length and train B is 370 m in length. A has a speed of 40 km/hr and B has a speed of 38 km/hr. If they move in opposite direction, find the time A will take in passing B completely.

4. Two trains 200 m and 175 m long are running on parallel tracks, in the same direction with speed of 46 km/hr and 28 km/hr respectively. How long will it take them to be clear of each other?

5. A 220 m long train is travelling at 60 km/hr. A man is running towards it from the opposite direction at 6 km/hr. In how many seconds, will the train cross the man?

6. When two trains were running in the same direction at 90 km/hr and 70 km/hr respectively, the faster train passed a man in the slower train in 36 seconds. Find the length of the faster train.

7. When two trains were running in the opposite directions at 40 km/hr and 30 km/hr respectively , the faster train passed a man in the slower train in 18 seconds. Find the length of the train.

8. At 10 a.m. a train leaves Delhi for Chennai at a speed of 72 km/hr. At 11 a.m. another train starts from Delhi for Chennai at a speed of 90 km/hr. At what time will it overtake the slower train?

9. Cyclist A started his journey on cycle at 7:30 a.m. at a speed of 8 km/hr. After 30 minutes , cyclist B started from the same place but with a speed of 10 km/hr. At what time did B overtake A?

10. A train 120 m long, travelling at 90 km/hr, overtakes another train travelling in the same direction at 72 km/hr and passes it completely in 50 seconds. Find (i) the length of the second train in metres and (ii) the time they would have taken to pass one another if they had been travelling at these speeds in opposite direction.

13.6 Problems on Boats and Streams

1. The flow of water in a river or sea is called **current** or **stream**.

2. The direction along the stream is called down stream and direction against the stream is called up stream.

3. If the speed of a boat in **still** water is x **km/hr** and the speed of stream is y **km/hr**, then
speed of boat down stream $= (x + y)$ km/hr, speed of boat up stream $= (x - y)$ km/hr.

4. If the speed of boat down stream is x km/hr and the speed up stream $= y$ km/hr, then

speed of the boat in still water $= \dfrac{1}{2}(x + y)$ km/hr , speed of stream $= \dfrac{1}{2}(x - y)$ km/hr .

[If l km/hr is the speed of the boat in still water and n km/hr is the speed of the stream, then

$l + n = x$ and $l - n = y$. Solving, $l = \dfrac{x + y}{2}$, $n = \dfrac{x - y}{2}$]

13.7 Solved Examples

Ex. 1. *The speed of a boat in still water is 8 km/hr and the speed of the stream is 1km/hr. Find* **(a)** *the time taken by the boat to go 63 km downstream.*

       (b) *the time taken by the boat to go 42 km upstream.*

Sol. (*a*) Speed of boat downstream = (8 +1) km/hr = 9 km/hr.

Distance travelled downstream = 63 km.

∴ Time taken by the boat downstream = $\dfrac{\text{Distance travelled}}{\text{Speed downstream}} = \dfrac{63 \text{ km}}{9 \text{ km/hr}} = \mathbf{7 \text{ hr.}}$

(*b*) Speed of boat upstream = (8 −1) km/hr = 7 km/hr.

Distance travelled upstream = 42 km

∴ Time taken by the boat upstream = $\dfrac{\text{Distance travelled}}{\text{speed upstream}} = \dfrac{42 \text{ km}}{7 \text{ km/hr}} = \mathbf{6 \text{ hr.}}$

Ex. 2. *The speed of boat in still water is 6 km/hr. It goes downstream for a distance of 31 km in 4 hours. Find the speed of the stream.*

Sol. Speed downstream = $\dfrac{\text{Distance covered downstream}}{\text{Time Taken}} = \dfrac{31 \text{ km}}{4 \text{ hours}} = 7.75 \text{ km/hr.}$

We know that, speed of a boat downstream = speed of boat in still water + speed of stream

∴ Speed of stream = speed of boat downstream – speed of boat in still water

           = 7.75 k/hr – 6 km/hr = **1.75 km/hr.**

Ex. 3. *The speed of a boat in still water in 6 km/hr and the speed of the stream is 2 km/hr. The boat is rowed downstream for a certain distance and then taken back to the starting point. Find the average speed for the whole journey.*

Sol. Let the distance travelled downstream as well as upstream be x km.

Speed of boat downstream = (6 + 2) km/hr = 8 km/hr.

Speed of boat upstream = (6 – 2) km/hr = 4 km/hr

Time taken downstream = $\dfrac{x \text{ km}}{8 \text{ km/hr}} = \dfrac{x}{8}$ hrs., Time taken upstream = $\dfrac{x \text{ km}}{4 \text{ km/hr}} = \dfrac{x}{4}$ hr.

∴ Total time taken = $\left(\dfrac{x}{8} + \dfrac{x}{4}\right)$ hr = $\left(\dfrac{x + 2x}{8}\right)$ hrs = $\dfrac{3x}{8}$ hr.

Total distance travelled = $(x + x)$ km = $2x$ km.

∴ Average speed = $\dfrac{\text{Total distance travelled}}{\text{Total time taken}}$

           = $\dfrac{2x \text{ km}}{\dfrac{3x}{8} \text{ hrs}} = \left(\dfrac{2x}{3x} \times 8\right)$ km/hr = $\dfrac{16}{3}$ km/hr = $\mathbf{5\dfrac{1}{3}}$**km/hr.**

EXERCISE 13 (c)

1. The speed of a boat in still water is 7 km/hr and the speed of the stream is 1.5 km/hr. Find :

   (*a*) the time taken by the boat to go 51 km downstream.

   (*b*) the time taken by the boat to go 44 km upstream.

2. A stream is flowing at the rate of 2 km/hr. A boat with a speed of 10 km/hr in still water is rowed downstream for 10 hours. Find the distance rowed. How long will it take to return to the starting point?

3. The speed of a current in a river is 1.5 km/hr. If a boat is rowed upstream for a distance of 46 km in 4 hours, find the speed of the boat in still water.

4. The speed of a boat in still water is 8.5 km/hr. If it is rowed downstream for a distance of 45 km in 4.5 hours, find the speed of the current.

5. The speed of a boat in still water is 8 km/hr and the speed of the stream is 2 km/hr. The boat is rowed upstream for a certain distance and then taken back to the starting point. Find the average speed for the whole journey.

LOOKING BACK
Summary of Key Facts

1. (*i*) Speed = $\dfrac{\text{Distance}}{\text{Time}}$ (*ii*) Distance = Speed × Time   (*iii*) Time = $\dfrac{\text{Distance}}{\text{Speed}}$

2. To convert m/sec to km/hr, multiply by $\dfrac{18}{5}$. **3.** To convert km/hr to m/sec, multiply by $\dfrac{5}{18}$.

4. Time taken by a train *a* metres long to pass a stationary object = Time Taken by it to cover *a* metres.

5. Time Taken by a train *a* metres long to pass a platform or tunnel *b* metres long = Time taken by it to cover (*a* + *b*) metres.

6. If two bodies are moving in the same direction at *u* km/hr and *v* km/hr, their relative speed is (*u* – *v*) km/hr, *u* > *v*.

7. If two bodies are moving in direction opposite to each other at *u* km/hr and *v* km/hr, then their relative speed is (*u* + *v*) km/hr.

8. If the speed of the boat in still water is *x* km/hr and the speed of the current is *y* km/hr, then.
   (*a*) Speed of boat downstream = (*x* + *y*) km/hr.
   (*b*) Speed of boat upstream = (*x* – *y*) km/hr.

MENTAL MATHS – 11

1. Convert 18 km/hr to m/sec.
2. Convert 20 m/sec to km/hr.
3. A car travels 100 km at 25 km/hr and the next 80 km at 20 km/hr. Find the average speed of the car.
4. A train 150 m long, passes a railway platform 200 m long in 35 sec. Find the speed in km/hr.
5. A man is running on a road parallel to a railway track at 5 km/hr. A train travelling in the opposite direction at 31 km/hr passes him in 14 sec. Find the length of the train.
6. A boat can travel at 12 km/hr upstream and 14 km/hr down stream. What is the speed of the stream ?
7. A man walks a certain distance at the rate of 5 km/hr in 36 min. What is the distance covered by him?

UNIT REVIEW – 3

1. Divide Rs 4950 in the ratio $\dfrac{2}{5} : \dfrac{1}{2} : \dfrac{3}{4}$.

2. A bag contains 50 paise, 25 paise, 20 paise, coins in the ratio 3 : 5 : 6. If the total money amounts to Rs 237, find the number of coins of each type in the bag.

3. If A : B = 4 : 7 and A : C = 8 : 9, find B : C and A : B : C.

4. Check whether 1.5, 0.6 and 0.24 are in continued proportion or not.

5. Find the third proportional to 9, 15.

6. Two numbers are in the ratio 11 : 5. If the smaller number is 165, find the larger.

7. Radha weaves 15 baskets in 9 days. In how many days will she weave 55 baskets ?

8. A garrison has ration for 400 soldiers to last for 30 days. How long will it last if 40 soldiers leave the garrison?

9. In making a model, the height of 10m high statue is reduced in the ratio 15 : 12. Find the height of the model.

10. 9 men can weed 10 acres of land in 15 days, how many acres can 21 men weed in 18 days?

11. 54% of the population of a town are female. Find the total population of the town if there are 6670 males.

12. A's income is 40% more than B's income. What per cent is B's income less than A's income?

13. After a 15% hike, the cost of cycle becomes Rs 2990. What was the original price of the cycle?

14. The area of rectangle with dimensions 9 m × 5 m was accidently read as 54 m^2. Find the error per cent.

15. If by selling an article for Rs 276 a man loses 10%, for what amount should he sell it so as to gain 20%?

16. If the S.P. of 8 articles is equal to C.P. of 10 articles, find the gain%.

17. Two second hand television sets were sold at Rs 7200 each. On one there was a gain of 20% and on the other a loss of 20%. Find the gain or loss% on the whole transaction.

18. A shopkeeper bought 100 purses at the rate of Rs 36 each. He sold 40 of them at the rate of Rs 40 each. At what rate should he sell the remainder so as to gain 20% on the whole ?

19. A can do a certain job in 10 days and B alone in 20 days. A started the work and was joined by B after 8 days. In how many days was the rest of the work completed?

20. A pipe can fill a tank in 15 hours. Due to a leak in the bottom, it is filled in 25 hours. If the tank is full, how much time will the leak take to empty it?

21. In what time will a certain sum become two and a half times of itself at 15% p.a. S.I. ?

22. Ravi and Sanjay borrowed Rs 1200 and Rs 800 respectively at the same rate of simple interest for 3 years. If Ravi paid Rs 96 more than Sanjay as a interest, find the rate per cent p.a.

23. A sum of money lent out at S.I. amounts to Rs 3520 in 2 years and Rs 4600 in 5 years. Find the sum and rate of interest.

24. Find the compound interest on a sum of Rs 8000 at the rate of 15% p.a. payable after 2 years. Calculate also the amount payable at the end of two years.

25. A man travels from Delhi to Roorkee at 40 km/hr and returns at 60 km/hr. This return journey takes $1\frac{1}{2}$ hours less than the forward journey. What is the distance between Delhi and Roorkee?

26. Ajay cycles at $\frac{6}{5}$th of his usual speed and reaches the school 7 minutes earlier. What is his usual time?

27. A train passes a station platform in 36 seconds and a man standing on the platform in 20 seconds. If the speed of the train is 54 km/hr. Find the length of the platform.

28. A train 180 m long is running at a speed of 60 km/hr. In what time will it pass a man running with a speed of 6km/hr in the same direction ?

29. A train running at a speed of 62 km/hr takes 15 secs to pass a man running with a speed of 10 km/hr in the opposite direction. Find the length of the train.

30. A train crosses a telegraph post in 8 seconds and a bridge 200 m long in 24 seconds. Find the speed of the train.

ANSWERS

EXERCISE 13 (a)

1. 18.75 km	2. 30km/hr	3. 40 sec.	4. The boy with the speed of 8.5km/hr.	5.864 km/hr

6. 53 min. 20 sec.	7. 32 km/hr	8. $17\frac{1}{7}$ km/hr.	9. 14.4 km/hr	10. 58.5 km/hr	11. 48 km/hr	12. 3 km

13. Walked for 15 min a distance of $1\frac{1}{2}$ km   14. 51 km/hr   15. 39.6 sec, 29.7 sec.   16. 25.2 km/hr.

17. 72km/hr   18. 45km/hr   19. 180km   20. 16 sec

EXERCISE 13 (b)

1. 24 sec	2. 36 sec	3. 30 sec	4. 1 min 15 sec	5. 12 sec	6. 200m	7. 350 m

8. After 4 hours (At 3 p.m.)   9. 9 : 30 a.m   10. (a) 130m   (b) $5\frac{5}{9}$ sec

EXERCISE 13 (c)

1. (*a*) 6 hours   (*b*) 8 hours   2. 120 km, 15 hours   3. 13 km/hr   4. 1.5 km/hr   5. 7.5 km/hr

MENTAL MATHS – 11

1. 5 m/sec   2. 72 km/hr   3. 22.5 km/hr   4. 36 km/hr   5. 140 m   6. 1 km/hr   7. 3 km

UNIT REVIEW – 3

1. Rs 1200, Rs 1500, Rs 2250   2. 50p $\rightarrow$ 180, 25p $\rightarrow$ 300, 20p $\rightarrow$ 360   3. 14 : 9; 8 : 14 : 9

4. Yes   5. 25   6. 363   7. 33 days   8. $33\frac{1}{3}$ days   9. 8 m   10. 28 acres

11. 14, 500   12. $28\frac{4}{7}\%$ 13. Rs 2600   14. 20%   15. Rs 368   16. 25%   17. Loss% = 4%

18. Rs 45.33 approx   19. $1\frac{1}{3}$ days   20. 37.5 hr.   21. 10 years   22. 8%

23. Rs 2800, $12\frac{6}{7}\%$ (**Hint :** Type Solved Ex. 12)   24. Rs 2580, Rs 10580   25. 180 km   26. 42 min

27. 240 m   28. 12 sec   29. 300 m   30. 45 km/hr.

14. Fundamental Concepts and Operations

14.1 Introduction

In the previous class, you have learnt about algebraic expressions, their addition, subtraction, multiplication and division. First we will revise them and then extend our study further.

14.2 Review of Concepts Learnt in Previous Classes

1. **Constants and Variables :** A symbol in algebra having a fixed value is called a constant, whereas a symbol which can be assigned different values is called a variable.

   e.g. $\frac{1}{3}$, -8, π, $\sqrt{2}$ etc. are all **constants** and x, y, z etc. are all **variables**.

2. **Algebraic expression :** A combination of constants and variables connected by the signs +, –, × and ÷ is called an algebraic expression. The several parts of an expression separated by + or – sign are called the **terms** of the expression. Thus $5 - 3x + 4y + 8xy + 7x^2y$ is an algebraic expression containing five terms and $5x - 7y$ is an algebraic expression containing two terms.

3. **Polynomial :** A polynomial is an algebraic expression in which the variables have non-negative integral exponents only.

   For example :

   (1) $10 + 3x + 2x^2 - \frac{1}{5}x^3 + \sqrt{2}x^4$ is a polynomial in one variable x.

   (2) $5x^3 + 3x^2y - \sqrt{5}\,xy^2 + 21y^3$ is a polynomial in two variables x and y.

   (3) $7 + 3x^{-2} + x^3$ is not a polynomial since it contains a term with a negative exponent.

   (4) $4x^3 - 2x^{\frac{3}{2}} + 7x^2 + 8$ is not a polynomial since it contains a term with power $\frac{3}{2}$ which is not a positive integer.

4. A **monomial** is a polynomial of one term. A polynomial of *two* terms is called a **binomial**, and a polynomial of *three* terms is called a **trinomial**. An algebraic expression containing more than three terms is referred to as polynomial. Thus, $\sqrt{7}x$ and $-23m^3n^2$ are monomials, $y - 7$, $3x^2 - 5xy$ are binomials; $x^2 + 5x + 6$, $7z + 5y^2$ $z - 2$ are trinomials and $x^3 + x^2 - 5x + 11$, $xy - y + y^2z - 2y^2 + 13$ are polynomials.

5. (*a*) **Degree of a polynomial in one variable :** If the polynomial is in one variable, then the highest power of the variable is called the degree of the polynomial.

   For example :

   (*i*) $3x - 5$ is polynomial in x of degree one.

   (*ii*) $3x^2 - 5x + 2$ is a polynomial in x of degree 2.

   (*iii*) $5y^4 - 2y^3 + 7$ is a polynomial in y of degree 4.

   (*b*) **Degree of a polynomial in two or more variables :** In the case of polynomials in two or more than two variables, the sum of the powers of the variables in each term is found and the highest sum so obtained is called the degree of the polynomial.

For example :

(i) $3x^2 - 5x^2y^2 + x^3 + 2y^3$ is a polynomial of degree 4.

degree of the term
$-5x^2y^2 = 2 + 2 = 4$

(ii) $7x^2y - 8y^4 + 2x^3y^4 - 5x^4 + 11$ is a polynomial of degree 7 in x and y.

degree of the term
$2x^3y^4 = 3 + 4$

(iii) The degree of a constant polynomial like 7, 23 is 0.

6. A polynomial is said to be simplified, or in **simplest form**, when no two of its terms are similar. For example, $7x^2 - 3x + 2$ is in simplest form, but $5y^2 + 9y - 2y + 3$ is not in simplest form. Its simplified form will be $5y^2 + 7y + 3$.

7. (a) **Linear polynomial :** A polynomial of degree 1 is called a linear polynomial.

For example : $4x + 2, \frac{3}{5} + 7z$ are linear polynomials.

(b) **Quadratic polynomial :** A polynomial of degree 2 is called a quadratic polynomial.

For example : $2x^2 + x + 3, 4a^2 - 3a + 5$ are quadratic polynomials.

(c) **Cubic Polynomial :** A polynomial of degree 3 is called a cubic polynomial.

For example : $6x^3 - 3x^2 + 2x + 5, 4z^3 - 4z + 7$ are cubic polynomials.

8. **Factors :** Each of the quantity (constant or variable) multiplied together to form a product is called a factor of the product.

A constant factor is the **numerical factor** and the factor containing a variable is called a **literal factor.**

For example : In $\frac{6}{5}xy, \frac{6}{5}$ is the numerical factor and x, y, xy are the literal factors.

9. **Coefficient :** In any term of an algebraic expression, the numerical part is called the numerical coefficient and the literal part, the literal coefficient.

Term	Numerical coefficient	Literal coefficient
$8x^2y^2$	8	x^2y^2
$-\frac{2}{3}yz$	$-\frac{2}{3}$	yz
x	1	x

10. **Like Terms :** Terms of an algebraic expression having the same literal coefficient are called like terms otherwise they are called unlike terms.

For example : $8a^2b, 7a^2b, -14a^2b$ etc. are like terms whereas $-\frac{2}{3}ab, 4ab^2, 6a^2b$ are all unlike terms.

11. The terms of a polynomial are said to be in **ascending** or **descending order** if they increase or decrease in degrees respectively.

Thus (i) The terms of the polynomial $7x^3 - 2x^2 + 5x - 11$ are in descending order.

(ii) The terms of the polynomial $3 - 5x + 2x^2 - 8x^3$ are in ascending order.

EXERCISE 14 (a)

1. Which of the following expressions are not polynomials?

(a) $\frac{1}{2}x^2 - 6x - \frac{1}{7} + x^3$ (b) $10p^2 + \frac{7}{p} - 2$ (c) $5z^3 - \sqrt{7}z^2 + 11$ (d) $\frac{5x - 8x^2}{1 + x}$

(e) $\sqrt{3}x^{1/2} + 5x^2 - 9x^2 + 7$ (f) $x^2 + \frac{1}{x^2}$ (g) $2x^4 - 7x^2 + 5x - 2$

(h) 45   (i) $\frac{x}{2} + 5$ (j) $7x^{-2} + x^{-1} + 8$

2. Write Monomial, Binomial, Trinomial or Polynomial to classify each polynomial and also state their degree.

(a) $5x$ (b) $17x^3y^2z$ (c) $-11-7x$ (d) x^2+3x+7

(e) $-z+\sqrt{3}z^3$ (f) $m-8m^3+m^4-2m^2$ (g) y^4-3y^2+19 (h) $\frac{1}{2}p^4-3p+5-p^6+11p^3$

3. Write polynomials in (c), (e), (f) and (h) of Q.2 in descending order.

4. Arrange the polynomial $4x^2y^2-7xy^3+2x^4-3y^4+x^3y$ in decreasing degree in x.

5. Give the degree of each of the following polynomials.

(a) $5x^3+6x^2-3x+20$ (b) $-2x+9$ (c) $x^2y^3+5x^2-9xy$ (d) -23
(e) $3x^2y^3-2y^3+6x^5-11x^3y^7$

6. Write down the numerical as well as literal coefficients of the following monomials.

(a) $2\pi r$ (b) $6x^2y^2$ (c) $\frac{\sqrt{2}}{3}x^2yz$ (d) $-5ab^2$ (e) $\frac{6}{y}$ (f) $\frac{4ab}{3cz}$

7. Identify the pairs of like terms :

(a) $4yz, -6yz$ (b) $\frac{4}{3}x^2y, 11xy^2$ (c) $7xy, -3yz$ (d) $8p^2, -\frac{6}{5}q^2$ (e) $12x^2y^2, -16y^2x^2$

OPERATIONS ON POLYNOMIALS

14.3 Addition and Subtraction of Polynomials

For addition or subtraction of two or more polynomials :

1. We collect the like terms together.
2. Find the sum or difference of the numerical coefficients of these terms.
3. The resulting expression should be in the simplest form and can be written according to the ascending or descending order of the terms.

Some solved examples are given below to help you strengthen your understanding of these concepts.

Ex. 1. *Add :* $-5x^2y^2, -\frac{11}{5}x^2y^2, 7x^2y^2, \frac{2}{3}x^2y^2.$

Sol. $\left(-5x^2y^2\right)+\left(-\frac{11}{5}x^2y^2\right)+7x^2y^2+\frac{2}{3}x^2y^2$

$=\left(-5-\frac{11}{5}+7+\frac{2}{3}\right)x^2y^2=\left(\frac{-75-33+105+10}{15}\right)x^2y^2 = \frac{7}{15}x^2y^2.$

Ex. 2. *Subtract :* $-7x^2y$ *from* $-9x^2y.$

Sol. Required difference $=-9x^2y-(-7x^2y)=-9x^2y+7x^2y=(-9+7)x^2y=$ **$-2x^2y$**.

Ex. 3. *Add together :* $7a^3-3a^2b+5ab^2-b^3, 2a^3-3ab^2-4a^2b$ *and* $b^3-4a^3+ab^2.$

Sol. **First method :**

$\quad$ Sum $= (7a^3-3a^2b+5ab^2-b^3)+(2a^3-3ab^2-4a^2b)+(b^3-4a^3+ab^2)$

$\qquad = (7a^3+2a^3-4a^3)+(-3a^2b-4a^2b)+(5ab^2-3ab^2+ab^2)-b^3+b^3$

$\qquad = 5a^3-7a^2b+3ab^2.$

> **Note :** After practice, you may be able collect the similar terms mentally and write the sum directly.

Second method : By arranging like terms in columns and adding them up, we have

$$7a^3 - 3a^2b + 5ab^2 - b^3$$
$$2a^3 - 4a^2b - 3ab^2$$
$$-4a^3 \qquad + ab^2 + b^3$$

Sum $= 5a^3 - 7a^2b + 3ab^2$

Ex. 4. *Subtract : $13xy - 6x^2 + 4a^2 - 1$ from $25x^2 + 16xy - 3b^2 - 2$.*

Sol. Arranging the terms properly, changing the signs in the subtrahend and adding the columns, we have

$$25x^2 + 16xy - 3b^2 - 2$$
$$-6x^2 + 13xy \qquad - 1 + 4a^2$$
$$+ \qquad - \qquad + \quad -$$
$$31x^2 + 3xy - 3b^2 - 1 - 4a^2$$

We may also set our work as under :

$(25x^2 + 16xy - 3b^2 - 2) - (13xy - 6x^2 + 4a^2 - 1)$
$= 25x^2 + 16xy - 3b^2 - 2 - 13xy + 6x^2 - 4a^2 + 1$
$= 31x^2 + 3xy - 3b^2 - 1 - 4a^2$.

| Combining like terms mentally |

Ex. 5. *Simplify : $5a + 7a + 2b + 8b - a + 1$.*

Sol. Combining mentally like terms together we have

$5a + 7a - a = 11a$ and $2b + 8b = 10b$

∴ Given expression $= 5a + 7a - a + 2b + 8b + 1 = 11a + 10b + 1$.

Ex. 6. *Simplify : $3ax^2y - 5a^2xy + 6ax^2y - 4axy^2 + 7a^2xy - 13axy^2$.*

Sol. Given expression $= 3ax^2y + 6ax^2y - 5a^2xy + 7a^2xy - 4axy^2 - 13axy^2$
$\qquad\qquad\qquad = 9ax^2y + 2a^2xy - 17axy^2$.

| Collecting like terms together |

Ex. 7. *Simplify : $a - \{5a - (3a - \overline{4a - 2})\}$.*

Sol. Exp. $= a - \{5a - (3a - 4a + 2)\}$
$\qquad = a - \{5a - 3a + 4a - 2\}$
$\qquad = a - \{6a - 2\} = a - 6a + 2 = \mathbf{-5a + 2}$.

| Operating '——' |
| Operating '( )' |
| Combining like terms mentally |

Note : We cannot add or subtract two unlike terms to form a single term. We can simply connect them with the + or – sign. For example : $6x + 3a$ or $4y - 3a$.

EXERCISE 14 (b)

Add the following expressions :

1. $2a^2b + 3b^2$ and $5a^2b + 7b^2$

2. $2x^2 + 3xy$ and $6xy - 4x^2$

3. $5x^2 - 11x + 7$ and $10x^2 - 18 + 7x$

4. $y^3 - 3y^2 + 7y - 17$ and $2y^2 - 5y - 8y^3 + 20$

5. $4x^2 - 7xy + 8z, x^2 - 2xy + 9z, -3x^2 + 8xy$

6. $9a^2 + 3b^2 - ab, a^2 + 2ab + 3b^2, 4ab - 3a^2 - b^2$

Subtract as indicated :

7. $(4a - 5b - c) - (3a + 2b - 7c)$

8. $4x^2 - 5x + 3$ from $4x^2 - 3x + 2$

9. $4xy - 6 + y^2$ from $5x^2 + 6xy - 8$

10. $(x^2 + 2x + 1) - (x^2 - 2x + 1)$

11. $(-4x^2 - x + 9) - (3x^2 - x)$

12. From the sum of $x + 3y$ and $-3x - y$ subtract $x - y$.

13. Subtract $x^2 - y^2 - z^2$ from the sum of $2x^2 + 3y^2 - z^2$ and $4x^2 - 3y^2 + 5z^2$.

14. Subtract the sum of $(4x^3 + 2x^2 - 5)$ and $(15x - x^3 - x^2)$ from the sum of $(9 + 6x - 2x^2)$ and $(4x - 1 - 5x^3 + x^2)$.

15. The perimeter of a triangle is $9a + 7b - 6c$. Two of its sides are $2a - 3b + 4c$ and $6c - 4a + 8b$. Find the third side.

16. How much is $6x^3 + 2x^2 - 8$ greater than $-2x^3 + x^2 + 7x - 11$?

17. What should be subtracted from $8a^2b^2 - 9a^3 + 11y^3$ to get $6y^3$?

14.4 Multiplication of Polynomials

Case 1. **Multiplication of Monomials**

> *Product of monomials = (product of numerical coefficients) × (product of literal factors).*

Ex. 1. *Multiply :*

(a) $16x^2y^3$ *by* $4x^4y^3z$.   (b) $-\dfrac{3}{5}a^2bc^5$ *by* $\dfrac{15}{27}ab^2c$.

Sol. (a) $16x^2y^3 \times 4x^4y^3z = (16 \times 4) \times (x^2y^3 \times x^4y^3z) = 64x^6y^6z$.

$x^m \times x^n = x^{m+n}$, *i.e.,* Add the exponents

(b) $-\dfrac{3}{5}a^2bc^5 \times \dfrac{15}{27}ab^2c = \left(-\dfrac{3}{5} \times \dfrac{15}{27}\right) \times \left(a^2bc^5 \times ab^2c\right) = -\dfrac{1}{3}a^3b^3c^6$.

Case 2. **Multiplication of polynomials**

> *Multiply each term of one polynomial with each term of the other polynomial and simplify by taking the like terms together.*

Ex. 2. *Multiply :* (a) $(5x^2 - 3x + 2)$ *by* $7x$ (b) $4a^2 - 6a + 5$ *by* $3a + 2$.

Sol. (a) Product $= 7x(5x^2 - 3x + 2) = -7x \times 5x^2 + 7x \times -3x + 7x \times 2$

$$= 35x^3 - 21x^2 + 14x.$$

(b) Product $= (3a + 2)(4a^2 - 6a + 5)$

$$= 3a(4a^2 - 6a + 5) + 2(4a^2 - 6a + 5)$$
$$= 12a^3 - 18a^2 + 15a + 8a^2 - 12a + 10$$
$$= \mathbf{12a^3 - 10a^2 + 3a + 10}$$

Combining like terms

We may also write it as :

$$
\begin{array}{r}
4a^2 - 6a + 5 \\
3a + 2 \\
\hline
12a^3 - 18a^2 + 15a \\
+ 8a^2 - 12a + 10 \\
\hline
12a^3 - 10a^2 + 3a + 10
\end{array}
$$

$\therefore$ **Product $= 12a^3 - 10a^2 + 3a + 10$.**

Ex. 3. *Multiply* $(x^2 + xy - y^2)$ *by* $(x^2 - xy + y^2)$

Sol. Product $= (x^2 + xy - y^2)(x^2 - xy + y^2) = x^2(x^2 - xy + y^2) + xy(x^2 - xy + y^2) - y^2(x^2 - xy + y^2)$

$$= x^4 - x^3y + x^2y^2 + x^3y - x^2y^2 + xy^3 - y^2x^2 + xy^3 - y^4$$
$$= x^4 - x^2y^2 + 2xy^3 - y^4.$$

Combining like terms and arranging in descending powers of x

You may also write as under :

$$
\begin{array}{r}
x^2 + xy - y^2 \\
x^2 - xy + y^2 \\
\hline
x^4 + x^3y - x^2y^2 \\
- x^3y - x^2y^2 + xy^3 \\
+ x^2y^2 + xy^3 - y^4 \\
\hline
x^4 \qquad - x^2y^2 + 2xy^3 - y^4
\end{array}
$$

$\therefore$ **Product $= x^4 - x^2y^2 + 2xy^3 - y^4$.**

EXERCISE 14 (c)

1. Multiply :

(a) $12xy$ by $-8x^2$

(b) $-16a^2b^2$ by $-5ab^2$

(c) $\left(-\dfrac{3}{5}a^2b^2\right)$ by $\left(\dfrac{10}{27}ab^4\right)$

(d) $\left(\dfrac{4}{3}x^2y^5\right)$ by $\left(\dfrac{6}{7}x^2y^3\right)$

(e) $\left(-\dfrac{11}{8}xy^3\right)$ by $\left(-\dfrac{24}{55}x^4\right)$

2. Multiply :

(a) $(6x-5)$ by $-3x$

(b) $(3pq+4p^2+3q-5r^2)$ by $6pqr^2$

(c) $(12x^2-4x+5)$ by $8x^3$

(d) $(3a^3x^3-4ay^2+7a^2y)$ by $-4x^2ya^2$

3. Find the product :

(a) $(x+6)(x+11)$

(b) $(2a+5)(3a-6)$

(c) $(5x+2b)(5x-2b)$

(d) $(6a-5b)(5a+6b)$

(e) $(6x^2-11x+7)(3x-4)$

(f) $(2x^2-3x-1)(x-5)$

(g) $(8x^2-2x-3)(-2x+3)$

(h) $(a^4-a^2b^2+b^4)(a^2+b^2)$

4. Multiply :

(a) $(a-b+c)$ by $(a-b-c)$

(b) (x^3-4x^2+5x-2) by (x^2+2x-1)

(c) $(2x^2-5x+3)$ by $(5x^2-6x-4)$

(d) $(3x^4-x^2+6x-7)$ by (x^2-3x+4)

14.5 Division of Polynomials

Case 1. Division of monomial by a monomial

Quotient of two monomials = (Quotient of their numerical coefficients) × (Quotient of their literal coefficients)

Ex. 1. *Divide :* (a) $32a^3b^3$ by $-8ab$ (b) $-81a^5b^4c^3$ by $-9a^2b^2c$

Sol. (a) $\dfrac{32a^3b^3}{-8ab}=\left(\dfrac{32}{-8}\right)\times\left(\dfrac{a^3b^3}{ab}\right)=-4a^2b^2$.

$$\boxed{x^m\div x^n=x^{m-n},\ i.e.,\ \text{Subtract the exponents}}$$

(b) $\dfrac{-81a^5b^4c^3}{-9a^2b^2c}=\left(\dfrac{-81}{-9}\right)\times\left(\dfrac{a^5b^4c^3}{a^2b^2c}\right)=9a^3b^2c^2$.

Case 2. Division of a polynomial by a monomial

Method : *Divide each term of the polynomial by the monomial*

Ex.2. *Divide :* (a) $18x^4y^2+15x^2y^2-27x^2y$ by $-3xy$

(b) $\dfrac{3}{4}ab^2c^3-\dfrac{2}{5}a^2b^2c^2+\dfrac{1}{3}ab^2c$ by $\dfrac{1}{2}abc$

Sol. (a) $\dfrac{18x^4y^2+15x^2y^2-27x^2y}{-3xy}=\dfrac{18x^4y^2}{-3xy}+\dfrac{15x^2y^2}{-3xy}-\dfrac{27x^2y}{-3xy}=-6x^3y-5xy+9x.$

(b) $\dfrac{\dfrac{3}{4}ab^2c^3-\dfrac{2}{5}a^2b^2c^2+\dfrac{1}{3}ab^2c}{\dfrac{1}{2}abc}=\dfrac{\dfrac{3}{4}ab^2c^3}{\dfrac{1}{2}abc}-\dfrac{\dfrac{2}{5}a^2b^2c^2}{\dfrac{1}{2}abc}+\dfrac{\dfrac{1}{3}ab^2c}{\dfrac{1}{2}abc}$

$$\boxed{\dfrac{\frac{3}{4}}{\frac{1}{2}}=\dfrac{3}{4}\times\dfrac{2}{1}=\dfrac{3}{2},\ \dfrac{\frac{2}{5}}{\frac{1}{2}}=\dfrac{2}{5}\times\dfrac{2}{1}=\dfrac{4}{5},\ \dfrac{\frac{1}{3}}{\frac{1}{2}}=\dfrac{1}{3}\times\dfrac{2}{1}=\dfrac{2}{3}}$$

$=\dfrac{3}{2}bc^2-\dfrac{4}{5}abc+\dfrac{2}{3}b.$

Case 3. **Division of a polynomial by a polynomial**

Method :

1. *Set up as a form of long division in which both the divisor and dividend are arranged in descending order, leaving space for missing terms.*
2. *Divide the first term of the dividend by the first term of the divisor and write it as the first term of the quotient.*
3. *Multiply the first term of the quotient by each term of the divisor and write the product below the dividend.*
4. *Subtract like terms and bring down one or more terms as needed.*
5. *Now use the remainder as the new dividend and repeat steps 2 to 4.*
6. *Repeat this process till we get the remainder either equal to 0 or a polynomial of degree lower than that of the divisor.*

Ex. 3. *Divide :* $14x^2 - 53x + 45$ *by* $7x - 9$

Sol.

$$
\begin{array}{r}
2x - 5 \\
7x - 9 \overline{\big)\, 14x^2 - 53x + 45} \\
14x^2 - 18x \\
\underline{\quad - \qquad +} \\
-35x + 45 \\
-35x + 45 \\
\underline{\quad + \qquad -} \\
0
\end{array}
$$

1.	Dividing $14x^2$ (1st term of dividend) by $7x$ (1st term of divisor), we get $2x$ (1st term of the quotient).
2.	Multiply $2x$ by $7x-9$ (each term of the divisor) and subtract.
3.	Now bring down 45 and then the remainder $-3x + 45$ is the new dividend.
4.	Repeat steps 1 to 3 till we get 0 or remainder as a polynomial of degree lower than that of the divisor.

$\therefore$ $(14x^2 - 53x + 45) \div (7x - 9) = $ **$(2x - 5)$**.

Ex. 8. *Divide :* $(x^3 - 4x^2 + 7x - 2)$ *by* $(x - 2)$.

Sol.

$$
\begin{array}{r}
x^2 - 2x + 3 \\
x - 2 \overline{\big)\, x^3 - 4x^2 + 7x - 2} \\
x^3 - 2x^2 \\
\underline{\quad - \qquad +} \\
-2x^2 + 7x \\
-2x^2 + 4x \\
\underline{\quad + \qquad -} \\
3x - 2 \\
3x - 6 \\
\underline{\quad - \qquad +} \\
4
\end{array}
$$

$\therefore$ For $(x^3 - 4x^2 + 7x - 2) \div (x - 2)$, we have
Quotient = $x^2 - 2x + 3$
Remainder = **4.**

In case of algebraic expressions also we can check by using the **Division Algorithm** *i.e.*

Dividend = Divisor × Quotient + Remainder.

In the question given above

Divisor = $(x - 2)$, Quotient = $(x^2 - 2x + 3)$, Remainder = 4

∴ Divisor × Quotient + Remainder = $(x - 2)(x^2 - 2x + 3) + 4$

$= x(x^2 - 2x + 3) - 2(x^2 - 2x + 3) + 4 = x^3 - 2x^2 + 3x - 2x^2 + 4x - 6 + 4$

$= x^3 - 4x^2 + 7x - 2$ = Dividend.

Ex. 5. *Divide $a^4 - b^4$ by $a - b$.*

Sol. Leaving space for missing terms, we have

$$
\begin{array}{r}
a^3 + a^2b + ab^2 + b^3 \\
a - b \,\overline{)\, a^4 \qquad\qquad - b^4} \\
a^4 - a^3b \\
\underline{-\quad +\quad} \\
a^3b \\
a^3b - a^2b^2 \\
\underline{-\quad +\quad} \\
a^2b^2 \\
a^2b^2 - ab^3 \\
\underline{-\quad +\quad} \\
ab^3 - b^4 \\
ab^3 - b^4 \\
\underline{-\quad +\quad} \\
0
\end{array}
$$

∴ $(a^4 - b^4) \div (a - b) = a^3 + a^2b + ab^2 + b^3$.

Ex. 6. *Divide $(8x^3 - 27)$ by $(2x - 3)$*

Sol. Leaving space for missing terms, we have

$$
\begin{array}{r}
4x^2 + 6x + 9 \\
2x - 3 \,\overline{)\, 8x^3 \qquad\quad - 27} \\
8x^3 - 12x^2 \\
\underline{-\quad +\quad} \\
12x^2 \\
12x^2 - 18x \\
\underline{-\quad +\quad} \\
18x - 27 \\
18x - 27 \\
\underline{-\quad +\quad} \\
0
\end{array}
$$

∴ $(8x^3 - 27) \div (2x - 3) = \mathbf{4x^2 + 6x + 9}$.

EXERCISE 14 (d)

1. Divide :

   (*i*) $28a^3b^2c$ by $7ab$ (*b*) $48a^4b^5c^6$ by $-16a^2c^2$ (*c*) $45x^5y^5$ by $-9x^6y$ (*d*) $-\dfrac{4}{5}a^2b^2c^4$ by $-\dfrac{6}{15}abc^2$

2. Divide :

   (*a*) $16pr^2 - 8pr^3 - 4p^2r^5$ by $-4pr^2$ (*b*) $6x^7 - 8x^6 + 4x^5 - 10x^4 + 6x^3$ by $-2x^3$

   (*c*) $7x^4y^2 - 14x^3y^3 + 35x^2y^4 - 56x^7y^5 + 21y^6$ by $7x^2y^2$ (*d*) $\dfrac{3}{4}abc - \dfrac{2}{5}a^2bc^2 + \dfrac{1}{7}ab^2$ by $\dfrac{1}{3}abc$

Divide :

3. $(x^2 + 8x + 15)$ by $(x + 3)$ **4.** $(2x^2 + 7x + 6)$ by $(x + 2)$ **5.** $(-2x^2 - 3x + 2)$ by $(x + 2)$

6. $(12x^2 + 7xy - 10y^2)$ by $(3x - 2y)$ **7.** $(6 + x - 4x^2 + x^3)$ by $(x - 3)$ **8.** $19x - 13x^2 + 2x^3 - 6$ by $(2x - 3)$

9. $-21 + 71x - 31x^2 - 24x^3$ by $(x + 2)$ **10.** $(x^3 - 125y^3 - 15x^2y + 75xy^2)$ by $(x - 5y)$

Divide :

11. $x^3 - 125$ by $(x - 5)$ **12.** $64a^3 + 27b^3$ by $(4a + 3b)$ **13.** $(a^4 - 16)$ by $(a + 2)$ **14.** $x^5 - y^5$ by $(x - y)$

Divide and in each case check your answer using the relation : dividend = divisor × quotient + remainder

15. $(2x^2 + x - 7)$ by $(x + 3)$ **16.** $(x^3 + 4x - 3)$ by $(x + 5)$ **17.** $(9x^3 + 3x^2 - 5x + 7)$ by $(3x - 1)$

LOOKING BACK
Summary of Key Facts

1. Algebraic expression in which the variables involved have only non-negative integral exponents are called **polynomials.**

2. A polynomial that involves only one variable is called a polynomial in one variable.

3. (*i*) Polynomials having only one term are called **monomials.**

   (*ii*) Polynomials having only two terms are called **binomials.**

   (*iii*) Polynomials having three terms are called **trinomials.**

4. (*i*) The highest exponent of the variable in a polynomial in one variable is called the **degree** of the polynomial.

   (*ii*) A constant is a polynomial of degree 0.

   (*iii*) In a polynomial in more than one variable, the highest sum of the powers of the variables is called the degree of the polynomial.

5. The standard form of a polynomial in one variable is that in which the terms of the polynomial are written in the decreasing or descending order of the exponents of the variable.

6. A polynomial is said to be **linear, quadratic, cubic** or **biquadratic,** if its degree is 1, 2, 3, or 4 respectively.

7. The sum or difference of two like terms is the like term whose numerical coefficient is the sum or difference of the numerical coefficients of the given terms.

8. (*i*) Product of monomials = (Product of numerical coefficients) × (Product of their variable parts).

   (*ii*) To multiply a polynomial by a polynomial, we multiply each term of one polynomial by each term of the other polynomial, and then simplify by combining the like terms together.

9. (*i*) Quotient of two monomials = (Quotient of their numerical coefficients) × (Quotient of their literal coefficients).

   (*ii*) If a polynomial is divided by another polynomial then we have

   Dividend = (divisor × quotient) + remainder.

   (*iii*) Before performing long division, the divisor and the dividend must be written in the standard form.

   (*iv*) The degree of the remainder is always lower than that of the divisor.

MENTAL MATHS – 12

1. Is $5x^3 - 3x^2 + \dfrac{5}{9}x - 2$ a polynomial ?

2. Is $\sqrt{ax} - 2x^2 + 7$ a polynomial ?

3. $5x^3 + \dfrac{1}{x} + x^{-3} + 11$ is a polynomial. **True or False ?**

4. Write $5y + 3y^3 + 7y^4 - 7 - 2y^2$ in the standard form.

5. Simplify : $x^{3a} \times x^{4a} \div x^{2a}$.

6. State the quotient if $7p^3 - 6p^2 + 12p$ is divided by $3p$.

7. Multiply $(4x + 2)(3x + 4)$

8. State the degree of the following polynomials :

   (*i*) $7x - 2x^2 + 9 - 4x^5$ (*ii*) $x^6 - 2x^6y^2 + 5x^3y^7 + y^8$

9. What is the degree of -23 ?

10. Divide $-21x^3y^2$ by $-3xy$.

ANSWERS

EXERCISE 14 (a)

1. (*b*), (*d*), (*e*), (*f*), (*j*)   2. (*a*) monomial, degree 1   (*b*) monomial, degree 6   (*c*) binomial, degree 1

   (*d*) trinomial, degree 2   (*e*) binomial, degree 3   (*f*) polynomial, degree 4 (*g*) trinomial, degree 4

   (*h*) Polynomial, degree 6.   3. $-7x - 11$, $\sqrt{3}z^3 - z$, $m^4 - 8m^3 - 2m^2 + m$, $-p^6 + \dfrac{1}{2}p^4 + 11p^3 - 3p + 5$

4. $2x^4 + x^3y + 4x^2y^2 - 7xy^3 - 3y^4$ 5. (*a*) 3   (*b*) 1   (*c*) 5   (*d*) 0   (*e*) 10

6.

	Numerical coefficient	Literal coefficient			Numerical coefficient	Literal coefficient
(a)	2π	r		(d)	-5	ab^2
(b)	6	$x^2 y^2$		(e)	6	$\dfrac{1}{y}$
(c)	$\dfrac{\sqrt{2}}{3}$	$x^2 yz$		(f)	$\dfrac{4}{3}$	$\dfrac{ab}{cz}$

7. (a) and (e)

EXERCISE 14 (b)

1. $7a^2 b + 10b^2$ 2. $-2x^2 + 9xy$ 3. $15x^2 - 4x - 11$ 4. $-7y^3 - y^2 + 2y + 3$ 5. $2x^2 - xy + 17z$ 6. $7a^2 + 5b^2 + 5ab$

7. $a - 7b + 6c$ 8. $2x - 1$ 9. $5x^2 + 2xy - y^2 - 2$ 10. $4x$ 11. $-7x^2 + 9$ 12. $-3x + 3y$

13. $5x^2 + y^2 + 5z^2$ 14. $-8x^3 - 2x^2 - 5x + 13$ 15. $11a + 2b - 16c$ 16. $8x^3 + x^2 - 7x + 3$ 17. $8a^2 b^2 - 9a^3 + 5y^3$

EXERCISE 14 (c)

1. (a) $-96x^3 y$ (b) $80a^3 b^4$ (c) $-\dfrac{2}{9} a^3 b^6$ (d) $\dfrac{8}{7} x^4 y^8$ (e) $\dfrac{3}{5} x^5 y^3$ 2. (a) $-18x^2 + 15x$

(b) $18p^2 q^2 r^2 + 24p^3 qr^2 + 18pq^2 r^2 - 30pqr^4$ (c) $96x^5 - 32x^4 + 40x^3$ (d) $-12a^5 yx^5 + 16a^3 y^3 x^2 - 28x^2 y^2 a^4$

3. (a) $x^2 + 17x + 66$ (b) $6a^2 + 3a - 30$ (c) $25x^2 - 4b^2$ (d) $30a^2 + 11ab - 30b^2$ (e) $18x^3 - 57x^2 + 65x - 28$

(f) $2x^3 - 13x^2 + 14x + 5$ (g) $-16x^3 + 28x^2 - 9$ (h) $a^6 + b^6$

4. (a) $a^2 - 2ab + b^2 - c^2$ (b) $x^5 - 2x^4 - 4x^3 + 12x^2 - 9x + 2$ (c) $10x^4 - 37x^3 + 37x^2 + 2x - 12$

(d) $3x^6 - 9x^5 + 11x^4 + 9x^3 - 29x^2 + 45x - 28$

EXERCISE 14 (d)

1. (a) $4a^2 bc$ (b) $-3a^2 b^5 c^4$ (c) $\dfrac{-5y^4}{x}$ (d) $2abc^2$ 2. (a) $-4 + 2r + pr^3$ (b) $-3x^4 + 4x^3 - 2x^2 + 5x - 3$

(c) $x^2 - 2xy + 5y^2 - 8x^5 y^3 + \dfrac{3y^4}{x^2}$ (d) $\dfrac{9}{4} - \dfrac{6}{5} ac + \dfrac{3b}{7c}$ 3. $(x + 5)$ 4. $2x + 3$ 5. $-2x + 1$

6. $4x + 5y$ 7. $x^2 - x - 2$ 8. $x^2 - 5x + 2$ 9. $Q = -24x^2 + 17x + 37, R = -95$ 10. $x^2 - 10xy + 25y^2$

11. $(x^2 + 5x + 25)$ 12. $16a^2 - 12ab + 9b^2$ 13. $a^3 - 2a^2 + 4a - 8$ 14. $x^4 + x^3 y + x^2 y^2 + xy^3 + y$

15. $Q = 2x - 5, R = 8$ 16. $Q = x^2 - 5x + 29; R = -148$ 17. $Q = 3x^2 + 2x - 1; R = 6$

MENTAL MATHS – 12

1. Yes   2. No   3. False   4. $7y^4 + 3y^3 - 2y^2 + 5y - 7$ 5. x^{5a} 6. $\dfrac{7}{3} p^2 - 2p + 4$

7. $12x^2 + 22x + 8$ 8. (i) 5 (ii) 10   9. 0   10. $7x^2 y$

15. Algebraic Identities (Some Special Products)

15.1 Meaning of an Identity

Consider the sentence $5x + 3 = 2x + 15$. If you put various values of x in this sentence, you will find that L.H.S. = R.H.S. only when $x = 4$. Such a mathematical sentence containing an unknown variable x which is satisfied only for a particular value of x and for no other value is called an **equation**. The number, that is the value of x which satisfies an equation is called the **solution** of the equation.

x	L.H.S	R.H.S
1	18	17
2	13	19
3	18	21
4	23	23
5	28	25

Now consider the sentence $(x + 3)^2 = x^2 + 6x + 9$. On putting various values of x, you find that L.H.S. = R.H.S. for all values of x. Such a mathematical sentence containing an unknown variable x which is satisfied for all values of x is called an **identity**.

x	L.H.S	R.H.S
1	16	16
2	25	25
3	36	36
4	49	49

15.2 Product of Two Binomials

IDENTITY 1. $(x + a)(x + b) = x^2 + (a + b)x + ab$.

Suppose we have to find the product $(x + a)(x + b)$, x, a and b are all numbers. By the closure property of addition for numbers, $x + a$ is also a number. This means that we may treat $(x + a)$ as we would 4 or –7 or any other number. Thus we have

$(x + a)(x + b) = (x + a)x + (x + a)b = x^2 + ax + bx + ab$

Therefore, $(x + a)(x + b) = x^2 + (a + b)x + ab$.

Second Method: $x + a$

$$\underline{x + b}$$

$$x^2 + ax$$

$$\underline{+ bx + ab}$$

The product is : $x^2 + ax + bx + ab = x^2(a + b)x + ab$.

This result is true for all values of a and b.

Thus, $(x + 3)(x + 4) = x^2 + (3 + 4)x + 3 \times 4 = x^2 + 7x + 12$.

$(x - 3)(x - 4) = x^2 + (-3 - 4)x + (-3)(-4) = x^2 - 7x + 12$.

$(x - 3)(x + 4) = x^2 + (-3 + 4)x + (-3)(+4) = x^2 + x - 12$.

$(x + 3)(x - 4) = x^2 + (+3 - 4)x + (+3)(-4) = x^2 - x - 12$.

In general, $(x + a)(x + b) = x^2 + $ **(algebraic sum of second terms)** $x + $ **product of second terms.**

Note : ax is sometimes called the "inner product" and bx the "outer product".

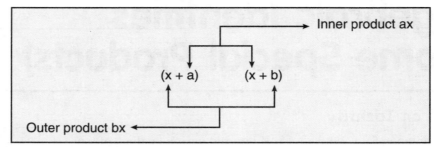

The following examples will illustrate how the product of two such binomials can be written down mentally:

Ex.1. *Expand :* **(a) $(x + 2)(x + 3)$,**   **(b) $(x + 2)(x - 5)$.**

Sol.

			You get
(1)	**1st Step :** Multiply the first terms of each binomial.	$(x + 2) \quad (x + 3)$	x^2
	2nd Step : Take the algebraic sum of the inner and outer products.	$(x + 3) \quad (x + 2)$	$2x + 3x = 5x$
	3rd Step : Multiply the last terms of each binomial. **Last Step :**	$(x + 3) \quad (x + 2)$	6
	The product is		$x^2 + 5x + 6$
(2)	**1st Step :**	$(x + 2) \quad (x - 5)$	x^2
	2nd Step :	$(x + 2) \quad (x - 5)$	$2x - 5x = -3x$
	3rd Step :	$(x + 2) \quad (x - 5)$	-10
	Last Step :		$x^2 - 3x - 10$

Now Suppose you have to find product of any two binomials $ax + by$ and $cx + dy$.

$$(ax + by)(cx + dy) = (ax + by)cx + (ax + by)dy = acx^2 + bcxy + adxy + bdy^2$$

$$= acx^2 + (bc + ad)xy + bdy^2.$$

Method :

> **Step 1 :** *Multiply the first terms of the binomials.*
> **Step 2 :** *Find the inner and outer products and take their algebraic sum.*
> **Step 3 :** *Multiply the last terms of the binomials.*
> **Last step :** *The required product is the algebraic sum of the products obtained in steps 1 to 3.*

Ex. 2. *Multiply : (3x +5) (2x +7).*

Sol.

Step 1. $(3x)(2x) = 6x^2$

Step 2. $(+5)(2x) + 7(3x)$

$= +10x + 21x = 31x$

Step 3. $(+5)(+7) = +35$

Last Step. The product is $6x^2 + 31x + 35$

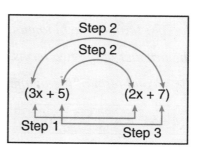

Ex. 3. *Find* $(7x - 2)(5x - 8)$ *by inspection.*

Sol.

The product is $35x^2 - 66x + 16$.

> **Think**
>
> $7x \times 5x = 35x^2$
>
> $(7x)(-8) + (-2)(5x) = -56x - 10x = -66x$
>
> $(-2)(-8) = +16$.

EXERCISE 15 (a)

Multiply mentally and write only the products for each of the following :

1. $(x+4)(x+2)$ 2. $(a+1)(a+8)$ 3. $(c+3)(c+2)$ 4. $(b-2)(b-5)$

5. $(n-1)(n-6)$ 6. $(3-x)(5-x)$ 7. $(y-7)(y+3)$ 8. $(m+3)(m-2)$

9. $(x-4)(x+6)$ 10. $(p+10)(p-9)$ 11. $(xy+6)(xy-5)$ 12. $(5-xy)(3+xy)$

13. $(x^2+3)(x^2-8)$ 14. $(4-x^2)(10+x^2)$ 15. $(ab-13)(ab-4)$ 16. $(2x+3)(3x+2)$

17. $(4x+7)(5x+6)$ 18. $(7x+1)(x+3)$ 19. $(2a^2+3b^2)(2a^2-5b^2)$

20. $(2x^2-7y^2)(3x^2+8y^2)$ 21. $(7x^2-5y)(x^2+3y)$

22. **Find by inspection the coefficient of x in the following expansions :**

   (i) $(x+17)(x+2)$ (ii) $(x+1)(3-x)$ (iii) $(x-p)(x-q)$

   (iv) $(2+3x)(3-5x)$ (v) $(5-x)(x+8)$ (vi) $(px-1)(px-1)$

15.3 Squaring a Binomial

IDENTITY 2. $(a+b)^2 = a^2 + 2ab + b^2$.   **IDENTITY 3.** $(a-b)^2 = a^2 - 2ab + b^2$.

(1)	(2)
$(a+b)^2 = (a+b)(a+b)$	$a + b$
$\quad = (a+b)a + (a+b)b$	$\dfrac{a + b}{a^2 + ab}$
$\quad = a^2 + ba + ab + b^2$	$\dfrac{\quad + ab + b^2}{a^2 + 2ab + b^2}$
$\quad = a^2 + (ab) + (1)(ab) + b^2$	
$\quad = a^2 + 2ab + b^2$.	

Method :

$$(a+b)^2 = a^2 + 2ab + b^2$$

1. *Square the first term of the binomial.*

2. *Double the product of the two terms.*

3. *Square the second term of the binomial.*

Thus $\boxed{(a+b)^2 = a^2 + 2ab + b^2}$

Similarly, when you square the binomial $a - b$, you obtain the identity

$$\boxed{(a-b)^2 = a^2 - 2ab + b^2}$$

$$\begin{array}{r} a-b \\ a-b \\ \hline a^2 - ab \\ -ab + b^2 \\ \hline a^2 - 2ab + b^2 \end{array}$$

Note that the signs of the square terms in the trinomial on the right side are always plus while the sign of the product $2ab$ is the same as the sign between the two terms of the binomial.

15.4 Other Formulas

1. $(a+b)^2 = a^2 + 2ab + b^2$

$\Rightarrow$ $a^2 + 2ab + b^2 = (a+b)^2$

$\boxed{a^2 + b^2 = (a+b)^2 - 2ab}$

Also, $x^2 + \dfrac{1}{x^2} = \left(x + \dfrac{1}{x}\right)^2 - 2$

Similarly, from $(a-b)^2 = a^2 - 2ab + b^2$
we have

$\boxed{a^2 + b^2 = (a-b)^2 + 2ab,}$ $x^2 + \dfrac{1}{x^2} = \left(x - \dfrac{1}{x}\right)^2 + 2$

3. $(a-b)^2 = a^2 + b^2 - 2ab$

$= a^2 + b^2 + 2ab - 4ab = (a+b)^2 - 4ab$

$\therefore$ $\boxed{(a-b)^2 = (a+b)^2 - 4ab}$

2. $(a+b)^2 = a^2 + b^2 + 2ab$

$= a^2 + b^2 - 2ab + 4ab$

(adding and subtracting $2ab$)

$= (a-b)^2 + 4ab$

$\therefore$ $\boxed{(a+b)^2 = (a-b)^2 + 4ab}$

4. $(a+b)^2 = a^2 + b^2 + 2ab$

$(a-b)^2 = a^2 + b^2 - 2ab$

Adding, we get

$(a+b)^2 + (a-b)^2 = 2a^2 + 2b^2$

$\therefore$ $\boxed{(a+b)^2 + (a-b)^2 = 2(a^2 + b^2)}$

Illustrations :

1. $(y+3)^2 = y^2 + 2 \times y \times 3 + 3^2 = y^2 + 6y + 9$.

2. $(p-7)^2 = p^2 - 2 \times p \times 7 + 7^2 = p^2 - 14p + 49$.

3. $(2m+3n)^2 = (2m)^2 + 2 \times (2m) \times (3n) + (3n)^2 = 4m^2 + 12mn + 9n^2$.

4. $\left(4a^2 - 7\right)^2 = \left(4a^2\right)^2 - 2.\left(4a^2\right)(7) + 7^2 = 16a^4 - 56a^2 + 49$.

5. $\left(12x^3 + 1\right)^2 = \left(12x^3\right)^2 + 2.\left(12x^3\right)(1) + 1^2 = 144x^6 + 24x^3 + 1$.

6. $\left(3x + \dfrac{1}{3x}\right)^2 = (3x)^2 + 2.(3x).\left(\dfrac{1}{3x}\right) + \left(\dfrac{1}{3x}\right)^2 = 9x^2 + 2 + \dfrac{1}{9x^2}$.

7. $\left(\dfrac{3a}{b} - \dfrac{b}{2a}\right)^2 = \left(\dfrac{3a}{b}\right)^2 - 2.\left(\dfrac{3a}{b}\right)\left(\dfrac{b}{2a}\right) + \left(\dfrac{b}{2a}\right)^2 = \dfrac{9a^2}{b^2} - 3 + \dfrac{b^2}{4a^2}$.

15.5 Perfect Square

Since $a^2 + 2ab + b^2$ is equal to $(a+b)^2$ and $a^2 - 2ab + b^2$ is equal to $(a-b)^2$, therefore, these polynomials are perfect squares.

A given polynomial will be a perfect square if
  (i) *it has three terms.*
  (ii) *two of the three terms are perfect squares;*
  (iii) *the third term is equal to twice the product of the square roots of the two perfect square terms.*

Thus, (*a*) $4x^2 + 20xy + 25y^2$ is a perfect square, because

  (*i*) it has three terms,

  (*ii*) two terms that is $4x^2$ and $25y^2$ are perfect squares. They are $(2x)^2$ and $(5y)^2$.

  (*iii*) The third term $20xy = 2(2x)(5y)$, that is, it is equal to twice the product of square roots of $4x^2$ and $25y^2$

$\therefore \quad 4x^2 + 20xy + 25y^2 = (2x + 5y)^2$.

Ex. 1. *State whether the following expressions are perfect squares.*

  (a) $9a^2 + 15ab + 25b^2$ (b) $a^2 - 12a - 36$ (c) $4x^4 + 36x^2 + 81$ (d) $x^2 - 8x + 9$

Sol. (*a*) $9a^2 + 15ab + 25b^2 = (3a)^2 + 15ab + (5b)^2$

For the given expression to be a perfect square the middle term should be equal to 2 (3*a*) (5*b*), that is, 30 ab which it is not. Therefore, it is not a perfect square.

(*b*) The square term 36 in the expression is negative, therefore, it is not a perfect square.

(*c*) $4x^4 + 36x^2 + 81 = \left(2x^2\right) + 2.\left(2x^2\right)(9) + (9)^2$.

Since two terms are perfect squares and third term is twice the product of the square roots of these terms, the given trinomial is a perfect square.

$\therefore \quad 4x^4 + 36x^2 + 81 = \left(2x^2 + 9\right)^2$.

(*d*) $x^2 - 8x + 9 = x^2 - 8x + (3)^2$

Since the middle term is not equal to twice the product of *x* and 3, therefore, it is not a perfect square.

Ex. 2. *What must be added to each of the following to make it a perfect square?*

(a) $49x^2 - 42x$ (b) $4a^2 + 9b^2$

Sol. (a) $49x^2 - 42x + ? = (7x)^2 - 2(7x)(3) + ?$

To make it a perfect square, we should add $(3)^2$, that is 9 to the given expression. On adding 9, the expression becomes $49x^2 - 42x + 9 = (7x - 3)^2$.

(b) $4a^2 + 9b^2 = (2a)^2 + (3b)^2$. It will be a perfect square if it is equal to

$$= (2a)^2 + 2(2a)(3b) + (3b)^2 = (2a + 3b)^2.$$

Therefore, we should add $2(2a)(3b)$ that is $12ab$ to make $4a^2 + 9b^2$ a perfect square.

15.6 Applications

Squaring numbers and simplification.

Ex. 1. *Square :* (a) *93*   (b) *99*

Sol. (a) $93^2 = (90 + 3)^2 = 90^2 + 2 \times 90 \times 3 + 3^2 = 8100 + 540 + 9 = \textbf{8,649.}$

(b) $99^2 = (100 - 1)^2 = (100)^2 - 2 \times 100 \times 1 + (1)^2 = 10000 - 200 + 1 = \textbf{9,801.}$

Ex. 2. *Simplify :* (a) *0.645 × 0.645 + 2 × 0.645 × 0.355 + (0.355)²*

(b) *5.82 × 5.82 − 2 × 5.82 × 4.32 + (4.32)².*

Sol. (a) Given exp. $= (0.645)^2 + 2 \times 0.645 \times 0.355 + (0.355)^2 = (0.645 + 0.355)^2 = (1.000)^2 = 1.$

(b) Given exp. $= (5.82)^2 - 2 \times 5.82 \times 4.32 + (4.32)^2 = (5.82 - 4.32)^2 = (1.5)^2 = \textbf{2.25.}$

Ex.3. *Find the value of $a^2 + b^2$ when* (a) $a + b = 7, ab = 12$,   (b) $a - b = 7, ab = 18.$

Sol. (a) $a^2 + b^2 = (a + b)^2 - 2ab = 7^2 - 2 \times 12 = 49 - 24 = \textbf{25}$

(b) $a^2 + b^2 = (a - b)^2 + 2ab = 7^2 + 2 \times 18 = 49 + 36 = \textbf{85}.$

Ex.4. (i) *If $x - \dfrac{1}{x} = 3$, find the value of $x^2 + \dfrac{1}{x^2}$*

(ii) *If $x + \dfrac{1}{x} = 4$, find the value of*   (a) $x^2 + \dfrac{1}{x^2}$ (b) $x^4 + \dfrac{1}{x^4}.$

Sol. (i) $x^2 + \dfrac{1}{x^2} = \left(x - \dfrac{1}{x}\right)^2 + 2 = 3^2 + 2 = 9 + 2 = \textbf{11}.$

(ii) (a) $x^2 + \dfrac{1}{x^2} = \left(x + \dfrac{1}{x}\right)^2 - 2 = (4)^2 - 2 = 16 - 2 = \textbf{14}.$

(b) $x^4 + \dfrac{1}{x^4} = \left(x^2 + \dfrac{1}{x^2}\right)^2 - 2 = 14^2 - 2 = 196 - 2 = \textbf{194}.$

Ex. 5. *Find the value of a − b if a + b = 3, ab = 2.*

Sol. $(a-b)^2 = (a+b)^2 - 4ab = 3^2 - 4 \times 2 = 9 - 8 = 1$

∴ $a - b = \pm\sqrt{1} = \pm 1$

Ex. 6. *Find the value of a + b if a − b = 3, ab = 40.*

Sol. $(a+b)^2 = (a-b)^2 + 4ab = 3^2 + 4 \times 40 = 9 + 160 = 169$

∴ $a + b = \pm\sqrt{169} = \pm 13$.

Ex. 7. *Find the value of $a^2 + b^2$ if a + b = 10 and a − b = 2.*

Sol. $2(a^2 + b^2) = (a+b)^2 + (a-b)^2 = 10^2 + 2^2 = 100 + 4 = 104$

∴ $a^2 + b^2 = \dfrac{104}{2} = 52$.

EXERCISE 15 (b)

Expand the following :

1. (a) $(x+5)^2$ (b) $(3x+4)^2$ (c) $(3x+5y)^2$ (d) $(1+10mn)^2$ **2.** (a) $(7y-8)^2$ (b) $(p-2q)^2$

(c) $(5y-3z)^2$ **3.** (a) $(a^2+1)^2$ (b) $(3a^2+b^2)^2$ (c) $(xy-4z)^2$ (d) $(5a^2-7b^2)^2$ **4.** (a) $\left(x+\dfrac{1}{x}\right)^2$

(b) $\left(2y-\dfrac{1}{2y}\right)^2$ **5.** (a) $(1.5p+2q)^2$ (b) $\left(5p-\dfrac{1}{4q}\right)^2$ (c) $(3.2d-5f)^2$ (d) $\left(2x^2-\dfrac{1}{3x^2}\right)^2$ (e) $\left(\dfrac{1}{2}x^2y+\dfrac{1}{3xy^2}\right)^2$

6. **Simplify :**

(a) $(x+3y)^2 + (3x+y)^2$ (b) $(x-2y)^2 + (2x-y)^2$ (c) $(2x+5y)^2 - (x+3y)^2$ (d) $(4x-7y)^2 - (2x+3y)^2$

7. **Without actual multiplication, find the square of :**

(a) 401 (b) 1003 (c) 999 (d) 99.99.

8. **Simplify :**

(a) $7.61 \times 7.61 + 2 \times 7.61 \times 2.39 + 2.39 \times 2.39$ (b) $79.01 \times 79.01 + 2 \times 79.01 \times 20.99 + 20.99 \times 20.99$

(c) $0.768 \times 0.768 - 2 \times 0.768 \times 0.568 + 0.568 \times 0.568$.

9. **State which of the following expansions is a perfect square :**

(a) $4m^2 + 4m + 1$ (b) $25q^2 - 40q + 16$ (c) $a^2 - 6ab - 9b^2$ (d) $4x^2 - 2 + \dfrac{1}{4x^2}$.

10. **What term should be added to each of the following expressions to make it a perfect square?**

(a) $4a^2 + 28a$ (b) $16 + 8y$ (c) $a^2 - 2a$ (d) $9 - 6x$

11. **Find the missing term in the following perfect squares :**

(a) $9m^2 - (\ ) + 64n^2$. (b) $(\ ) + 48x + 64$. (c) $25a^2 + 120ab + (\ )$ (d) $(\ ) - 90xy + 81y^2$.

12. **Find the value of $a^2 + b^2$ when :**

(a) $a+b = 9, \ ab = 20$ (b) $a-b = 5, \ ab = 14$

13. Find the value of $x^2 + \dfrac{1}{x^2}$ when

     (a) $x + \dfrac{1}{x} = 3$ (b) $x - \dfrac{1}{x} = 11$ (c) $x - \dfrac{1}{x} = -4$

14. Find the value of $x^4 + \dfrac{1}{x^4}$ when $x + \dfrac{1}{x} = 3$

15. **Find the value of :**

     (a) $m - n$ if $m + n = 7, mn = 12$ (b) $l + m$ if $l - m = 3, lm = 7$ (c) $p^2 + q^2$ if $p - q = 6$ and $p + q = 14$

     (d) $x^2 + y^2$ if $x + y = 11, x - y = 3$ (e) $4ab$ if $a + b = 9$ and $a - b = 5$ (f) mn if $m + n = 8, m - n = 2$

     (g) $4cd\left(c^2 + d^2\right)$ if $c + d = 11, c - d = 1$.

15.7 Identity : $(a + b)(a - b) = a^2 - b^2$

(1)	(2)
$(a+b)(a-b) = a(a+b) - (a+b)b$	$a + b$
$\qquad = a^2 + ab - ab - b^2$	$\underline{a - b}$
$\qquad = a^2 - b^2$	$a^2 + ab$
	$\underline{\qquad -ab - b^2}$
	$a^2 \qquad - b^2$

> $(a+b)(a-b) = a^2 - b^2$
>
> *i.e.*, **Product of the sum and the difference of the same two terms = difference of their squares.**
>
> *i.e.*, **(1st term + 2nd term) (1st term − 2nd term) = (1st term)^2 − (2nd term)^2**

Ex. 1. *Expand the following:*

     (a) $(x + 3)(x - 3)$ **(b)** $(4x + 1)(4x - 1)$ **(c)** $(5x + 7y)(5x - 7y)$

     (d) $(a - b - c)(a - b + c)$ **(e)** $(1 + x)(1 + x^2)(1 - x)$

Sol. (a) $(x + 3)(x - 3) = (x)^2 - 3^2 = x^2 - 9$.

     (b) $(4x + 1)(4x - 1) = (4x)^2 - 1^2 = \mathbf{16x^2 - 1}$.

     (c) $(5x + 7y)(5x - 7y) = (5x)^2 - (7y)^2 = \mathbf{25x^2 - 49y^2}$.

     (d) $(a - b - c)(a - b + c) = (a - b)^2 - c^2 = \mathbf{a^2 - 2ab + b^2 - c^2}$.

     (e) $(1 + x)(1 + x^2)(1 - x) = (1 + x)(1 - x)(1 + x^2) = (1 - x^2)(1 + x^2) = \mathbf{1 - x^4}$.

Ex. 2. *Simplify:* $(x + 2y - 5z)^2 - (x - 2y + 5z)^2$.

Sol. Given exp. $= (x + 2y - 5z)^2 - (x - 2y + 5z)^2$

                  $= \left[(x + 2y - 5z) + (x - 2y + 5z)\right]\left[(x + 2y - 5z) - (x - 2y + 5z)\right]$ $\because \ a^2 - b^2 = (a + b)(a - b)$

                  $= 2x(x + 2y - 5z - x + 2y - 5z) = 2x(4y - 10z) = \mathbf{8xy - 20xz}$.

Ex.3. *Without actual multiplication, find the value of :*

    (a) 41×39 **(b)** 1001×999 **(c)** $687 \times 687 - 313 \times 313$

Sol. (*a*) $41 \times 39 = (40+1)(40-1) = (40)^2 - 1^2 = 1600 - 1 = \mathbf{1599}$.

     (*b*) $1001 \times 999 = (1000+1)(1000-1) = (1000)^2 - 1^2 = 1000000 - 1 = \mathbf{999999}$.

     (*c*) $687 \times 687 - 313 \times 313 = (687)^2 - (313)^2 = (687+313)(687-313) = 1000 \times 374 = \mathbf{374000}$.

Ex. 4. *Simplify :* $\dfrac{5718 \times 5718 - 4135 \times 4135}{5718 + 4135}$

Sol. $\dfrac{5718 \times 5718 - 4135 \times 4135}{5718 + 4135} = \dfrac{(5718)^2 - (4135)^2}{5718 + 4135}$

$= \dfrac{(5718 + 4135)(5718 - 4135)}{5718 + 4135} = 5718 - 4135 = \mathbf{1583}$.

EXERCISE 15 (c)

Write down the following products :

  1. $(y+2)(y-2)$ **2.** $(p+1)(p-1)$ **3.** $(x-4)(x+4)$ **4.** $(3b+7)(3b-7)$

  5. $(9a+10b)(9a-10b)$ **6.** $(5p^2-7q)(5p^2+7q)$ **7.** $(a^2+b^2)(a^2-b^2)$ **8.** $(ab-c)(ab+c)$

  9. $\left(\dfrac{1}{3}-5x\right)\left(\dfrac{1}{3}+5x\right)$ **10.** $(a^2b^3-x^3y^4)(a^2b^3+x^3y^4)$ **11.** $(x+y+z)(x+y-z)$

 12. $(l+m+n)(l-m+n)$ **13.** $(x+y)(x-y)(x^2+y^2)$ **14.** $(2-x)(2+x)(4+x^2)$

Simplify :

 15. $(x+2y-3z)^2 - (x-2y+3z)^2$.   **16.** $(a+b)(a-b) + (b+c)(b-c) + (c+a)(c-a)$.

 17. $(x^2+y^2)(x^2-y^2) + (y^2+z^2)(y^2-z^2) + (z^2+x^2)(z^2-x^2)$.

Find the value of :

  18. 102×98 **19.** 505×495 **20.** 1.97×2.03 **21.** 200.04×199.96 **22.** $1003^2 - 997^2$

Simplify :

 23. $6.73 \times 6.73 - 3.37 \times 3.37$ **24.** $\dfrac{3.59 \times 3.59 - 2.41 \times 2.41}{3.59 + 2.41}$

 25. $\dfrac{3532 \times 3532 - 1458 \times 1458}{3532 + 1458}$ **26.** $\dfrac{37.85 \times 37.85 - 12.15 \times 12.15}{37.85 - 12.15}$

15.8 Square of a Trinomial

IDENTITY 5 : $(a+b+c)^2 = a^2 + b^2 + c^2 + 2ab + 2bc + 2ca$.

Let $a+b = x$. Then $(a+b+c)^2 = (x+c)^2 = x^2 + 2xc + c^2$.

Substituting the value of $x = (a+b)^2 + 2(a+b)c + c^2 = a^2 + 2ab + b^2 + 2ac + 2bc + c^2$

$\therefore \quad (a+b+c)^2 = a^2 + b^2 + c^2 + 2ab + 2bc + 2ca$

    i.e., The square of an algebraic expression containing 3 terms

    = (1st term)^2 + (2nd term)^2 + (3rd term)^2 + 2 (1st term) (2nd term)

           + 2(2nd term) (3rd term) + 2 (3rd term) (1st term)

Ex. 1. *Expand the following :*

(a) $(2x + 4y + z)^2$ (b) $(a - b - c)^2$ (c) $\left(3x^2 - \dfrac{1}{3}p + 3q^2\right)^2$

Sol. (a) $(2x + 4y + z)^2$

$= (2x)^2 + (4y)^2 + (z)^2 + 2(2x)(4y) + 2(4y)(z) + 2(z)(2x)$

$= 4x^2 + 16y^2 + z^2 + 16xy + 8yz + 4zx$.

(b) $(a - b - c)^2$

$= (a)^2 + (-b)^2 + (-c)^2 + 2(a)(-b) + 2(-b)(-c) + 2(-c)(a)$

$= a^2 + b^2 + c^2 - 2ab + 2bc - 2ca$.

(c) $\left(3x^2 - \dfrac{1}{3}p + 3q^2\right)^2$

$= (3x^2)^2 + \left(-\dfrac{1}{3}p\right)^2 + \left(3q^2\right)^2 + 2\left(3x^2\right)\left(-\dfrac{1}{3}p\right) + 2\left(-\dfrac{1}{3}p\right)\left(3q^2\right) + 2\left(3q^2\right)\left(3x^2\right)$

$= 9x^4 + \dfrac{1}{9}p^2 + 9q^4 - 2x^2p - 2pq^2 + 18q^2x^2$.

Ex. 2. *Simplify :* $(x + y + z)^2 + (x - y - z)^2$.

Sol. $(x + y + z)^2 + (x - y - z)^2$

$= x^2 + y^2 + z^2 + 2xy + 2yz + 2zx + x^2 + (-y)^2 + (-z)^2 + 2(x)(-y) + 2(-y)(-z) + 2(-z)(x)$

$= x^2 + y^2 + z^2 + 2xy + 2yz + 2zx + x^2 + y^2 + z^2 - 2xy + 2yz - 2zx$

$= 2x^2 + 2y^2 + 2z^2 + 4yz$.

Ex. 3. *Find the value of* $a^2 + b^2 + c^2$ *if* $a + b + c = 13$ *and* $ab + bc + ca = 27$.

Sol. $(a + b + c)^2 = a^2 + b^2 + c^2 + 2ab + 2bc + 2ca$

i.e, $(a + b + c)^2 = a^2 + b^2 + c^2 + 2(ab + bc + ca)$

$\therefore$ $(13)^2 = a^2 + b^2 + c^2 + 2(27)$ *or* $169 = a^2 + b^2 + c^2 + 54$

or $169 - 54 = a^2 + b^2 + c^2$ or $115 = a^2 + b^2 + c^2$

$\therefore$ $a^2 + b^2 + c^2 = 115$·

EXERCISE 15 (d)

1. Expand the following :

1. $(x + 3y + 2z)^2$ **2.** $(4x + y + 5z)^2$ **3.** $(2a + 3b + 4c)^2$ **4.** $(4a - 3b - 5c)^2$ **5.** $(5p - q - 2r)^2$

6. $\left(x + \dfrac{1}{2}y + \dfrac{1}{2}z\right)^2$ **7.** $\left(4y - \dfrac{1}{5}p + 5q\right)^2$ **8.** $(x^2 + y^2 + z^2)^2$ **9.** $\left(7x - \dfrac{1}{2}y + \dfrac{1}{3}z\right)^2$

II. Simplify :

10. $(a - b - c)^2 + (-a + b + c)^2$ **11.** $(2x + p - c)^2 - (2x - p + c)^2$

III. Find the value of :

12. $a^2 + b^2 + c^2$ if $a + b + c = 7$ and $ab + bc + ca = 15$ **13.** $a + b + c$ if $a^2 + b^2 + c^2 = 41$ and $ab + bc + ca = 20$

14. $ab + bc + ca$ if $a + b + c = 15$ and $a^2 + b^2 + c^2 = 77$ **15.** $ab + bc + ca$ if $a + b + c = 27$ and $a^2 + b^2 + c^2 = 105$

LOOKING BACK
A Summary of Key Facts

1. $(x + a)(x + b) = x^2 + (a + b)x + ab$ 2. $(a + b)^2 = a^2 + 2ab + b^2$ 3. $(a - b)^2 = a^2 - 2ab + b^2$

4. $a^2 + b^2 = (a + b)^2 - 2ab$ 5. $x^2 + \dfrac{1}{x^2} = \left(x + \dfrac{1}{x}\right)^2 - 2$ 6. $(a + b)^2 = (a - b)^2 + 4ab$

7. $(a - b)^2 = (a + b)^2 - 4ab$ 8. $(a + b)^2 + (a - b)^2 = 2(a^2 + b^2)$

9. Expression of the form $a^2 + 2ab + b^2 = (a + b)^2$ and $a^2 - 2ab + b^2 = (a - b)^2$ are called perfect squares. They are of the form $(1\text{st term})^2 \pm 2(\text{sq. root of 1st term}) (\text{square root 2nd term}) + (2\text{nd term})^2$

10. $(a + b)(a - b) = a^2 - b^2$ 11. $(a + b + c)^2 = a^2 + b^2 + c^2 + 2ab + 2bc + 2ca$

MENTAL MATHS – 13

Find the product of the following :

1. $(x + 2)(x + 3)$ 2. $(x + 5)(x - 2)$ 3. $(2x + 5)(2x - 5)$ 4. $\left(x^2 + y^2\right)\left(x^2 - y^2\right)$

5. $(a + b)^2 - (a - b)^2 = \ldots$ 6. $(2x + y + 3z)^2$ 7. $(a - b + c)^2$ 8. If $\left(x + \dfrac{1}{x}\right) = 7$, find $\left(x^2 + \dfrac{1}{x^2}\right)$

Evaluate : 9. $91^2 - 9^2$ 10. $8.7^2 - 1.3^2$ 11. Is $4x^2 + 12xy + 9y^2$ a perfect square?

12. Is $25x^2 - 30xy + 16y^2$ a perfect square?

ANSWERS

EXERCISE 15 (a)

1. $x^2 + 6x + 8$ 2. $a^2 + 9a + 8$ 3. $c^2 + 5c + 6$ 4. $b^2 - 7b + 10$ 5. $n^2 - 7n + 6$

6. $15 - 8x + x^2$ 7. $y^2 - 4y - 21$ 8. $m^2 + m - 6$ 9. $x^2 + 2x - 24$ 10. $p^2 + p - 90$

11. $x^2 y^2 + xy - 30$ 12. $15 + 2xy - x^2 y^2$ 13. $x^4 - 5x^2 - 24$ 14. $40 - 6x^2 - x^4$ 15. $a^2 b^2 - 17ab + 52$

16. $6x^2 + 13x + 6$ 17. $20x^2 + 59x + 42$ 18. $7x^2 + 22x + 3$ 19. $4a^4 - 4a^2 b^2 - 15b^4$

20. $6x^4 - 5x^2 y^2 - 56y^4$ 21. $7x^4 + 16x^2 y - 15y^2$ 22. (i) 19 (ii) 2 (iii) $-(p + q)$ (iv) -1 (v) -3 (vi) $-2p$

EXERCISE 15 (b)

1. (a) $x^2 + 10x + 25$ (b) $9x^2 + 24x + 16$ (c) $9x^2 + 30xy + 25y^2$ (d) $1 + 20mn + 100m^2 n^2$

2. (a) $49y^2 - 112y + 64$ (b) $p^2 - 4pq + 4q^2$ (c) $25y^2 - 30yz + 9z^2$ 3. (a) $a^4 + 2a^2 + 1$ (b) $9a^4 + 6a^2 b^2 + b^4$

(c) $x^2 y^2 - 8xyz + 16z^2$ (d) $25a^4 - 70a^2 b^2 + 49b^4$ 4. (a) $x^2 + 2 + \dfrac{1}{x^2}$ (b) $4y^2 - 2 + \dfrac{1}{4y^2}$

5. (a) $2.25p^2 + 6pq + 4q^2$ (b) $25p^2 - \dfrac{5p}{2q} + \dfrac{1}{16q^2}$ (c) $10.24d^2 - 32d + 25f^2$ (d) $4x^4 - \dfrac{4}{3} + \dfrac{1}{9x^4}$

(e) $\dfrac{1}{4}x^4 y^2 + \dfrac{x}{3y} + \dfrac{1}{9x^2 y^4}$

6. (a) $10x^2 + 12xy + 10y^2$ (b) $5x^2 - 8xy + 5y^2$ (c) $3x^2 + 14xy + 16y^2$ (d) $12x^2 - 68xy + 40y^2$

7. (a) 1,60,801 (b) 10,06,009 (c) 998001 (d) 9998.0001

8. (a) 100 (b) 10,000 (c) 0.04 9. (a), (b) and (d) 10. (a) 49 (b) y^2 (c) 1 (d) x^2

11. (a) 48 mn (b) $9x^2$ (c) $144b^2$ (d) $25x^2$ 12. (a) 41

(b) 53 13. (a) 7 (b) 123 (c) 18 14. 47

15. (a) ± 1 (b) $\sqrt{37}$ (c) 116 (d) 65 (e) 56 (f) 15 (g) 7320

EXERCISE 15 (c)

1. $y^2 - 4$　　2. $p^2 - 1$　　3. $x^2 - 16$　　4. $9b^2 - 49$　　5. $81a^2 - 100b^2$

6. $25p^4 - 49q^2$　　7. $a^4 - b^4$　　8. $a^2b^2 - c^2$　　9. $\dfrac{1}{9} - 25x^2$　　10. $a^4b^6 - x^6y^8$

11. $(x+y)^2 - z^2$　　12. $(l+n)^2 - m^2$　　13. $x^4 - y^4$　　14. $16 - x^4$　　15. $2x(4y - 6z)$ or $8xy - 12xz$

16. 0　　17. 0　　18. $9,996$　　19. $2,49,975$　　20. 3.9991

21. 39999.9984　　22. $12,000$　　23. 33.936　　24. 1.18　　25. $2,074$　　26. 50

EXERCISE 15 (d)

1. $x^2 + 9y^2 + 4z^2 + 6xy + 12yz + 4zx$

2. $16x^2 + y^2 + 25z^2 + 8xy + 10yz + 40zx$

3. $4a^2 + 9b^2 + 16c^2 + 12ab + 24bc + 16ca$

4. $16a^2 + 9b^2 + 25c^2 - 24ab + 30bc - 40ca$

5. $25p^2 + q^2 + 4r^2 - 10pq + 4qr - 20pr$

6. $x^2 + \dfrac{1}{4}y^2 + \dfrac{1}{4}z^2 + xy + \dfrac{1}{2}yz + zx$

7. $16y^2 + \dfrac{1}{25}p^2 + 25q^2 - \dfrac{8}{5}py - 2pq + 40qy$

8. $x^4 + y^4 + z^4 + 2x^2y^2 + 2y^2z^2 + 2z^2x^2$

9. $49x^2 + \dfrac{1}{4}y^2 + \dfrac{1}{9}z^2 - 7xy - \dfrac{1}{3}yz + \dfrac{14}{3}zx$

10. $2\left(a^2 + b^2 + c^2 - 2ab + 2bc - 2ca\right)$

11. $8px - 8cx$　　12. 19　　13. 9　　14. 74　　15. 312

MENTAL MATHS – 13

1. $x^2 + 5x + 6$　　2. $x^2 + 3x - 10$　　3. $4x^2 - 25$　　4. $x^4 - y^4$　　5. $4ab$

6. $4x^2 + y^2 + 9z^2 + 4xy + 6yz + 12zx$　　7. $a^2 + b^2 + c^2 - 2ab - 2bc + 2ca$　　8. 47

9. 8200　　10. 74　　11. yes　　12. No.

PUZZLE

1. I saw a farmer tending his cows and ducks in his yard. When I enquired how many of each he had, he replied," I have altogether 60 eyes and 86 feet between them. Can you tell the answer?

2. Ananya who is in primay four, says she can write even numbers 2,4,6,8 etc. using only odd digits 1,3,5, and 7. Is she that smart?

FUN WITH NUMBERS

```
        1              1
       21             12
      3 21           1 2 3
     4 3 21         1 2 3 4
    5 4 3 21       1 2 3 4 5
   6 5 4 3 21     1 2 3 4 5 6
  7 6 5 4 3 21   1 2 3 4 5 6 7
 8 7 6 5 4 3 21  1 2 3 4 5 6 7 8
9 8 7 6 5 4 3 21 1 2 3 4 5 6 7 8 9
```

Which sum is greater? How could you tell?

Answers :

Puzzle :　1. Since there are 60 eyes, total number of animals is 30. Now, by trial we find that there are 13 cows and 17 ducks. They have in all $13 \times 4 + 17 \times 2 = 86$ legs.

2. Yes; $1\dfrac{1}{1} = 2$, $3\dfrac{3}{3} = 4$, $5\dfrac{5}{5} = 6$, $7\dfrac{7}{7} = 8$ etc.

Fun with numbers : Both are equal. The sum of the units column of the first addition is $9 = 9 \times 1$. The sum of the units column of the second addition is $1 \times 9 = 9$. Both are same. Similarly for other columns.

16. Factorisation

You have already been introduced to the concept of factorisation in class VII. Here we will study the meaning of factorisation and the methods of factorising various types of polynomials in more detail.

16.1 Type 1. Monomial Factors

You have been told that the basis for multiplication of polynomials is the distributive property of numbers. This property states

Multiplication

$\longrightarrow$

$$a(b+c) = ab + ac$$

$\longleftarrow$

Factorising

This shows how, a sum of two terms, which have a factor in common, can be expressed as a product. Thus, the factor a in each term on the left side can be taken out as a *common* factor of the whole expression and we can write $ab + ac = a(b + c)$

Just as in $21 = 3 \times 7$, 3 and 7 are factors of 21, so in $ab + bc = a(b+c)$, a and $b + c$ are factors of $ab + ac$. A factor such as a is a **common monomial factor** in the terms ab and ac. Just as we divide 21 by 3 to find the factor 7, so we divide each term of $ab + ac$ by a to find the factor $(b + c)$.

$$a \,\overline{\left| ab + ac \right.}$$
$$\qquad b + c$$

In $6p + 6q$, the common monomial factor is 6, and $p + q$ is the other factor. Notice that you usually do not factorise the number when you are factorising a polynomial. You do not need to write $6p + 6q$ as $2 \times 3(p + q)$.

Again you can factorise $28x^3 - 70x^2$ in the following ways,

$$14\left(2x^3 - 5x^2\right); x\left(28x^2 - 70x\right); x^2\left(28x - 70\right); 2x\left(14x^2 - 35x\right); 14x\left(2x^2 - 5x\right); 14x^2\left(2x - 5\right)$$

The accepted correct way is to write $28x^3 - 70x^2 = 14x^2\left(2x - 5\right)$.

Notice that $14x^2$ is the **greatest common factor** of the terms of the given polynomial. It is understood that in complete factorisation the greatest common factor is to be removed even if it is not a prime number.

Ex. 1 *Factorise* : (a) $6y + 18$, (b) $-15m^2 + 5$ (c) $4x^2 - 8x + 12$.

Sol. (a) $6y + 18 = 6(y + 3)$

(b) $-15m^2 + 5 = 5\left(-3m^2 + 1\right)$ or $-5\left(3m^2 - 1\right)$

> Notice that the greatest common monomial factor which is 6 here is not resolved into prime factors.

(c) $4x^2 - 8x + 12 = 4\left(x^2 - 2x + 3\right)$.

Ex. 2. *Factorise* : $xy + x$.

Sol. The common factor is x, and dividing each term by x we obtain the other factor $y + 1$.

so $xy + x = x(y + 1)$.

Ex. 3 *Factorise* : $25a^2 + 5ab$.

Sol. $25a^2 + 5ab = 5a(5a + b)$.

> **Mental Work**
> The common factor is $5a$
> $$5a \,\overline{\left| 25a^2 + 5ab \right.}$$
> $$\qquad 5a + b$$

167

Ex. 4 *Factorise :* $4x^4 y^3 - 12x^2 y^2 - 16x^3 y$.

Sol. The H.C.F. of the terms of the given polynomial is $4x^2 y$.

Therefore, $4x^4 y^3 - 12x^2 y^2 + 16x^3 y = 4x^2 y\left(x^2 y^2 - 3y + 4x\right)$.

EXERCISE 16 (a)

Factorise completely by removing a monomial factor :

1. $3y - 9$	**2.** $5x + 10$	**3.** $2x - 4$	**4.** $5m + 5n$	**5.** $4a + 8b$
6. $7x - 14y$	**7.** $-3m - 15n$	**8.** $-7p - 14q$	**9.** $6x^2 + 11x$	**10.** $3y^2 + 7y$
11. $ax + bx$	**12.** $x^2 y + xy^2$	**13.** $4 + 12x^2$	**14.** $ax + ay + az$	**15.** $a^3 b + ab^3$
16. $x^2 y^2 + x^2$	**17.** $p^2 - 3pq + pq^2$	**18.** $7y^3 - 5y^2$	**19.** $6x^3 - 10x^2$	
20. $2ab^2 - 6bc + 8abc$	**21.** $12p^5 + 16p^4 - 20p^3$			

16.2 Type 2. When the Common Factor is a Polynomial

Form : $x(a + b) + y(a + b) + z(a + b)$

In $ab + ac = a(b + c)$, for all a, b, c.

You may replace a, b, c, by expression involving more that one term, *e.g.*,

$(x + 5)x + (x + 5)y = (x + 5)(x + y)$.

$(a - 1)(x + 4) + (a - 1)(y - 5) = (a - 1)[(x + 4) + (y - 5)] = (a - 1)(x + y - 1)$.

and also, $x(a + b) + y(a + b) + z(a + b) = (a + b)(x + y + z)$.

Ex. 1. *Factorise :* $x(a + b)^2 + y(a + b)^4 + z(a + b)^3$.

Sol. The greatest common factor is $(a + b)^2$.

So $x(a + b)^2 + y(a + b)^4 + z(a + b)^3 = (a + b)^2 \{x + y(a + b)^2 + z(a + b)\}$.

EXERCISE 16 (b)

Factorise :

1. $(x + 3)x + (x + 3)y$	**2.** $(a + 1)x + (a + 1)y$	**3.** $a(m + n) + b(m + n)$
4. $2(x - a)^2 + 4m(x - a)$	**5.** $a(a + b) - b(b + a)$	**6.** $(p + q)^2 + 3(p + q)$
7. $(x + y)^2 + (x + y)$	**8.** $(x + y) - (x + y)^2$	**9.** $a(x - y) - b(x - y)^2$
10. $a(x + y + z) + b(x + y + z) + c(x + y + z)$	**11.** $(a - b)^4 + (a - b)^3$	**12.** $(a + b)^3 - 3ab(a + b)$

16.3 Type 3. By Grouping the Terms

Form : $ax + ay + bx + by$

Some polynomials with four terms that do not have a common factor in each term, but do have some similar terms, such as $3m + 3n - an - am$, can be factorised by grouping. This means grouping in a manner that will express the given polynomial in the form of a binomial with a common binomial factor.

The first step in this process is to separate the given terms into binomial groups having a common factor in each group. Thus,

$$3m + 3n - an - am = (3m + 3n) + (-am - an)$$

When this can be done, each binomial in the expression may be factorised as a binomial with a common monomial factor. That is,

$$(3m + 3n) + (-am - an) = [3(m + n)] + [-a(m + n)] = (m + n)(3 - a).$$

Notice that a polynomial factorable by grouping has (i) four terms, (ii) that can be grouped into two binomials with a common factor in each,(iii) such that the binomials factor in each group is the same.

Ex. 1. *Fatorise : ax + bx + ay + by .*

Sol. **Write**

$$ax + bx + ay + by$$
$$= (ax + bx) + (ay + by)$$
$$= x(a + b) + y(a + b)$$
$$= (a + b)(x + y)$$

> **Think**
> Four terms.
> Grouped into two binomials, x common factor in one, y in the other.
> Binomial expression with common factor in each term. The common factor is $a + b$. The quotient is $(x + y)$obtained by dividing each term by the common factor $(a + b)$.

The same factors could have been obtained if we had proceeded as under:

$$ax + bx + ay + by$$
$$= (ax + ay) + (bx + by)$$
$$= a(x + y) + b(x + y)$$
$$= (x + y)(a + b).$$

> Same four terms.
> Grouped with a and b as common factor.
> The common factor is $a + b$. The quotient is $(x + y)$ obtained by dividing each term by the common factor $(a + b)$.

Ex. 2. *Factorise : 3 ab + 6bc + 4ad + 8cd.*

Sol. Exp. $= 3ab + 6bc + 4ad + 8cd = 3b(a + 2c) + 4d(a + 2c)$
$$= (a + 2c)(3b + 4d).$$

Ex. 3. *Factorise : $a^2 + bc + ab + ac.$*

Sol. Exp. $= a^2 + bc + ab + ac = a^2 + ab + bc + ac$
$$= a(a + b) + c(b + a) = a(a + b) + c(a + b)$$
$$= (a + b)(a + c).$$

> Interchanging the positions of bc and ab

Ex. 4. *Factorise : $x^3 + x^2 + x + 1.$*

Sol. Exp. $= (x^3 + x^2) + (x + 1) = x^2(x + 1) + 1(x + 1) = (x + 1)(x^2 + 1).$

EXERCISE 16 (c)

Factorise :

1. $x(m + n) + ym + yn$
2. $px + py + x(x + y)$
3. $ax + ay + 8x + 8y$
4. $m(m + 4) - 8m - 32$
5. $3x + 3y + px + py$
6. $ax + bx + 7a + 7b$
7. $xy - zx - 2y + 2z$
8. $x^2 + y - x - xy$
9. $3xy - 5x + 6y - 10$
10. $6x^2 + 3x - 4xy - 2y$
11. $1 - 2a - 2a^2 + 4a^3$
12. $(a - 2b)^2 + 3a - 6b$
13. $32(x + y)^2 - 2x - 2y$
14. $ax^2 + (1 + a^2)x + a$
15. $x^5 + x^4 + x^3 + x^2$

16.4 Type 4. Factorising Perfect Square Trinomials

Form : $a^2 + 2ab + b^2$ *and* $a^2 - 2ab + b^2$

(Trinomials in which two terms are perfect squares and the third term is twice the product of the square roots of these two perfect square terms).

Formulas : $a^2 + 2ab + b^2 = (a+b)^2$; $a^2 - 2ab + b^2 = (a-b)^2$

Ex. 1. *Factorise :* $36x^2 + 60xy + 25y^2$.

Sol. **Exp.** $= 36x^2 + 60xy + 25y^2$

$= (6x)^2 + 2(6x)(5y) + (5y)^2 = (6x+5y)^2 = (6x+5y)(6x+5y)$.

Ex. 2. *Factorise :* $4x^4 - 12x^2 + 9$.

Sol. **Exp.** $= 4x^4 - 12x^2 + 9 = (2x^2)^2 - 2(2x^2)(3) + (3)^2 = (2x^2 - 3)^2 = (2x^2 - 3)(2x^2 - 3)$.

Ex. 3. *Factorise :* $4y - y^2 - 4$.

Sol. Whenever a polynomial has a negative leading coefficient, the student can write –1 ( ) and then work more easily with a polynomial inside the brackets that has a positive leading coefficient.

Exp. $= 4y - y^2 - 4 = -y^2 + 4y - 4 = -1(y^2 - 4y + 4) = -1(y-2)^2 = (-1)(y-2)(y-2)$.

EXERCISE 16 (d)

Factorise :

1. $x^2 + 4x + 4$
2. $x^2 + 6x + 9$
3. $x^2 - 10x + 25$
4. $4x^2 - 4x + 1$

5. $a^2 + 10ab + 25b^2$
6. $x^2 - 8xy + 16y^2$
7. $4x^2 + 20xy + 25y^2$
8. $64x^2 - 80xy + 25y^2$

9. $x^4 + 6x^2 + 9$
10. $4x^4 - 12x^2 + 9$
11. $a^2 - 2 + \dfrac{1}{a^2}$
12. $x^2 + x + \dfrac{1}{4}$

16.5 Type 5. Difference of Two Squares

Pattern : $a^2 - b^2 = (a+b)(a-b)$.

You are familiar with products of the following type:

$(a+b)(a-b) = a^2 - b^2$

$(3x+y)(3x-y) = 9x^2 - y^2$

$(4x-7y)(4x+7y) = 16x^2 - 49y^2$

Since in each expresion on the right hand side, two perfect squares are separated by a subtraction sign, therefore, each of these expression is referred to as the *differences* of two *squares*.

You can reverse this pattern to find a pattern for factorising the difference of two squares.

Since the first term of the difference of two squares is the square of some expression, the first term of each factor must be the square root of the first square.

Similarly, the second term of each factor is the square root of the second square. One factor must have + between the terms, and the other must have '–'.

Ex. 1. *Factorise :* $4x^2 - 9y^2$.

Sol.

(1) This is the difference of two squares, so you find the square root of the first term. $(2x)(2x)$

(2) Next, you find the square root of the second term. $(3y)(3y)$

(3) Now fill in the signs. One has a plus sign, the other has a minus sign. Although it does not matter which comes first, you must have one of each. $(2x - 3y)(2x + 3y)$.

> **Note :** Your teacher will explain to you that the *sum* of two squares, say $a^2 + b^2$ cannot be factorised over the set of real numbers.

Ex. 2. *Factorise :* $\dfrac{x^2}{25} - \dfrac{y^2}{36}$.

Sol. $\dfrac{x^2}{25} - \dfrac{y^2}{36} = \left(\dfrac{x}{5}\right)^2 - \left(\dfrac{y}{6}\right)^2 = \left(\dfrac{x}{5} - \dfrac{y}{6}\right)\left(\dfrac{x}{5} + \dfrac{y}{6}\right)$.

Ex. 3. *Factorise* $a^{10}b^{24} - 0.09x^{36}$.

Sol. Exp. $= a^{10}b^{24} - 0.09x^{36} = \left(a^5 b^{12}\right)^2 - \left(0.3x^{18}\right)^2$ Using $x^{mn} = (x^m)^n$

$= \left(a^5 b^{12} - 0.3x^{18}\right)\left(a^5 b^{12} + 0.3x^{18}\right)$.

Ex. 4. *Find the value of* $687 \times 687 - 313 \times 313$.

Sol. $687 \times 687 - 313 \times 313 = \left(687\right)^2 - \left(313\right)^2$

$= \left(687 + 313\right)\left(687 - 313\right) = 1000 \times 374 = \mathbf{374000.}$

Ex. 5. *Simplify :* $\dfrac{725 \times 725 - 413 \times 413}{725 + 413}$.

Sol. $\dfrac{725 \times 725 - 413 \times 413}{725 + 413} = \dfrac{\left(725\right)^2 - \left(413\right)^2}{725 + 413}$

$= \dfrac{\left(725 + 413\right)\left(725 - 413\right)}{725 + 413} = 725 - 413 = \mathbf{312.}$

EXERCISE 16 (e)

Factorise :

1. $x^2 - 9$	**2.** $x^2 - 4$	**3.** $a^2 - 25$	**4.** $p^2 - 1$	**5.** $16a^2 - 121$
6. $16x^2 - 25y^2$	**7.** $36m^2 - 169n^2$	**8.** $-64 + 25x^2$	**9.** $x^2 y^2 - a^2$	**10.** $x^4 - 9$
11. $a^8 - 36$	**12.** $x^6 - 16$	**13.** $1 - 4c^{12}$	**14.** $25x^6 - 49y^8$	**15.** $2.25a^2 - b^2$
16. $x^2 y^2 - 0.81$	**17.** $25p^2 - \dfrac{1}{9}$	**18.** $\dfrac{16a^2}{25b^2} - \dfrac{x^2}{100y^2}$	**19.** $-36 + \dfrac{1}{49}m^2$	**20.** $\dfrac{4}{9}p^2 - \dfrac{25}{36}q^4$

Find the value of :

21. $2003^2 - 1997^2$ **22.** $100.6^2 - 99.4^2$

Simplify :

24. $\dfrac{5682 \times 5682 - 3432 \times 3432}{5682 + 3432}$ **25.** $\dfrac{4.987 \times 4.987 - 3.013 \times 3.013}{4.987 - 3.013}$

16.6 Factorisation of Difference of Two Squares (continued) Harder Examples.

Ex. 1. Factorise : $(5x + 4y)^2 - (3x - 2y)^2$.

Sol. Exp. $= (5x + 4y)^2 - (3x - 2y)^2 = \{(5x + 4y) - (3x - 2y)\}\{(5x + 4y) + (3x - 2y)\}$

$= (5x + 4y - 3x + 2y)(5x + 4y + 3x - 2y) = (2x + 6y)(8x + 2y),$ Combining like terms.

$= 2(x + 3y) \cdot 2(4x + y) = 4(x + 3y)(4x + y).$ Taking out common factor 2 from both brackets.

Ex. 2. _Factorise :_ $16a^2 - 9(b - c)^2$.

Sol. Exp. $= 16a^2 - 9(b - c)^2 = 4^2 a^2 - 3^2 (b - c)^2$

$= (4a)^2 - (3b - 3c)^2$ ⟵ Note this step. 3 has been taken inside the bracket.

$= (4a - 3b + 3c)(4a + 3b - 3c).$

Ex. 3. Factorise : $48ax^2 - 75ay^2$.

Sol. First take out the greatest common factor.

$\quad$ **Exp.** $= 48ax^2 - 75ay^2 = 3a(16x^2 - 25y^2) = 3a\{(4x)^2 - (5y)^2\} = 3a(4x - 5y)(4x + 5y).$

Ex. 4. Factorise : $5(3x - 4y)^2 - 20(2x - y)^2$.

Sol. Exp. $= 5[(3x - 4y)^2 - 4(2x - y)^2]$ First take out the common factor '5'

$= 5[(3x - 4y)^2 - 2^2 (2x - y)^2]$

$= 5[(3x - 4y)^2 - (4x - 2y)^2]$ Write $2^2 (2x - y)^2 = [2(2x - y)]^2 = (4x - 2y)^2$

$= 5(3x - 4y - 4x + 2y)(3x - 4y + 4x - 2y)$

$= 5(-x - 2y)(7x - 6y) = -5(x + 2y)(7x - 6y).$

Ex. 5. _Factorise :_ $16x^4 - y^4$.

Sol. Exp. $= (4x^2)^2 - (y^2)^2 = (4x^2 - y^2)(4x^2 + y^2)$

The factor $(4x^2 - y^2)$ can be factorised further

$= [(2x)^2 - (y)^2](4x^2 + y^2) = (2x - y)(2x + y)(4x^2 + y^2).$

EXERCISE 16 (f)

Factorise :

1. $(a + b)^2 - 1$ **2.** $(3x - 2y)^2 - 9z^2$ **3.** $1 - (x - y)^2$ **4.** $4x^2 - 9(2x - y)^2$

5. $16(x + y)^2 - 25(x - y)^2$ **6.** $ab^2 - ac^2$ **7.** $36x^3 - x$

8. $3 - 12b^2$ **9.** $18ax^2 - 98ay^2$ **10.** $2x^2 - \dfrac{1}{2}$ (**Hint.** Given Exp. $= 2\left(x^2 - \dfrac{1}{4}\right)$)

11. $x^4 - y^4$ **12.** $x^4 - 625$ **13.** $16y^4 - 81$ **14.** $xy^5 - yx^5$

15. $(a + b)^2 - (b - a)^2$ **16.** $(x + 2y - 5z)^2 - (x - 2y + 5z)^2$

16.7 Factorising Trinomials of the Form x² + bx + c

Ex. 1. **Factorise :** $x^2 + 6x + 8$.

Sol. First check to see if there is a common monomial factor. Since there is none, we can start the trial and error factorising into the product of two binomials as follows :

First clue :	Since the product of the linear terms of the binomials must be x^2, therefore, the factors are of the form shown at the right.	$(x+?)(x+?)$
Second clue :	The product of the constant terms of the binomials must be 8. The factors of 8 are 1,2,4,8. Thus, the constant term should be 8×1 or 2×4. Of these, we choose that pair the sum of whose components gives the coefficient of the middle term 6. The sum of 2 and 4 is 6. Therefore, 2 and 4 are the second terms of binomials.	$(x \; 2)(x \; 4)$
Third clue :	The product of the constant terms, of the binomials must be 8.Therefore, both constant terms must be positive numbers or both must be negative numbers. Hence, the only integral choices are 2, 4, or –2, –4. Since the middle term is $+6x$, we choose +2 and +4.	$(x+2)(x+4)$

Study the following also :   **Factors**

(i) $x^2 + 2x - 8$ $(x+4)(x-2)$

(ii) $x^2 - 2x - 8$ $(x-4)(x+2)$

In (i), since the product is negative, one constant term should be positive and the other negative.

Since the middle term is $+2x$, the greater constant term should be positive and the smaller negative. Therefore, we choose +4 and –2.

In (ii), since the middle term is $-2x$, the greater constant term should be negative, and the smaller positive. Therefore, we choose –4 and +2.

Ex. 2. _Factorise :_ **(a)** $x^2 + 9x + 20$ **(b)** $x^2 + 7x + 12$ ·

Sol. (a) We have to find two numbers whose sum is +9 and the product is +20.

These numbers are 5 and 4.

Exp. = $x^2 + 9x + 20 = x^2 + 5x + 4x + 20$

       = $x(x + 5) + 4 (x + 5) = (x + 5) (x + 4)$

(b) We have to find two numbers whose product is 12 and the sum is –7. The numbers are –4 and –3.

∴ $x^2 - 7x + 12 = x^2 - 4x - 3x + 12 = x(x - 4) - 3 (x - 4) = (x - 4) (x - 3)$.

Ex. 3. _Factorise :_ **(a)** $x^2 + 5x - 24$ **(b)** $x^2 - 11x - 80$.

Sol. (a) The two numbers, whose product is –24 and the sum is 5, are 8 and –3.

$x^2 + 5x - 24 = x^2 + 8x - 3x - 24$

         $= x(x + 8) - 3 (x + 8)$

         $= (x + 8) (x - 3)$.

> **Think**
>
> Constant term is –24 which is negative. So one of the numbers will be –ve and another +ve. Since the coeff. of x is +5 which is +ve, therefore, the greater number will be +ve.

(*b*) The two numbers whose product is –80 and the sum is –11, are –16 and +5.

Exp. = $x^2 - 11x - 80 = x^2 - 16x + 5x - 80$

$\qquad = x(x - 16) + 5(x - 16) = (x - 16)(x + 5).$

EXERCISE 16 (g)

Factorise :

1. $a^2 + 5a + 6$ 2. $x^2 + 7x + 12$ 3. $m^2 + 13m + 42$ 4. $a^2 + 25a - 54$ 5. $t^2 + 9t - 36$

6. $a^2 + 5a - 50$ 7. $x^2 - 4x - 5$ 8. $y^2 - 10y + 16$ 9. $x^2 - 2x - 24$ 10. $y^2 + 2y - 48$

11. $n^2 - 3n - 40$ 12. $y^2 - 11y + 24$ 13. $48 + 22x - x^2$ 14. $c^2 - 18c + 65$ 15. $x^2 - 29x + 204$

16. $p^2 - 5p - 176$ 17. $n^2 - 19n - 92$ 18. $j^2 - 11j - 102$

19. $2a^3 + 10a^2 - 28a$ [**Hint.** First take out the common factor 2a.]

20. $12b + 15 - 3b^2$ 21. $3c^5 - 18c^4 - 48c^3$ 22. $-2y^3 + 22y^2 + 24y$

23. $b^2c^3 + 8bc^4 + 12c^5$ 24. $a^4 - 5a^2 - 36$ 25. $y^4 + 4y^2 - 32$

16.8 Factorising Trinomials of the Form ax² + bx + c

The difference in the two quadratic polynomials, $x^2 + bx + c$, considered so far and $ax^2 + bx + c$ which we will take up now, is that while in the first expression the coefficient of x^2 is 1, in the latter it is *a*. Now we will find two numbers such that.

  (*i*) Sum is equal to the coeffcient of x in the middle term.

  (*ii*) Product is equal to ac, that is, equal to (coeff. of x^2 × constant term).

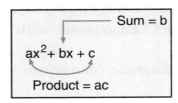

Ex. 1. *Factorise:* $2x^2 + 7x + 5$.

  Sol. We have to find two numbers whose sum is 7 and the product is 2 × 5, that is, 10. The two such numbers are 2 and 5.

$\qquad \therefore$ Given exp. $= 2x^2 + 7x + 5 = 2x^2 + 2x + 5x + 5$

$\qquad\qquad\qquad = 2x(x + 1) + 5(x + 1) = (x + 1)(2x + 5).$

Ex. 2. *Factorise :* $2x^2 + 9x - 5$

  Sol.   Exp. $= 2x^2 + 9x - 5$

$\qquad\qquad = 2x^2 + 10x - x - 5$

$\qquad\qquad = 2x(x + 5) - 1(x + 5)$

$\qquad\qquad = (x + 5)(2x - 1).$

Think
The two numbers whose sum is + 9 and the product 2 × (–5) *i.e.* –10, are 10 and –1

Ex. 3. **Factorise :** $12x^2 - x - 1$.

  Sol. Exp. $= 12x^2 - x - 1$

$\qquad\qquad = 12x^2 - 4x + 3x - 1$

Think
The two numbers whose sum is –1 and the product is 12(–1), that is –12, are –4 and +3.

$= 4x(3x - 1) + 1(3x - 1)$

$= (3x - 1)(4x + 1).$

Ex. 4. *Factorise :* $-5x^2 - x + 4.$

Sol. Exp. $= -5x^2 - x + 4.$

$= -(5x^2 + x - 4)$ | Change sign for the sake of covenience |

$= -(5x^2 + 5x - 4x - 4) = -[5x(x + 1) - 4(x + 1)]$

$= -(5x - 4)(x + 1).$

Ex. 5. *Factorise :* $12y^3 - 14y^2 - 10y.$

Sol. Exp. $= 12y^3 - 14y^2 - 10y.$

$= 2y(6y^2 - 7y - 5)$

$= 2y(6y^2 - 10y + 3y - 5)$

$= 2y\{2y(3y - 5) + 1(3y - 5)\}$

$= 2y(3y - 5)(2y + 1).$

Think
$6 \times -5 = -30$

2	30
3	15
	5

$-10 + 3 = -7$
$-10 \times 3 = -30$

Ex. 6. *Factorise:* $15x^4 + 3x^2 - 18.$

Sol. Exp.$= 15x^4 + 3x^2 - 18 = 3(5x^4 + x^2 - 6)$

Take out the common factor 3

$= 3(5x^4 + 6x^2 - 5x^2 - 6)$

$= 3[x^2(5x^2 + 6) - 1(5x^2 + 6)]$

$= 3(5x^2 + 6)(x^2 - 1)$

can be factorised further. | $x^2 - 1 = (x - 1)(x + 1)$ |

$= 3(5x^2 + 6)(x - 1)(x + 1)$

EXERCISE 16 (h)

Factorise :

1. $4x^2 + 5x + 1$ **2.** $2x^2 + 11x + 14$ **3.** $2x^2 + 11x + 12$ **4.** $3x^2 + 13x + 4$ **5.** $2x^2 - 5x - 12$

6. $4x^2 + 8x - 5$ **7.** $13x^2 + 37x - 6$ **8.** $40n^2 + n - 6$ **9.** $4z^2 - 16z + 15$ **10.** $6 - 9c - 27c^2$

11. $1 - t - 6t^2$ **12.** $2a^2 + 7ab - 15b^2$ **13.** $4x^2 + 24x + 20$ **14.** $12a^2 + 2a - 4$ **15.** $12m^3 + 6m^2 - 6m$

16. $6x^5 - 22x^3 - 8x$ **17.** $6z^6 - 21z^4 - 12z^2$ **18.** $-12b^5 - b^3 + b$

MENTAL MATHS – 14

Find the factors of the following :

1. $3x^2 + 5x$ **2.** $x^3y^2 + x^2y^3$ **3.** $3x(5x - y) + 4y(5x - y)$ **4.** $16x^2 - 25y^2$

5. $4x^2 + 12x + 9$ **6.** $36 - 60y + 25y^2$ **7.** $a^4 - 25$ **8.** $\dfrac{1}{x^2} - 16$

9. $\dfrac{x^2}{4} - \dfrac{y^2}{9}$ **10.** $x^2 + 16x + 63$

LOOKING BACK
Summary of Key Facts

1. Factorization means expressing a given algebraic expression as the product of two or more expressions. Each of the expressions occuring in the product is called a **factor**.
   Thus, $x^3 - 9 = (x - 3)\ (x + 3)$

   Factors

2. You have studied the following methods of finding factors of a given polynomial
   (*i*) By taking out the common factor

   e.g. $\mathbf{5x^2 + 25x}$ $= 5x\ (x + 5),\ 7x(x + 2) + 5\ (x + 2) = (x + 2)\ (7x + 5).$

   (*ii*) By grouping the terms :
   $5x + 5y + ax + ay = 5(x + y) + a\ (x + y) = (x + y)\ (5 + a).$

   (*iii*) By expressing as difference of two squares and using the formula $a^2 - b^2 = (a + b)\ (a - b).$

   (*iv*) Factorising the trinomials of the form $x^2 + bx + c$ and $ax^2 + bx + c$.

ANSWERS

EXERCISE 16 (a)

1. $3(y - 3)$
2. $5(x + 2)$
3. $2(x - 2)$
4. $5(m + n)$
5. $4(a + 2b)$
6. $7(x - 2y)$
7. $-3(m + 5n)$
8. $-7(p + 2q)$
9. $x(6x + 11)$
10. $y(3y + 7)$
11. $x(a + b)$
12. $xy(x + y)$
13. $4(1 + 3x^2)$
14. $a(x + y + z)$
15. $ab(a^2 + b^2)$
16. $x^2(y^2 + 1)$
17. $p(p - 3q + q^2)$
18. $y^2(7y - 5)$
19. $2x^2(3x - 5)$
20. $2b(ab - 3c + 4ac)$
21. $4p^3(3p^2 + 4p - 5)$

EXERCISE 16 (b)

1. $(x + 3)\ (x + y)$
2. $(a + 1)\ (x + y)$
3. $(m + n)\ (a + b)$
4. $2(x - a)\ (x - a + 2m)$
5. $(a + b)\ (a - b)$
6. $(p + q)\ (p + q + 3)$
7. $(x + y)\ (x + y + 1)$
8. $(x + y)\ (1 - x - y)$
9. $(x - y)\ (a - bx + by)$
10. $(x + y + z)\ (a + b + c)$
11. $(a - b)^3(a - b + 1)$
12. $(a + b)(a^2 + b^2 - ab)$

EXERCISE 16 (c)

1. $(m + n)\ (x + y)$
2. $(x + y)\ (p + x)$
3. $(x + y)\ (a + 8)$
4. $(m + 4)\ (m - 8)$
5. $(x + y)\ (3 + p)$
6. $(a + b)\ (x + 7)$
7. $(x - 2)\ (y - z)$
8. $(x - 1)\ (x - y)$
9. $(3y - 5)\ (x + 2)$
10. $(2x + 1)\ (3x - 2y)$
11. $(1 - 2a^2)(1 - 2a)$
12. $(a - 2b)\ (a - 2b + 3)$
13. $2(x + y)\ (16x + 16y - 1)$
14. $(x + a)\ (ax + 1)$
15. $x^2(x + 1)(x^2 + 1)$

EXERCISE 16 (d)

1. $(x + 2)\ (x + 2)$
2. $(x + 3)\ (x + 3)$
3. $(x - 5)\ (x - 5)$
4. $(2x - 1)\ (2x - 1)$
5. $(a + 5b)(a + 5b)$
6. $(x - 4y)(x - 4y)$
7. $(2x + 5y)(2x + 5y)$
8. $(8x - 5y)(8x - 5y)$
9. $(x^2 + 3)\ (x^2 + 3)$
10. $(2x^2 - 3)(2x^2 - 3)$
11. $\left(a - \dfrac{1}{a}\right)\left(a - \dfrac{1}{a}\right)$
12. $\left(x + \dfrac{1}{2}\right)\left(x + \dfrac{1}{2}\right)$

EXERCISE 16 (e)

1. $(x - 3)\ (x + 3)$
2. $(x - 2)\ (x + 2)$
3. $(a - 5)\ (a + 5)$
4. $(p - 1)\ (p + 1)$
5. $(4a - 11)(4a + 11)$
6. $(4x - 5y)\ (4x + 5y)$
7. $(6m - 13n)\ (6m + 13n)$
8. $(5x - 8)(5x + 8)$
9. $(xy + a)(xy - a)$
10. $(x^2 - 3)(x^2 + 3)$
11. $(a^4 - 6)(a^4 + 6)$
12. $(x^3 - 4)(x^3 + 4)$
13. $(1 - 2c^6)(1 + 2c^6)$
14. $\left(5x^3 - 7y^4\right)\left(5x^3 + 7y^4\right)$

15. $(1.5a-b)(1.5a+b)$ 16. $(xy-0.9)(xy+0.9)$ 17. $\left(5p-\dfrac{1}{3}\right)\left(5p+\dfrac{1}{3}\right)$ 18. $\left(\dfrac{4a}{5b}-\dfrac{x}{10y}\right)\left(\dfrac{4a}{5b}+\dfrac{x}{10y}\right)$

19. $\left(\dfrac{m}{7}-6\right)\left(\dfrac{m}{7}+6\right)$ 20. $\left(\dfrac{2}{3}p-\dfrac{5}{6}q^2\right)\left(\dfrac{2}{3}p+\dfrac{5}{6}q^2\right)$ 21. $24,000$ 22. 240

23. 2250 24. 8

EXERCISE 16 (f)

1. $(a+b-1)(a+b+1)$ 2. $(3x-2y-3z)(3x-2y+3z)$ 3. $(1-x+y)(1+x-y)$ 4. $(-4x+3y)(8x-3y)$

5. $(9x-y)(-x+9y)$ 6. $a(b-c)(b+c)$ 7. $x(6x-1)(6x+1)$ 8. $3(1-2b)(1+2b)$

9. $2a(3x-7y)(3x+7y)$ 10. $2\left(x-\dfrac{1}{2}\right)\left(x+\dfrac{1}{2}\right)$ 11. $(x-y)(x+y)\left(x^2+y^2\right)$ 12. $(x-5)(x+5)\left(x^2+25\right)$

13. $(2y-3)(2y+3)\left(4y^2+9\right)$ 14. $xy(y-x)(y+x)\left(y^2+x^2\right)$

15. $4ab$ 16. $4x(2y-5z)$

EXERCISE 16 (g)

1. $(a+3)(a+2)$ 2. $(x+4)(x+3)$ 3. $(m+7)(m+6)$ 4. $(a+27)(a-2)$ 5. $(t+12)(t-3)$

6. $(a+10)(a-5)$ 7. $(x-5)(x+1)$ 8. $(y-8)(y-2)$ 9. $(x-6)(x+4)$ 10. $(y+8)(y-6)$

11. $(n-8)(n+5)$ 12. $(y-8)(y-3)$ 13. $(24-x)(2+x)$ 14. $(c-13)(c-5)$ 15. $(x-12)(x-17)$

16. $(p-16)(p+11)$ 17. $(n-23)(n+4)$ 18. $(j-17)(j+6)$ 19. $2a(a+7)(a-2)$ 20. $-3(b-5)(b+1)$

21. $3c^3(c-8)(c+2)$ 22. $-2y(y-12)(y+1)$ 23. $c^3(b+6c)(b+2c)$

24. $(a-3)(a+3)\left(a^2+4\right)$ 25. $(y-2)(y+2)\left(y^2+8\right)$

EXERCISE 16 (h)

1. $(4x+1)(x+1)$ 2. $(x+2)(2x+7)$ 3. $(2x+3)(x+4)$ 4. $(3x+1)(x+4)$ 5. $(2x+3)(x-4)$

6. $(2x+5)(2x-1)$ 7. $(13x-2)(x+3)$ 8. $(8n-3)(5n+2)$ 9. $(2z-5)(2z-3)$ 10. $3(1-3c)(2+3c)$

11. $(1+2t)(1-3t)$ 12. $(2a-3b)(a+5b)$ 13. $4(x+1)(x+5)$ 14. $2(2a-1)(3a+2)$ 15. $6m(2m-1)(m+1)$

16. $2x(x+2)(x-2)\left(3x^2+1\right)$ 17. $3z^2(z+2)(z-2)\left(2z^2+1\right)$

18. $b(1-2b)(1+2b)\left(1+3b^2\right)$

MENTAL MATHS – 14

1. $x(3x+5)$ 2. $x^2y^2(x+y)$ 3. $(5x-y)(3x+4y)$ 4. $(4x+5y)(4x-5y)$

5. $(2x+3)(2x+3)$ 6. $(6-5y)(6-5y)$ 7. $\left(a^2+5\right)\left(a^2-5\right)$ 8. $\left(\dfrac{1}{x}+4\right)\left(\dfrac{1}{x}-4\right)$

9. $\left(\dfrac{x}{2}+\dfrac{y}{3}\right)\left(\dfrac{x}{2}-\dfrac{y}{3}\right)$ 10. $(x+9)(x+7)$

17. Simplification of Algebraic Expressions

17.1 H.C.F. of Two Polynomials

A common factor of two or more monomials is a polynomial which divides each of them exactly. Thus a^2b^2 is a common factor of a^3b^5, a^6b^3.

The **highest common factor** of two polynomials is the polynomial of the highest degree and greatest numerical coefficient which divides both the polynomials exactly. It is shortly written as H.C.F. or G.C.F.

Type 1. **H.C.F. of Monomials**

Method 1. *Find the H.C.F. of the numerical coefficients of all the monomials.*

2. *Find the highest power of each of the variables common to all the monomials. Omit the variables which are not common.*

3. *Multiply (1) and (2). The product is the H.C.F. of the given monomials.*

Ex. 1. *Find the H.C.F. $16x^2y^4, 20x^5y^3, 12x^3y^8z$.*

Sol. H.C.F. of 16, 20, 12 = 4

Highest power of x common to all = x^2, highest power of y common to all = y^3

z is not common

∴   H.C.F. of the given monomials = $4x^2y^3$.

Ex. 2. *Find the H.C.F. of $27a^{28}b^{11}c^5, 81a^7c^8b^9d^{19}$ and $9a^3b^{10}c^{13}d^5$.*

Sol. H.C.F. of 27, 81 and 9 = 9

Highest power of a common to all = a^3.

Highest power of b common to all = b^9.

Highest power of c common to all = c^5.

d is not common ∴   H.C.F. of the given monomials $= 9a^3b^9c^5$.

Type 2. **H.C.F. of polynomials which can be easily factorised.**

Method 1. *Find the factors of the polynomials.*

2. *Find the H.C.F. of the numerical factors.*

3. *Find the set of common factors of the given polynomials.*

4. *The product of all such common factors and the H.C.F. of the numerical factors is the H.C.F. of the given polynomials.*

Ex. 3. **Find the H.C.F. of :** $x^2 + x - 2, x^3 + 5x^2 + 6x$.

Sol. $x^2 + x - 2 = x^2 + 2x - x - 2 = x(x+2) - 1(x+2) = (x-1)(x+2)$ ...(i)

$x^3 + 5x^2 + 6x = x(x^2 + 5x + 6)$

$$= x\left(x^2+3x+2x+6\right) = x\left[x(x+3)+2(x+3)\right]$$

$$= x(x+2)(x+3) \qquad\qquad\qquad ...(ii)$$

The common factor to (*i*) and (*ii*) is $x+2$ ∴ H.C.F. $= x+2$.

Ex. 4. *Find the H.C.F. of* $2x^2 - x, 6x^2 + x - 2, 14x^2 + 3x - 5, 4x^2 - 1$ *and* $(2x - 1)^2$.

Sol. 1st polynomial $= 2x^2 - x = x(2x-1)$

2nd polynomial $= 6x^2 + x - 2$

$$= 6x^2 + 4x - 3x - 2 = 2x(3x+2) - 1(3x+2)$$

$$= (3x+2)(2x-1)$$

3rd polynomial $= 14x^2 + 3x - 5$

$$= 14x^2 + 10x - 7x - 5 = 2x(7x+5) - 1(7x+5)$$

$$= (2x-1)(7x+5)$$

4th polynomial $= 4x^2 - 1 = (2x)^2 - 1^2 = (2x-1)(4x+1)$

5th polynomial $= (2x-1)^2$

The common factor to all the polyomials is $2x-1$. ∴ H.C.F. $= 2x-1$.

17.2 L.C.M. of Two Polynomials

■ Definitions

1. **A Common Multiple** of two or more polynomials is a polynomial which is exactly divisible by each of them.

   For example, x^5 is a common multiple of x^3 and x^5 and $6x^2yz$ is a common multiple of $2x^2$ and $3xz$.

2. **The Lowest Common Multiple (L.C.M.)** of polynomials is the polynomial of the lowest degree and smallest numerical coefficient which is exactly divisible by both the given polynomials.

■ Method of determining L.C.M.

Type 1. L.C.M. of Monomials

Ex.1. *Find the L.C.M. of* $16x^2y^4, 20x^5y^3$ *and* $12x^3y^8$.

Sol. L.C.M. of 16, 20 and 12 $= 4 \times 3 \times 4 \times 5 = 240$

L.C.M. of x^2, x^3 and $x^5 = x^5$, L.C.M. of y^4, y^3, and $y^8 = y^8$

∴ L.C.M. of the given monomials $= 240x^5y^8$.

4	12	16	20
	3	4	5

Type 2. L.C.M. of polynomials which can be easily factorised.

Step 1. *Write each polynomial in factorised form.*

Step 2. *Include in the L.C.M. the factors that are common to the given polynomials and then the remaining factors that are not common.*

Step 3. *The L.C.M. is the product of all the common factors and the remaining factors.*

Ex. 2. *Find the L.C.M. of the following :* $6a^2 - 5a - 6, 12a^2 + 11a + 2$.

Sol.   1st exp. $= 6a^2 - 5a - 6 = 6a^2 - 9a + 4a - 6 = 3a(2a - 3) + 2(2a - 3) = (2a - 3)(3a + 2)$

     2nd exp. $= 12a^2 + 11a + 2 = 12a^2 + 8a + 3a + 2 = 4a(3a + 2) + 1(3a + 2) = (3a + 2)(4a + 1)$

     The common factor is $(3a+2)$. The remaining factors are $(2a - 3)$ and $(4a + 1)$

    $\therefore$ L.C.M. $= (3a + 2)(2a - 3)(4a + 1)$.

Ex. 3. *Find the L.C.M. of the following :* $8x^2 y(x^4 - y^4), 12x^3 y^2 (x^2 + 2xy - 3y^2),$

     $24x^4 y^3 (x^3 + xy^2 + x^2 y + y^3)$.

Sol.   1st. exp. $= 8x^2 y\left[(x^2)^2 - (y^2)^2\right] = 8x^2 y(x^2 - y^2)(x^2 + y^2) = 8x^2 y(x - y)(x + y)(x^2 + y^2)$

     2nd. exp. $= 12x^3 y^2 (x^2 + 2xy - 3y^2) = 12x^3 y^2 \left(x^2 + 3xy - xy - 3y^2\right)$

             $= 12x^3 y^2 \left\{x(x + 3y) - y(x + 3y)\right\} = 12x^3 y^2 (x + 3y)(x - y)$

     3rd. exp. $= 24x^4 y^3 \left(x^3 + xy^2 + x^2 y + y^3\right) = 24x^4 y^3 \left\{x\left(x^2 + y^2\right) + y\left(x^2 + y^2\right)\right\}$

4	8,	12,	24
3	2,	3,	6,
2	2,	1,	2,
	1,	1,	1,

             $= 24x^4 y^3 (x + y)(x^2 + y^2)$

    $\therefore$ L.C.M. of 8, 12, 24 $= 4 \times 3 \times 2 = 24$

     L.C.M. of $x^2, x^3, x^4 = x^4$, L.C.M. of $y, y^2, y^3 = y^3$

    $\therefore$ Reqd. L.C.M. $= 24x^4 y^3 (x - y)(x + y)(x + 3y)(x^2 + y^2)$

EXERCISE 17 (a)

Find the H.C.F. and L.C.M. of the following monomials :

1. $a^2 b, \ ab^2$ **2.** $5a^2 b^4, \ 10a^4 b^3$ **3.** $12a^3 b^3 d^5, \ 20a^2 d^2 b^4$

4. $26x^4 y^7 z^{10}, \ 13xy^5 z^4, \ 78x^3 y^8 z^7$ **5.** $15p^{27} q^{12} r^{21}, \ 90p^{20} q^{10} r^{11}, \ 135p^{10} q^{11} z^{30}$

Find the H.C.F. of the following polynomials:

6. $x^2 - y^2, \ (x - y)^2$ **7.** $x^2 - 7x + 12, \ x^2 - 16$ **8.** $x^3 - x, \ x^3 + 2x^2 + x$ **9.** $6x^2 - 11x + 3, \ 3x^2 + 26x - 9$

Find the L.C.M of the follwing polynomials

10. $x^2 - 1, (x - 1)^2$ **11.** $3y + 12, \ y^2 - 16$ **12.** $x - y$ and $y - x$ **13.** $x^2 - 2xy + y^2, \ x^2 - y^2$

14. $3x^2 + 15x + 18, \ 2x^2 - 2x - 12$ **15.** $2x^2 - 10x + 12, \ x^2 - 6x + 5$ **16.** $x^2 + x - 6, \ x^3 - 4x$

17.3 Rational Expressions or Algebraic Fractions

     Definition. A fraction is any expression which appears in the form of a quotient like $\dfrac{m}{n}$ where m and n represent any numbers or expressions.

Fractions like $\dfrac{x-3}{x+5}, \dfrac{x^2-3x+2}{5x^2-x+1}, \dfrac{2}{x-3}, \dfrac{x+1}{7x^2+x-1}$ having polynomials in the numerator or denominator or both

are called **algebraic fractions** or **rational expressions.**

Equality of algebraic fractions. You know that two rational numbers are equal, only if the following relationship exists:

$$\frac{a}{b} = \frac{c}{d} \text{, if and only if } ad = bc.$$

In a similar manner two algebraic fractions $\dfrac{A}{B}$ and $\dfrac{C}{D}$ are equal if and only if AD = BC.

17.4 Simplifying Algebraic Fractions

In arithmetic, you learnt to change fractions to lowest terms. By this, you understood that an equivalent fraction was to be found out so that the numerator and denominator did not contain a common factor. Similarly, an algebraic fraction is in simplest form when the polynomials in the numerator and denominator do not have a common factor.

Ex. 1. *Reduce to lowest terms* : $\dfrac{18x^4 y^9}{24x^{10} y^5}$.

Sol. $\dfrac{18x^4 y^9}{24x^{10} y^5} = \dfrac{18}{24} \cdot \dfrac{x^4}{x^{10}} \cdot \dfrac{y^9}{y^5} = \dfrac{3}{4} \cdot \dfrac{1}{x^6} \cdot y^4 = \dfrac{3y^4}{4x^6}.$

Ex.2. *Reduce* $\dfrac{3c+15}{c^2-25}$ *to lowest terms.*

Sol. $\dfrac{3c+15}{c^2-25} = \dfrac{3(c+5)}{(c+5)(c-5)} = \dfrac{3}{c-5}.$

Sometimes factors of the numerator and denominator are opposite of one another as in the next example.

Ex. 3. *Simplify:* $\dfrac{4-x}{x^2-x-12}$.

Sol. $x^2-x-12 = x^2-4x+3x-12 = x(x-4)+3(x-4) = (x-4)(x+3)$

Express the numerator as a product having -1 as a factor.

$$4-x = -1(x-4)$$

$\therefore$ fraction $= \dfrac{-1(x-4)}{(x-4)(x+3)} = \dfrac{-1}{x+3}.$

EXERCISE 17 (b)

Simplify :

1. $\dfrac{16xy}{20xz}$

2. $\dfrac{9x^2 y}{15xy^2}$

3. $\dfrac{-45a^4 b^3}{10a^3 b^2}$

4. $\dfrac{5m+5n}{7m+7n}$

5. $\dfrac{a^2-b^2}{a+b}$

6. $\dfrac{9x+27}{x^2-9}$

7. $\dfrac{x^2-9}{x^2-6x+9}$

8. $\dfrac{x^2+2x-15}{x^2+7x+10}$

9. $\dfrac{x^4+a^2 x^2}{x^4-a^4}$

10. $\dfrac{4p^2-100}{p^2-2x-35}$

11. $\dfrac{x-7}{2x^2-11x-21}$

12. $\dfrac{x^2-13x+42}{x^2-8x+12}$

13. $\dfrac{6x^2-5x+1}{9x^2-6x+1}$

14. $\dfrac{(x-3)(x^2-5x+4)}{(x-4)(x^2-2x-3)}$

15. $\dfrac{x^2-xy}{x^3 y-xy^3}$

17.5 Multiplication and Division of Algebraic Fractions

You know how to multiply two rational numbers. Two algebraic fractions are multiplied in the same manner.

Ex. 1   (i) $\dfrac{3x}{y} \cdot \dfrac{w}{5z} = \dfrac{3xw}{5zy}$.

> Multiply the numerators
> multiply the denominators

(ii) $\dfrac{5x}{y^2} \cdot \dfrac{7yz^2}{10x^2} = \dfrac{5 \times 7}{10} \cdot \dfrac{x}{x^2} \cdot \dfrac{y}{y^2} \cdot z^2 = \dfrac{7z^2}{2xy}$.

(iii) $\dfrac{-2ab^3}{3ac^2} \cdot \dfrac{abc}{c^3d^3} \cdot \dfrac{c^2d^4}{-4a^2b} = \dfrac{-2ab^3 \cdot abc \cdot c^2d^4}{3ac^2 \cdot c^3d^3 \cdot -4a^2b} = \dfrac{-2a^2b^4c^3d^4}{-12a^3bc^5d^3} = \dfrac{b^3d}{6ac^2}$.

(iv) $\left(\dfrac{a}{b}\right)^2 = \dfrac{a}{b} \cdot \dfrac{a}{b} = \dfrac{a^2}{b^2}$.

(v) $\dfrac{6x^2y}{5ab^2} \div \dfrac{18xy}{25a^2b^2} = \dfrac{6x^2y}{5ab^2} \times \dfrac{25a^2b^2}{18xy} = \dfrac{6 \times 25}{5 \times 18} \cdot \dfrac{x^2y}{xy} \cdot \dfrac{a^2b^2}{ab^2} = \dfrac{5}{3} \times xa = \dfrac{5}{3}ax.$

Ex. 2. *Multiply:* $\dfrac{8x^2}{x^2 - y^2} \cdot \dfrac{x+y}{2x}$

> **Method :** Factorise numerators and denominators when necessary.

Sol. $\dfrac{8x^2}{x^2 - y^2} \cdot \dfrac{x+y}{2x} = \dfrac{8x^2}{(x+y)(x-y)} \cdot \dfrac{x+y}{2x} = \dfrac{4x}{x-y}$.

Ex. 3. *Simplify :* $\dfrac{5x+5y}{x^2-y^2} \cdot \dfrac{2x^2+xy-3y^2}{(x+y)^2}$.

Sol. $5x + 5y = 5(x+y); x^2 - y^2 = (x-y)(x+y)$

$2x^2 + xy - 3y^2 = 2x^2 + 3xy - 2xy - 3y^2$

$= x(2x+3y) - y(2x+3y) = (2x+3y)(x-y)$

$\therefore \quad \dfrac{5x+5y}{x^2-y^2} \cdot \dfrac{2x^2+xy-3y^2}{(x+y)^2} = \dfrac{5(x+y)}{(x+y)(x-y)} \cdot \dfrac{(2x+3y)(x-y)}{(x+y)^2} = \dfrac{5(2x+3y)}{(x+y)^2}$.

EXERCISE 17 (c)

Simplify :

1. $\dfrac{x}{y^2} \cdot \dfrac{y}{xz} \cdot \dfrac{z^2}{xy}$

2. $\dfrac{4x^2y}{5ab} \cdot \dfrac{3ab^2}{9xy^2}$

3. $\dfrac{2g-2h}{g+h} \cdot \dfrac{2g+2h}{4g}$

4. $\dfrac{x}{x+5} \cdot \dfrac{x^2-25}{x^2+3x}$

5. $\dfrac{a^2-b^2}{a^2-2ab+b^2} \cdot \dfrac{a-b}{a+b}$

6. $\dfrac{3x^2-27}{x+3} \cdot \dfrac{1}{10x-30}$

7. $\dfrac{z^2-2z}{z+1} \cdot \dfrac{z^2-1}{z^2-2z+1}$

8. $\dfrac{4t^2+4t-3}{9t^2-1} \cdot \left(\dfrac{4t^2-8t+3}{6t^2-7t-3}\right)^{-1}$

9. $\left(\dfrac{5a^2-4a-1}{5a-5}\right)^{-1} \cdot \left(\dfrac{2a^2+a-3}{25a^2+10a+1}\right)^{0}$

10. $\dfrac{x-2}{x^2-5x+6} \cdot \dfrac{x^2-9}{x^2-3x}$

17.6 Addition and Subtraction of Fractions

As we do in case of fractions involving integers, in case of algebraic fractions also, we first find the L.C.M. of the polynomials in the denominators, which we may call the L.C.D. (lowest common denominator).

Ex. 1. *Simplify* : $\dfrac{x^2 + 5x}{x^2 - 9} - \dfrac{7x + 3}{x^2 - 9}$.

Sol. Here the denominators are the same

$$\textbf{Exp.} \ = \frac{x^2 + 5x}{x^2 - 9} - \frac{(7x+3)}{x^2 - 9} = \frac{x^2 + 5x - (7x+3)}{x^2 - 9}$$

$$= \frac{x^2 + 5x - 7x - 3}{x^2 - 9} = \frac{x^2 - 2x - 3}{x^2 - 9} = \frac{x^2 - 3x + x - 3}{x^2 - 9}$$

$$= \frac{x(x-3) + 1(x-3)}{x^2 - 9} = \frac{(x-3)(x+1)}{(x-3)(x+3)} = \frac{x+1}{x+3}.$$

Ex. 2. **Add :** $\dfrac{a}{5xy} + \dfrac{b}{10xz} + \dfrac{c}{15yz}$.

Sol. By inspection, the L.C.D. is $30xyz$.

$$\therefore \quad \frac{a}{5xy} + \frac{b}{10xz} + \frac{c}{15yz} = \frac{6az + 3by + 2cx}{30xyz}.$$

Ex. 3. *Simplify* : $\dfrac{5x + 2}{4x - 8} - \dfrac{2x + 5}{x^2 - x - 2}$.

Sol. $4x - 8 = 4(x-2)$

$$x^2 - x - 2 = x^2 - 2x + x - 2 = x(x-2) + 1(x-2) = (x-2)(x+1)$$

$\therefore$ L.C.D. $= 4(x-2)(x+1)$.

$$\frac{5x+2}{4x-8} - \frac{2x+5}{x^2 - x - 2} = \frac{5x+2}{4(x-2)} - \frac{2x+5}{(x-2)(x+1)}$$

$$= \frac{(5x+2)(x+1) - 4(2x+5)}{4(x-2)(x+1)} = \frac{5x^2 + 5x + 2x + 2 - 8x - 20}{4(x-2)(x+1)} = \frac{5x^2 - x - 18}{4(x-2)(x+1)}$$

$$= \frac{5x^2 - 10x + 9x - 18}{4(x-2)(x+1)} = \frac{5x(x-2) + 9(x-2)}{4(x-2)(x+1)} = \frac{(x-2)(5x+9)}{4(x-2)(x+1)} = \frac{5x+9}{4(x+1)} = \frac{5x+9}{4x+4}.$$

Ex. 4. *Simplify* : $\dfrac{1}{x^2 + 7x + 10} - \dfrac{1}{x^2 + 2x - 15}$

Sol. We have

$$x^2 + 7x + 10 = x^2 + 5x + 2x + 10$$

$$= x(x+5) + 2(x+5) = (x+2)(x+5)$$

$$x^2 + 2x - 15 = x^2 + 5x - 3x - 15 = x(x+5) - 3(x+5)$$

$$= (x-3)(x+5)$$

$$\therefore \quad \frac{1}{x^2+7x+10} - \frac{1}{x^2+2x-15} = \frac{1}{(x+2)(x+5)} - \frac{1}{(x-3)(x+5)}$$

$$= \frac{(x-3)-(x+2)}{(x+2)(x-3)(x+5)} = \frac{x-3-x-2}{(x+2)(x-3)(x+5)} = \frac{-5}{(x+2)(x-3)(x+5)}.$$

EXERCISE 17 (d)

Simplify :

1. $\dfrac{4}{5x} + \dfrac{2}{5x} - \dfrac{3}{5x}$

2. $\dfrac{3x}{4y} - \dfrac{x-2}{4y}$

3. $\dfrac{p-3q}{6} - \dfrac{2p+7q}{6}$

4. $\dfrac{5m}{m+n} + \dfrac{5n}{m+n}$

5. $\dfrac{a}{a-b} - \dfrac{b}{a-b}$

6. $\dfrac{pq}{(p+q)^2} + \dfrac{q^2}{(p+q)^2}$

7. $\dfrac{x+y}{x} + \dfrac{x+y}{y}$

8. $\dfrac{a-b}{ab} + \dfrac{b-c}{bc} + \dfrac{c-a}{ca}$

9. $\dfrac{5}{x+a} + \dfrac{3}{5x+5a}$

10. $\dfrac{a^2-b^2}{a^2b^2} + \dfrac{b^2-c^2}{b^2c^2} + \dfrac{c^2-a^2}{c^2a^2}$

11. $\dfrac{7}{x^2-y^2} - \dfrac{4}{3x+3y}$

12. $\dfrac{a+b}{a-b} - \dfrac{a-b}{a+b}$

13. $\dfrac{x-1}{x^2+5x} - \dfrac{x+1}{x^2-25}$

14. $\dfrac{3}{x-y} + \dfrac{5}{y^2-x^2}$

15. $\dfrac{3x+2}{x^2-16} + \dfrac{x-5}{(x+4)^2}$

16. $\dfrac{1}{x^2-9x+20} - \dfrac{1}{x^2-11x+30}$

17. $\dfrac{1}{x^2-7x+12} + \dfrac{1}{x^2-5x+6}$

18. $\dfrac{x+1}{x^2-4x+3} - \dfrac{x-3}{x^2-1}$

19. $\left(\dfrac{1}{1-a} - \dfrac{2a}{1-a^2}\right) \times \dfrac{a^2-2a-3}{a^2-6a+9}$

20. $\dfrac{1}{4x^2+8x+3} + \dfrac{1}{4x^2+16x+15} + \dfrac{1}{4x^2+12x+5}$

17.7 Removal of Brackets

In an expression involving brackets, we must remove them in the order (*i*) Bar $\overline{\qquad}$ (*ii*) Parenthesis( ) (*iii*) Curly brackets { } (*iv*) Square brackets [ ] .

Note that : When there is minus sign before a bracket, remove the bracket by changing the sign of the terms inside the bracket.

Ex.1. *Simplifty :* $4\left[a - 6\{a - 2(3a - \overline{4a+3}\,)\}\right]$

Sol. Given exp. $= 4\left[a - 6\{a - 2(3a - \overline{4a+3})\}\right]$

$= 4\left[a - 6\{a - 2(3a - 4a - 3)\}\right]$ (Removing bar)

$= 4\left[a - 6\{a - 2(-a - 3)\}\right]$

$= 4\left[a - 6\{a + 2a + 6\}\right]$ (Removing parenthesis)

$= 4\left[a - 6\{3a + 6\}\right]$

$= 4\left[a - 18a - 36\right]$ (Removing curly brackets)

$= 4\left[-17a - 36\right] = \mathbf{-68a - 144}$.   (Removing square brackets)

17.8 Bodmas

An algebraic expression containing the various mathematical opertations as $+, -, \div, \times$ and **'of'** is solved by keeping the **BODMAS** rule in mind .

Simplification of the algebraic expressions is done in the following the order :

(*i*) Brackets (*ii*) Of (*iii*) Division (*iv*) Multiplication (*v*) Addition (*iv*) Subtraction.

Ex.2. *Simplify :* $24x + 14x \div 7x - \dfrac{1}{3} \, of \, 36x.$

Sol. Given exp. $= 24x + 14x \div 7x - \dfrac{1}{3} \, of \, 36x$

$= 24x + 14x \div 7x - 12x$ (Simplifying 'of')

$= 24x + 2x - 12x$ (Simplifying $\div$)

$= 26x - 12x$ (Simplifying $+$)

$= \mathbf{14x.}$ (Simplifying $-$)

EXERCISE 17 (e)

Simplfy :

1. $4x - \left[3y - 2\left\{3x - 3(6y - 2x)\right\}\right]$

2. $\left\{8 - (3a - 5b) - \overline{6a + 7b}\right\}$

3. $2(2b - 3c) - 2\left[4c - 2\{c - 3\,(b - c)\} - 3b\right]$

4. $\left(x^2 - y^2 + z^2\right) - \left(x^2 - \overline{y^2 + z^2}\right)$

5. $-2\left[a + b - \left\{3a - 4b - 6\left(3a - \overline{2b - 6}\right)\right\}\right]$

6. $\left\{6 - 2a + 8b - (3a - 2b)\right\} - \left\{7a - \left(2a - \overline{4a + 2b}\right)\right\}$

Simplfy :

7. $(35x \times 2 - 28x \div 4) \div 9x$

8. $6x \text{ of } \dfrac{2}{3} \div 2x + 9x$

9. $4m \times 16m - 7m^2 \text{ of } 8m \div 7m$

10. $-13x + 6x^2 \div (7x - 4x)$

11. $42x^2 \div \left(16x - \overline{8x + 2x}\right)$

12. $(6a^2 - 10ab) \div (-2a) - (12ab - 9b^2) \div (-3b)$

LOOKING BACK

A Summary of Key Facts

1. An algebraic fraction is a rational expression of the form $\dfrac{p}{q}$ where p and q are polynomials and $q \neq 0$.

2. The H.C.F. of two polynomials is the polynomial of highest degree and greatest numerical coefficient which divides both the polynomials exactly.

3. The L.C.M. of two polynomials is the polynomial of the lowest degree and smallest numerical coefficient which is exactly divisible by both the polynomials.

4. An algebraic fraction is in its simplest form when the polynomials in the numerator and denominator do not have a common factor.

5. An algebraic expression is simplified by removing the brackets in the order: (*i*) **Bar** (*ii*) **Parenthesis** (*iii*) **Curly Brackets** (*iv*) **Square Brackets** and following the rule of **BODMAS**.

MENTAL MATHS–15

1. Find the H.C.F. of $5x^2y^3$, $10x^3y$, $15x^3y^3$.

2. Find the L.C.M. of $4x^3y^2$, $8xyz$, $16x^4y^2z$.

3. Find the H.C.F. of $(x+1)(x-3)(x+2)^2$ and $(x+1)^2(x+2)$.

4. Find the L.C.M. of $(x-1)(x-2)$ and $(x-2)(x-7)$.

5. Express $\dfrac{x^2+5x+6}{x^2+4x+4}$ in its lowest terms

6. Add $\dfrac{1}{x^2-16}$ and $\dfrac{1}{x+4}$

7. Simplify : $\dfrac{x^2-36}{x+6}$

8. Simplify : $\dfrac{x^2+3x+2}{x+1}.(x-2).$

ANSWERS

EXERCISE 17 (a)

1. H.C.F. $= ab$, L.C.M. $= a^2b^2$

2. H.C.F. $= 5a^2b^3$, L.C.M. $= 10a^4b^4$

3. H.C.F. $= 4a^2b^3d^2$, L.C.M. $= 60a^3b^4d^5$

4. H.C.F. $= 13xy^5z^4$, L.C.M. $= 78x^4y^8z^{10}$

5. H.C.F. $= 15p^{10}q^{10}$, L.C.M. $= 270p^{27}q^{12}r^{21}z^{30}$

6. $x-y$ **7.** $x-4$ **8.** $x(x^2+x+1)$

9. $3x-1$ **10.** $(x-1)^2(x+1)$ **11.** $3(y+4)(y-4)$ **12.** $-(x-y)$ **13.** $(x-y)^2(x+y)$

14. $6(x+2)(x+3)(x-3)$ **15.** $2(x-2)(x-3)(x-1)(x-5)$ **16.** $x(x-2)(x+3)(x+2)$

EXERCISE 17 (b)

1. $\dfrac{4y}{5z}$ **2.** $\dfrac{3x}{5y}$ **3.** $\dfrac{-9}{2}ab$ **4.** $\dfrac{5}{7}$ **5.** $a-b$ **6.** $\dfrac{9}{x-3}$ **7.** $\dfrac{x+3}{x-3}$ **8.** $\dfrac{x-3}{x+2}$

9. $\dfrac{x^2}{x^2-a^2}$ **10.** $\dfrac{4(p-5)}{(p-7)}$ **11.** $\dfrac{1}{2x+3}$ **12.** $\dfrac{x-7}{x-2}$ **13.** $\dfrac{(2x-1)}{(3x-1)}$ **14.** $\dfrac{(x-1)}{(x+1)}$ **15.** $\dfrac{1}{y(x+y)}$

EXERCISE 17 (c)

1. $\dfrac{z}{xy^2}$ **2.** $\dfrac{4bx}{15y}$ **3.** $\dfrac{g-h}{g}$ **4.** $\dfrac{x-5}{x+3}$ **5.** 1 **6.** $\dfrac{3}{10}$

7. $\dfrac{z(z-2)}{z-1}$ **8.** $\dfrac{2t+3}{3t-1}$ **9.** $\dfrac{5}{5a+1}$ **10.** $\dfrac{x+3}{x(x-3)}$

EXERCISE 17 (d)

1. $\dfrac{3}{5x}$ **2.** $\dfrac{x+1}{2y}$ **3.** $\dfrac{-(p+10q)}{6}$ **4.** 5 **5.** 1 **6.** $\dfrac{q}{p+q}$

7. $\dfrac{(x+y)^2}{xy}$ **8.** 0 **9.** $\dfrac{28}{5x+5a}$ **10.** 0 **11.** $\dfrac{21-4x+4y}{3(x^2-y^2)}$ **12.** $\dfrac{4ab}{a^2-b^2}$

13. $\dfrac{-7x+5}{x(x+5)(x-5)}$ **14.** $\dfrac{3x+3y-5}{x^2-y^2}$ **15.** $\dfrac{4x^2+5x+28}{(x-4)(x+4)^2}$ **16.** $\dfrac{-2}{(x-4)(x-5)(x-6)}$ **17.** $\dfrac{2}{(x-2)(x-4)}$

18. $\dfrac{8}{(x+1)(x-3)}$ **19.** $\dfrac{1}{a-3}$ **20.** $\dfrac{3}{(2x+1)(2x+5)}$

EXERCISE 17 (e)

1. $22x-39y$ **2.** $8-9a-2b$ **3.** $2c-2b$ **4.** $2z^2$ **5.** $-32a+14b-72$ **6.** $6-14a+8b$

7. 7 **8.** $9x+2$ **9.** $56m^2$ **10.** $-11x$ **11.** $7x$ **12.** $a+2b$

MENTAL MATHS – 15

1. $5x^2y$ **2.** $16x^4y^2z$ **3.** $(x+1)(x+2)$ **4.** $(x-1)(x-2)(x-7)$ **5.** $\dfrac{x+3}{x+2}$ **6.** $\dfrac{x-3}{x^2-16}$ **7.** $x-6$ **8.** x^2-4

18. Formula

18.1 Definitions

Formula : A formula is an algebraic rule used for evaluation. When we use a formula for evaluation we replace the letters in the formula by particular numbers. We call this **substituting in the formula**.

Subject of a Formula : The subject of a formula is a variable which is expressed in terms of other variables.

18.2 Framing a Formula

Ex. 1. *The selling price P of an article is $\left(1-\dfrac{1}{10}\right)$ times its marked price m after a discount of 10%.*

Sol. $P = \left(1-\dfrac{1}{10}\right)m$.

Ex. 2. *A two digit number is 7 more than three times the sum of the digits. If x is the digit at the ten's place and y the digit at the units place, write an equation in x and y.*

Sol. Sum of digits $= x + y$

The number in expanded form $= 10x + y$ ($\because$ x is the digit at ten's place and y at unit's place)

Given : Two digit number = 7 more than 3 times sum of digits.

i.e., $10x + y = 7 + 3 (x + y)$.

Ex. 3. *A cyclist rides x kilometres at a km/hr, takes half an hour for tea, rides back along the same road at b km/hr. Frame a formula to show the number, t, of hours taken.*

Sol. Time taken to travel x km $= \dfrac{\text{Distance}}{\text{Speed}} = \dfrac{x}{a}$ hours, Time taken to have tea $= \dfrac{1}{2}$ hour

Time taken to come back x km $= \dfrac{\text{Distance}}{\text{Speed}} = \dfrac{x}{b}$ hours

$\therefore$ Total time taken $t = \left(\dfrac{x}{a} + \dfrac{1}{2} + \dfrac{x}{b}\right)$ hours.

EXERCISE 18 (a)

Frame the formula for the following statements

1. The volume V of a sphere is $\dfrac{4}{3}$ of the product of constant π and the cube of its radius.
2. To change a temperature of $b°$ Farenheit into corresponding temperature of $a°$ Centigrade, subtract 32 from b and multiply the result by five - ninths.
3. The time t taken by me, if I walk x kms at 4 km/hr, rest for 15 minutes and then again walk y km at 3 km/hr.
4. When a is decreased by $x\%$, it becomes equal to b.
5. The area A sq.m, to be papered of the walls of a room l m long and b m wide and h in high allowing B sq m for the combined area of doors, windows, fire place etc.
6. The reciprocal of the focal length f equals the sum of the reciprocals of the object distance u and image distance v.
7. Rohan earns Rs x a week ; spends Rs y per month and his savings are Rs z in a year.

8. Half the product of the greatest and least of four consecutive whole numbers is 1 less than a half the product of the other two numbers, the least being x.

9. A two-digit number having x as the ten's digit and y as the unit's digit is 9 less than 4 times the sum of its digits.

10. In a class of z children, each one of the x children pay Rs 4 and the remaining children pay Rs 6 each, the total collection being Rs A.

11. A man has in his wallet total money 'M', which is as : x notes of Rs 50, y notes of Rs 10, z notes of Rs 5, a coins of 50 paise and b coins of 25 paise. Express M in rupees.

12. A train covers a distance in a hours at a speed of x km/hr and covers another distance in b hours at a speed of y km/hr. Find the average speed (s) of the train for the whole journey.

13. Ranjana is x years old and Sanju is twice as old as Ranjana. 10 years hence Sanju will be 3 times as old as Ranjana.

14. If the sum of m and n is multiplied by the amount by which p is less than 10, the product is equal to t.

18.3 Changing the Subject of the Formula

In the formula $v = u + ft$, v is the subject of the formula. Changing the subject of the formula means making one of the other variables used in the formula as subject.

The same formula can be written as :

(1) $u = ft - v$; u is the subject   (2) $f = \dfrac{v-u}{t}$; f is the subject   (3) $t = \dfrac{v-u}{f}$; t is the subject.

Ex. 4. *Given $s = (u + v)t$; make v the subject of the formula.*

Sol. $s = (u + v)\,t$ $\Rightarrow$ $s = ut + vt$

$\Rightarrow s - ut = vt$ $\Rightarrow$ $v = \dfrac{s-ut}{t}$

Ex.5. *Given $\dfrac{t-x}{1+tx} = 1$; make t the subject of the formula.*

Sol. $\dfrac{t-x}{1+tx} = 1$ $\Rightarrow$ $t - x = 1 + tx$ $\Rightarrow t - tx = 1 + x$

$\Rightarrow t\,(1 - x) = (1 + x) \Rightarrow t = \dfrac{1+x}{1-x}$.

Ex. 6. *Given $\sqrt{\dfrac{x}{a}} = 3$; make x the subject of the formula.*

Sol. $\sqrt{\dfrac{x}{a}} = 3$

Squaring both the sides, we have $\dfrac{x}{a} = 9 \Rightarrow$ **$x = 9a$.**

18.4 Evaluation by Substituting

Ex. 7. *Given $A = P\left(1 + \dfrac{rt}{100}\right)$*

    (a) Make t the subject of the formula.

    (b) Find the value of t, when $A = 2000$, $P = 1600$, $r = 5$.

Sol. Given $A = P\left(1 + \dfrac{rt}{100}\right)$

(a) $A = P + \dfrac{Prt}{100} \Rightarrow A - P = \dfrac{Prt}{100} \Rightarrow t = \dfrac{100(A-P)}{Pr}$.

(b) $t = \dfrac{100(A-P)}{Pr}$ and given $A = 2000$, $P = 1600$, $r = 5$

Substituting, we get,

$$t = \dfrac{100(2000-1600)}{1600 \times 5} = \dfrac{100 \times 400}{1600 \times 5} = 5.$$

Ex. 8. *Given* $\dfrac{1}{p} = \dfrac{qr}{q+r}$;

(a) *make r the subject of the formula.*

(b) *Calculate r if* $p = \dfrac{qr}{q+r}$ *and* $q = 1\dfrac{1}{3}$.

Sol. Given $\dfrac{1}{p} = \dfrac{qr}{q+r}$

(a) On cross multiplication $q + r = pqr \Rightarrow pqr - r = q \Rightarrow (pq-1)r = q \Rightarrow r = \dfrac{q}{pq-1}$.

(b) $r = \dfrac{q}{pq-1}$ and given $p = 1\dfrac{1}{2} = \dfrac{3}{2}$; $q = 1\dfrac{1}{3} = \dfrac{4}{3}$

Substituting, we get

$$r = \dfrac{\dfrac{4}{3}}{\dfrac{3}{2} \times \dfrac{4}{3} - 1} = \dfrac{\dfrac{4}{3}}{2-1} = \dfrac{4}{3} \div 1 = \dfrac{4}{3}.$$

EXERCISE 18 (b)

1. Given $z = \dfrac{8x}{4+x}$;

   (a) Make x the subject of the formula.   (b) Evaluate x when $z = 2$.

2. Given $l = a + (n - 1)d$.

   (a) Make d the subject of the formula.   (b) Find the value of d when $l = 40$, $a = 12$ and $n = 8$.

3. Given $A = \dfrac{1}{2}(a+b)h$.

   (a) Make a the subject of the formula   (b) Find the value of a when $A = 400$, $b = 30$, $h = 20$.

4. Given $2A + 3B = \dfrac{3B - A}{2C}$, express B in terms of A and C. Find the value of B, when $C = -3$ and $A = 2$.

5. Given $R = \sqrt{\dfrac{3v}{4\pi}}$,

   (a) Make V the subject of the formula.   (b) Find the value of V when $R = 2.1$, $\pi = \dfrac{22}{7}$.

6. If $c = \sqrt{a^2 + b^2}$, express b in terms of a and c. Find the value of b when $c = 5$, $a = 3$.

7. If a cricketer scores altogether r runs in x innings. n times not out, his average $a = r$ runs. Express n in terms of a, x and r. Find the number $x - n$ of times he was not out when he scores 204 runs in 15 innings and his averatge is 17 runs.

8. The area of a trapezim is given by the formula $A = \frac{1}{2}h(x+y)$. Make x the subject of the formula. Evaluate x, when $A = 36$ cm^2, $h = 7.2$ cm, $y = 3$ cm.

9. The penimeter of a recangle is $P = 2(l + b)$ and the area of a rectangle is $A = lb$.

   (a) Express P in terms of A and b only.   (b) Express A in terms of l and P only.

10. **In an examination a candidate had to answer 25 questions, each requiring a single answer "True" or "False". It was marked by giving 2 marks for the correct answer and –1 for each incorrect answer.**

    (a) Write down a formula for the marks M obtained by a candidate who answered all questions, but had only x of them correct.

    (b) Use your formula to find out how many of his answers were correct, if he answered all the questions and scored a total of 5 marks.

LOOKING BACK

A Summary of Key Facts

1. A formula expresses a relationship between two or more variables.
2. Subject of a formula is a variable expressed in terms of the variables.
3. To find the value of the subject by replacing the other variables by values is called substitution.

ANSWERS

EXERCISE 18 (a)

1. $V = \frac{4}{3}\pi r^3$

2. $a°C = \frac{5}{9}(b°F - 32)$

3. $t = \left(\frac{x}{4} + \frac{1}{4} + \frac{y}{3}\right)$ hours

4. $b = a\left(1 - \frac{x}{100}\right)$

5. $A = [2(l+b)h - B]$ sq m

6. $\frac{1}{f} = \frac{1}{u} + \frac{1}{v}$

7. $z = \text{Rs }(52x - 12y)$

8. $\frac{1}{2}x(x+3) = \frac{1}{2}(x+1)(x+2) - 1$

9. $10x + y = 4(x+y) - 9$

10. $A = \text{Rs }(4x + 6(z - x))$

11. $M = \text{Rs }\left(50x + 10y + 5z + \frac{a}{2} + \frac{b}{4}\right)$

12. $s = \left(\frac{xa + yb}{a+b}\right)$ km/hr.

13. $2x + 10 = 3(x + 10)$

14. $t = (m+n)(10 - p)$

EXERCISE 18 (b)

1. (a) $x = \frac{4z}{8-z}$ (b) $\frac{4}{3}$

2. (a) $d = \frac{l-a}{n-1}$ (b) 4

3. (a) $a = \frac{2A}{h} - b$ (b) 10

4. (a) $B = \frac{4AC + A}{3 - 6C}$ (b) $\frac{-22}{21}$

5. (a) $V = \frac{4}{3}\pi R^3$ (b) 38.808

6. (a) $b = \sqrt{c^2 - a^2}$, 4

7. 3 times not out

8. $\frac{2A}{h} - y$; $x = 7$ cm

9. (a) $P = \frac{2A}{b} + 2b$ (b) $A = \frac{1}{2}l(P - 2l)$

10. (a) $M = 3x - 25$ (b) 10

19. Exponents

19.1 Quick Review-Exponents

Recall that a short cut for writing product of a number by itself several times such as

$$\underbrace{2 \times 2 \times 2 \times 2 \times 2}_{\text{2, multiplied by itself 5 times}} \text{ is } 2^5$$

The expression 2^5 is read as *two to the fifth power*. In this expression, 2 is called the **base** and 5 is called the **exponent**. The expression 2^5, or 32, is called a power of 2. The expression 2^5 is called the **exponential** form of the power. Any number can be used as a base in an expression involving exponents.

Bases can be positive numbers, zero or negative numbers. Thus

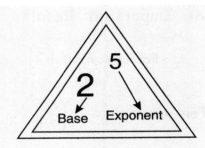

4^5 mean $\underbrace{4 \times 4 \times 4 \times 4 \times 4}_{\text{five 4's}} = 1024$

$(-2)^4$ mean $\underbrace{-2 \times -2 \times -2 \times -2}_{\text{four }-2\text{'s}} = 16$

0^3 means $\underbrace{0 \times 0 \times 0}_{\text{three 0's}} = 0$

Notice the importance of parentheses around the -2. Is it true that $(-2)^4 = -2^4$? Can you see the difference that $(-2)^4 = -16$ but $-2^4 = -16$?

Also, $\left(\sqrt{3}\right)^2 = \sqrt{3} \times \sqrt{3} = \sqrt{3 \times 3} = \sqrt{9} = 3$

$\left(-\sqrt{2}\right)^5 = -\sqrt{2} \times -\sqrt{2} \times -\sqrt{2} \times -\sqrt{2} \times -\sqrt{2} = (-1)^2 \times \sqrt{2 \times 2 \times 2 \times 2 \times 2} = -2 \times 2\sqrt{2} = -4\sqrt{2}$

$(0.02)^3 = 0.02 \times 0.02 \times 0.02 = 0.000008$

Zero Exponent : For every real number $a \neq 0$, $a^0 = 1$.

Ex. $7^0 = 1$, $\left(-\dfrac{2}{3}\right)^0 = 1$, $(3702)^0 = 1$, $(\pi)^0 = 1$, $(573.129)^0 = 1$

Negative Exponent : For any real number $a \neq 0$, and an integer n, $a^{-n} = \dfrac{1}{a^n}$.

Ex. $2^{-3} = \dfrac{1}{2^3} = \dfrac{1}{8}$, $\dfrac{1}{4^{-2}} = 4^2 = 16$, $(-3)^{-3} = \dfrac{1}{(-3)^3}$, $\dfrac{1}{-27} = -\dfrac{1}{27}$, $\dfrac{1}{(-6)^{-2}} = (-6)^2 = -6 \times -6 = 36$.

In general,

$a^n = \underbrace{a \times a \times a \ldots\ldots\ldots \times a}$ (n times), where a is any real number and n is an integer. a^n is read as **"a to the nth power"**.

191

19.2 Laws of Exponents

If $a \neq 0$ be any number and m, n be any integers, then

	Statement	Illustration
Law I	$a^m \times a^n = a^{m+n}$	$2^3 \times 2^7 = 2^{3+7} = 2^{10}$ $2^4 \times 2^{-3} = 2^{4+(-3)} = 2^1 = 2$
Law II	$(a^m)^n = a^{mn}$	$(4^2)^{-3} = 4^{2 \times -3} = 4^{-6}$ $(9^{-5})^{-3} = 9^{-5 \times -3} = 9^{15}$
Law III	$(ab)^m = a^m b^n$	$(6 \times 5)^4 = 6^4 \times 5^4$
Law IV	$\left(\dfrac{a}{b}\right)^m = \dfrac{a^m}{b^n}, (b \neq 0)$	$\left(\dfrac{2}{3}\right)^4 = \dfrac{2^4}{3^4}$
Law V	$\dfrac{a^m}{a^n} = a^{m-n}$	$\dfrac{5^7}{5^4} = 5^{7-4} = 5^3, \dfrac{6^8}{6^{-3}} = 6^{8-(-3)} = 6^{11}$

An Important Result

For $a \neq 0, b \neq 0, \left(\dfrac{a}{b}\right)^{-m} = \left(\dfrac{b}{a}\right)^m$, where m is a +ve integer.

For example : $\left(\dfrac{5}{7}\right)^{-2} = \left(\dfrac{7}{5}\right)^2 = \dfrac{7^2}{5^2} = \dfrac{49}{25}; \left(\dfrac{-3}{4}\right)^{-3} = \left(-\dfrac{4}{3}\right)^3 = \dfrac{(-4)^3}{3^3} = \dfrac{-64}{27}.$

$$\left[(a+3)^4\right]^{-1} = (a+3)^{4 \times -1} = (a+3)^{-4} = \dfrac{1}{(a+3)^4}$$

19.3 Solved Examples

Ex. 1. *Evaluate*

    (a) $\dfrac{7^{-2} \times 7^4}{7^{-5}}$ **(b)** $2^3 \times (-9)^0 \times 3^3$ **(c)** $\left[\left(\dfrac{x^2}{y^2}\right)^{-2}\right]^0$

Sol. *(a)* $\dfrac{7^{-2} \times 7^4}{7^{-5}} = 7^{-2+4-(-5)} = 7^{-2+4+5} = \mathbf{7^7}.$

    (b) $2^3 \times (9)^0 \times 3^3 = 2^3 \times 1 \times 3^3 = 2^3 \times 3^3 = (2 \times 3)^3 = 6^3 = \mathbf{216.}$

    (c) $\left[\left(\dfrac{x^2}{y^2}\right)^{-2}\right]^0 = \left(\dfrac{x^2}{y^2}\right)^{-2 \times 0} = \left(\dfrac{x^2}{y^2}\right) = 1.$

Ex. 2. *Simplify :* **(a)** $\dfrac{3^{2n+4} - 5.3^{2(n+1)}}{(9)^{n-1}}$ **(b)** $\left\{\left(\dfrac{1}{3}\right)^{-3} - \left(\dfrac{1}{2}\right)^{-3}\right\} \div \left(\dfrac{1}{4}\right)^{-3}$

Sol. (a) $\dfrac{3^{2n+4}-5.3^{2(n+1)}}{(9)^{n-1}} = \dfrac{3^{2n}\cdot 3^4 - 5\cdot 3^{2n}\cdot 3^2}{(3^2)^{n-1}} = \dfrac{3^{2n}\cdot 81 - 3^{2n}\cdot 45}{3^{2n}\cdot 3^{-2}}$

$$= \dfrac{3^{2n}\cdot(81-45)\times 3^2}{3^{2n}} = 36\times 9 = \mathbf{324}.$$

(b) $\left\{\left(\dfrac{1}{3}\right)^{-3} - \left(\dfrac{1}{2}\right)^{-3}\right\} \div \left(\dfrac{1}{4}\right)^{-3} = \left\{(3)^3 - (2)^3\right\} \div 4^3$

$$= (27 - 8) \div 64 = 19 \div 64 = \dfrac{\mathbf{19}}{\mathbf{64}}.$$

Ex. 3. *Express as a positive power of 3 :* $\dfrac{(9^{-1})\times(27)^{-2}}{(81)^{-2}\times 3^6}.$

Sol. $\dfrac{(9^{-1})\times(27)^{-2}}{(81)^{-2}\times 3^6} = \dfrac{(3^2)^{-1}\times(3^3)^{-2}}{(3^4)^{-2}\times 3^6} = \dfrac{3^{-2}\times 3^{-6}}{3^{-8}\times 3^6} = \dfrac{3^{-2+(-6)}}{3^{-8+6}} = \dfrac{3^{-8}}{3^{-2}}$

$$= 3^{-8-(-2)} = 3^{-8+2} = 3^{-6} = \dfrac{\mathbf{1}}{\mathbf{3^6}}.$$

Ex. 4. *Simplify :* $\left[\left(\dfrac{2}{3}\right)^2\right]^3 \times \left(\dfrac{1}{3}\right)^{-4} \times 3^{-1} \times \dfrac{1}{6}$

Sol. $\left[\left(\dfrac{2}{3}\right)^2\right]^3 \times \left(\dfrac{1}{3}\right)^{-4} \times 3^{-1} \times \dfrac{1}{6} = \left(\dfrac{2}{3}\right)^6 \times 3^4 \times \dfrac{1}{3} \times \dfrac{1}{6}$

$$= \dfrac{2^6}{3^6} \times 3^4 \times \dfrac{1}{3} \times \dfrac{1}{6}$$

$$= \dfrac{2^6}{3^6} \times 3^4 \times \dfrac{1}{3} \times \dfrac{1}{2} \times \dfrac{1}{3} = \dfrac{2^6 \times 3^4}{3^8 \times 2}$$

$$= 2^{6-1} \times 3^{4+(-8)}$$

$$= 2^5 \times 3^{-4} = \dfrac{2^5}{3^4} = \dfrac{\mathbf{32}}{\mathbf{81}}.$$

Ex. 5. *Find x so that* $\left(\dfrac{2}{9}\right)^3 \times \left(\dfrac{2}{9}\right)^{-6} = \left(\dfrac{2}{9}\right)^{2m-1}.$

Sol. $\left(\dfrac{2}{9}\right)^3 \times \left(\dfrac{2}{9}\right)^{-6} = \left(\dfrac{2}{9}\right)^{2m-1} \Rightarrow \left(\dfrac{2}{9}\right)^{3+(-6)} = \left(\dfrac{2}{9}\right)^{2m-1}$

$$\Rightarrow \left(\dfrac{2}{9}\right)^{-3} = \left(\dfrac{2}{9}\right)^{2m-1}.$$

In an equation when bases on both the sides are equal, their powers must also be equal.

$$\therefore \quad 2m - 1 = -3 \quad \Rightarrow \quad 2m = -3 + 1 \quad \Rightarrow \quad 2m = -2 \quad \Rightarrow \quad m = \frac{-2}{2} \quad \Rightarrow \quad \mathbf{m = -1.}$$

Ex. 6. *Show that* $\left(\dfrac{x^a}{x^b}\right)^c \times \left(\dfrac{x^b}{x^c}\right)^a \times \left(\dfrac{x^c}{x^a}\right)^b = 1.$

Sol. $\left(\dfrac{x^a}{x^b}\right)^c \times \left(\dfrac{x^b}{x^c}\right)^a \times \left(\dfrac{x^c}{x^a}\right)^b \quad \Rightarrow \quad \left(x^{a-b}\right)^c \times \left(x^{b-c}\right)^a \times \left(x^{c-a}\right)^b$

$\Rightarrow \quad x^{(a-b)c} \times x^{(b-c)a} \times x^{(c-a)b} = x^{ac-bc} \times x^{ba-ca} \times x^{cb-ab}$

$\Rightarrow \quad x^{ac-bc+ba-ca+cb-ab} = x^0 = \mathbf{1.}$

Ex. 7. *If* $\dfrac{9^n(3^2)(3^{-n/2})^{-2} - 27^n}{3^{3m} \cdot (2^3)} = \dfrac{1}{27}$, *find the value of m − n.*

Sol. Given expression $= \dfrac{3^{2n} \cdot 3^2 \cdot 3^{-n/2 \times -2} - (3^3)^n}{3^{3m} \cdot 2^3} = \dfrac{1}{3^3}$ $\qquad\qquad \left[\because 9^n(3^2)^n = 3^{2n}\right]$

$\Rightarrow \quad \dfrac{3^{2n} \cdot 3^2 \cdot 3^n - 3^{3n}}{3^{3m} \cdot 2^3} = \dfrac{1}{3^3} \quad \Rightarrow \quad \dfrac{3^{3n} \cdot 3^2 - 3^{3n}}{3^{3m} \cdot 2^3} \quad \Rightarrow \quad \dfrac{3^{3n}(3^2 - 1)}{3^{3m} \cdot 8} = \dfrac{1}{3^3}$

$\Rightarrow \quad \dfrac{3^{3n}(9-1)}{3^{3m} \cdot 8} = \dfrac{3^{3n}}{3^{3m}} = \dfrac{1}{3^3} \quad \Rightarrow \quad 3^{3n-3m} = 3^{-3} \quad \Rightarrow \quad 3^{3(n-m)} = 3^{-3}$

$\Rightarrow \quad 3(n - m) = -3 \quad \Rightarrow \quad n - m = -1 \quad \text{or} \quad \mathbf{m - n = 1.}$

EXERCISE 19

Expand the following :

1. Evaluate :

(a) 2^{-3} (b) 6^0 (c) $(-3)^{-2}$ (d) $8^5 \cdot 8^{-5}$ (e) $\dfrac{1}{2^{-2}}$

(f) $3(8-1)^0$ (g) $\dfrac{1}{2^{-1}} + \dfrac{1}{3^{-1}}$ (h) $7x^0$ (i) $a^3 \div a^{-2}$ (j) $\dfrac{y^{-6}}{y^4}$

(k) $(x^{-3})^0$ (l) $d^{2t} \div d^{-2t}$ (m) $\dfrac{1}{a^0 + b^0}$ (n) $(5^0 - 3^0) \times 7^0$ (o) $\left[\left(\dfrac{5}{7}\right)^{-6}\right]^0$

(p) $6^0 + 6^{-1} + 3^{-1}$

2. Simplify :

(a) $x^5 \cdot x^3$ (b) $\dfrac{x^8}{x^3}$ (c) $(x^3)^2$ (d) $(3x^2)^3$ (e) $(5x^{-3}yz^2)^{-2}$

3. In the following exercise write the number that indicates the correct meaning of the given expression :

(a) $4n^3$ means :

(i) 4 times $n + n + n$ (ii) $4n \cdot 4n \cdot 4n$ (iii) $4 \cdot n \cdot n \cdot n$

(b) $6x^3y^2$ means

(i) $6 \cdot xy \cdot xy \cdot xy \cdot xy \cdot xy$ (ii) $(6 \cdot x \cdot x \cdot x \cdot y)(7 \cdot x \cdot x \cdot x \cdot y)$ (iii) $6 \cdot x \cdot x \cdot x \cdot y \cdot y$.

4. Simplify :

(a) $\dfrac{(a^0 b^{-2})^5}{2a^{-1}}$ (b) $\dfrac{4a^{-3} b^0}{2a^2 b^{-1}}$ (c) $\dfrac{2x^2 y^{-2}}{2^{-1} x^2 y^2}$ (d) $\dfrac{(t^{-4})^3}{(t^3)^{-4}}$ (e) $4k^2(4^{-1}k + 4k^{-2})$

(f) $\left(\dfrac{3x^{-2}}{2y^{-1}}\right)^{-2}$ (g) $\left[\dfrac{3^{-1}}{(-2)^{-2}}\right]^{-2}$

5. Express each of the following as a power of 2 : $8, 8^x, 16^{x+3}$.

6. If $a = 2^m$ and $b = 2^{m+1}$, Show that $\dfrac{8a^3}{b^2} = 2^{m+1}$.

7. If $x = 2^k$ and $y = 2^{k+3}$, what is the value of $\dfrac{x}{y}$?

8. Write each expression such that there is no variable in the denominator,

(a) $\dfrac{3r^{-2} s^3}{12r^{-3} s^7}$ (b) $\dfrac{12x^3 y^{-2} z^4}{6x^7 y^{-5} z^{-3}}$ (c) $\dfrac{(5m)^0 n^{-2}}{4mn^{-3}}$ (d) $\dfrac{14a^{-4} k}{7^0 a^3 k^8}$

Simplify :

9. $\dfrac{2^{-n} \cdot 8^{2n+1} \cdot 16^{2n}}{4^{3n}}$. (**Hint :** Express each factor as a power of 2)

10. $\dfrac{2^{n+4} - 2 \cdot 2^n}{2 \cdot 2^{n+3}} + 2^{-3}$ **11.** $\dfrac{(0.6)^0 - (0.1)^{-1}}{\left(\dfrac{3}{2^3}\right)^{-1} \cdot \left(\dfrac{3}{2}\right)^3 + \left(-\dfrac{1}{3}\right)^{-1}}$.

12. If $\dfrac{9^n \times 3^5 \times (27)^3}{3 \times (81)^4} = 27$, then find the value of n.

13. Show that :

(a) $\left(\dfrac{x^a}{x^b}\right)^{a+b} \times \left(\dfrac{x^b}{x^c}\right)^{b+c} \times \left(\dfrac{x^c}{x^a}\right)^{c+a} = 1$ (b) $\dfrac{x^{a+b} \times x^{b+c} \times x^{c+a}}{(x^a \times x^b \times x^c)^2} = 1$

14. Find x such that :

(a) $\left(\dfrac{7}{4}\right)^{-3} \times \left(\dfrac{7}{4}\right)^{-5} = \left(\dfrac{7}{4}\right)^{3x-2}$ (b) $\left(\dfrac{125}{8}\right) \times \left(\dfrac{125}{8}\right)^x = \left(\dfrac{5}{2}\right)^{18}$

15. Find the value x such that

(a) $3^{2x-1} = \dfrac{1}{27^{x-3}}$ (b) $\left(\dfrac{p}{q}\right)^{3x+2} = \left(\dfrac{q}{p}\right)^{2-x}$

LOOKING BACK
A Summary of Key Facts

Laws of Exponents

For any real number $a \neq 0$ and any integral exponents m, n

(i) $a^m \times a^n = a^{m+n}$ (ii) $a^m \div a^n = a^{m-n}$ (iii) $(a^m)^n = a^{mn}$

(iv) $(a \times b)^m = a^m \times b^m$ (v) $\left(\dfrac{a}{b}\right)^m = \dfrac{a^m}{b^m}$ (vi) $a^0 = 1$ (vii) $a^{-n} = \dfrac{1}{a^n}$

(viii) $\left(\dfrac{a}{b}\right)^{-m} = \left(\dfrac{b}{a}\right)^m$ (ix) $\dfrac{1}{a^{-n}} = a^n$

MENTAL MATHS – 16

1. If m and n are whole numbers such that $m^n = 121$, then find the value of $(m-1)^{n+1}$.

Evaluate :

2. $(-2)^{-4}$ **3.** $\left[\left\{\left(-\dfrac{1}{3}\right)^{-2}\right\}^2\right]^1$ **4.** State True or False : $8^{0.25} \times 2^{0.25} = 2$.

5. Fill in the blanks :

(a) $7^9 \div 7^5 = \left(\dfrac{1}{7}\right)^{\cdots\cdots}$ (b) $\left(-\dfrac{4}{5}\right)^4 \div \left(-\dfrac{4}{5}\right)^{-2} = \left(-\dfrac{5}{4}\right)^{\cdots\cdots}$

ANSWERS

EXERCISE 19

1. (a) $\dfrac{1}{8}$ (b) 1   (c) $\dfrac{1}{9}$ (d) 1   (e) 4   (f) 3   (g) 5   (h) 7

(i) a^5 (j) y^{-10} (k) 1   (l) d^{4t} (m) $\dfrac{1}{2}$ (n) 0   (o) 1   (p) $\dfrac{3}{2}$

2. (a) x^8 (b) x^5 (c) x^6 (d) $27x^6$ (e) $\dfrac{x^6}{25y^2z^4}$

3. (a) (iii)   (b) (iii)   **4.** (a) $\dfrac{a}{2b^{10}}$ (b) $\dfrac{2b}{a^5}$ (c) $\dfrac{4}{y^4}$ (d) 1   (e) $k^3 + 16$

(f) $\dfrac{4x^4}{9y^2}$ (g) $\dfrac{9}{16}$ **5.** $2^3, 2^{3x}, 2^{4x+12}$ **7.** $\dfrac{1}{8}$

8. (a) $\dfrac{rs^{-4}}{4}$ (b) $2x^{-4}y^3z^7$ (c) $\dfrac{nm^{-1}}{4}$ (d) $14a^{-7}k^{-7}$ **9.** 2^{7n+3} **10.** 1   **11.** $-\dfrac{3}{2}$

12. 3   **14.** (a) $x = -2$ (b) $x = 5$ **15.** (a) $x = 2$ (b) $x = -2$.

MENTAL MATHS – 16

1. 1000   **2.** $\dfrac{1}{16}$ **3.** 81   **4.** True   **5.** (i) –4   (ii) –6

20. Linear Equations

20.1 Linear Equations in One Variable

A linear equation in one variable is also called a simple equation. You have already learnt in class VII the method of solving simple equations.

Revise with the help of the following examples.

Ex. 1. *Solve : $8x - 11 - 5x + 3 = 2x + 4 - 3x$.*

Sol. Transposing all the terms containing x to the left side and all those not containing x to the right, we get

$8x - 5x - 2x + 3x = 4 + 11 - 3$

or $4x = 12$ $\qquad$ $\therefore$ $\quad x = \dfrac{12}{4} = 3$.

Ex. 2. *Solve : $\dfrac{3x - 2}{10} - \dfrac{x + 3}{7} + \dfrac{4x - 7}{3} = x - 1$.*

Sol. Multiplying by 210, the L.C.M. of the denominators, we get

$\qquad 21(3x - 2) - 30(x + 3) + 70(4x - 7) = 210x - 210$

$\Rightarrow$ $63x - 42 - 30x - 90 + 280x - 490 = 210x - 210$

$\Rightarrow$ $63x - 30x + 280x - 210x = -210 + 42 + 90 + 490$

$\Rightarrow$ $103x = 412$ $\quad \therefore \quad x = \dfrac{412}{103} = 4$.

20.2 Equations of the Form $\dfrac{ax + b}{cx + d} = \dfrac{p}{q}$.

Method. From the given equation, we have $q(ax + b) = p(cx + d)$. This process is called cross multiplication.

Ex.3. *Solve : $\dfrac{3x + 2}{4x + 11} = \dfrac{4}{7}$.*

Sol. By cross multiplication, we have

$\qquad 7(3x + 2) = 4(4x + 11)$

$\Rightarrow$ $21x + 14 = 16x + 44 \Rightarrow 21x - 16x = 44 - 14$

$\Rightarrow$ $5x = 30$ $\quad \therefore \quad x = \dfrac{30}{5} = 6$.

$$\boxed{\dfrac{ax + b}{cx + d} \diagdown\!\!\!\!\times\diagup = \dfrac{p}{q}}$$

Ex. 4. *Solve : $\dfrac{m - 3}{m + 4} = \dfrac{m + 1}{m - 2}$.*

Sol. Cross multiplying, we get

$\qquad (m - 3)(m - 2) = (m + 4)(m + 1)$

$\Rightarrow$ $m^2 - 5m + 6 = m^2 + 5m + 4$

$\Rightarrow$ $m^2 - 5m - m^2 - 5m = 4 - 6$

$\Rightarrow$ $-10m = -2$ $\quad \therefore \quad m = \dfrac{-2}{-10} = \dfrac{1}{5}$.

$$\boxed{\dfrac{m - 3}{m + 4} \diagdown\!\!\!\!\times\diagup = \dfrac{m + 1}{m - 2}}$$

Ex. 5. *Solve :* $\dfrac{x^2-9}{5+x^2}=\dfrac{-5}{9}$ *for positive value of x.*

Sol. $\dfrac{x^2-9}{5+x^2}=\dfrac{-5}{9}$

Cross multiplying, we get

$9(x^2-9)=-5\,(5+x^2)$

$\Rightarrow\ 9x^2-81=-25-5x^2 \qquad\qquad \Rightarrow\ 9x^2+5x^2=-25+81$

$\Rightarrow\ 14x^2=56 \qquad\qquad \Rightarrow\ x^2=\dfrac{56}{14}=4=(+2)^2$

$\therefore\ x=2.$ (Taking the positive value)

Ex. 6. *Solve* $\dfrac{(x+2)(2x-3)-2x^2+6}{x-5}=2.$

Sol. $(x+2)(2x-3)=x(2x-3)+2(2x-3)$

$$=2x^2-3x+4x-6$$

$$=2x^2+x-6 \qquad\qquad\qquad\qquad\text{...(1)}$$

The given equation is

$$\frac{(x+2)(2x-3)-2x^2+6}{x-5}=2$$

$\Rightarrow\ \dfrac{2x^2+x-6-2x^2+6}{x-5}=2 \quad\Rightarrow\ \dfrac{x}{x-5}=\dfrac{2}{1}$ \qquad [using (1)]

Cross multiplying, $1\times x=2\,(x-5) \quad\Rightarrow\quad x=2x-10 \quad\Rightarrow\quad x-2x=-10 \quad\Rightarrow\quad -x=-10$

$\therefore \qquad\qquad\qquad x=10.$

EXERCISE 20 (a)

Solve the following equations :

1. $16x-35=7x-8$ **2.** $2(x+3)=15+x$ **3.** $-(x-4)=3x-20$

4. $16-2\,(3y+5)=4(y-2)$ **5.** $10p-(3p-4)=4(p+1)+9$ **6.** $7m-4(m+6)=7(m-8)+4$

7. $\dfrac{x}{2}+\dfrac{x}{3}=15$ **8.** $\dfrac{2}{3}\left(x+\dfrac{3}{5}\right)=\dfrac{7}{2}$ **9.** $\dfrac{1}{6}(4y+5)-\dfrac{2}{3}(2y+7)=\dfrac{3}{2}$

10. $\dfrac{x+3}{2}-\dfrac{4}{3}=\dfrac{3x-7}{3}$

Solve the following equations :

11. $\dfrac{3}{x+1}=\dfrac{5}{2x}$ **12.** $\dfrac{6}{3m+1}=\dfrac{9}{5m-3}$ **13.** $\dfrac{2x+3}{5}=\dfrac{4x+9}{11}$ **14.** $\dfrac{9x-5}{7}=\dfrac{6x+2}{5}$

15. $\dfrac{5x-7}{3x}=2$ **16.** $\dfrac{0.4z-3}{1.5z+9}=\dfrac{7}{5}$ **17.** $\dfrac{x-2}{x-4}=\dfrac{x+4}{x-2}$ **18.** $\dfrac{y-2}{y-5}=\dfrac{y+3}{y+5}$

19. $\dfrac{2y-4}{3y+2}=-\dfrac{2}{3}$ $\left(\text{Hint}: \text{Write }\dfrac{-2}{3}\text{ for }-\dfrac{2}{3}\right)$ **20.** $\dfrac{\frac{x}{4}-\frac{3}{5}}{\frac{4}{3}-7x}=-\dfrac{3}{20}$ **21.** $\dfrac{(2x+3)-(5x-7)}{6x+11}=-\dfrac{8}{3}$

22. $\dfrac{17(2-x)-5(x+12)}{1-7x}=8$ **23.** $\dfrac{(4+x)(5-x)}{(2+x)(7-x)}=1$ **24.** $\dfrac{x^2-(x+1)(x+2)}{5x+1}=6$

Solve and give the positive value of y which satisfies given equation : 25. $\dfrac{y^2+4}{3y^2+7}=\dfrac{1}{2}$

20.3 Applications of Linear Equations to Practical Problems

You have already learnt in earlier classes how to solve some real life problems by converting them into linear equations in one variable. Here we will take up more problems of a slightly higher level.

Recall that to solve such problems we denote the unknown quantity by x and from the given relation, construct a linear equation in x.

20.4 Type 1. Problems on Numbers

Ex. 1. *Find three consecutive odd numbers whose sum is 45.*

Sol. Let the three consecutive odd numbers be $2x + 1, 2x + 3, 2x + 5$. Then

$(2x + 1) + (2x + 3) + (2x +5) = 45 \Rightarrow 6x + 9 = 45$

$\Rightarrow \quad 6x = 45 - 9 = 36 \quad \therefore \quad x = \dfrac{36}{6} = 6$

So the required numbers are $2 \times 6 + 1, 2 \times 6 + 3, 2 \times 6 + 5$, i.e., **13, 15 and 17.**

Ex. 2. *One number is 3 times another number. If 15 is added to both the numbers, then one of the new numbers becomes twice that of the other new number. Find the numbers.*

Sol. Let one number be x. Then the other number $= 3x$

By the given condition, one number $+15 = 2$ (other number $+15$)

i.e. $\quad 3x + 15 = 2(x +15) \qquad \Rightarrow \qquad 3x + 15 = 2x + 30$

$\Rightarrow \qquad 3x - 2x = 30 - 15 \qquad \Rightarrow \qquad x = 15.$

Hence, one number is 15 and the other number is $3 \times 15 = 45$.

Ex. 3. *Sum of the digits of a two-digit number is 9. The number obtained by interchanging the digits exceeds the given number by 27. Find the given number.*

Sol. Let the units digit be x; Then tens digit $= (9 - x)$

Number formed by these digits $= 10 \times$ ten's digit $+$ unit's digit $= 10(9 - x) + x = 90 - 9x$

When the digits are interchanged, unit's digit becomes $9 - x$ and ten's digit becomes x.

$\therefore \quad$ Number formed on interchanging the digits $= 10x + (9 - x) = 9x + 9$.

It is given that new number exceeds the given number by 27

i.e., new number $-$ given number $= 27$

i.e., $(9x + 9) - (90 - 9x) = 27 \Rightarrow 9x + 9 - 90 + 9x = 27 \Rightarrow 18x - 81 = 27$

$\Rightarrow \qquad 18x = 27 + 81 \quad \Rightarrow 18x = 108 \quad \therefore \quad x = \dfrac{108}{18} = 6.$

$\therefore \quad$ Required number $= (90 - 9x) = 90 - 9 \times 6 = 90 - 54 = \mathbf{36.}$

Ex. 4. *The denominator of a rational number is greater than its numerator by 8. If the numerator is increased by 17 and the denominator is decreased by 1, the number obtained is $\frac{3}{2}$. Find the rational number.*

Sol. Let the numerator be x then the denominator $= x + 8$

$\therefore$ Required rational number $= \dfrac{x}{x+8}$

New rational number $= \dfrac{\text{Numerator} + 17}{\text{Denominator} - 1} = \dfrac{x+17}{(x+8)-1} = \dfrac{x+17}{x+7}$

It is given that new rational number $= \dfrac{3}{2}$ $\therefore$ $\dfrac{x+17}{x+7} = \dfrac{3}{2}$

$\Rightarrow$ $2(x + 17) = 3(x + 7)$ $\Rightarrow$ $2x + 34 = 3x + 21$

$\Rightarrow$ $2x - 3x = 21 - 34$ $\Rightarrow$ $-x = -13 \Rightarrow x = 13$.

$\therefore$ Reqd. rational number $= \dfrac{x}{x+8} = \dfrac{13}{13+8} = \dfrac{\mathbf{13}}{\mathbf{21}}$.

20.5 Type 2. Age Related Problems

Ex. 5. *Kiran is 24 years older than Rakesh. 10 years ago Kiran's age was five times the age of Rakesh. Find their ages.*

Sol. Let Kiran's present age be x years.

Then Rakesh's present age $= (x - 24)$ years

10 years ago, Kiran's age $= (\text{present age} - 10)$ years $= (x - 10)$ years

Also, 10 years ago, Rakesh's age $= \{(x - 24) - 10\}$ years $= (x - 34)$ years

Given : 10 years ago, Kiran's age $= 5$ times Rakesh's age

$\therefore$ $x - 10 = 5(x - 34) \Rightarrow x - 5x = -170 + 10 \Rightarrow -4x = -160$ $\therefore$ $x = \dfrac{-160}{-4} = 40$.

Therefore, Kiran's age is 40 years and Rakesh's age is $(40 - 24)$ or **16 years.**

Ex. 6. *The ages of Ravi and Hema are in the ratio 5 : 7. Four years later, their ages will be in the ratio 3 : 4. Find their ages.*

Sol. Let Ravi's present age be $5x$ years and that of Hema be $7x$ years.

4 years later, Ravi's age $= (5x + 4)$ years, Hema's age $= (7x + 4)$ years.

By the given condition, $(5x + 4) : (7x + 4) = 3 : 4$

or $\dfrac{5x+4}{7x+4} = \dfrac{3}{4} \Rightarrow 4(5x + 4) = 3(7x + 4) \Rightarrow 20x + 16 = 21x + 12$

$\Rightarrow$ $20x - 21x = 12 - 16 \Rightarrow -x = -4 \Rightarrow x = 4$.

$\therefore$ Ravi's age $= 5 \times 4 = \mathbf{20 \ years}$, Hema's age $= 7 \times 4 = \mathbf{28 \ years.}$

20.6. Type 3. Problems on Mensuration

Ex. 7. *The width of Sudha's garden is $\frac{2}{3}$ of its length. If its perimeter is 40 m, find its dimensions.*

Sol. Let the length of the garden be x m. Then, width $= \dfrac{2}{3} x$ m.

Perimeter $= 2 \ (\text{length} + \text{width}) = 2\left(x + \dfrac{2}{3}x\right)$

$\therefore$ Equation is $2x + 2\left(\dfrac{2x}{3}\right) = 40 \Rightarrow 2x + \dfrac{4x}{3} = 40$ | Given : Perimeter is 40 m. |

$\Rightarrow$ $6x + 4x = 120 \Rightarrow 10x = 120 \therefore x = \dfrac{120}{10} = 12$ | Clear off fractions. |

$\therefore$ Length is **12 m** and width is $\dfrac{2}{3} \times 12 = $ **8 m.**

Ex. 8. *Each side of a triangle is increased by 10 cm. If the ratio of the perimeters of the new triangle and the given triangle is 5 : 4, find the perimeter of the given triangle.*

Sol. Let sides of the given triangle be a, b, c. Then perimeter of the triangle $= a + b + c = x$ (say)

Perimeter of the new triangle $= (a + 10) + (b + 10) + (c + 10) = (a + b + c) + 30 = (x + 30)$.

By the given condition, $(x + 30) : x = 5 : 4 \Rightarrow \dfrac{x+30}{x} = \dfrac{5}{4} \Rightarrow 4(x + 30) = 5x$

$\Rightarrow$ $4x + 120 = 5x \Rightarrow 4x - 5x = -120 \Rightarrow -x = -120 \Rightarrow x = 120$.

$\therefore$ Perimeter of the given triangle $= x =$ **120 cm.**

Ex. 9. *The perimeter of a rectangle is 240 cm. If its length is decreased by 10% and its breadth is increased by 20%, we get the same perimeter. Find the length and breadth of the rectangle.*

Sol. Given perimeter $= 240$, *i.e.*, $2(l + b) = 240 \Rightarrow l + b = 120$ cm.

Let length of the rectangle be x cm. Then, breadth of the rectangle $= (120 - x)$ cm

The length is decreased by 10%, so new length $= x - x \times \dfrac{10}{100} = x - \dfrac{x}{10} = \dfrac{9x}{10}$ cm.

Breadth is increased by 20%, so new breadth is

$(120 - x) + (120 - x) \times \dfrac{20}{100} = (120 - x) + (120 - x) \times \dfrac{1}{5}$

$= \dfrac{5(120-x) + (120-x)}{5} = \dfrac{600 - 5x + 120 - x}{5} = \dfrac{720 - 6x}{5}$ cm

| **Short Cut** |
| Length $= \dfrac{90}{100} x$ |
| Breadth $= \dfrac{120}{100}(120 - x)$ |

By the condition, perimeter remains the same, *i.e.*, 240 cm

| Perimeter $= 2$(length + breadth) |

So, $2\left(\dfrac{9x}{10} + \dfrac{720 - 6x}{5}\right) = 240 \Rightarrow \dfrac{9x}{10} + \dfrac{720 - 6x}{5} = 120$

$\Rightarrow$ $\dfrac{9x + 1440 - 12x}{10} = 120$

$\Rightarrow$ $1440 - 3x = 120 \times 10 = 1200 \Rightarrow -3x = 1200 - 1440 = -240 \Rightarrow x = \dfrac{-240}{-3} = 80$.

$\therefore$ Length of the rectangle $= x =$ **80 cm** and breadth $= 120 - x = 120 - 80 =$ **40 cm.**

20.7 Type. 4. Problems on Speed Time and Distance

Ex. 10. *A car travelling at 60 km/hr left Dehradun at 3 P.M. One hour later another car travelling at 80 km/hr started over the same road to overtake the first. How long must the second car travel?*

Sol. Let the second car overtake the first, x hours after it started. First car travelled for $(x + 1)$ hours and distance covered by both the cars is the same.

Distance covered by 1st car in $(x + 1)$ hours $= 60(x + 1)$ km | Distance = Speed × Time |

Distance covered by 2nd car in x hours $= 80x$ km

$\therefore$ $60(x + 1) = 80x \Rightarrow 60x + 60 = 80x \Rightarrow$ $60 = 80x - 60x = 20x \therefore x = \dfrac{60}{20} =$ **3.**

Hence, the second car travelled for **3 hours.**

Ex.11. *A motor boat covers a certain distance downstream in a river in five hours. It covers the same distance upstream in five hours and a half. Find the speed of the boat in still water.*

Sol. Let the speed of the boat $= x$ km/hr.

Then speed of the boat downstream $= (x + 1.5)$ km/hr

and speed of the boat upstream $= (x - 1.5)$ km/hr

Distance covered by the boat down stream in 5 hours $= (x + 1.5) \times 5 = (5x + 7.5)$ km

> Distance = Speed × time

Distance covered by the boat upstream in $5\frac{1}{2}$, *i.e.*, $\frac{11}{2}$ hours $= (x - 1.5) \times \frac{11}{2} = \frac{11x - 16.5}{2}$ km

By the given condition $5x + 7.5 = \frac{11x - 16.5}{2} \Rightarrow 2(5x + 7.5) = 11x - 16.5$

$\Rightarrow$ $10x + 15 = 11x - 16.5 \Rightarrow 10x - 11x = -16.5 - 15 \Rightarrow -x = -31.5 \Rightarrow x = 31.5$

$\therefore$ Speed of the boat $= x = $ **31.5 km/hr.**

20.8 Other Problems

Ex.12. *Saurabh can finish a work in 18 hours while Vinod can complete the same work in 24 hours. How long will it take them together to complete this work if Saurabh is called away for 2 hours while Vinod continues with the work?*

Sol. Suppose Vinod continues with the work for x hours.

Then Saurabh is available to do the work for $(x - 2)$ hours.

$\therefore$ Work done by Saurabh in 1 hr $= \frac{1}{18} \Rightarrow$ Work done by Saurabh in $(x - 2)$ hrs $= \frac{x - 2}{18}$

Similarly, work done by Vinod in x hrs. $= \frac{x}{24}$

Work done by them together $= \frac{x - 2}{18} + \frac{x}{24}$

Since this is the whole work 1 completed, therefore,

$\frac{x - 2}{18} + \frac{x}{24} = 1 \Rightarrow 72 \times \frac{x - 2}{18} + 72 \times \frac{x}{24} = 72 \times 1 \Rightarrow 4x - 8 + 3x = 72$

> To clear the fractions multiply by the LCM of 18, 24 *i.e.*, 72

$\Rightarrow$ $7x = 72 + 8 = 80$ $\therefore$ $x = \frac{80}{7} = 11\frac{3}{7}$ hours.

Hence, together, they finish the work in $11\frac{3}{7}$ **hours.**

Ex. 13. *Prema receives a certain amount of money on her retirement from her employer. She gives half of this money and an additional sum of Rs 10,000 to her daughter. She also gives one third of the money received and an additional sum of Rs 3000 to her son. If the daughter gets twice as much as the son, find the amount of money Prema received on her retirement.*

Sol. Let amount of money received by Prema be Rs x.

Money given to her daughter $= $ Rs $\left(\frac{x}{2} + 10000\right) = $ Rs $\left(\frac{x + 20000}{2}\right)$

Money given to her son $= $ Rs $\left(\frac{x}{3} + 3000\right) = $ Rs $\left(\frac{x + 9000}{3}\right)$

By the given condition, daughter's share $= $ twice the son's share

$\therefore$ $\frac{x + 20000}{2} = 2\left(\frac{x + 9000}{3}\right) = \frac{2x + 18000}{3}$

> Multiplying both sides by L.C.M. of 2 and 3 is 6

$\Rightarrow \quad 3(x + 20000) = 2(2x + 18000) \Rightarrow 3x + 60000 = 4x + 36000 \Rightarrow 3x - 4x = 36000 - 60000$

$\Rightarrow \quad -x = -24000 \qquad \therefore \quad x = 24000.$

$\therefore \qquad$ Amount of money received by Prema = **Rs 24000.**

EXERCISE 20 (b)

1. The larger of two numbers is 12 more than the smaller and the sum of the two numbers is 10. Find the numbers.

2. One number is 5 times another. If 18 is subtracted from the larger, the remainder will be 3 times the smaller. Find the numbers.

3. (*i*) Find three consecutive numbers whose sum is 108.
   (*ii*) Find three consecutive odd numbers whose sum is 93.
   (*iii*) Find three consecutive even numbers whose sum is 246.
   (*iv*) The sum of three consecutive multiples of 7 is 777. Find these multiples.
   (**Hint :** Let the numbers be $7x$, $7x + 7$ and $7x + 14$)

4. Divide 534 into three parts such that the second part will be 32 less than twice the first, and the third will be 18 more than the first.

5. Three times the smallest of three consecutive odd numbers decreased by 7 equals twice the largest one. Find the numbers.

6. One number is 7 more than another and its square is 77 more than the square of the smaller number. What are the numbers?

7. The square of the larger of two consecutive even numbers exceeds the square of the smaller by 36. Find the numbers.

8. The denominator of a fraction is 3 more than the numerator. If 5 is added to both parts, the resulting fraction is equivalent to $\dfrac{4}{5}$. Find the fraction.

9. The difference between two positive integers is 50 and the ratio of these integers is 1:3. Find these integers.

10. The sum of the digits of a two-digit number is 7. The number obtained by interchanging the digits exceeds the original number by 27. Find the number.

11. Sushma is now 15 years older than Vijay but in 3 more years she will be 8 times as old as Vijay was 3 years ago. How old are they now?

12. Mary is 3 times as old as Bhawna, and the sum of their ages 5 years from now will be twice Mary's present age. How old are they now?

13. Sanjay is now $\dfrac{1}{2}$ as old as his brother. In 6 more years he will be $\dfrac{3}{5}$ as old as his brother then. What is the present age of each boy?

14. (*a*) If the area is $3x$ cm^2, make an equation, and find x.
    (*b*) If the perimeter is 40 cm, make an equation, and find x.

8 cm	225 m^2
$x - 5$ cm	25 m
Fig. Q.14	**Fig. Q.15**

15. $4(x - 2)$ metres of rope is used to fence this rectangular enclosure. Find x.

16. Madhu's flower garden is now a square. If she enlarges it by increasing the width 1 metre and the length 3 metres, the area will be 19 sq metres more than the present area. What is the length of a side now?

17. The sides (other than hypotenuse) of a right triangle are in the ratio 3 : 4. A rectangle is described on its hypotenuse, the hypotenuse being the longer side of the rectangle. The breadth of the rectangle is four-fifth of its length. Find the shortest side of the right triangle, if the perimeter of the rectangle is 180 cm.

[**Hint :** Hypotenuse = $\sqrt{\text{sum of squares of sides}} = \sqrt{(3x)^2 + (4x)^2} = \sqrt{25x^2} = 5x$

∴ Breadth fo the rectangle = $\frac{4}{5}(5x) = 4x$]

18. Two cars leave Delhi at the same time, travelling in opposite directions. If the average speed of one car is 5 km/h more than that of the other and they are 425 km apart at the end of 5 hrs, what is the average speed of each?

19. Two automobiles start out at the same time from cities 595 km apart. If the rate of one is $\frac{8}{9}$ of the rate of the other and if they meet in 7 hours, what is the rate of each?

20. A motorboat goes downstream in a river and covers the distance between two coastal towns in five hours. It covers this distance upstream in six hours. If the speed of the stream is 2 km/h, find the speed of the boat in still water.

21. A steamer, going downstream in a river, covers the distance between two towns in 20 hours. Coming back upstream, it covers this distance in 25 hours. The speed of water is 4 km/h. Find the distance between the two towns.

    (**Hint :** First find the speed of the steamer in still water.)

22. Ranjana's mother gave her Rs 245 for buying New Year cards. If she got some 10-rupee cards, $\frac{2}{3}$ as many 5 rupee cards, and $\frac{1}{5}$ as many 15-rupee cards, how many of each kind did she buy?

23. The enrolment in a school this year is 552. This is an increase of 15% over last year's enrolment. How many were enrolled last year?

24. A fruit vendor buys some oranges at the rate of Rs 5 per orange. He also buys an equal number of bananas at the rate of Rs 2 per banana. He makes a 20% profit on oranges and a 15% profit on bananas. At the end of the day, all the fruit is sold out. His total profit is Rs 390. Find the number of oranges purchased.

ANSWERS

EXERCISE 20 (a)

1. $x = 3$
2. $x = 9$
3. $x = 6$
4. $x = 1.4$
5. $p = 3$
6. $m = 7$
7. $x = 18$
8. $x = 4\frac{13}{20}$
9. $y = -8$
10. $x = 5$
11. $x = 5$
12. $m = 9$
13. $x = 6$
14. $x = 13$
15. $x = -7$
16. $z = -9.18$
17. $x = 5$
18. $y = -1$
19. $y = \frac{1}{3}$
20. $x = -\frac{1}{2}$
21. $x = -\frac{118}{39}$
22. $x = 1$
23. $x = \frac{3}{2}$
24. $x = -\frac{8}{33}$
25. $y = 1$

EXERCISE 20 (b)

1. $-1, 11$
2. $9, 45$
3. (a) 35, 36, 37   (b) 29, 31, 33   (c) 80, 82, 84   (d) 252, 259, 266
4. 137, 242, 155
5. 15, 17, 19
6. 2, 9
7. 8, 10
8. $\frac{7}{10}$
9. 25, 75
10. 25
11. 21 years, 6 years
12. 5 years, 15 years
13. 12 years, 24 years
14. (a) $x = 8$ (b) $x = 17$
15. $x = 19$
16. 7 m
17. 30 cm.
18. 40 km/hr, 45 km/hr
19. 45 km/hr, 40 km/hr
20. 22 km/hr
21. 800 km
22. 15 of 10 rupees each, 10 of 5 rupees each, 3 of 15 rupees each
23. 480
24. 300

21. Simultaneous Linear Equations

LINEAR EQUATIONS IN TWO VARIABLES

21.1 Introduction

Consider the linear equation in two variables

$$2x + y = 8$$

To solve such an equation in two variables, you must determine all the values of x and the corresponding values of y for which the equation is satisfied. Some trial values of x and y for the equation "$2x + y = 8$" are shown in the table. Note that the statement is true for the pair $(2, 4)$, but for the pair $(4, 2)$ it is false. Therefore, you must report the pairs in an agreed upon order. If you choose the order (x, y) in this case, you can say that $(2, 4)$ is a solution and $(4, 2)$ is not a solution of the equation $2x + y = 8$.

x	y	$2x + y$	$2x + y = 8$
2	4	$4 + 4$	True
3	5	$6 + 5$	False
4	2	$8 + 2$	False
1	6	$2 + 6$	True
$\dfrac{1}{2}$	7	$1 + 7$	True

Since the order in which the numbers written in the pair, *i.e.*, the pair $(2, 4)$ is not the same as the pair $(4, 2)$ for our purpose, we call a pair like $(4, 2)$ an **ordered pair**.

If you try values of x in succession and for each such value find the corressponding value of y, you will find that there is an unlimited number of ordered pairs, such as $(0, 8)$, $(1, 6)$, $(2, 4)$, $(3, 2)$, $(4, 0)$, $(1/2, 7)$, $(-1, 10)$, $(-2, 12)$, etc., that satisfy the equation $2x + y = 8$, but there is no single "solution" as in equations with one variable. If instead, we are given two linear equations in two variables such as $x + y = 8$ and $x - y = 2$, it is generally possible (barring special cases) to find a single ordered pair that will satisfy both the equations. The two equations form what is called a **system of linear equations**. They are also called simultaneous linear equations. **Simultaneous linear equations** or simply **simultaneous equations** are those equations for which there is at least one pair of numbers that will satisfy each equation.

21.2 Solving Simultaneous Equations

There are two methods :

(1) Graphical method (2) Algebraic method

In this chapter we will take up the algebraic method.

Simultaneous equations can be solved algebraically by eliminating one of the variables. This elimination is done by any one of the following two methods :

1. **The addition method.** This method involves adding or subtracting the given equations so that one of the variables is eliminated and an equation in one variable only is obtained. If necessary, we multiply the given equations by such numbers as will make the coefficients of one unknown in the resulting equations numerically equal.

21.3 Type 1. When the coefficients of one of the variables in the two equations are equal.

Ex. 1. *Solve :* (a) $x - y = 3$ (b) $x - y = 5$
$\qquad\qquad\quad x + y = 5$ $\qquad\quad x + 5y = 11$

205

Sol. (a) $x - y = 3$ ...(1)

               $x + y = 5$ ....(2)

Adding (1) and (2), we obtain

$$2x = 8 \qquad \therefore \quad x = \frac{8}{2} = 4$$

Now putting $x = 4$ in (1), we get

        $4 - y = 3$ or $4 - 3 = y$ $\therefore$ $y = 1$

The solution is $x = 4, y = 1$ or **(4, 1)**.

(b) $x - y = 5$ ...(1)

              $x + 5y = 11$ ...(2)

Subtracting (1) from (2), we obtain

$$6y = 6 \qquad \therefore \quad y = \frac{6}{6} = 1$$

Putting $y = 1$ in (1), we get

        $x - 1 = 5$ $\therefore$ $x = 5 + 1 = 6$

The solution is $x = 6, y = 1$ or **(6, 1)**.

21.4 Type II. When the coefficients of one of the variables in the two equations are different.

Method I. *Make the coefficients of one of the variables in the two equations equal by multiplying both sides of the given equation by suitable numbers.*

Ex. 2. Solve : $3x - 2y = 19$ ... (1)

               $4x + y = 18$ ... (2)

Sol. In this example, you can see that adding or subtracting will not eliminate either variable. However, if both members of the second equation are multiplied by 2, the coefficients of y will become equal. Then by adding the equations we can eliminate the variable as follows :

             $3x - 2y = 19$ *Rewrite* (1)

             $\underline{8x + 2y = 36}$ *Multiply* (2) *by* 2

                $11x = 55$ *Add the equations*

      $\Rightarrow$ $x = 5$

Now, $3(5) - 2y = 19$ *Put the value of x in* (1)

      $\Rightarrow$ $15 - 2y = 19$

      $\Rightarrow$ $-2y = 19 - 15 = 4$ $\therefore$ $y = \dfrac{4}{-2} = -2$ $\therefore$ The solution is **(5, – 2)**.

Ex. 3. Solve :

         $3x - 5y = 14$ ...(1)

         $2x - 7y = 2$ ...(2)

Sol. In this example we will have to transform each equation to obtain the same numerical coefficients of one of the variables. To do this we multiply the first equation by 2 and the second equation by 3. The variable x in each equation then has the same coefficient.

$$6x - 10y = 28 \qquad \textit{Multiply (1) by 2.}$$
$$6x - 21y = 6 \qquad \textit{Multiply (2) by 3.}$$

$$\underline{- \quad + \qquad -}$$
$$11y = 22 \qquad \textit{Subtract}$$

$$\therefore \qquad\qquad y = \frac{22}{11} = 2.$$

Putting $y = 2$ in (1), we get
$$3x - 5(2) = 14 \quad \Rightarrow \quad 3x - 10 = 14$$

$$3x = 14 + 10 = 24 \quad \Rightarrow \quad x = \frac{24}{3} = 8 \quad \therefore \text{ The solution is } \textbf{(8, 2)}.$$

> **Note :** You should check the solution in each equation. Remember that a solution is correct only when it satisfies each equation in the system.

Check : Putting $x = 8$, $y = 2$ in (1), we get $3 \times 8 - 5 \times 2 = 14$ or $24 - 10 = 14$ or $14 = 14$ which is true.

Putting $x = 8$, $y = 2$, in (2), we get $2 \times 8 - 7 \times 2 = 2$ or $16 - 14 = 2$ or $2 = 2$ which is true.

Hence, the solution $x = 8$, $y = 2$, *i.e.*, (8, 2) is correct.

21.5 Method II. The Substitution Method

In this method, one equation is solved for one of the variables in terms of the other variable. Then this value is substituted for the variable in the second equation. The resulting equation contains only one variable.

Ex. 1. *Solve :* $2x - y = 4$ ...(1)
                  $x + 2y = -3$ ...(2)

Sol. From (1), $y = 2x - 4$

Substituting this value in (2), we get
$$x + 2(2x - 4) = -3 \qquad \Rightarrow \quad x + 4x - 8 = -3$$
$$\Rightarrow \qquad\qquad 5x = -3 + 8 \quad \Rightarrow 5x = 5 \quad \therefore \quad x = 1$$

Putting $x = 1$ in (1) or (2) we obtain $y = -2$. $\therefore$ The solution is $\textbf{(1, -2)}$.

A modification of the substitution method is called the **comparison method**. Two equations are solved for the same variable, and the resulting expressions are then equated.

Ex. 2. *Solve :* $3x - y = -15$ ...(1)
                  $2x + 3y = 23$ ...(2)
                                           ...(3)

Sol. From (1), $y = 3x + 15$

From (2), $y = \dfrac{23 - 2x}{3}$ ...(4)

Equating the two expressions in (3) and (4) we get

$$3x + 15 = \frac{23 - 2x}{3} \quad \Rightarrow \quad 9x + 45 = 23 - 2x \qquad \boxed{\text{Cross multiplying}}$$

$$\Rightarrow 9x + 2x = 23 - 45 = -22$$

$$\Rightarrow 11x = -22 \quad \therefore \quad x = \frac{-22}{11} = -2$$

Substituting in (3), we get, $y = 3(-2) + 15 = -6 + 15 = 9$

$\therefore$ The solution is $\textbf{(-2, 9)}$.

Note : You may employ any method, addition or substitution or comparison, whichever you may find convenient for a given system of equations. Generally, the addition method is used more commonly.

21.6 Equations Involving Fractions

Ex. 1. *Solve :*

$$\frac{7+x}{5} - \frac{2x-y}{4} = 3y - 5 \qquad \text{...(1)}$$

$$\frac{5y-7}{2} + \frac{4x-3}{6} = 18y - 5x \qquad \text{...(2)}$$

Sol. First remove fractions by multiplying both sides of each equation by the corresponding L.C.M. of the numbers in the denominators.

The L.C.M. of 5 and 4 is 20, therefore, we multiply both sides of (1) by 20. The L.C.M. of 2 and 6 is 6, therefore, we multiply both sides of (2) by 6.

Removing fractions from (1)

$$20 \times \frac{7+x}{5} - 20 \times \frac{2x-y}{4} = 20(3y - 5)$$

$$\Rightarrow \qquad 4(7 + x) - 5(2x - y) = 20(3y - 5)$$

$$\Rightarrow \qquad -6x - 55y = -128 \qquad \text{...(3)}$$

Removing fractions from (2),

$$6 \times \frac{5y-7}{2} + 6 \times \frac{4x-3}{6} = 6(18 - 5x)$$

$$\Rightarrow \qquad 3(5y - 7) + 4x - 3 = 6(18 - 5x)$$

$$\Rightarrow \qquad 34x + 15y = 132 \qquad \text{... (4)}$$

Multiplying (3) by 17 and (4) by 3,

$$-102x - 935y = -2176 \qquad \text{...(5)}$$

$$102x + 45y = 396 \qquad \text{... (6)}$$

Adding (5) and (6), $-890y = -1780 \qquad \therefore \quad y = \frac{-1780}{-890} = 2$

Substituting the value of y in (4),

$$34x + 15 \times 2 = 132$$

$$\Rightarrow \qquad 34x = 132 - 30 = 102 \quad \Rightarrow \quad x = \frac{102}{34} = 3.$$

$\therefore$ The solution is **(3, 2).**

Ex. 2. Solve algebraically : $\dfrac{2}{x} + \dfrac{2}{3y} = \dfrac{1}{6}, \dfrac{3}{x} + \dfrac{2}{y} = 0.$

Sol. Let $\dfrac{1}{x} = u$, and $\dfrac{1}{y} = v$. Then

$$2u + \frac{2}{3}v = \frac{1}{6} \qquad \text{...(1)}$$

$$3u + 2v = 0 \qquad \text{...(2)}$$

From (2) , $2v = -3u$. Substituting in (1), we get

$$2u + \frac{-3u}{3} = \frac{1}{6}, \quad \text{or} \quad 2u - u = \frac{1}{6}, \quad \text{or} \quad u = \frac{1}{6}$$

$$\therefore \qquad 2v = -3u = -3 \times \frac{1}{6} = -\frac{1}{2}, \text{ or } v = -\frac{1}{2} \times \frac{1}{2} = -\frac{1}{4}$$

$$\therefore \qquad x = \frac{1}{u} = 6, \, y = \frac{1}{v} = -4 \quad \therefore \text{ The solution is } \mathbf{(6, -4)}.$$

We can also solve the given equations as under :

Clearing fractions, we have

$$\frac{6}{x} + \frac{2}{y} = \frac{1}{2} \qquad \qquad \qquad \qquad \qquad \qquad \qquad \text{... (1)}$$

[Multiplying the first eqn. by the L.C.M. 3]

$$\frac{3}{x} + \frac{2}{y} = 0 \qquad \qquad \qquad \qquad \qquad \qquad \qquad \qquad \text{... (2)}$$

Subtracting (2) and (1), $\dfrac{6}{x} - \dfrac{3}{x} = \dfrac{1}{2} \quad \Rightarrow \quad \dfrac{6-3}{x} = \dfrac{1}{2} \quad \Rightarrow \quad \dfrac{3}{x} = \dfrac{1}{2} \quad \Rightarrow \quad \mathbf{x = 6}.$

Substituting in (2), $\dfrac{3}{6} + \dfrac{2}{y} = 0 \quad \Rightarrow \quad \dfrac{1}{2} + \dfrac{2}{y} = 0 \quad \Rightarrow \quad \dfrac{2}{y} = \dfrac{1}{2} \quad \Rightarrow \quad \mathbf{y = -4}.$

EXERCISE 21 (a)

Solve the following systems of equations :

1. $2x - y = 4$
   $x + y = 5$

2. $3x + y = 4$
   $2x - y = 6$

3. $2x - y = 5$
   $3x + y = 25$

4. $x + 2y = 12$
   $x - y = 4$

5. $4x - y = 4$
   $4x + 2y = -5$

6. $3x + 2y = 2$
   $5x + 6y = 4$

7. $4x + 3y = 14$
   $9x - 2y = 14$

8. $7(x + y) = 14$
   $x = 7y - 6$

9. $2x + 3y = 16$
   $x + y = 6$

10. $3x - 4y = 8$
    $x - y = 3$

11. $2n - 3p = 20$
    $5n + p = -1$

12. $2x + 5y = 23$
    $5x - 17 = y$

13. $5x - 3y = -1$
    $-x + 3y = -7$

14. $6p - 7q = 11$
    $8p + 3q = -47$

15. $4x + 12y = -8$
    $3x - 5y = 8$

16. $4(x + y) = 8(y - 4)$
    $2(x - 1) = y - 15$

17. $4(p + q) = 6(q - 1)$
    $8(p + 1) = q + 1$

Solve :

18. $\dfrac{x}{2} + \dfrac{y}{3} = 6$

    $3x - 2y = 12$

19. $\dfrac{x}{7} + y = \dfrac{-11}{7}$

    $x - \dfrac{5y}{3} = 2$

20. $\dfrac{m}{2} + n = \dfrac{1}{2}$

    $\dfrac{m}{7} + 1 = \dfrac{4n}{7}$

21. $4x + \dfrac{6}{y} = 15$

    $6x - \dfrac{8}{y} = 14$

22. $x - y = 0.9$

    $\dfrac{11}{2(x + y)} = 1$

23. $\dfrac{7}{x} + \dfrac{8}{y} = 2$

    $\dfrac{2}{x} + \dfrac{12}{y} = 20$

24. $\dfrac{5}{x} - \dfrac{3}{y} = -17$

    $\dfrac{1}{x} + \dfrac{2}{y} = 7$

25. $\dfrac{5}{2x} + \dfrac{3}{y} = \dfrac{7}{6}$

    $\dfrac{3}{2x} - \dfrac{4}{y} = \dfrac{1}{18}$

21.7 Application of Simultaneous Equations to Practical Problems

Ex. 1. *The sum of two numbers is 126 and their difference is 18. Find the numbers.*

Sol. Let the numbers be x and y. Then

$$x + y = 126 \qquad \qquad \qquad \text{... (1)}$$
$$x - y = 18 \qquad \qquad \qquad \text{... (2)}$$

Adding (1) and (2), we obtain

$$2x = 144 \quad \therefore \quad x = \frac{144}{2} = \mathbf{72}$$

Now putting $x = 72$ in (*i*), we have $72 + y = 126 \quad \Rightarrow \quad y = 126 - 72 \quad \Rightarrow \quad y = \mathbf{54}$

$\therefore$ The two numbers are **72** and **54**.

Ex. 2. *Two numbers differ by 6. Three times the larger number is 2 more than five times the smaller number. Find the numbers.*

Sol. Let the numbers be x and y. Then

$$x - y = 6$$

Three times the larger number ($3x$) is 2 more than five times the smaller number ($5y$). So we get

$$3x - 5y = 2$$

$\therefore$ We have to solve

$$x - y = 6 \qquad \qquad \qquad \text{... (1)}$$
$$3x - 5y = 2 \qquad \qquad \qquad \text{... (2)}$$

$5x - 5y = 30$	Multiply (1) by 5
$3x - 5y = 2$	Rewrite (2)
$-\quad+\quad-$	
$2x \quad\quad = 28$	Subtract
$x \quad\quad = 14$	

Putting $x = 14$ in (1)

$$14 - y = 6 \quad \Rightarrow \quad y = 14 - 6 \quad \Rightarrow \quad y = \mathbf{8}$$

$\therefore$ The two numbers are **14** and **8**.

Ex. 3. *A fraction becomes $\frac{4}{5}$ if 1 is added to each of the numerator and denominator. However if we subtract 5 from each, the fraction becomes $\frac{1}{2}$. Find the fraction.*

Sol. Let the fraction be $\dfrac{x}{y}$.

Given, $\dfrac{x+1}{y+1} = \dfrac{4}{5}$ and $\dfrac{x-5}{y-5} = \dfrac{1}{2}$

$\Rightarrow$ $5(x+1) = 4(y+1)$ $\Rightarrow$ $2(x-5) = y-5$

$\Rightarrow$ $5x + 5 = 4y + 4 \Rightarrow 5x - 4y = -1$ $\Rightarrow$ $2x - 10 = y - 5 \quad \Rightarrow \quad 2x - y = 5$

∴   We have to solve the equations

$$5x - 4y = -1 \qquad \qquad \text{...(1)}$$
$$2x - y = 5 \qquad \qquad \text{....(2)}$$

$5x - 4y = -1$	Rewrite (1)
$8x - 4y = 20$	Multiply (2) by 4

    $- \quad + \quad -$

$$-3x = -21 \qquad \text{Subtract}$$
$$x = 7$$

Substituting $x = 7$ in (2), we have

$$14 - y = 5 \Rightarrow y = 14 - 5 \Rightarrow y = 9 \quad \therefore \text{ The required fraction is } \frac{7}{9}.$$

Ex. 4. *William is six years older than John. In four years' time the sum of their ages will be 30 years. What are their ages now ?*

  Sol. Let William's age be x years and that of John be y years.

According to the given conditions :

$$x - y = 6$$
$$x + 4 + y + 4 = 30 \quad (\because \text{ after 4 years their ages will be } (x + 4) \text{ years and } (y + 4) \text{ years})$$

i.e. the equations are : $x - y = 6$ ...(1)

                    $x + y = 22$ ...(2)

Adding (1) and (2), we get $2x = 28 \Rightarrow x = 14$

Substituting $x = 14$ in (2), we have $14 + y = 22 \quad \Rightarrow \quad y = 8$.

∴   William's age is **14 years** and John's age is **8 years.**

Ex. 5. *The sum of the digits of a two digit number is 8. The number obtained by interchanging the two digits exceeds the given number by 36. Find the number.*

  Sol. Let the ten's digit be x and the one's digit be y.

Thus the number in the expanded form is written as $10x + y$ (Original number).

When the digits are reversed, then x becomes the one's digit and y becomes the ten's digit. Therefore, the number in the expanded form is

    $10y + x$ (New number after reversing the digits).

According to the given conditions, we have

    $x + y = 8$ ...(1)

    $(10y + x) - (10x + y) = 36$ | New number exceeds the old number by 36. |

$\Rightarrow$ $-9x + 9y = 36$ ...(2)

$9x + 9y = 72$	Multiply (1) by 9
$-9x + 9y = 36$	Rewrite (2)

Adding (1) and (2), we get

    $18y = 108 \Rightarrow y = 6$

Substituting $y = 6$ in (1), we have $x + 6 = 8 \quad \Rightarrow \quad x = 2$.

∴   The original number is $10 \times 2 + 6 = 20 + 6 = $ **26.**

Ex. 6. *5 pens and 6 pencils together cost Rs 9 and 3 pens and 2 pencils cost Rs 5. Find the cost of 1 pen and 1 pencil.*

Sol. Let the cost of 1 pen be Rs x and the cost of 1 pencil be Rs y. According to the given question:

$5x + 6y = 9$ ...(1)

$3x + 2y = 5$ ...(2)

$15x + 18y = 27$ Multiply (1) by 3

$15x + 10y = 25$ Multiply (2) by 5

$\underline{\quad\quad - \quad\quad - \quad\quad\quad - \quad\quad\quad\quad\quad\quad\quad}$

$\qquad\qquad 8y = 2$ Subtract

$\Rightarrow \quad y = \dfrac{1}{4}$

Substituting $y = \dfrac{1}{4}$ in (i) $5x + \dfrac{6}{4} = 9$ $\Rightarrow$ $5x = 9 - \dfrac{3}{2} = \dfrac{15}{2}$ $\Rightarrow$ $x = \dfrac{15}{2 \times 5} = \dfrac{3}{2}$.

$\therefore$ Cost of 1 pen = Rs $\dfrac{3}{2}$ = **Rs 1.50** and cost of **1 pencil** = Re $\dfrac{1}{4} = \dfrac{1}{4} \times 100$ = **25 paise.**

Ex. 7. *The area of a rectangle gets reduced by 9 square units, if its length is reduced by 5 units and the breadth is increased by 3 units. If we increase the length by 3 units and the breadth by 2 units, the area is increased by 67 square units. Find the length and breadth of the reactangle.*

Sol. Let the length and breadth of the rectangle be x units and y units respectively.

Then area = xy sq units.

Given : If the length is reduced by 5 units and breadth increased by 3 units, the area is reduced by 9 square units *i.e.*, $xy - 9 = (x - 5)(y + 3)$

$\Rightarrow \qquad xy - 9 = xy - 5y + 3x - 15 \Rightarrow 3x - 5y = 6.$

Given : When the length is increased by 3 units and breadth by 2 units, the area is increased by 67 sq units *i.e.*,

$xy + 67 = (x + 3)(y + 2) \Rightarrow xy + 67 = xy + 3y + 2x + 6 \Rightarrow 2x + 3y = 61$

$\therefore$ We have to solve the equations :

$3x - 5y = 6$ ...(1)

$2x + 3y = 61$ ...(2)

$6x - 10y = 12$ Multiply (1) by 2

$6x + 9y = 183$ Multiply (2) by 3

$\underline{\quad\quad - \quad\quad - \quad\quad\quad - \quad\quad\quad\quad\quad\quad}$ Subtract

$-19y = -171$ $\Rightarrow y = \dfrac{-171}{-19} = \mathbf{9}$

Putting $y = 9$ in (1), we have $3x - 45 = 6 \Rightarrow 3x = 51 \Rightarrow x = \mathbf{17}.$

$\therefore$ The length and breadth of the rectangle are 17 units and 9 units respectively.

Ex. 8. *A boat goes 36 km downstream in 4 hours and 30 km upstream in 5 hours. Find **(i)** the speed of boat in still water **(ii)** speed of the current.*

Sol. Speed downstream = $\dfrac{\text{Distance}}{\text{Time}} = \dfrac{36 \text{km}}{4 \text{hrs.}} = 9$ km/hr,

Speed upstream = $\dfrac{\text{Distance}}{\text{Time}} = \dfrac{30 \text{km}}{5 \text{hrs.}} = 6$ km/hr.

Let the speed of the boat in still water be x km/hr and speed of the current be y km/hr.

Then speed downstream = $(x + y)$ km/hr and speed upstream = $(x - y)$ km/hr

According to the question.

$$x + y = 9 \qquad \qquad ...(1)$$
$$x - y = 6 \qquad \qquad ...(2)$$

Adding (1) and (2), we get $2x = 15 \implies x = 7.5$

Substituting $x = 7.5$ in (1), we have $7.5 + y = 9 \implies y = 9 - 7.5 \implies y = 1.5$.

∴ The speed of the boat in still water is **7.5 km/hr** and the speed of the current is **1.5 km/hr.**

Ex. 9. *2 men and 7 boys can do a piece of work in 4 days. The same work is done by 4 men and 4 boys in 3 days. How long would it take 1 man and 1 boy to do it ?*

Sol. Let one man alone take x days and 1 boy alone take y days to complete the work.

One man's one day's work = $\dfrac{1}{x}$, ∴ 2 men's one day's work = $\dfrac{2}{x}$

One boy's one day's work = $\dfrac{1}{y}$ $\implies$ 7 boys' one day's work = $\dfrac{7}{y}$

∵ Together they take 4 days to complete the work, therefore working together their one day's work = $\dfrac{1}{4}$.

∴ According to the question $\dfrac{2}{x} + \dfrac{7}{y} = \dfrac{1}{4} \implies \dfrac{8}{x} + \dfrac{28}{y} = 1$

Similarly $\dfrac{4}{x} + \dfrac{4}{y} = \dfrac{1}{3} \implies \dfrac{12}{x} + \dfrac{12}{y} = 1$

Let $\dfrac{1}{x} = u$ and $\dfrac{1}{y} = v$. Then

$$8u + 28v = 1 \qquad \qquad ...(1)$$
$$12u + 12v = 1 \qquad \qquad ...(2)$$
$$24u + 84v = 3 \qquad \text{Multiply (1) by 3}$$
$$24u + 24v = 2 \qquad \text{Multiply (2) by 2}$$
$$\overline{}$$
$$\underset{-}{} \quad \underset{-}{} \quad \underset{-}{}$$
$$60v = 1 \qquad \text{Subtract}$$

$$\implies v = \dfrac{1}{60}$$

Substituting $v = \dfrac{1}{60}$ in (i), we have

$$8u + \dfrac{28}{60} = 1 \implies 8u = 1 - \dfrac{28}{60} = \dfrac{60 - 28}{60} = \dfrac{32}{60} \implies u = \dfrac{32}{60} \times \dfrac{1}{8} = \dfrac{1}{15}$$

∴ $x = \dfrac{1}{u} = \dfrac{1}{\dfrac{1}{15}} = 15$, $y = \dfrac{1}{v} = \dfrac{1}{\dfrac{1}{60}} = 60$.

Hence, 1 man takes **15 days** to complete the work alone and 1 boy takes **60 days** to complete the work alone.

Ex. 10. *A man has only 20 paisa coins and 25 paisa coins in his purse. If he has 50 coins in all worth Rs 12, how many coins of each type does he have?*

Sol.   Let the man have x, 20 paise coins and y, 25 paisa coins. Then $x + y = 50$

    Value of 20 paisa coins $= 20x$ paise, Value of 25 paisa coins $= 25y$ paise

$\therefore$ $20x + 25y = 1200$ or $4x + 5y = 240$

Thus, we have the following equations :

$x + y = 50$	... (1)
$4x + 5y = 240$	...(2)
$4x + 4y = 200$	Multiplying (1) by 4.
$4x + 5y = 240$	Rewrite (2)
$-\quad -\quad -$	Subtract

             $-y = -40 \implies y = 40$

Substituting $y = 40$ in (1), we get

       $x + 40 = 50 \implies x = 10.$

$\therefore$ The man has **10** twenty paisa coins and **40** twenty five paisa coins.

> **Check :** Sum of the coins $= 10 + 40 = 50$
>
> Value of 10 twenty paisa coins $= $ Rs $\left(10 \times \dfrac{1}{5}\right) = $ Rs 2
>
> Value of 40 twenty paisa coins $= $ Rs $\left(40 \times \dfrac{1}{4}\right) = $ Rs 10
>
> Total value of 50 coins $= $ Rs 2 $+$ Rs 10 $=$ Rs 12.

EXERCISE 21 (b)

1. If one number is added to twice another number, the answer is 68. If twice the first number is added to three times the other number, the answer is 112. What are the numbers?

2. Three times one number is 24 more than twice another number. The sum of the numbers is eleven times their difference. Find the numbers.

3. Divide a straight line 24 cm long into two parts so that twice the length of one part is 3 cm more than the length of the other part.

4. Ten years later A will be twice as old as B and ten years ago A was twelve times as old as B. What are the present ages of A and B ?

5. If twice the son's age in years is added to the father's age, the sum is 70. But if twice the father's age is added to the son's age, the sum is 95. Find the ages of father and son.

6. If a man walks for 2 hours and then cycles for 1 hour, he covers 17 km. If he walks for 1 hour and then cycles for 2 hours, still at the same speeds, he covers 22 km. What are his speeds of walking and cycling?

7. The wages of 6 men and 5 boys amount to Rs 260 per day. For 4 men and 7 boys, paid at the same rates, the wage bill for a day is Rs 232. Find the wages per day of a man and a boy.

8. Two audio casettes and three video casettes cost Rs 340. But three audio casettes and two video cassettes cost Rs 260. Find the price of one audio cassette and one video casette.

9. 4 kg of potatoes and 3 kg of tomatoes together cost Rs 36.50. While 3 kg of potatoes and 2 kg of tomatoes together cost Rs 26.50. What is the price per kg of tomatoes and potatoes ?

10. A man has 50 paise and 25 paise coins worth Rs 5. The value of the 50 paise coins is equal to that of the 25 paise coins. How many coins of each has he ?

11. A fraction is such that if the numerator is multiplied by 3 and the denominator is reduced by 3, we get 18/11, but if numerator is increased by 8 and denominator doubled, we get 2/5. Find the fraction.

12. The sum of the digits of a two digit number is 9. The number obtained by reversing the order of digits of the given number exceeds the given number by 9. Find the given number.

13. A boat goes 20km upstream in 5 hours and 35 km downstream in 7 hours. Find (*i*) the speed of boat in still water (*ii*) speed of the current.

14. A person starts his job with a certain yearly income and earns a fixed increment every year. If his salary was Rs 4500 after 4 years of service and Rs 5400 after 10 years of service, find his initial salary and annual increment.

15. If in a rectangle, the length is increased and breadth is reduced by 2 units each, the area is reduced by 28 square units. If the length is reduced by 1 unit, and the breadth increased by 2 units, the area is increased by 33 square units. Find the dimensions of the rectangle.

16. In a $\triangle$ ABC $\angle A = y°$, $\angle B = (y - 9)°$, $\angle C = x°$. Also $\angle B - \angle C = 48°$. Find the three angles.

17. 3 men and 6 boys can together finish a work in 3 days, while 1 man and 1 boy can finish it in 12 days. Find the time taken by 1 man alone to finish the work.

18. The incomes of A and B are in the ratio 3 : 4 and their expenditures are in the ratio of 5 : 7. If each of them saves Rs 1000 per month, find their monthly income.

   (**Hint :** Let the incomes be Rs $3x$ and Rs $4x$; expenditures be Rs $5y$ and Rs $7y$. Then $3x - 5y = 1000$ and $4x - 7y = 1000$).

19. A and B each has certain number of oranges. A says to B "if you give me 10 of your oranges I will have twice the number of oranges left with you". B replies, "If you give me 10 of your oranges, I will have the same number of oranges as left with you". Find the number of oranges with A and B separately.

LOOKING BACK
Summary of Key Facts

1. A pair of linear equations in two variables satisfied by the same pair of values for the variable is said to form a system of simultaneous linear equations.

2. Algebraic methods for solving the equations are :
   (*i*) Elimination by equating the coefficient.
   (*ii*) Substitution.

ANSWERS

EXERCISE 21 (a)

1. $(3, 2)$
2. $(2, -2)$
3. $(6, 7)$
4. $\left(\dfrac{20}{3}, \dfrac{8}{3}\right)$
5. $\left(\dfrac{1}{4}, -3\right)$
6. $\left(\dfrac{1}{2}, \dfrac{1}{4}\right)$
7. $(2, 2)$
8. $(1, 1)$
9. $(2, 4)$
10. $(4, 1)$
11. $(1, -6)$
12. $(4, 3)$
13. $(-2, -3)$
14. $(-4, -5)$
15. $(1, -1)$
16. $(-5, 3)$
17. $\left(-\dfrac{2}{3}, \dfrac{5}{3}\right)$
18. $(8, 6)$
19. $\left(-\dfrac{1}{2}, -\dfrac{3}{2}\right)$
20. $\left(-\dfrac{5}{3}, \dfrac{4}{3}\right)$
21. $(3, 2)$
22. $(3.2, 2.3)$
23. $\left(-\dfrac{1}{2}, \dfrac{1}{2}\right)$
24. $\left(-1, \dfrac{1}{4}\right)$
25. $(3, 9)$

EXERCISE 21 (b)

1. $20, 24$
2. $18, 15$
3. 9 cm, 15 cm
4. 34 years, 12 years
5. 40 years, 15 years
6. 4 km/hr., 9 km/hr.
7. Rs 30, Rs 16
8. Rs 20, Rs 100
9. Rs 6.50, Rs 3.50
10. 50 paisa – 5 coins, 25 paisa – 10 coins
11. $\dfrac{12}{25}$
12. 45
13. (*i*) 4.5 km/hr. (*ii*) 0.5 km/hr.
14. Rs 3900, Rs 150
15. $l = 23$ units, $b = 11$ units
16. $82°, 73°, 25°$
17. 18 days
18. Rs 6000, Rs 8000
19. A $\to$ 70, B $\to$ 50.

22. Linear Graphs

22.1 Coordinates

There are many occasions when you need to describe the position of an object. For example, telling a friend how to find your house, finding a square in the game of battleships, describing the position of an aeroplane showing up on a radar screen. In mathematics we need a quick way to describe the position of a point.

Rene Descartes- a French mathematician and philosopher who lived from 1596 to 1650 developed a method for locating the position of a point by giving its distances from two reference lines *OX* and *OY* called **axes** at right angles to each other.

O is called the **origin**, *OX* is called the X-axis, *OY* is called the Y-axis.

It is said that Descartes found it very difficult to get up in the morning and that he preferred to stay in bed and think. The strain of getting up at 5 O' clock in the morning to teach Queen Christine of Sweden is supposed to have killed him.

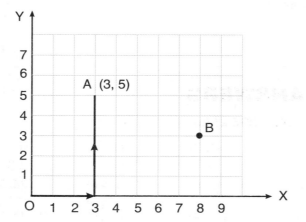

The position of a point A can be described as follows :

Start from O and move 3 squares along OX, then move 5 squares up from OX.

We always use the same method to describe the position of a point, *i.e.*, start from O, finish move along the *x*-axis and then up.

The description of the position of the point A is shortened to the **number pair (3, 5).**

The number pair (3, 5) is referred to as the **coordinates** of A. The first number, 3, is called the ***x*-coordinate** or the **abscissa** of A.

The second number, 5, is called the ***y*-coordinate** or the **ordinate** of A.

A point like B may be referred to simply as the point (8, 3). This tells us all that we need to know about the position of B. The origin is the point (0, 0)

Remark : The point (3, 5) is an **ordered pair** since it is always the *x*-coordinate that is given before the *y*-coordinate. *x* comes before *y* in the alphabet.

The abscissa of a point is its perpendicular distance from the *y*-axis, and the ordinate is its perpendicular distance from the *x*-axis.

Quadrants

The axes can be extended to create four quadrants. Counting anti-clockwise, they are referred to as 1st quadrant, 2nd quadrant, 3rd quadrant and 4th quadrant.

The convention of signs is as follows :

Distances measured from O along the x-axis to the right of y-axis are taken as positive and those measured to the left as negative. Similarly, distances measured from O along the y-axis, above x-axis are taken as positive and those measured below the x-axis are taken as negative. In keeping with the above convention, the coordinates of a point would be as follows :

1st quadrant ; (+, +)   2nd quadrant : (–, +)

3rd quadrant : (–, –)   4th quadrant : (+, –)

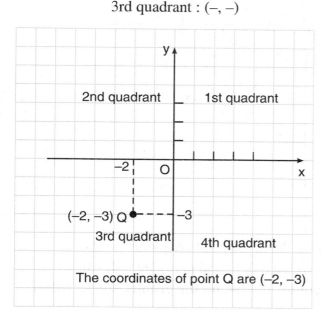

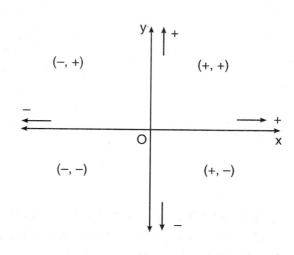

Remark : In general, the coordinates of a point are represented by the ordered pair (x, y).

■ **Any point on the x-axis.**

The ordinate of any point on x-axis is 0. So the coordinates of any point on the x-axis are **$(x, 0)$**

■ **Any point on the y-axis**

The abscissa of any point on the y-axis is 0. So the coordinates of any point on the y-axis are **$(0, y)$**.

22.2 Solved Examples

Ex. 1. *Draw a set of axes from –6 to 6. Use the same scale for each axis. Plot the points whose coordinates are given below and join them up in the given order :*

(a) **(i)** *(–4, 5), (–3, 6), (–2, 5), (–3, 2)*

 (ii) *(–6, –4), (–5, –2), (–2, –2), (–3, –4)*

 (iii) *(4, 3) (1, 6) (6, 5)*

 (iv) *(5, –2) (3, –4), (–1, 2).*

(b) *Draw the diagonals inside the shapes **(i)** and **(ii)**. Write the coordinates of the intersection of these diagonals.*

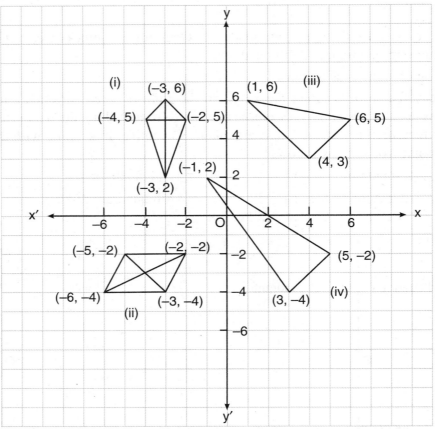

(a) Let $X'OX$ and YOY' be the coordinate axes. Then, the given point are plotted as shown.

(b) The coordinates of the points of intersection in (i) are (**−3, 5**) and in (ii) are (**−4, −3**).

Ex. 2. Write down the coordinates of the lettered points, plotted on the graphs, shown below.

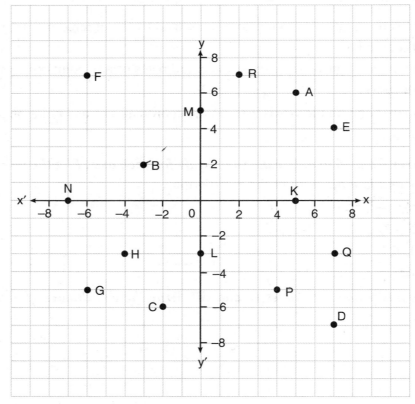

Sol. Look at the point A. It is in the first quadrant. So, its coordinates are (+, +). It is at a distance of 5 units from the *y*-axis, so its abscissa, *i.e.*, the *x*-coordinate is 5. Also, it is at a distance of 6 units from the *x*-axis, so its ordinate, *i.e.*, the *y*-coordiante is 6.

∴   Coordinates of A are (5, 6).

Similarly, you can read the coordinates of other points plotted in the graph keeping in mind that the coordinates of a point are (−, +) in quadrant II, (−, −) in quadrant III and (+, −) in quadrant IV.

Hence, we have B(−3, 2), C(−2, −6), D(7, −7), E(7, 4), F(−6, 7), G(−6, − 5), H(−4, −3), P(4, −5), Q(7, −3), R(2, 7), K(5, 0), M(0, 5) N(−7, 0), L(0, −3).

EXERCISE 22 (a)

1. Draw your own set of axes on a graph paper and plot the following points.

(*a*) A(5, 3)   (*b*) B(−4, 6)   (*c*) C(−3, −7)   (*d*) D(6, −5)

(*e*) E(6, 6)   (*f*) F(−6, 3)   (*g*) G(−8, −6)   (*h*) H(−1, 8)

2. Write down the coordinates of :

(*a*) The vertices P, Q and R of triangle PQR.

(*b*) The vertices A, B, C and D of the parallelogram ABCD. How long is AB? How long is DC?

(*c*) The centre, L, of the circle. What is the length of diameter of the circle?

(*d*) The vertices of the trapezium EFGH. How long is FG? How long is EH?

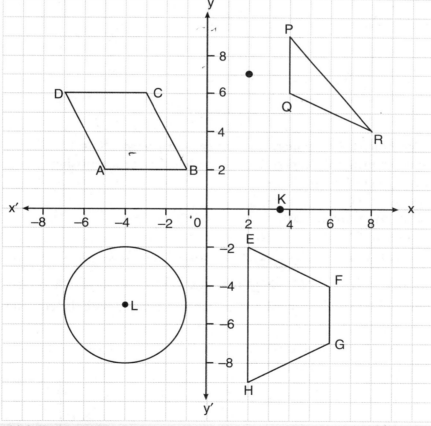

3. Name the points which lie on (*i*) the *x*-axis, (*ii*) the *y*-axis.
A(5, 0), B(0, 3), C(−8, 0), D(0, −4)

4. Plot the points A(−3, 4), B(−1, 4), C(1, 3), D(1, 2), E(−1, 1), F(1, 0), G(1, −1), H(−1, −2), K(−3, −2). Join the points in alphabetical order and join K to A.

5. Plot the points A(2, 1), B(−1, 3), C(−3, 0), D(0, −2). Join the points to make the figure ABCD. What is the name of the figure?

6. The points A(–2, –1), B(–2, 3), C(–6, 3) are three corners of a square ABCD. Plot the points and find the point D. Give the coordinates of D.

7. Plot the points A(–7, –3), B(5, 3) and mark the point C, the midpoint of the line segment AB. Give the coordinates of C.

8. The radar screen shows aircraft positions. Write down the coordinates of the aircraft in various positions A, B, C, D, E, F and G.

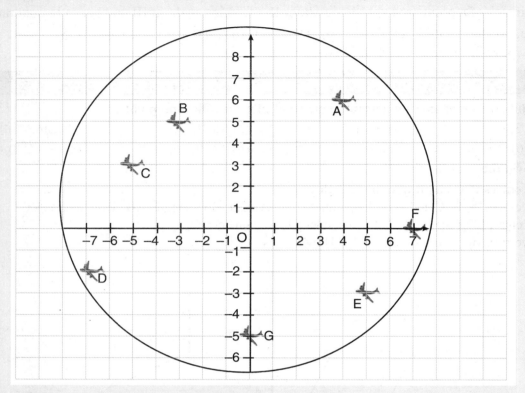

9. **Draw a coordinate grid on squared paper. Number each axis from –10 to 10.**
   Plot these points and complete the shapes. Each shape has one corner missing.
   Write down the missing coordinates.
   (*a*) square : (1, 1), (5, 1), (1, 5), (–, –),
   (*b*) rectangle : (2, 7), (7, 7) (7, 10), (–, –),
   (*c*) parallelogram : (–9, 10), (–7, 10), (–6, 7), (–, –),
   (*d*) octagon : (–6, –1), (–4, –3), (–2, –3), (0, –1), (0, 1), (–2, 3), (–4, 3), (–, –).

22.3 Graphing Linear, i.e., First Degree Equations in one and two variables

Each of the following three diagrams shows a graph associated with the equation.

$$x + y = 2$$

In Fig. (*i*), the replacement set of variables x and y is the set of whole numbers W, and so the graph consists of just three points (0, 2), (1, 1) and (2, 0).

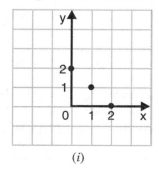 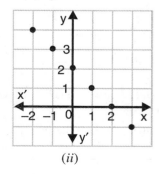 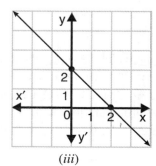

         (*i*)   (*ii*)   (*iii*)

In Fig. (*ii*), you see only a partial graph; the replacement set of each variable is the set of integers, Z, and the resulting graph is an infinte set of isolated points.

In Fig. (*iii*), the replacement set of each variable is the set of real numbers R, and the graph is an infinite set of points that together form a line. The line is called the **graph of the equation** on the coordinate plane, and the equation is called an **equation of the line**.

Any equation of the form $ax + by + c = 0$, where a, b and c are real numbers and a and b are not both zero, is called a **linear equation in two variables**, x and y.

> *A linear equation is an equation whose graph is a straight line.*

Thus, $5x - 7y = 8$, $5x = 9$, and $3y = 17$ are linear equations.

Ex. 1. *Graph $3x - y = 5$.*

Sol. $3x - y = 5 \implies -y = 5 - 3x \implies y = -5 + 3x \implies y = 3x - 5$.

Now, make a table as follows :

Let $x =$	Then $y =$	(Ordered pair) Point
2	$3 \times 2 - 5 = 1$	$\rightarrow (2, 1)$
0	$3 \times 0 - 5 = -5$	$\rightarrow (0, -5)$
−1	$3 \times (-1) - 5 = -8$	$\rightarrow (-1, -8)$
3	$3 \times 3 - 5 = 4$	$\rightarrow (3, 4)$
1	$3 \times 1 - 5 = -2$	$\rightarrow (1, -2)$

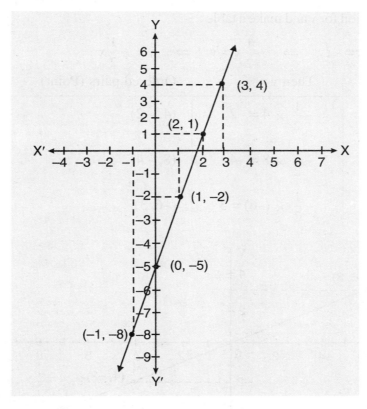

Graphing the ordered pairs listed in the table, suggests that the points all lie on a line. In fact, it can be proved that all the points of this line make up the graph of the entire solution set of $3x - y = 5$.

Method. To graph any linear equation in two variables.

1. *Write the given equation in the form showing one variable in terms of the other (most commonly, in the form y = mx + c) and find at least three sets of values for these variables.*
2. *Draw the x- and y-axes and choose a suitable scale.*
3. *Plot three points named by the ordered pairs.*
4. *Draw the straight line joining any two of these points and check it with the third point.*

Ex. 2. *Graph the equation 2x – y = 6.*

Sol. **Step 1.** Write the equation in the form $y = 2x - 6$

Step 2. Make a table by substituting values for x

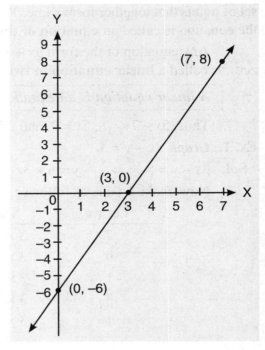

If $x =$	then $y =$
7	8
3	0
0	– 6

ordered pairs :

Step 3. Plot these three points.

Step 4. Draw a straight line through first and third points.

Check : Does the second point lie on this line?

Ex. 3. *Graph 2x = x – 2y.*

Sol. Solve the given equation for y and make a table :

$$2x = x - 2y \implies x = -2y \implies -\frac{1}{2}x = y \implies y = -\frac{1}{2}x$$

Let $x =$	Then $y =$	Ordered pairs (Point)
4	$-\frac{1}{2} \times 4 = -2$	$(4, -2)$
8	$-\frac{1}{2} \times 8 = -4$	$(8, -4)$
–6	$-\frac{1}{2} \times (-6) = 3$	$(-6, 3)$

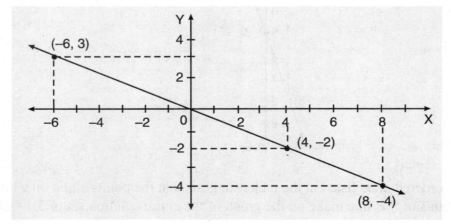

Plot the points $(4, -2)$, $(8, -4)$, $(-6, 3)$ and join.

> **Maths Alert** : Two points determine a line, so you need to graph only two points of the given equation. As a check, graph at least three points. (If the points you locate are not on a line, you have made an error).

Ex. 4. *Graph the equations* (i) $y = 4$, (ii) $x = -5$.

Sol.

(i) Writing the equation as $0 \cdot x + y = 4$, we see that there is no restriction on x. The condition simply requires that for every value of x in R, the value of y is 4.

Some solutions are $(1, 4)$, $(-3, 4)$ and $(5, 4)$. The graph is shown in Fig. Ex. 4(i). It should be noted that the graph of equation $y = k$ is the line parallel to the x-axis at a distance k units from it.

(ii) The equation can be written as $x + 0 \cdot y = -5$.

The condition requires that for every value of y in R, the value of x is -5. Some solutions are $(-5, 1)$, $(-5, 3$ and $(-5, -3)$. The graph is shown in Fig. Ex. 4(ii).

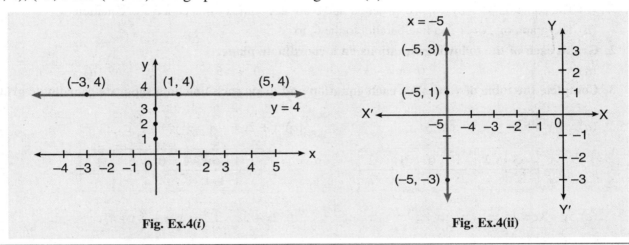

Fig. Ex.4(i)   Fig. Ex.4(ii)

> **Note :**
>
> (1) The graph of a first degree equation in only one unknown quantity is either the x-axis, the y-axis or a line parallel to one of the axes. Thus,
>
> (2) The graph of $y = 0$ is the *x*-axis and the graph of $x = 0$ is the *y*-axis.
>
> (3) The graph of $y = 5$ and $y = -5$ are lines parallel to the *x*-axis.
>
> (4) The graphs of $x = 4$ and $x = -4$ are lines parallel to the *y*-axis at distances 4 and -4 units respectively from it.

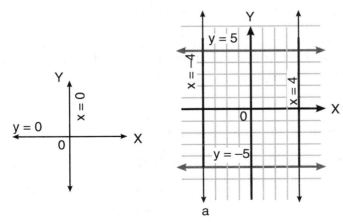

Fig. Note 2   Fig. Note 3 and 4

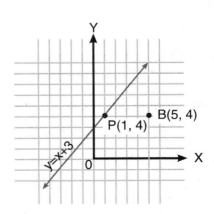

Fig. Note 5 and 6

Also,

(5) If a point is **on the graph** of an equation, its coordinates satisfy the equation. Thus, if $x = 1$ and $y = 4$, the coordinates of P(1, 4) on the graph of $y = x + 3$ satisfy the equation $y = x + 3$, *i.e.*, if we substitute $x = 1$ and $y = 4$ in the equation $y = x + 3$, the **L. H. S = R. H. S.**

(6) If a point is **not on the graph** of an equation, its coordinates **do not satisfy** the equation.

Thus, if $x = 5$ and $y = 4$, the coordinates of B(5, 4) which is not on the graph of $y = x + 3$, do not satisfy the equation $y = x + 3$.

EXERCISE 22 (b)

1. Fill in the blanks :

(a) The graph of $x = 1$ is a line parallel to the .... axis.

(b) The graph of $y = 1$ is a line parallel to the ... axis.

(c) The equation $ax + by + c = 0$ (where a and b are not both zero) is called a ... equation.

(d) The graph of $2x = 1$ is a line parallel to the ... axis.

2. Graph each of the following equations on a coordinate plane.

(a) $x = 4$ (b) $x = -3$ (c) $y = 5$ (d) $y = -1$

3. Complete the table of values for each equation and draw each line on a separate coordinate grid.

(a) $x + y = 5 \Rightarrow y = 5 - x$

x	–3	–2	–1	0	1	2
y	8					7

(b) $x + 2y = -4 \Rightarrow y = -\dfrac{1}{2}x - 2$

x	–6	–4	0	6	4
y	1		–2		

(c) $5y - 3x = 15 \Rightarrow y = \dfrac{3}{5}x + 3$

x	–15	–10	–5	0	5	10
y	6					

(d) $2x + 3y = 12 \Rightarrow y = -\dfrac{2}{3}x + 4$

x	–9	–6	3	0	9	6	3
y							

4. Draw a coordinate grid from –10 to 10 on both axes. Using table of values draw each line on the same grid.

(a) $y = x - 4$ (b) $y = 2x - 4$ (c) $y = 3x - 4$ (d) $y = 4x - 4$

22.4 Solving a Pair of Simultaneous Equations Graphically

Simultaneous mean 'at the same time'

You know that simultaneous equations are equations that are true at the same time.

When two lines cross, they cross only once. Each line can have an equation

e.g., $y = x - 2$, $y = -x + 4$

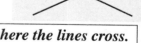

> *When you solve a pair of simultaneous equations you are finding the point where the lines cross. This point is called the point of intersection of the lines.*

Ex. 1. *Solve graphically the equations :* $x + y = 3$, $3x - 2y = 4$.

Sol. **Step 1.** *Draw the graphs of the two equations on the same co-ordinate plane.*

To draw graph of $x + y = 3 \Rightarrow y = 3 - x$, we have

x	0	1	3
y	3	2	0

Plot the points (0, 3) (1, 2) and (3, 0) and join.

To draw graph of $3x - 2y = 4 \Rightarrow y = \dfrac{3}{2}x - 2$, we have

x	0	2	4
y	–2	1	4

Plot the point (0, –2), (2, 1) and (4, 4) and join.

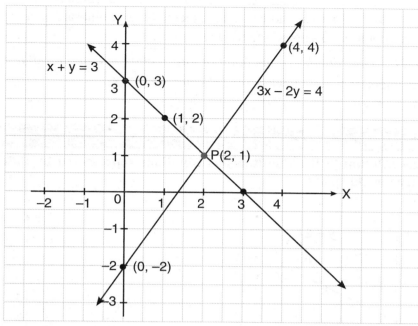

Step. 2. *Read the co-ordinates of the point of intersection of the two lines that you have drawn.*

Here the lines intersect at point P whose coordinates are (2, 1). Hence, *x = 2, y = 1* is the solution of the given equation.

Ex. 2. *Solve the system : 2x – 3y = – 6, 2x – y = 2.*

Sol. **Step. 1.** *Draw graphs of the two equations on the same co-ordinate plane.*

The table of values for the equation

$2x - 3y = -6 \Rightarrow y = \frac{2}{3}x + 2$, is

x	0	3	– 3
y	2	4	0

The table of values for the equation

$2x - y = 2 \Rightarrow y = 2x - 2$, is

x	0	1	2
y	– 2	0	2

Plot the points (0, 2), (3, 4), (– 3, 0). Join to obtain the graph of $2x - 3y = -6$. Now plot the points (0, – 2), (1, 0) and (2, 2) and join to obtain the graph of $2x - y = 2$.

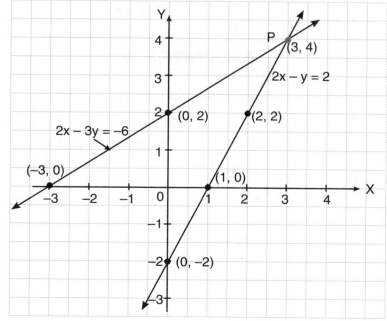

Maths Alert : We wish to remind you that, in fact only two points are enough to obtain the graph. We have taken three points to safeguard against any error.

Step. 2. Read the co-ordinates of the point of intersection of two lines that you have drawn.

Here the lines intersect at point P whose coordinates are $(3, 4)$.

Hence, $x = 3, y = 4$ is the solution of the given equations.

EXERCISE 22 (c)

1. **Write down the solution to the simultaneous equations represented by these lines. Show that both equations are true at this point.**

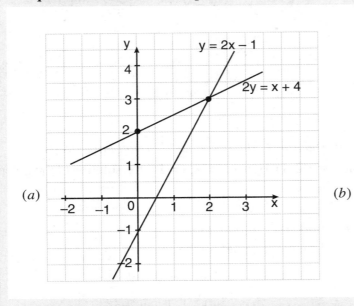
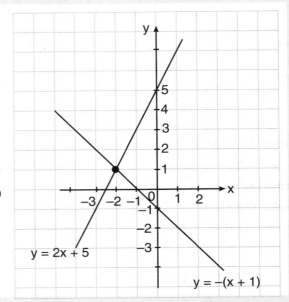

(a)   (b)

Solve these simultaneous equations using graphs :

2. $y + x = 0$ **3.** $y = 2x + 2$ **4.** $x + y = 3$

     $y - x = -4$ $3y = -x - 15$ $2x + 5y = 12$

5. $x - 2y = 5$ **6.** $3x + y + 1 = 0$ **7.** $2x - y = 8$

     $2x + 3y = 10$ $2x - 3y + 8 = 0$ $4x + 3y = 6$

ANSWERS

EXERCISE 22 (a)

2. (a) P $(4, 9)$, Q $(4, 6)$, R $(8, 4)$

    (b) A $(-5, 2)$, B $(-1, 2)$, C $(-3, 6)$; D$(-7, 6)$

       AB = DC = 4 units

    (c) L $(-4, -5)$; diameter = 6 units

    (d) E$(2, -2)$, F$(6, -4)$, G$(6, -7)$, H$(2, -9)$; EH = 7 units

3. On x-axis : A$(5, 0)$, C$(-8, 0)$;

    On y- axis : B$(0, 3)$, D $(0, -4)$

5. Square   **6.** D$(-6, -1)$ **7.** $(-1, 0)$

8. A$(4, 6)$, B$(-3, 5)$, C$(-5, 3)$, D$(-7, -2)$, E$(5, -3)$,

    F$(7, 0)$, G$(0, -5)$

9. (a) $(5, 5)$,   (b) $(2, 10)$ (c) $(-8, 7)$,

    (d) $(-6, 1)$

EXERCISE 22 (b)

1. (a) y-axis   (b) x-axis   (c) linear   (d) y-axis

2. (a)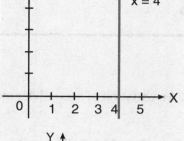

    (b)

    (c)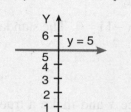

    (d)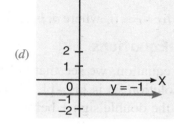

3. (a) $x + y = 5 \implies y = 5 - x$

x	–3	–2	–1	0	1	2
y	8	7	6	5	4	3

    (b) $x + 2y = -4 \implies y = -\dfrac{1}{2}x - 2$

x	–6	–4	0	6	4
y	1	0	–2	–5	–4

(c) $5y - 3x = 15 \implies y = \dfrac{3}{5}x + 3$

x	–15	–10	–5	0	5	10
y	–6	–3	0	3	6	9

    (d) $2x + 3y = 12 \implies y = -\dfrac{2}{3}x + 4$

x	–9	–6	–3	0	9	6
y	10	8	6	4	–2	0

EXERCISE 22 (c)

1. (a) $(2, 3)$ (b) $(-2, 1)$ 2. $(2, -2)$ 3. $(-3, -4)$ 4. $(1, 2)$ 5. $(5, 0)$

6. $(-1, 2)$ 6. $(3, -2)$

INTERESTING FACT ABOUT A MATHEMATICIAN

Throughout most of history, women were not given much education. Therefore, there have been few women mathematicans, although many women became eminent mathematicians. One famous woman mathematician was **Maria Agnesi** (1718-1799) of Milan, Italy.

A remarkable thing about Maria Agnesi was that she could do mathematical problems in her sleep. She was a sleep-walker. Often in the morning she would find that she had sleepwalked to her desk and completed a problem she had been unable to solve the night before.

PUZZLE

A woman was travelling with her young son, a carton of cakes, and a wolf. She had to cross a river in a small boat large enough only for herself and one of the three. If she left her son alone with the cakes, he would eat them. If she left the wolf alone with the boy, the wolf would eat him. How could she make the crossing? See below.

(**Hint :** Which two of the three could be left alone on the river bank?)

Answer : The woman takes the boy across, returns alone. She takes the carton of cakes across, returns with boy. she takes wolf across, returns alone. Then she takes the boy across.

23. Quadratic Equations

23.1 Definition

A quadratic equation is a polynomial equation of second degree. An equation of second degree is one in which the variable appears to the second power and to no higher power.

Examples of quadratic equations are $x^2 - 36 = 0$, $x^2 + 7x + 12 = 0$, $5x^2 - 7x - 11 = 0$. The standard form of the quadratic equation is $ax^2 + bx + c = 0$, where a, b, c, are constants and $a \neq 0$.

23.2 Solving Quadratic Equations

If $x^2 = 1$ is the given equation, we see that either $+1$ or -1 can replace x and make a true sentence. A common way to write this solution set is $\{1, -1\}$. Mathematicians have devised a way of writing $+1$ and -1 as simple expression by using the double sign $\pm$ before the number. The roots of the equation $x^2 = 1$ are often written as $x = \pm 1$.

Ex. 1. *Solve:* $2(x^2 - 8) = 11 - x^2$

> **Step 1.** $\qquad 2(x^2 - 8) = 11 - x^2$
>
> $\qquad \Rightarrow 2x^2 - 16 = 11 - x^2$
>
> $\qquad \Rightarrow 3x^2 = 27$

Step 1. *Express the given equation in standard form, $ax^2 = k$ where k is a constant.*
Step 2. *Divide both sides by the coefficient of x^2.*
Step 3. *Take square root of both members of the equation.*

Step 2. $\Rightarrow x^2 = \dfrac{27}{3} = 9$

Step 3. $\Rightarrow x = \pm 3$

$2\left[(-3)^2 - 8\right] = 11 - (-3)^2$
$\Rightarrow 2(9 - 8) = 11 - (9)$
$\Rightarrow 2 = 2$

Check: $2(3^2 - 8) = 11 - 3^2 \Rightarrow 2 \times 1 = 11 - 9 \Rightarrow 2 = 2$

The roots of the given equation are $x = 3$ and $x = -3$.

A root is any replacement of the variable that makes the equation true. Since each root satisfies the equation, it is seen that there are two roots for this quadratic equation.

Ex. 2. *Solve:* $5x^2 = 15x$.

Sol. $5x^2 - 15x = 0$

$\Rightarrow 5x(x - 3) = 0$

$\Rightarrow 5x = 0 \quad$ or $\quad x - 3 = 0$

$\Rightarrow x = 0 \quad$ or $\qquad x = 3$

Hence, $x = 0, 3$

1. *Express in the form $ax^2 + bx = 0$.*
2. *Factorise.*
3. *Let each factor = 0 (if ab = 0, then either a= 0 or b =0).*
4. *Solve for each resulting equation.*

23.3 Solving Quadratic Equation by Factorising

Procedure :   **1.** *Express the given equation in the standard form*

$$ax^2 + bx + c = 0.$$

     2. *Factorise the left number.*   (that is, $ax^2 + bx + c$)

     3. *Let each factor = 0.*

     4. *Solve each resulting equation.*

     5. *Check each root in original equation .*

Ex. 3. *Solve:* $x^2 - 3x - 10 = 0.$

Sol. $x^2 - 3x - 10 = 0$ **1.** *The equation is in standard form.*

$\Rightarrow x^2 - 5x + 2x - 10 = 0$ **2.** *Factorise the left member.*

$\Rightarrow x(x-5) + 2(x-5) = 0$

$\Rightarrow \quad\quad (x-5)(x+2) = 0$

$x - 5 = 0$ or $x + 2 = 0$ **3.** *Let each factor = 0.*

$x = 5$ or $x = -2$ **4.** *Solve each resulting equation.*

Check : $x = 5$ | **Check :** $x = -2$

$5^2 - (3 \times 5) - 10 = 0$ | $(-2)^2 - (3 \times -2) - 10 = 0$

$25 - 15 - 10 = 0$ | $4 + 6 - 10 = 0$

$25 - 25 = 0$ | $10 - 10 = 0$

$0 = 0$ | $0 = 0$

$$\therefore \; x = 5, -2.$$

Maths Alert : Before checking, we can only say 5 or –2. After checking, we can say that the roots are 5 and –2.

Ex. 4 *Solve :* $9t^2 - 3t - 2 = 0.$

Sol. $9t^2 - 3t - 2 = 0$

$9t^2 - 6t + 3t - 2 = 0$ $\Rightarrow$ $3t(3t-2) + 1(3t-2) = 0$

$\Rightarrow (3t-2)(3t+1) = 0 \Rightarrow 3t - 2 = 0$ or $3t + 1 = 0$

$\Rightarrow 3t = 2$ or $3t = -1 \Rightarrow t = \dfrac{2}{3}$ or $-\dfrac{1}{3}$

$$\therefore \; t = \frac{2}{3}, \; t = -\frac{1}{3}.$$

> **Check :** When $t = \dfrac{2}{3}$, L.H.S. $= 9 \times \left(\dfrac{2}{3}\right)^2 - 3 \times \dfrac{2}{3} - 2$
>
> $= 4 - 2 - 2 = 0 =$ R.H.S.
>
> When $t = -\dfrac{1}{3}$, L.H.S. $= 9 \times \left(-\dfrac{1}{3}\right)^2 - 3 \times \left(-\dfrac{1}{3}\right) - 2$
>
> $= 1 + 1 - 2 = 0 =$ R.H.S.

Ex. 5 *Solve* $\dfrac{x+3}{x+2} = \dfrac{3x-7}{2x-3}.$

Sol. $\dfrac{x+3}{x+2} = \dfrac{3x-7}{2x-3}$

Cross multiplying $(x+3)(2x-3) = (3x-7)(x+2)$

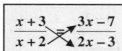

$\Rightarrow \quad 2x^2 + 6x - 3x - 9 = 3x^2 - 7x + 6x - 14$

$\Rightarrow \quad 2x^2 + 3x - 9 = 3x^2 - x - 14$

$\Rightarrow \quad x^2 - 4x - 5 = 0$

$\Rightarrow \quad x^2 - 5x + x - 5 = 0 \quad \Rightarrow \quad x(x-5) + 1(x-5) = 0$ | Factorising

$\Rightarrow \quad (x+1)(x-5) = 0$

$\quad x + 1 = 0 \quad$ or $x - 5 = 0$ | Let each factor be 0.

$\quad x = -1 \quad$ or $x = 5$

$\therefore \quad \mathbf{x = -1, 5.}$

On checking, you will find that the both the values satisfy the given equation.

Ex. 6. *Solve* $\dfrac{1}{x-3} - \dfrac{1}{x+5} = \dfrac{1}{6}$.

Sol. $\dfrac{1}{x-3} - \dfrac{1}{x+5} = \dfrac{1}{6} \qquad \Rightarrow \dfrac{(x+5) - (x-3)}{(x-3)(x+5)} = \dfrac{1}{6}$

$\Rightarrow \dfrac{x+5-x+3}{x^2 - 3x + 5x - 15} = \dfrac{1}{6}$

$\Rightarrow \dfrac{8}{x^2 + 2x - 15} = \dfrac{1}{6} \quad \Rightarrow 48 = x^2 + 2x - 15$ | on cross multiplication

$\Rightarrow x^2 + 2x - 15 - 48 = 0 \Rightarrow x^2 + 2x - 63 = 0$

$\Rightarrow x^2 + 9x - 7x - 63 = 0 \Rightarrow x(x+9) - 7(x+9) = 0$ | Factorising

$\Rightarrow (x+9)(x-7) = 0$

$\Rightarrow x + 9 = 0 \qquad$ or $x - 7 = 0$ | Let each factor be equal to 0

$\Rightarrow x = -9 \qquad$ or $x = 7$

Since, both the values satisfy the given equation.

$\therefore \quad \mathbf{x = -9}$ or $\mathbf{x = 7}$

EXERCISE 23

Solve each of the following equations :

1. $x^2 = 25$ **2.** $x^2 - 49 = 0$ **3.** $x^2 - 7 = 0$ **4.** $x^2 = 75$ **5.** $2x^2 = 8$

6. $4 = 100y^2$ **7.** $\dfrac{x^2}{3} - 12 = 0$ **8.** $\dfrac{x^2 - 9}{5} = 8$ **9.** $\dfrac{2x}{3} = \dfrac{6}{x}$ **10.** $\dfrac{y+2}{5} = \dfrac{9}{y-2}$

11. $2x^2 - 4x = 0$ **12.** $x^2 - \dfrac{1}{2}x = 0$ **13.** $x^2 - 3x - 10 = 0$ **14.** $x^2 - 7x + 12 = 0$ **15.** $x^2 - 5x - 6 = 0$

16. $2x^2 - 10x + 12 = 0$ **17.** $6a^2 + a - 2 = 0$ **18.** $x + \dfrac{16}{x} = 8$ **19.** $\dfrac{7}{x} = 9 - 2x$

20. $3x^2 + x = 10$ **21.** $2a^2 - 15a + 27 = 0$ **22.** $(c-5)^2 = 64$ **23.** $\dfrac{3}{x} - \dfrac{6}{x+1} = 2$

24. $\dfrac{x}{4} + \dfrac{10}{x-2} = 6$ **25.** $\dfrac{x+3}{x-2} - \dfrac{1-x}{x} = \dfrac{17}{4}$ **26.** $\dfrac{x-1}{x-2} + \dfrac{x-3}{x-4} = 3\dfrac{1}{3}(x \neq 2, 4)$

27. $\dfrac{2x}{x-4} + \dfrac{2x-5}{x-3} = \dfrac{25}{3}(x \neq 3, 4)$

LOOKING BACK
A Summary of Key Facts

1. A quadratic equation is a polynomial equation of second degree.

2. A root is a value of the variable that make the equation true. There are two roots for each quadratic equation.

3. For the quadratic equation, $x^2 = a$ we have $x \pm a$.

MENTAL MATHS – 17

Find the roots of:

1. $3z - z^2 = 0$ **2.** $5z^2 - 30z = 0$ **3.** $x^2 + 5x + 6 = 0$ **4.** $x^2 - 3x - 10 = 0$

5. $y^2 + 3y - 18 = 0$ **6.** $5x^2 - 20 = 0$ **7.** $x^2 + 9x + 14 = 0$ **8.** $x^2 + 4x - 12 = 0$

ANSWERS
EXERCISE 23

1. $-5, 5$ **2.** $-7, 7$ **3.** $-\sqrt{7}, \sqrt{7}$ **4.** $-5\sqrt{3}, 5\sqrt{3}$ **5.** $-2, 2$ **6.** $-\dfrac{1}{5}, \dfrac{1}{5}$

7. $-6, 6$ **8.** $-7, 7$ **9.** $-3, 3$ **10.** $-7, 7$ **11.** $0, 2$ **12.** $0, \dfrac{1}{2}$

13. $-2, 5$ **14.** $3, 4$ **15.** $-1, 6$ **16.** $2, 3$ **17.** $-\dfrac{2}{3}, \dfrac{1}{2}$ **18.** $4, 4$

19. $1, \dfrac{7}{2}$ **20.** $-2, \dfrac{5}{3}$ **21.** $\dfrac{9}{2}, 3$ **22.** $13, -3$ **23.** $-3, \dfrac{1}{2}$ **24.** $22, 4$

25. $4, \dfrac{-2}{9}$ **26.** $5, \dfrac{5}{2}$ **27.** $6, \dfrac{40}{13}$

MENTAL MATHS – 16

1. $0, 3$ **2.** $0, 6$ **3.** $-2, -3$ **4.** $5, -2$ **5.** $-6, 3$ **6.** ± 2

7. $-7, -2$ **8.** $-6, 2$

THE HUMAN CALCULATOR

SEPTEMBER 819202

Gordon Cherry of London can instantly calculate in his head that September 18 in the year 819202 will fall on a Wednesday.

S	M	T	W	T	F	S
1	2	3	4	5	6	7
8	9	10	11	12	13	14
15	16	17	18	19	20	21
22	23	24	25	26	27	28

WORKING WITH PRIMES

1. In the twentieth century the first year that was a prime was 1901. Can you find the other twelve?

2. Complete the magic square. Note that all the numbers except 1 are prime numbers.

Answers :

1. 1907, 1913, 1931, 1933, 1949, 1951, 1973, 1979, 1987, 1993, 1997, 1999.

2.

67	1	43
13	37	61
31	73	7

67	1	43
	37	
	43	7

24. Linear Inequations

24.1 Inequations in One Variable

Mathematical sentences of the type

$$5 \neq 7, \ 7 > 5, \ -1 < 2, \ 3y < 15, \ 5t > 20$$

are called inequalities or inequations. These sentences say that one thing is not equal to another.

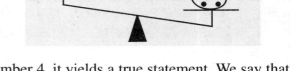

The bag on the left weighs less than the one on the right, so $x < 15$, or $15 > x$.

Consider the sentences

(a) $3x = 12$ (b) $2x < 3$

If the variable x in the equation (a) is replaced by the number 4, it yields a true statement. We say that the equation is satisfied. Similarly, the inequation (b) is satisfied if the variable x is replaced by the numbers.

$$..., -3, -2, -1; \ 0, \ 1 \ (x \text{ is an integer})$$

24.2 Solution Set or Truth Set

Consider the inequation $1 + x > 5$. We can obtain the following solutions for the replacement sets shown.

Replacement set	Solutions
$A = \{0, 1, 2, 5, 7, 8)$	5, 7 and 8
$B = \{0, 1, 2, 3, 4, 6)$	6
$C = \{0, 1, 2, 3, 4\}$	ϕ

The above example illustrates the fact the solution of an inequation depends upon the replacement set used. It also follows from the above that an inequation may have one, many or no solution depending upon the replacement set. The solution or solutions of a given inequation form a set which we call the **solution set** or the **truth set**. It is obviously a subset of the replacement set.

24.3 Notation

Recall from the chapter on sets the following notations that are used for sets of numbers.

> **N** = *Set of all natural numbers,*
> **W** = *Set of all whole numbers,*
> **Z** = *Set of all integers*
> **Z^{+}** = *Set of all positive integers*
> **Z^{-}** = *Set of all negative integers.*
> **R** = *Set of all real numbers.*

24.4 Properties of Inequalities.

1. **Adding to or subtracting from both sides of an inequality any non-zero number produces an equivalent inequality.**

   (*i*) $x-3>5$ is equivalent to $x-3+3>5+3$ or $x>5+3$ or $x>8$.

   (*ii*) $x+1>3$ is equivalent to $x+1-1>3-1$, or $x>3-1$ or $x>2$.

2. **Multiplying or dividing both sides of an inequality by the same positive number produces an equivalent inequality.**

   (*i*) $5x>15$ is equivalent to $\dfrac{5x}{5}>\dfrac{15}{5}$, or $x>\dfrac{15}{5}$ or $x>3$.

   (*ii*) $\dfrac{x}{3}>2$ is equivalent to $\dfrac{x}{3}\times3>2\times3$, or $x>2\times 3$, or $x>6$.

3. **Multiplying both sides of an inequality by the same negative number produces an inequality with its direction reversed.**

   (*i*) $3<4$ is equivalent to $(-1)(3)>(-1)(4)$, or $-3>-4$.

   (*ii*) $x>8$ is equivalent to $(-1)(x)<(-1)(8),$ or $-x<-8$.

   (*iii*) $-x>-8$ is equivalent to $(-1)(-x)<(-1)(-8)$, or $x<8$.

4. **Dividing each side of an inequality by a positive number, does not change the inequality.**

   (*i*) $20>15$. Also, $\dfrac{20}{5}>\dfrac{15}{5}$, *i.e.*, $4>3$.

   (*ii*) $12x>48 \Rightarrow \dfrac{12x}{12}>\dfrac{48}{12}$, *i.e.*, $x>4$.

5. **Dividing each side of an inequality by a negative number, reverses the inequality.**

   e.g. $21>14 \Rightarrow \dfrac{21}{-7}<\dfrac{14}{-7}$, *i.e.* $-3<-2$.

   $-16<-12 \Rightarrow \dfrac{-16}{-4}>\dfrac{-12}{-4}$, *i.e.* $4>3$.

Maths Alert :

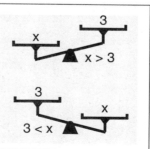

If we change over the sides of an inequality we must change the sign from < to > or from > to <.

Remark : Properties 3 and 5 tell us that we should not multiply or divide both sides of an inequality by a negative number unless it is desired to reverse the inequality.

24.5 Graphing Solution Set of an Inequality on a Number Line

The graph of a linear inequality in one variable is the collection of all points on the number line which correspond to the numbers in the solution set of the given inequality.

Illustrations :

1. The number line represents the inequality $x > 3$. The open dot at 3 indicates that this number is excluded.

   The coloured shading with an arrowhead indicates that all numbers greater than 3 are included in the graph.

   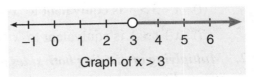

2. The solid dot at 3 indicates that the point 3 is also included in the graph.

   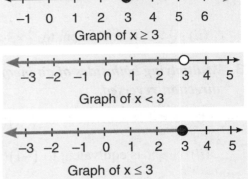

3. (*i*) The diagram shows that all numbers less than 3 are included in the graph.

   (*ii*) The diagram shows that graph of all numbers less than or equal to 3.

   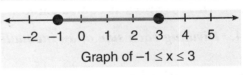

4. The graph is the line segment that includes −1 and 3 and all points between them.

   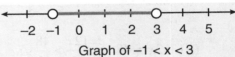

5. The graph of all points lying between −1 and 3 excluding end-points −1 and 3.

EXERCISE 24 (a)

Match the inqualities with the graphs.

1. $x \leq -2$ (*a*)

2. $-4 \leq x < 0$ (*b*)

3. $-3 < x \leq 4$ (*c*)

4. $0 \leq x \leq 5$ (*d*)

5. $x > 0$ (*e*)

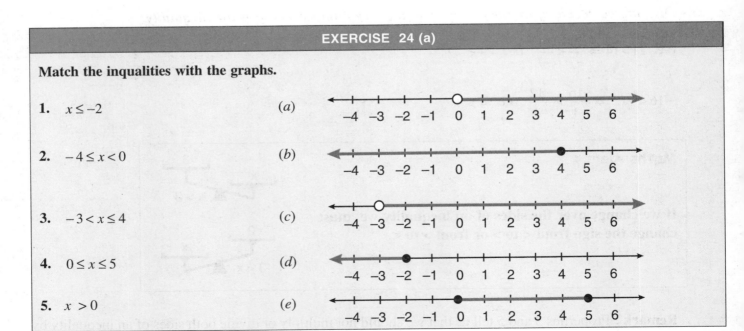

6.	$x \le 4$	(f)	
7.	$x > -3$	(g)	
8.	$x < 2$ or $x > 2$	(h)	

24.6 Solved Examples

Ex. 1. *Solve $x + 2 < 5$, choosing replacement from $\{0, 1, 2, 3, 4, 5\}$ and graph the solution set.*

Sol. $x + 2 < 5$

$x + 2 - 2 < 5 - 2$ Subtract 2 from each side

$\Rightarrow x < 3$

Choosing those numbers from the replacement set which are less than 3, we have $x = 0, 1, 2$. The graph consists of only the points 0, 1, 2 and so the graph is as shown.

Note that no other portion of the number line than the points 0, 1, and 2 is included in the graph.

Ex. 2. *Solve the inequality $3x + 5 > 20$, and graph the solution set.*

Sol. As with equations, we can add to or subtract the same value from each side. However we can multiply or divide by positive values only.

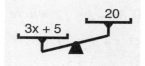

$3x > 20 - 5$ Subtract 5 from each side.

$3x > 15$

$x > \dfrac{15}{3}$ Divide by 3.

$x > 5$

The graph is as shown.

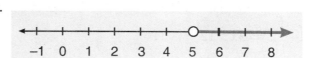

Ex. 3. *Solve the inquality $23 - 4x < 7$.*

Sol. Looking back at the method used for negative terms in equations, we have

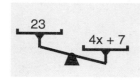

$23 < 4x + 7,$ Adding $4x$ to each side.

$23 - 7 < 4x$ Subtracting 7 from both sides.

$\Rightarrow 16 < 4x$

$\Rightarrow 4 < x$

$\Rightarrow x > 4.$

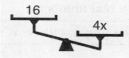

Ex. 4. *Solve the inequality* $12 - x > 3x - 5$.

Sol. As with equations, we need to have the 'x' term positive, and on one side.

$$12 - x > 3x - 5 \implies 12 > 4x - 5 \implies 17 > 4x \implies \frac{17}{4} > x \implies 4\frac{1}{4} > x, \ i.e., \ x < 4\frac{1}{4}.$$

Ex. 5. *Solve the inequality* $3n + 8 < 29$ *if* $n \in W$ *and graph the solution set.*

Sol. W = the set of whole numbers $\{0, 1, 2, 3, ...\}$

$$3n + 8 < 29 \implies 3n < 29 - 8 \implies 3n < 21 \implies n < \frac{21}{3} \quad \text{So, } n < 7$$

$\therefore$ The solution set S = all whole numbers less than 7 = **{0, 1, 2, 3, 4, 5, 6}**

The graph includes only the whole numbers 0 to 6 and is as shown :

Ex. 6. *Solve the following inequalities :*

(a) $x + 3 > 5$ *in the system of natural numbers.*

(b) $x - 4 \le 1$ *in the system of natural numbers.*

(c) $-3x > 15$ *in the system of integers.*

(d) $3x + 2 > 14$ *in the system of real numbers.*

(e) $7 - 4x < 15$ *in the system of real numbers.*

(f) $5x - 3 \le 12$ *where* $x \in \{-5, -3, -1, 1, 3, 5, 6\}$.

(g) $x + 5 < 20$ *where x is a prime number.*

Sol. (a) $x + 3 > 5 \implies x + 3 - 3 > 5 - 3 \implies \mathbf{x > 2}$.   Hence $x = 3, 4, 5, 6, ...$

(b) $x - 4 \le 1 \implies x - 4 + 4 \le 1 + 4 \implies \mathbf{x \le 5}$ Hence $x = 1, 2, 3, 4, 5$.

(c) $-3x > 15 \implies = \dfrac{-3x}{3} > \dfrac{15}{3} \implies -x > 5 \implies \mathbf{x < -5}$.   Hence $x = ..., -8, -7, -6$.

> **Note :** The graph will be as shown.

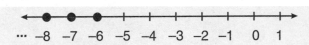

(d) $3x + 2 > 14 \implies 3x > 14 - 2 \implies 3x > 12$

$\implies \dfrac{3x}{3} > \dfrac{12}{3} \implies \mathbf{x > 4}$.

(e) $7 - 4x < 15 \implies -4x < 15 - 7 \implies -4x < 8$

$\implies \dfrac{-4x}{4} < \dfrac{8}{4} \implies -x < 2 \implies \mathbf{x > -2.}$

where x is a real number.

> **Note :** The graph will be as shown:

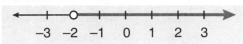

(f) if $5x - 3 \leq 12$, where $x\{\in -5, -3, -1, 1, 3, 5, 6\}$

then $5x \leq 12 + 3 \Rightarrow 5x \leq 15 \Rightarrow \dfrac{5x}{5} \leq \dfrac{15}{5} \Rightarrow x \leq 3$

Hence $x = -5, -3, -1, 1, 3$.

> **Note** : The graph will be as shown :

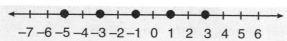

(g) if $x + 5 < 20$ where x is a prime number

then $x < 20 - 5 \Rightarrow x < 15$

We choose only those numbers which are primes numbers. Hence $x = 2, 3, 5, 7, 11, 13$.

Ex. 7. *Solve $x + 3 > 15$ when $x \in$ {all natural numbers less than 10}*

Sol. $x + 3 > 15 \quad \Rightarrow \quad x > 15 - 3 \quad \Rightarrow \quad$ So, $x > 12$

But the replacement set includes only numbers < 10

∴ Solution set $\mathbf{S = \phi.}$

Ex. 8. *Solve the inequality $7(x - 2) + 2 > 2(5x + 9)$ and graph its solution set.*

Sol. When nothing is mentioned we presume that x is a real number.

$7(x - 2) + 2 > 2(5x + 9)$

$\Rightarrow \quad 7x - 14 + 2 > 10x + 18$

$\Rightarrow \quad 7x - 12 > 10x + 18 \quad \Rightarrow \quad 7x - 10x > 18 + 12$

$\Rightarrow \quad -3x > 30 \Rightarrow -x > 10 \quad \Rightarrow \mathbf{\textit{x} < -10}$

The graph is as shown :

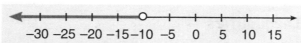

EXERCISE 24 (b)

1. **Which numbers out of the numbers shown here might x stand for in each inequation below?**

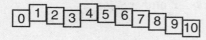

(a) $x > 7$ (b) $x < 5$ (c) $x > 9$ (d) $x \leq 2$

2. (a) Choose replacements from $\{-2, -1, 0, 1, 2\}$ to solve these inequations.

(b) Mark the solutions as dots on a number line. **For example,** the solution of $x > 0$ is 1, 2, which can be shown on the number line like this.

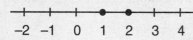

(a) $x + 3 > 3$ (b) $x - 5 < -5$ (c) $x - 2 < -3$

(d) $1 - x > 1$ (e) $-3 < -2 + x$ (f) $x + 6 > 7 + 2x$

Find the solution set for each of the following inequalities:

3. $x - 8 < 30$ where x is a square number.   **4.** $17x \leq 119$ where x is a positive odd number.

5. $\dfrac{z}{4} < 10$ where z is a positive integer divisible by 5.

6. $2x + 15 \le 51$ where x is a positive integer divisible by both 2 and 3.

7. $3p + 26 \le 98$ where p is a positive integer divisible by both 3 and 4.

8. $5x - 17 \le 28$ where x is an integer greater than 4.   9. $\dfrac{m}{2} + 6 < 11$ where m is not a prime number.

Solve the following inequations and show the solutions on a number line :

10. $x + 2 > 7$ in the system of (*a*) integers, and (*b*) real numbers.

11. $y + 3 > -4$ in the system of (*a*) integers less than –2. (*b*) real numbers.

12. $6 + 3t > 27$ in the system of (*a*) even numbers less than 15. (*b*) real numbers.

13. $13 - y < 9$ in the system of (*a*) prime numbers less than 20. (*b*) real numbers.

14. $4 - 5n \le +10 - 8n$ in the system of
    (*a*) non-negative integers   (*b*) integers,   (*c*) real numbers.

Solve each inequality in the system of real numbers and graph its solution set :

15. $0 > -4 - p$ 16. $\dfrac{t}{15} + 8 > 8$ 17. $8(y + 5) > -(20 - 3y)$

Match the inequality with the graph of its 'line' solution :–

18. $c - 7 > -25$ (*a*) 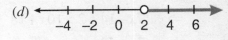   19. $5x - 7 \ge 2x - 10$ (*b*)

20. $-3x - 7 > -22$ (*c*)   21. $x \ge -1, x \in Z$ (*d*)

22. $\dfrac{u + 1}{-3} > -1$ (*e*)   23. $-2 < 2 + \dfrac{y}{3}$ (*f*)

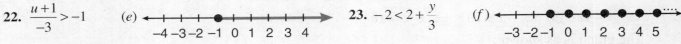

24.7 Solving Combined Inequalities

In this case there are two inequations to be satisfied. Such inequalities are also called compound inequalities.

Ex. 1. *Solve the inequation –2 < x ≤ 1 and represent the solution set on the numbers line.*

Sol. Given inequation contains two inequations namely, $x > -2$ and $x \le 1$.

This is shown here on the number line.

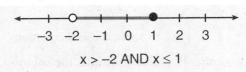

Remark : Sometimes two inequations cannot be written as one expression, *e.g.* $x < -2$ and $x \ge 1$.

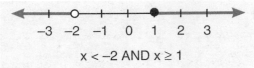

Ex. 2. *Solve the inequation –1 ≤ 2x + 4 < 5 and show the solution on a number line. Write down the possible values of x, if x is an integer.*

Sol. Given inequation can be spilt into two inequations.

$-1 \le 2x + 4$ AND $2x + 4 < 5$. Solve them separately.

$-1 \le 2x + 4$	$2x + 4 < 5$
$\Rightarrow \quad -1 - 4 \le 2x$	$\Rightarrow \quad 2x < 5 - 4$
$\Rightarrow \quad -5 \le 2x$	$\Rightarrow \quad 2x < 1$
$\Rightarrow \quad -\dfrac{5}{2} \le x$	$\Rightarrow \quad x < \dfrac{1}{2}$
$\Rightarrow \quad x \ge -2\dfrac{1}{2}$	

So $\quad -2\dfrac{1}{2} \le x < \dfrac{1}{2}$

This can be shown on the number line as under :

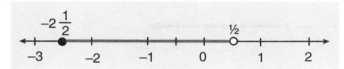

If x is an integer then $x = -2, -1$ or 0.

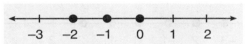

LOOKING BACK
Summary of Key facts

1. > means greater than; < means less than

$\ge$ means greater than or equal to.

$\le$ means less than or equal to.

2. To solve an inequation, you can:

  (*i*) Add the same number to both sides.

 (*ii*) Subtract the same number from both sides.

 (*iii*) Multiply both sides by the same positive number.

 (*iv*) Divide both sides by the same positive number.

  (*v*) Multiplying or dividing both sides by a negative number reverses the direction of the inequation.

3. The solution of an inequation depends on the replacement or truth set given and can be represented on a number line.

ANSWERS

EXERCISE 24 (a)

1. (*d*)   2. (*g*)   3. (*f*)   4. (*e*)   5. (*a*)   6. (*b*)   7. (*c*)   8. (*h*)

EXERCISE 24 (b)

1. (*a*) 8, 9, 10   (*b*) 0, 1, 2, 3, 4   (*c*) 10   (*d*) 0, 1, 2   2. (*a*) 1, 2   (*b*) –1, –2   (*c*) –2   (*d*) –1, –2   (*e*) 0, 1, 2   (*f*) –2

3. {1, 4, 9, 16, 25, 36}   4. {1, 3, 5, 7}   5. {5, 10, 15, 20, 25, 30, 35}   6. {6, 12, 18}

7. {12, 24}   8. {5, 6, 7, 8, 9}   9. {1, 4, 6, 8, 9}

10. $x > 5$ *(a)*   *(b)*

11. *(a)* $\{-6, -5, -4, -3\}$

    (b) $y > -7$

12. *(a)* $\{8, 10, 12, 14\}$

    (b) $t > 7$

13. *(a)* $\{5, 7, 11, 13, 17, 19\}$

    (b) $y > 4$

14. *(a)* $\{0, 1, 2\}$

    (b) $n \le 2, n \in Z$

    (c) $n \le 2, n \in R$

15. $p > -4$ **16.** $t > 0$

17. $y > -12$

18. *(c)*   **19.** *(e)*   **20.** *(a)*   **21.** *(f)*   **22.** *(d)*   **23.** *(b)*

EXERCISE 24 (c)

1. $-1 \le x < 2$

2. $-2 \le x \le 3$

3. $-2 \le x < 2$

4. $-3 \le x \le 3$

5. $-1 < x \le 3$

6. $-2, -1, 0, 1, 2$ **7.** $-2, -1, 0, 1, 2, 3$ **8.** $-2, -1, 0, 1$ **9.** $-1, 0, 1, 2, 3$

25. Relations and Functions

25.1 Review

You have studied in detail about relations and functions (also called mapping) in class VII. Let us review briefly the concepts learnt by you in that class.

- **Ordered pair.** An ordered pair is a pair of objects whose components occur in a special order. In the ordered pair (a, b), a is called the **first component** and b the **second component.**

> **Maths Alert :**
> 1. The ordered pair (a, b) is not the same as (b, a).
> 2. (a, b) is not the same $\{a, b\}$. The former denotes an ordered pair whereas the latter denotes a set.
> 3. Ordered pairs may have the same first and second component such as (a, a), $(3, 3)$, etc.
> 4. Two ordered pairs of numbers are said to be **equal** when the first components of both are equal and also their second components are equal.

Thus, $(-5, 7) = \left(-\dfrac{25}{5}, \dfrac{35}{5}\right)$ but $(-5, 7) \neq (7, -5)$ and $(3, 8) \neq (5, 8)$.

- **Cartesian product.** Let A and B be two non-empty sets. Then, their Cartesian product, denoted by $A \times B$ and read 'A cross B' is the set of all ordered pairs whose first components are elements of the first set A and second components are elements of the second set B.

> **Maths Alert :** The Cartesian product $A \times B$ is not the same as $B \times A$. In $A \times B$, the set A will be considered as the first set and the first component of the ordered pairs will be picked up from set A, while in $B \times A$, the set B will be considered as the first set and the first component of the ordered pairs in this case will be picked up from set B.

Ex. 1. *Let A = {2, 3, 5} and B = {2, 4}. Find :*

(a) $A \times A$ (b) $A \times B$ (c) $B \times A$ (d) $B \times B$

Sol. Given : A = {2, 3, 5}, B = {2, 4}

(a) $A \times A = \{(2, 2), (2, 3), (2, 5), (3, 2), (3, 3), (3, 5), (5, 2), (5, 3), (5, 5)\}$

(b) $A \times B = \{(2, 2), (2, 4), (3, 2), (3, 4), (5, 2), (5, 4)\}$

(c) $B \times A = \{(2, 2), (2, 3), (2, 5), (4, 2), (4, 3), (4, 5)\}$

(d) $B \times B = \{(2, 2), (2, 4), (4, 2), (4, 4)\}$

EXERCISE 25 (a)

Form ordered pairs by pairing the following :

1. Cricketers :	Dravid	Sachin	Sehwag	Ganguly	Dhoni
Runs scored in a match :	59	84	66	47	28
2. Students :	Rekha	Sunita	Vivek	Rahul	Anju
Marks in science	49	58	75	84	63

3. If $A = \{6, 7, 8\}$, $B = \{8, 9\}$, find the Cartesian products $A \times A$, $B \times B$, $A \times B$ and $B \times A$.

25.2 Relation

In our daily life, by relation, we mean an association of two objects, such as that of

    (*i*)   person, *e.g.*, father and son, husband and wife, brothers and sisters,

    (*ii*) Schools and their principals,

    (*iii*) States and their capitals etc.

In mathematics, any set of ordered pairs is called a relation. For example, the set

$$R = \{(0, 0), (-1, 1), (2, 4), (-3, 9), (-8, 5)\} \text{ is a relation.}$$

25.3. Domain and Range of a Relation

The set of all the first components of the ordered pairs is called the **domain** of the relation , while the set of all the second components is called the **range** of the **relation**.

Thus, for the above relation, we have

Domain of $R = \{0, -1, 2, -3, -8\}$, Range of $R = \{0, 1, 4, 9, 5\}$

25.4. Representation of a Relation

The representation of a relation as a set of ordered pairs as done above is called the **roster form**. Another way to picture a relation is by using an **arrow diagram**, which is also called the **mapping diagram**. Thus, we may picture the relation R as under :

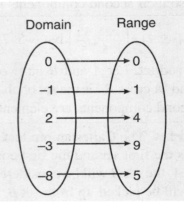

Domain	Range
0	0
–1	1
2	4
–3	9
–8	5

- **The equation form of a relation**

  Suppose we have the relation

  $$R = \{(-2, 4), (2, 4) \ (3, 9), (4, 16), (-8, 64)\}$$

  in which the second component of an ordered pair is the square of the first component then it may also be represented by means of the equation $y = x^2$.

  The variable x denotes an element of the domain and the variable y denotes an element of the range. Here, y is the square of x.

  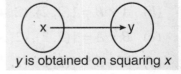

  y is obtained on squaring *x*

- **Rule of a relation**

  If a particular relationship exists between the second and first components of each ordered pair of a relation R, then this relationship is called the ***rule of the relation.***

  Thus, in the relation $R = \{(-2, 4), (2, 4), (3, 9), (4, 16), (-8, 64)\}$ the rule of the relation is '***the square of'.***

Ex. 1. *Let A = {10, 11, 12, 13, 14} and B = {7, 8, 9, 10, 11, 12}. Let R be a relation 'is 2 more than' from A to B. Find R. Show it by an arrow diagram and also by an equation.*

Sol. Here, the element of the second set is obtained on subtracting 2 from the element of the first set, so clearly, $R = \{(x, y) \mid y = x - 2, x \in A, y \in B\}$.

Hence, we form those pairs (x, y) in which x is 2 more than y.

∴ $R = \{(10, 8), (11, 9), (12, 10), (13, 11), (14, 12)\}$

Domain (R) = set of first components of the ordered pairs in $R = \{10, 11, 12, 13, 14\}$

Range (R) = set of second components of the ordered pairs in $R = \{8, 9, 10, 11, 12\}$

The arrow diagram is as shown

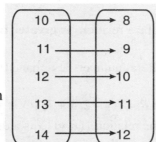

Ex. 2. *Write the following relations in roster form :*

(a)
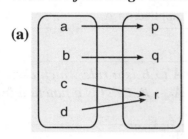

(b)
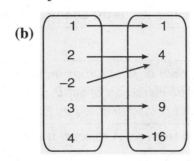

(c)
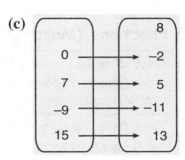

Write the domain and range in each case.

Sol. (a) $R = \{(a, p), (b, q), (c, r), (d, r)\}$

Domain $(R) = \{a, b, c, d\}$, Range $(R) = \{p, q, r\}$

(b) $R = \{(1, 1), (2, 4), (-2, 4), (3, 9), (4, 16)\}$

Domain $(R) = \{1, 2, -2, 3, 4\}$, Range $(R) = \{1, 4, 9, 16\}$

(c) $R = \{(0, -2), (7, 5), (-9, -11), (15, 13)\}$

Domain $(R) = \{0, 7, -9, 15\}$,

Range $(R) = \{-2, 5, -11, 13\}$

Remark : The relation may be written in the form $\{(x, y) \,|\, y = x - 2, x \in R, y \in R\}$.

EXERCISE 25 (b)

1. List the ordered pairs in each relation :

(a)
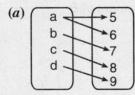

(b)
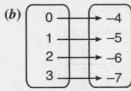

(c)
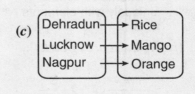

2. Let A = $\{a, b, c, d\}$, B = $\{x, y, z\}$. State which of the following is a relation from A to B :

   (a) $\{(a, x), (b, y), (c, z), (d, x)\}$ (b) $\{(a, x), (a, y), (a, z)\}$ (c) $\{(a, y), (b, x), (z, c)\}$

   (d) $\{(a, z)\}, (a, y), (d, x)\}$ (e) $\{(a, z), (d, z), (a, x), (b, x)\}$

   (**Hint.** R is a relation from A to B only when the ordered pairs in R belong to A × B, *i.e.*, R ⊆ A × B)

3. **In each of the following, state which of the ordered pairs belong to the given relations :**

   (a) $\{(x, y) \mid y = x^3\}$; R = $\{(1, 1), (2, 8), (3, 10), (4, 64), (-1, -1), (7, 49), (-5, -125)\}$

   (b) $\{(x, y) \mid xy = 20\}$; R = $\{(1, 20), (-20, -1), (4, 5), (5, 4), (0, 20), (20, 0), (-10, -2), (8, 3)\}$

4. Given A = $\{3, 4, 5, 6\}$ and B = $\{6, 7, 8, 9, 10, 11, 12\}$, find R if R is a relation '**is a factor of**' from A to B. Write the domain and range of R.

5. Given A = $\{6, 7, 8, 9\}$ and B = $\{5, 6, 8\}$, let R be a relation '**is greater than**' from A to B. Describe R in Roster form and find its domain and range.

6. Write the relation $\{(x, y) : x = 3y, x$ and y are natural numbers less than 10$\}$ in roster form and find its domain and range.

7. Determine the domain and range of the relation $R = \{(x - 2, x + 3) \mid x \in \{0, 1, 2, 3, 4, 5\}\}$

8. Given A = $\{2, 3, 4, 5, 6\}$, list the elements of the relation $\{(x, y) \mid x$ is a divisor of $y, (x, y) \in A \times A$ and $x \neq y\}$.

9. Z is the set of integers. Describe the relation $\{(0, -5), (3, -2), (5, 0), (7, 2), (-10, -15) ... \}$ in set builder form, giving its domain and range.

10. Given A = $\{-2, -1, 0, 1, 2\}$ find the relation R : '**is the additive inverse of**' applied on A.

25.5 Functions (Mappings)

> *Let A, B be two non-empty sets, then a function or mapping from A to B is a rule which associates every element x of set A to a unique element y of set B. We write $f : A \rightarrow B$, i.e., f is a function from A to B. y is called the image of x and is also denoted by f(x).*

Thus, for a function to be defined from set A to set B it is essential that

(i) All elements of set A are used up, i.e., domain of function = set A.

(ii) An element of set A is not paired with more than one element of set B, i.e., no two ordered pairs of the function should have the same first component.

Illustration :

Look at the following arrow diagrams of five relations R_1, R_2, R_3, R_4 and R_5. We will examine which of them are functions and which are not.

(i) R_1 is '**5 less than**'   (ii) R_2 is '**the additive inverse of**'   (iii) R_3 is '**the square of**'

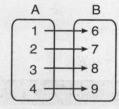

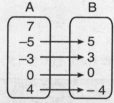

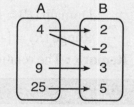

Elements of A match uniquely with elements of B.

Element 7 of A is not used up in forming pairs

Element 4 of A pairs with more than one element of B

(iv) R_4 is '**scores marks**'   (ii) R_5 is '**the multiple of**'

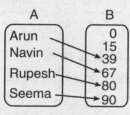

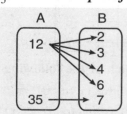

Some elements of B remain unpaired

More than one ordered pair have the same component in R_5

In the above examples,

   (i) R_1 is a function,

  (ii) R_2 is not a function because one element of the first set is not paired with any element of the second set '*B*'.

 (iii) $R_3 = \{(4, 2), (4, -2), (9, 3), (25, 5)$ is not a function because in it two ordered pairs (4, 2) and (4, -2) have the same first component '4'. *i.e.,* more than one arrow starts from the same element of *A*.

 (iv) R_4 is a function even though two elements of *B* remain unpaired.

  (v) $R_5 = \{(12, 2), (12, 3), (12, 4), (12, 6), (35, 7)\}$ is not a function as 4 ordered pairs have the same first component, viz., '12'. (*i.e.,* more than one arrow starts from the same element '12' of the first set *A*.

25.6 Representation of a Function

As you would have observed in the above discussion just like a relation *R*, a function *f* may also be described or represented in several ways. Some of these are (1) Roster form (2) An arrow diagram (3) A formula called an equation (4) set builder notation (5) A graph.

For example, we have the relation $R = \{(-2, -1), (-1, 2), (0, 5), (1, 8), (2, 11),\}$ which is a function.

The following are the different ways in which it can be represented.

  1. Roster form : $f = \{(-2, -1), (-1, 2), (0, 5), (1, 8), (2, 11)\}$,

  2. An arrow diagram

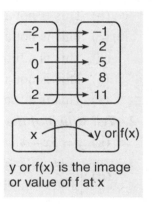

  3. An equation : $y = 3x + 5$ or $f(x) = 3x + 5$

     y or *f*(*x*) is the image of *x* under the rule '*5 more than 3 times*'.

  4. Set builder notation : $f\{(x, y) \mid y = 3x + 5\}$

  5. A graph

y or f(x) is the image
or value of f at x

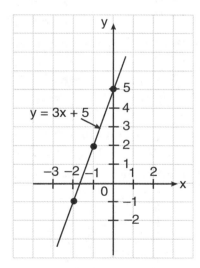

Ex. 1. *Which of the following relations are functions ? Give reasons. In case of a function, determine its domain and range.*

    (a) $R_1 = \{(5, -7), (2, 9), (-1, 6), (4, 13)\}$ **(b)** $R_2 = \{(3, 0), (3, -3), (1, 2), (5, 14)\}$

    (c) $R_3 = \{(a, x), (b, y), (c, z), (p, q), (m, n)\}$.

Sol. The relation R_1 and R_3 are functions because no two of their ordered pairs have the same first component. The relation R_2 is not a function since the two ordered pairs (3, 0) and (3, –3) have the same first component.

Ex. 2. *State whether or not each of the following diagram defines a function.*

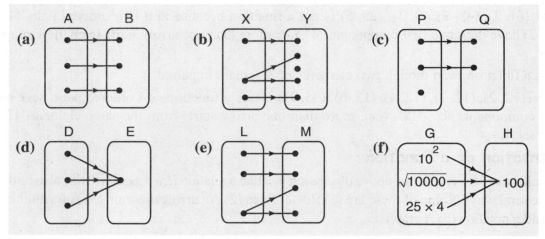

Sol.   (*a*) This is a function because each element of *A* is paired with a unique element of *B*.

      (*b*) This is not a function because one element of *X* is paired with two elements of *Y*.

      (*c*) This is not a function because one element of *P* is not paired with an element of *Q*.

      (*d*) This is a function because each element of *D* is paired with one element of *E*.

      (*e*) This is not a function because one element of *L* is paired with two elements of *M*.

      (*f*) This is a function because each element of *G* is paired with one element of *H*.

Ex. 2. *Tell which of the following relations are functions ?*

    (a) $y = 5x - 4$ **(b)** *x is the square of y*   **(c)** $y < x + 2$

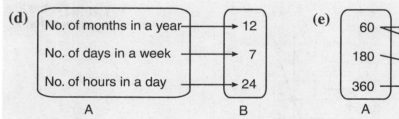 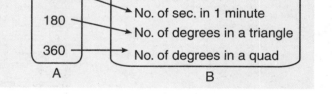

Sol.   (*a*) **Function.** Each replacement of *x* gives one and only one replacement of *y*. A few ordered pairs of the function are {(–2, –14), (–1, –9), (0, –4), (1, 1), (2, 6)}.

      (*b*) **Not a function.** A replacement of *x*, such as 4 pairs with two values of *y*.

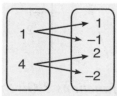

      (*c*) **Not a function.** For each replacement of *x* there are many replacements of *y*. Thus, if *x* = 1, then *y* may be 2, 1, 0, –1, ...

      (*d*) **Function.** Each element of *A* pairs with a unique element of *B*.

      (*e*) **Not a function.** One element '60' of *A* pairs with two elements of *B*.

Ex. 3. *The arrow diagram given here represents a mapping. Write this mapping in the form of an equation.*

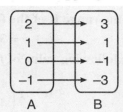

Sol. The mapping from *A* to *B* is $x \to 2x - 1$ and can be written in the form $y = 2x - 1$.

Ex. 4. *Given $f = x \to 3 - 5x$, find $f(0)$ and $f(2)$.*

Sol. $f(0) = 3 - 5 \times 0 = 3$, $f(2) = 3 - 5 \times 2 = -7$.

EXERCISE 25 (c)

1. State in each case whether the relation is a mapping from left to right, giving reasons :

(a) 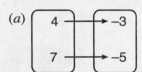 (b) 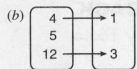 (c) 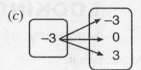 (d)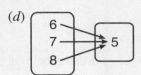

(e) 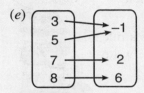 (f) 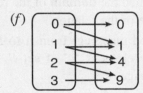 (g) 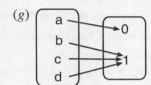 (h)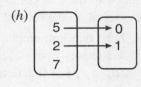

2. State the domain and range of each relation. Then tell whether or not the relation is a function :

(a) $\{(1, 1), (2, 2), (3, 3)\}$ (b) $\{(-5, 5), (-4, 4), (-3, 3)\}$ (c) $\{(5, 7), (5, 8), (5, 9)\}$

(d) $\{(3, a), (4, a), (5, a)\}$ (e) $\{(-7, 3), (-3, 2), (5, 2), (6, 3)\}$ (f) $\{(8, , -4), (2, -2), (8, -1)\}$

3. For each question state whether the relation A $\to$ B is a function, giving reasons :

(a) 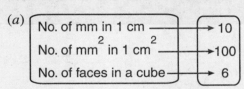   (b)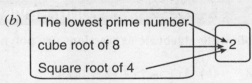

(c) 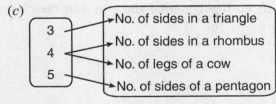   (d)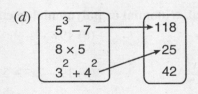

4. Write the mappings shown in the following diagrams in (a) roster form (b) equation form :

(a) 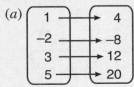   (b) 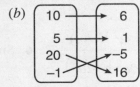   (c)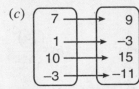

5. State the domain and range of each function then give a rule for the function letting x represent a member of the domain and y represent a member of the range :

(a) $\{(-2, 4), (-1, 1), (1, 1), (2, 4)\}$ (b) $\{(0, 0), (1, 6), (2, 12), (3, 18)\}$

(c) $\{(-8, -4), (-6, -3), (-2, -1), (0, 0)\}$ (d) $\{(0, 7), (2, 9), (-1, 6), (-5, 2)\}$

6. Let Domain = $\{-2, -1, 0, 1, 2\}$. Determine the range R of the function defined by each equation :

    (a) $y = x$ (b) $y = |x|$ (c) $y = 3x - 2$ (d) $y = x^3$

7. **Given the function** $f : x \rightarrow 5 - 4x$, **find the following value of** f :

    (a) $f(0)$ (b) $f(-2)$ (c) $f\left(\dfrac{1}{4}\right)$ (d) $f\left(-\dfrac{3}{2}\right)$

8. Let $f(x) = \dfrac{x-3}{2x+7}$, find $f(4) \cdot f(-1)$.   9. Let $f(x) = \dfrac{2x^2 - 1}{x - 2}$, $x \neq 2$, $x \in R$. Find the value of $\dfrac{f(5)}{f\left(\frac{1}{2}\right)}$.

10. Let $f(x) = \dfrac{3x^3 - 5x + 11}{x - 1}$, $x \neq 1$. Find the vlaue of $\dfrac{f(3)}{f(-2)}$.

LOOKING BACK
Summary of Key facts

1. Any set of ordered pairs is called a **relation.**

    The set of all the first components of the ordered pairs is called the **domain** of the relation and the set of all the second components is called the **range** of the relation.

2. Let A, B be two non-empty sets then a function (also called mapping) from A to B is a rule which associates every element 'x' of set A to a unique element 'y' of set B. We write $f : A \rightarrow B$, i.e., f is a function from A to B. Y is called the image of x.

3. A relation R from A to B is a function only if

    (i) The set A is entirely used up, i.e., no element of A remains unpaired.

    (ii) An element of set A is not paired with more than one element of B, i.e., no two ordered pairs of the function should have the same first component.

UNIT REVIEW – 4

1. **Which of the following algebraic expressions are polynomials ?**

    (a) $4x^3 - 6x + 8$ (b) $3x^{1/2} - 2x + 12$ (c) 43 (d) $\dfrac{7}{2x - 5}$ (e) $\dfrac{x^2}{2} + 4$

2. **Write monomial, binomial, trinomial or polynomial to classify each polynomial and also state their degree.**

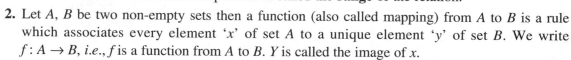

    (a) $4x^3 + 4x + 2$ (b) a^5 (c) $19x^2y^3 - 9y^3 + 18x^5y - 29y^6$

    (d) $3\sqrt{11}\, r^2 + 11s$ (e) $\dfrac{x^3}{3}$ (f) $19 - 7x^5 + 5x$

3. 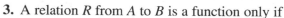 Add $x^2 - 6x + 7$, $8x - 15 - x^2$, $4x^2 + 6x - 9$, $7x + 10$

4. 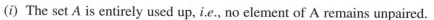 Subtract $x^2 - y^2 - z^2$ from the sum of $2x^2 + 3y^2 - z^2$ and $4x^2 - 3y^2 + 5z^2$

5. **Simplify :**

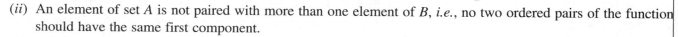

    (a) $(rs)^5\, r^5 s^5$ (b) $\dfrac{(x^6)^2}{x^6 x^2}$ (c) $\dfrac{(-3a^2)(-3a)^2}{-(3a^2)^2 (2a^3)^2}$ 6. **Simplify :** $\dfrac{(-5)^{-2} x^5 \left(y^{-1} z^{-2}\right)^2}{10^{-1} \left(x^{-1} y^2\right)^{-1} z^{-3}}$

7. **Multiply :**

    (a) $(4a^3 b)\,(-3a^2 b)\,(-12a^5 b^2)$ (b) $2pq(p^3 - p^2 q + pq^2 - q^3)$ (c) $(2x - 5)\,(5x + 6)$

    (d) $(2c + d)\,(3c^2 - 2cd - 5d^2)$ (e) $(3a^2 + 2ab + b^2)\,(a^2 - ab - b^2)$

8. Divide : $(x^3 - x^2 - 4x + 4)$ by $x + 2$

9. Simplify and express the quotient as a sum :

(a) $\dfrac{6c^2 - 2b^2c^2 + 3ac}{12a^2b^2c^2}$

(b) $(36x^8 - 72x^6 - 12x^4 + 48x^2) \div (-12x^4)$

10. Simplify using identities : $\left(2x + \dfrac{1}{3y}\right)^2 - \left(2x - \dfrac{1}{3}y\right)^2$

11. If $2l - 3m = -1$ and $l\,m = 20$. Find the value of $4l^2 + 9m^2$.

12. Find the value of $\dfrac{8.63 \times 8.63 - 1.37 \times 1.37}{7.26}$ using identities.

13. Factorise :

(a) $10a - 5b + 2ca - cb$ (b) $4m^3n - 7m^2n^2$ (c) $a(a-5) - 8(5-a)$

(d) $y^2 - 10y + 21$ (e) $7x^2 - 3x - 4$ (f) $49 - 9(y + 2b)^2$

14. Simplify : $\dfrac{(x^2-1)(x^2-6x+8)}{(x^2-4)(x^2-3x-4)}$.   **15. Simplify :** $\dfrac{3}{a^2-a-2} - \dfrac{2}{a^2-1}$.

16. Find the L.C.M. of : $n^2 + 3n + 2,\ n^2 + 5n + 6,\ n^2 + 4n + 3$.

17. Solve for x :

(a) $\dfrac{1}{x+1} - \dfrac{1}{9} = \dfrac{2}{3(x+1)}$

(b) $3(2x - 1) + 4(x - 1) = 1 - 2(x - 2)$

18. Solve :

(a) $2x = 3y;\ 3x - 2y = 5$

(b) $\dfrac{4}{x} + \dfrac{5}{y} = 41;\ \dfrac{5}{x} + \dfrac{4}{y} = 40$

19. The length of a certain rectangle is 2 m greater than its width. If the width were reduced by 20 m and the length increased by 100 m, the perimeter of the new rectangle would be twice the perimeter of the original rectangle. What are the dimensions of the original rectangle ?

20. Find a number of two digits which is equal to four times the sum of its digits and which is increased by 36 if its digits are interchanged.

21. There are two class rooms A and B having a certain number of students. If 5 students are shifted from room A to room B, the resulting number of students in both the rooms becomes equal. If 5 students are shifted from room B to room A, the resulting number of students in room A becomes double the number of students left in room B. Find the original number of students in both the rooms separately.

22. Solve and check the answer :

(a) $2x^2 = 5x$ (b) $y^2 - 11by - 60b^2 = 0$ (c) $\dfrac{x-1}{x-4} = \dfrac{2x-3}{3x-8}$ (d) $\dfrac{10}{n-1} - \dfrac{10}{n+2} = 3$

23. Make l the subject of the formula $s = \dfrac{n}{2}(a+l)$. If $s = 40$, $n = 8$ and $a = 2$, find l.

24. Frame a formula for the following statement : 'The distance s metres, which a falling body covers in t seconds is 4.8 times the square of the time t'.

25. Solve the inequality and show the solution on a number line.

$7(a + 4) + 117 < 13(13 + a) + 12$

26. State in each case whether the relation is a function from A to B, giving reasons.

(a)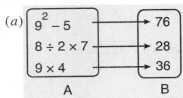

(b)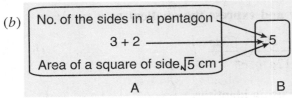

27. State the domain and range of the given relation. Then tell whether the relation is a function or not.

$\{(5, -3), (5, 5), (5, 5), (3, 5)\}$

28. Graph :

(a) $3x = 2x - 3y$ (b) $x = 0$ (c) $y = -2$

29. Solve graphically the system $2x - y = 5$, $x + 3y = 6$

30. In 2004 Shyam was twice as old as Rajeev. In 1999 the sum of their ages was 32.

(a) In which year was Shyam born ?

(b) In which year will Rajeev's age be three fourths Shyam's age?

ANSWERS

EXERCISE 25 (a)

1. (Dravid, 59), (Sachin, 84), (Sehwag, 66), (Ganguly, 47), (Dhoni, 28). 2. (Rekha, 49), (Sunita, 58), (Vivek, 75), (Rahul, 84), (Anju, 63),

3. $A \times A = \{(6, 6), (6, 7), (6, 8), (7, 6), (7, 7), (7, 8), (8, 6), (8, 7), (8, 8)\}$
   $B \times B = \{(8, 8), (8, 9), (9, 8), (9, 9), A \times B = \{(6, 8), (6, 9), (7, 8), (7, 9), (8, 8), (8, 9)\}$
   $B \times A = \{(8, 6), (8, 7), (8, 8), (9, 6), (9, 7), (9, 8)\}$

EXERCISE 25 (b)

1. (a) $\{(a, 5), (a, 6), (b, 7), (c, 8), (d, 9)\}$ (b) $\{(0, -4), (1, -5), (2, -6), (3, -7)\}$
   (c) $\{(\text{Dehradun, Rice}), (\text{Lucknow, Mango}), (\text{Nagpur, Orange})$

2. (a), (b), (d), (e) are relations. (c) is not a relation from A to B as the first component of the ordered pair (z, c) belongs to B and not A.

3. (a) (1, 1), (2, 8), (4, 64), (−1, −1), (−5, −125)   (b) (1, 20), (−20, −1), (4, 5), (5, 4), (−10, −2)

4. $R = \{(3, 6), (3, 9), (3, 12), (4, 8), (4, 12), (5, 10), (6, 12)\}$ Domain $(R) = \{3, 4, 5, 6\}$, Range $(R) = \{6, 8, 9, 10, 12\}$

5. $R = \{(6, 5), (7, 5), (7, 6), (8, 5), (8, 6), (9, 8)\}$ Domain $(R) = \{6, 7, 8, 9\}$, Range $(R) = \{5, 6, 8\}$

6. $R = \{(3, 1), (6, 2), (9, 3)\}$, Domain $= \{3, 6, 9\}$, Range $= \{1, 2, 3\}$

7. Relation $= \{(-2, 3), (-1, 4), (0, 5), (1, 6), (2, 7), (3, 8)\}$ Domain $R = \{-2, -1, 0, 1, 2, 3\}$, Range$=\{3, 4, 5, 6, 7, 8\}$

8. $R = \{(2, 4), (2, 6), (3, 6)\}$ 9. $R = \{(x, y) \mid y = x - 5, x, y \in Z\}$, domain $= \{0, 3, 5, 7, -10\}$, Range $= \{-5, -2, 0, 2, -15\}$

10. $R = \{(-2, 2), (-1, 1), (0, 0), (1, -1), (2, -2)\}$

EXERCISE 25 (c)

1. (a) Yes   (b) No   (c) No   (d) Yes   (e) Yes   (f) No   (g) Yes   (h) No

2. (a) Domain $= \{1, 2, 3\}$, Range $= \{1, 2, 3\}$; Yes   (b) Domain $= \{-5, -4, -3\}$, Range $= \{5, 4, 3\}$; Yes
   (c) Domain $= \{5\}$, Range $= \{7, 8, 9\}$; No   (d) Domain $= \{3, 4, 5\}$, Range $= \{a\}$; Yes
   (e) Domain $= \{-7, -3, 5, 6\}$, Range $= \{3, 2\}$; Yes   (f) Domain $= \{8, 2\}$, Range $= \{-4, -2, -1\}$; No

3. (a) Yes   (b) Yes   (c) No   (d) No

4. (a) Roster form $\{(1, 4), (-2, -8), (3, 12), (5, 20)\}$, Equation form : $y = 4x$
   (b) Roster form $\{(10, 6), (5, 1), (20, 16), (-1, -5)\}$, Equation form : $y = x - 4$
   (c) Roster form $\{(7, 9), (1, -3), (10, 15), (-3, -11)\}$, Equation form : $y = 2x - 5$

5. (a) Domain $= \{-2, -1, 1, 2\}$, Range $= \{4, 1\}$; Rule : $y = x^2$ (b) Domain $= \{0, 1, 2, 3\}$, Range $= \{0, 6, 12, 18\}$; Rule : $y = 6x$

   (c) Domain $= \{-8, -6, -2, 0\}$, Range $= \{-4, -3, -1, 0\}$; Rule : $y = \frac{1}{2}x$

   (d) Domain $= \{0, 2, -1, -5\}$, Range $= \{7, 9, 6, 2\}$; Rule : $y = x + 7$

6. (a) $\{-2, -1, 0, 1, 2\}$ (b) $\{0, 1, 2\}$ (c) $\{-8, -5, -2, 1, 4\}$ (d) $\{-8, -1, 0, 1, 8\}$

7. (a) 5   (b)   13   (c)   4   (d)   11   8. $\dfrac{-4}{75}$ 9. 49   10. 23.1

UNIT REVIEW – 4

1. (a) (c) and (e)

2. (a) Trinomial; degree 3   (b) Monomial; degree 5   (c) Polynomial; degree 6   (d) Binomial; degree 2
   (e) Monomial; degree 3   (f) Trinomial; degree 5   3. $4x^2 + 15x - 7$ 4. $5x^2 + y^2 + 5z^2$

5. (a) $r^{10}s^{10}$ (b) x^4 (c) $\dfrac{3}{4a^6}$ 6. $\dfrac{2x^4}{5z}$

7. (a) $144a^{10}b^4$ (b) $2p^4q - 2p^3q^2 + 2p^2q^3 - 2pq^4$ (c) $10x^2 - 13x - 30$ (d) $6c^3 - c^2d - 12cd^2 - 5d^3$
   (e) $3a^4 - a^3b - 4a^2b^2 - 3ab^3 - b^4$

8. $x^2 - 3x + 2$ 9. (a) $\dfrac{1}{2a^2b^2} - \dfrac{1}{6a^2} + \dfrac{1}{4ab^2c}$ (b) $-3x^4 + 6x^2 + 1 - \dfrac{4}{x^2}$ 10. $\dfrac{8x}{3y}$ 11. 241   12. 10

13. (a) $(2a - b)(5 + c)$ (b) $m^2n(4m - 7n)$ (c) $(a - 5)(a + 8)$ (d) $(y - 7)(y - 3)$
    (e) $(7x + 4)(x - 1)$ (f) $(7 + 3y + 6b)(7 - 3y - 6b)$

14. $\dfrac{x - 1}{x + 2}$ 15. $\dfrac{1}{(a - 2)(a - 1)}$ 16. $(n + 1)(n + 2)(n + 3)$ 17. (a) $x = 2$ (b) $x = 1$

18. (a) $x = 3, y = 2$ (b) $x = \dfrac{1}{4}, y = \dfrac{1}{5}$ 19. length = 41 m, width = 39 m   20. 48

21. Room A $\rightarrow$ 35, Room B $\rightarrow$ 25   22. (a) $x = 0, 2\dfrac{1}{2}$ (b) $y = 15b, -4b$ (c) $x = \pm 2$ (d) $x = 3, -4$

23. $l = \dfrac{2S}{n} - a$; 8   24. $s = 4.8t^2$ 25. $a > -6$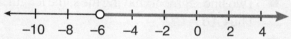

26. (a) Yes   (b)   Yes

27. Domain = $\{5, 3\}$; Range = $\{-3, 5\}$; No   29. (3, 1)

30. (a) 1976   (b)   2032 (**Hint :** Let Rajeev's age in 2004 be x years)

HISTORICAL NOTE
How much is a metre?

In A.D. 1120, the king of England decreed that in his country, the yard will be used as the unit of length. It was the distance from the tip of the king's nose to the end of his outstreched arm.

The original standard adopted by France was called a foot. It was equal to the royal foot of the king. In 1799, the kings foot was replaced by "metre". Then it was defined as one ten millionth distance from the equator to the North Pole along a longitudenal line that passes through Paris.

In 1889, one metre was defined as the distance between two lines on a specific platinum-iridium bar stored under controlled conditions. But progress in service and technology necessisated a more precise standard. So in 1960, Metre was redefined as 1,650,763.73 wavelengths of a particular orange-red light emitted by atoms of Krypton-86 in a gas discharge tube.

The metre was redefined again in 1983, this time as the distance which light travels in a vacuum in $\dfrac{1}{299, 792, 458}$ seconds.

This remains the current definition. Note that in all these redefinitions, the length of the metre was always taken as close as possible to the value fixed in 1799.

26. Basic Concepts of Geometry

26.1 Introduction

Geometry is everywhere around us, in man made structures, in nature, in sports, in art and in lots of more things. In geometry, we have four simple ideas or imaginary things *i.e.* point, line, plane and space and everything else is built on these simple concepts.

26.2 Point

A point is a location and it has absolutely no dimensions *i.e.* no length, no width and no depth. We use a dot, like point *P*, to represent a point.

26.3 Line

A line is a set of points that has only one dimension, length. A line *DE* is shown in the given diagram. The arrowheads on the line *DE* shows that it is extending endlessly in both the directions and has no end points. Hence it has no fixed length.

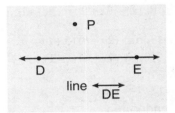

- **Line Segment :**

  A line segment is simply a part of a line that has a specific length and specific end points.

- Two line segments having the same length are called congruent line segments. Thus $AB \cong CD$.

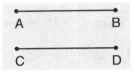

- **Ray :**

  A ray is a part of a line that has only one end point. It extends endlessly in one direction.

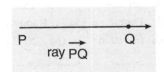

  Two lines can be related to each other in four different ways:

- Lines that have just one point in common are called **Intersecting Lines.**

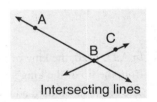

Intersecting lines

- Lines that lie in the same plane but never intersect even if produced endlessly in both directions are called **Parallel Lines.**

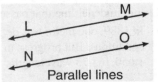

Parallel lines

- Two intersecting lines that form a right angle are called **Perpendicular Lines.**

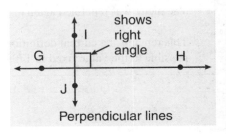

Perpendicular lines

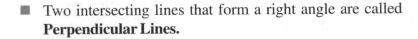

■ Lines that are not in the same plane and do not intersect are called **skew lines.**

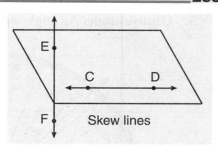

Skew lines

■ **Plane :**

The set of points all lying on one surface is called a plane. A wall, or surface of a table, floor etc. are all examples of a plane. A plane actually extends endlessly and the surface of a plane has no thickness. At least three points not on the same line are needed to define a plane.

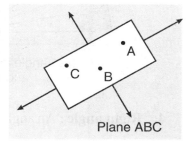

Plane ABC

26.4 Angle

Two rays that share a common endpoint form an angle. The common endpoint is called the **vertex.**

We measure the size of an angle in degrees using a protractor.

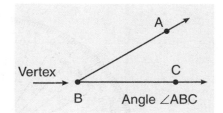

Angle ∠ABC

26.5 Types of Angles

There are five main type of angles.

1. **Straight angle :** An angle measuring 180° is called a straight angle.

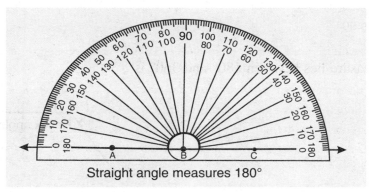

Straight angle measures 180°

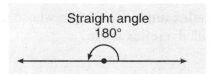

Straight angle 180°

2. **Acute angle:** An angle whose measure lies between 0° and 90° is called an acute angle.

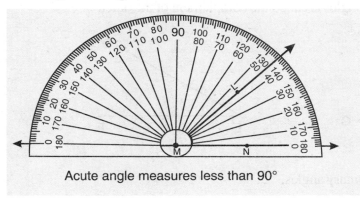

Acute angle measures less than 90°

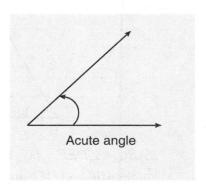

Acute angle

3. **Obtuse angle:** An angle whose measure lies between 90° and 180° is called an obtuse angle.

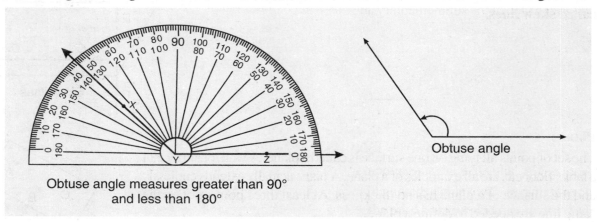

Obtuse angle measures greater than 90°
and less than 180°

Obtuse angle

4. **Right angle :** An angle whose measure is equal to 90° is called a right angle.

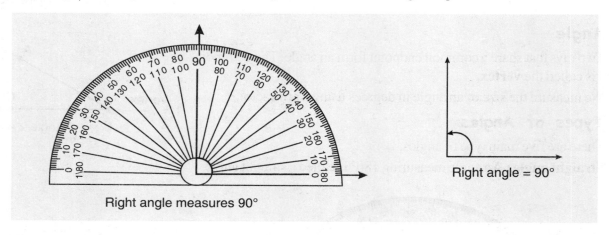

Right angle measures 90°

Right angle = 90°

5. **Reflex angle :** An angle whose measure lies between 180° and 360° is called a reflex angle.

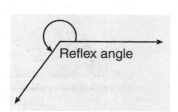

Reflex angle

26.6 More Types of Angles

1. **Complementary angles :** Two angles are called complementary angles if the sum of their degree measures equals 90°. One of the complementary angles is called the complement of the other.

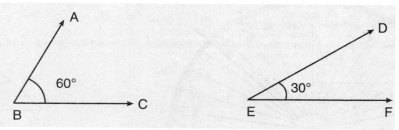

∵ $\angle ABC + \angle DEF = 60° + 30° = 90°$

∴ Angles ABC and DEF are complementary angles.

2. **Supplementary angles :** Two angles are called supplementary angles, if the sum of their degree measures equals 180°. One of the supplementary angles is called the supplement of the other.

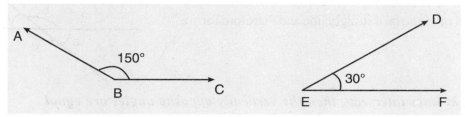

$\because$ $\angle ABC + \angle DEF = 150° + 30° = 180°$

$\therefore$ Angles *ABC* and *DEF* are supplementary angles.

3. **Adjacent angles :** Two angles having a common vertex and a common side (ray) are called adjacent angles. In the figure given below *a* and *b* are adjacent angles having a common vertex *O* and a common ray *OC*.

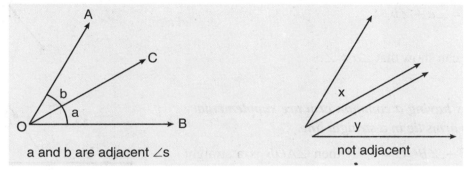

a and b are adjacent ∠s   not adjacent

4. **Linear pair :** Two adjacent angles form a linear pair if they are supplementary i.e their sum is 180° .

$\because$ $\angle AOB = 180°$ (a straight line)

$\therefore$ $\angle AOC$ and $\angle COB$ form a linear pair.

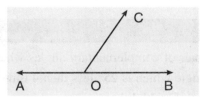

5. **Angles at point :** Sum of the angles round a point is 360°.

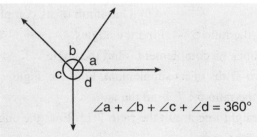

$\angle a + \angle b + \angle c + \angle d = 360°$

6. **Vertically opposite angles :** Vertically opposite angles are pairs of angles formed by two intersecting lines opposite to each other. They are always equal (or congruent).

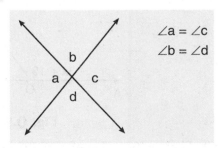

$\angle a = \angle c$
$\angle b = \angle d$

26.7 Some Important Properties

1. *If two straight lines intersect then the adjacent angles are supplementary (i.e form a linear pair).*
   For the two intersecting lines *l* and *m*,

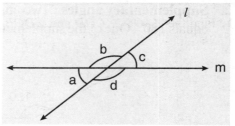

$\angle a + \angle b = 180°$, $\angle b + \angle c = 180°$

$\angle c + \angle d = 180°$, $\angle d + \angle a = 180°$

All these pairs of $\angle s$ lie on a straight line and therefore form a straight angle .

2. *If two straight lines intersect , then the vertically opposite angles are equal .*

For the two intersecting lines l and m, $\angle a = \angle c$, $\angle b = \angle d$.

Proof :

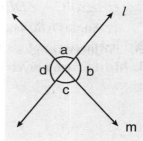

$\because \angle a + \angle d = 180°$ (straight $\angle$)

$\angle a + \angle b = 180°$ (straight $\angle$)

$\therefore \angle a + \angle d = \angle a + \angle b$

$\Rightarrow \angle d = \angle b$

Similarly, we can show that $\angle a = \angle c$.

3. *If two angles having a common arm are supplementary the other two arms lie in a straight line.*

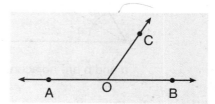

i.e. if $\angle AOC + \angle BOC = 180°$ then $\angle AOB$ is a straight angle and hence AOB is a straight line.

$\Rightarrow AO$ and OB lie on a straight line.

EXERCISE 26 (a)

1. Find the pair of complementary angles which differ by 34°.
2. Find an angle which is 25° less then 4 times its complement.
3. **Find an angle which is :**

   (*a*) 48° more than its supplement.   (*b*) One-ninth of its complement.
4. Two complementary angles are in the ratio 5 : 4. Find the angles.
5. The supplement of an angle is 6 times its complement. Find the angle.
6. The complement of an angle is two–fifths of its supplement. Find the angle.
7. Two supplementary angles are in the ratio 5 : 7. Find the angles.
8. Two adjacent angles lying on a straight line are in the ratio 7:11. Find the angles.
9. Find the value of x from the adjoining figure.

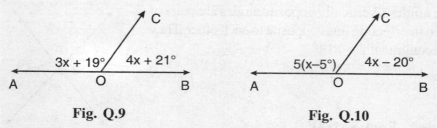

Fig. Q.9   Fig. Q.10

10. Find the (*a*) value of x (*b*) the measure of each angle from the figure.

11. Find the ∠AOC, ∠COD and ∠DOB from the given figure.

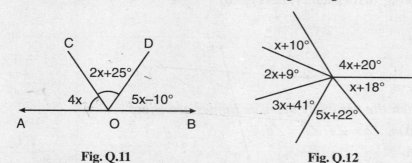

Fig. Q.11   Fig. Q.12   Fig. Q.13

12. Find the value of *x* from the given figure.

13. In the figure ∠AOB : ∠BOC : ∠COD : ∠DOA = 2 : 3 : 5 : 8. Find the angles.

14. **Find the values of *x*, *y* and *z* when the two lines AB and CD, intersect at a point P.**

(*a*)

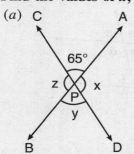

(*b*)

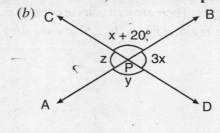

Fig. Q.14

15. Find *a* , *b* and *c* from the figure given below.

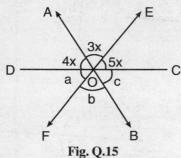

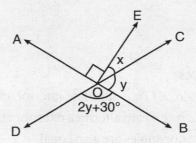

Fig. Q.15   Fig. Q.16

16. *AB* and *CD* intersect each other at *O*. Given ∠EOA=90°, ∠EOC = *x*, ∠BOC = *y* and ∠BOD = 2*y* + 30°. Find the values of *x* and *y* and ∠AOD.

PARALLEL LINES

26.8 Parallel Lines

Lines in a plane which do not intersect are called parallel lines. A pair of parallel lines like *l* and *m*, *p* and *q* are always the same distance (perpendicular distance) apart.

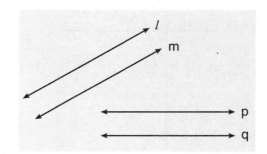

Transversal : A line which intersects two or more given lines in distinct points is called a **transversal** to the given lines. The lines may be intersecting lines Fig. (*a*) or parallel lines Fig. (*b*)

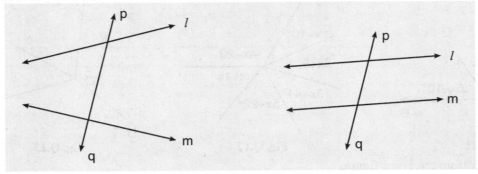

Fig. (a) **Fig (b)**

When two parallel lines are cut by a transversal, eight angles are formed, which may be classified as under :

1. **Corresponding angles :** There are four pairs of corresponding angles *i.e.* ($\angle a$, $\angle e$) ($\angle c$, $\angle g$) , ($\angle b$, $\angle f$) , ($\angle d$, $\angle h$) and they are equal .

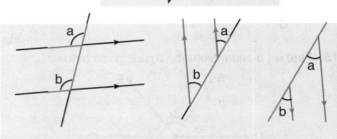

In all these figures,
You can find them by looking for an F shape.
$\angle a = \angle b$

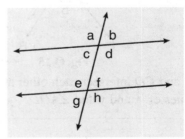

2. **Alternate angles :**
   ($\angle d$, $\angle e$) and ($\angle c$, $\angle f$) are alternate interior angles.
   ($\angle a$, $\angle h$) and ($\angle b$, $\angle g$) are alternate exterior angles.
   The alternate interior angles are also equal.
   For a pair of alternate angles, always look for a Z shape.

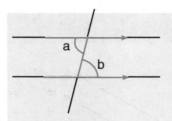
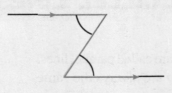
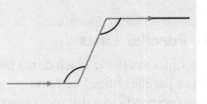

3. **Allied angles (or co-interior angles)** : Interior angles on the same
    side of the transversal are always supplementary, *i.e.,*
    $\angle c + \angle e = 180°$, $\angle d + \angle f = 180°$
    Look for C shape for co-interior $\angle$s.

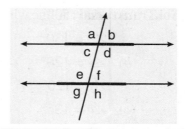

Theorem : *If two parallel lines are intersected by a transversal, then*

(a) *Corresponding angles are equal (b) Alternate Interior angles are equal (c) Alternate exterior angles are equal (d) Co-interior angles are supplementary.*

Conversely : *If two straight lines are intersected by a transversal such that:*

(a) *Corresponding angles are equal*
                OR
(b) *Alternate angles are equal*
                OR
(c) *Co-interior angles are supplementary, then the two lines are parallel to each other.*

26.9 Two Lines Parallel to the Same Line

■ *Two lines parallel to the same given line are parallel to each other.*

Proof : Let *l, m,* and *n* be three lines such that *l* ∥ *m* and *l* ∥ *n*. Let *t* be the
transversal cutting these lines.

Since : *l* ∥ *m*, therefore, $\angle 1 = \angle 2$ (*corresponding angles*)
Also, *l* ∥ *n*, therefore, $\angle 1 = \angle 3$ (*corresponding angles*)
∴ $\angle 2 = \angle 3$ (*both equal to the same* $\angle 1$)
But these are corresponding angles
∴ *m* ∥ *n*.

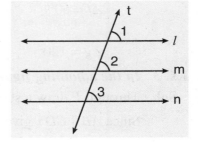

■ **Two lines perpendicular to the same line :** Two lines in a plane, perpendicular to the same given line
are parallel to each other.

Proof : Let m and n be two lines each perpendicular to a given line *l*
i.e., m ⊥ *l* and *n* ⊥ *l* ⇒ $\angle 1 = 90°$ and $\angle 2 = 90°$ ∴ $\angle 1 = \angle 2$
But these are corresponding angles ∴ *m* ∥ *n*.

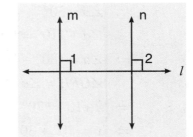

26.10 Solved Examples

Ex. 1 (a) *Find $\angle a$ and $\angle b$, giving reasons.*
       (b) *Find $\angle x$ and $\angle y$ giving reasons.*
       (c) *Find $\angle a$, $\angle b$, and $\angle c$.*

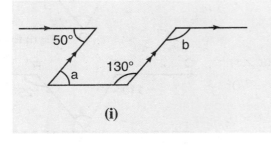

(i)

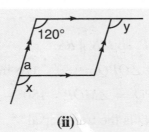

(ii)

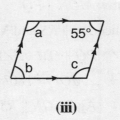

(iii)

Sol. (a) $\angle a = 50°$ *(Alternate with 50°)*

     $\angle b = 130°$ *(Alternate with 130°)*

   (b) $\angle x = 120°$ *(corresponding with 120°)*

     $\angle y = 120°$ *(corresponding with 120°)*

   (c) $\angle a = 125°$ *(allied to 55°)*

     $\angle b = 55°$ *(allied to $\angle a$)*

     $\angle c = 125°$ *(allied to $\angle b$).*

Ex. 2. *Find the marked angles, giving your reasons.*

Sol. $\angle a = 120°$ (Linear pair, adjacent to 60°)

    $\angle b = 60°$ (vertically opposite to 60° or adjacent to $\angle a$)

    $\angle c = 120°$ (adjacent to 60° or vertically opposite $\angle a$)

    $\angle d = 60°$ (alternate to $\angle b$ or allied to $\angle c$ or corresponding to 60°

    $\angle e = 120°$ (adjacent to angle $\angle d$ or allied to $\angle b$ or corresponding to a or alternate to $\angle c$)

    $\angle f = 60°$ (adjacent to angle $\angle e$ or vertically opposite to $\angle d$ or corresponding to $\angle b$)

    $\angle g = 120°$ (vertically opposite $\angle e$ or adjacent to both $\angle f$ and $\angle d$, or corresponding to $\angle c$)

Ex. 3. *In the adjoining figure, AB is parallel to CD. Find the value of x in degrees.*

Sol. Through P draw a st. line parallel to AB.

   Since $AB \parallel CD$ (given) and

   $AB \parallel EF$ (by construction), so

   $EF \parallel CD$.

   (Lines parallel to the same line are parallel to each other)

   ∴ $\angle b = 30°$ ($EF \parallel CD$, alternate $\angle s$)

    $\angle a + 110° = 180°$ ($EF \parallel AB$, co-interior $\angle s$)

  ⇒ $\angle a = 180° - 110° = 70°$

    $\angle GPH = \angle a + \angle b$

  ⇒ $x + 10° = 70° + 30°$

  ⇒ $x = 70° + 30° - 10° = \mathbf{90°}$.

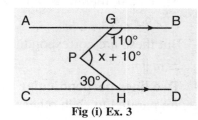

Fig (i) Ex. 3

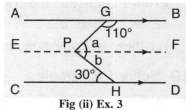

Fig (ii) Ex. 3

Ex. 4. *In the adjoining figure PQ $\parallel$ RS, find the value of a.*

Sol. Draw $MON \parallel PQ$

   Since $PQ \parallel RS$ and $MN \parallel QP$, so $MN \parallel RS$.

  ∵ $PQ \parallel OM$ ∴ $\angle MOP + \angle OPQ = 180°$ (co-interior $\angle s$)

  ⇒ $\angle MOP = 180° - \angle OPQ \Rightarrow \angle MOP = 180° - 110° = 70°$

   Again $ON \parallel RS$ and RO is the transversal

  ∴ $\angle SRO + \angle NOR = 180°$ (co-interior $\angle s$)

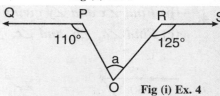

Fig (i) Ex. 4

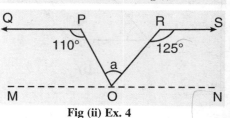

Fig (ii) Ex. 4

$\Rightarrow \quad 125° + \angle NOR = 180° \Rightarrow \quad \angle NOR = 180° - 125° = 55°$

Now, $\angle MOP + \angle a + \angle NOR = 180°$ (straight angle)

$\Rightarrow \quad 70° + \angle a + 55° = 180° \Rightarrow \quad \angle a = 180° - 70° - 55° = 180° - 125° = \mathbf{55°}.$

Ex. 5. *In the given figure, line segments DE, FG and HI are parallel to side AB of △ABC. How many pairs of parallel line segments are there in the figure ? Name each of them.*

Sol. Since *DE*, *FG*, *HI*, are all parallel to *AB*, so they are parallel to each other. Hence we have six pairs of parallel line segments in the figure. They are:

AB ‖ *DE*, *DE* ‖ *FG*, *FG* ‖ *HI*, *HI* ‖ *AB*, *HI* ‖ *DE*, *FG* ‖ *AB*.

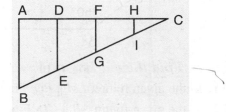

Ex. 6. *In the adjoining figure l ‖ m, p ⊥ m and p ⊥ n.*

     (a) *Is m ‖ n? Why?*

     (b) *Is l ‖ n ? Why ?*

     (c) *Is p ⊥ l ? Why?*

Sol.   (*a*) Since $p \perp m$ and $p \perp n$, so $m \parallel n$ because lines *m* and *n* are perpendicular to the same line.

     (*b*) Yes, because $l \parallel m$ (given) and $m \parallel n$ (proved in (i) above) so $l \parallel n$.

     (*c*) As $l \parallel n$ and $p \perp n$ so $p \perp l$.

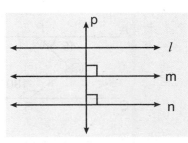

EXERCISE 26 (b)

Write down giving reasons the size of the angles or angles marked with letters :

1.

2.

3.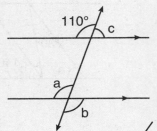

4.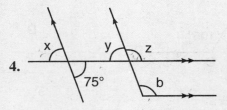

5.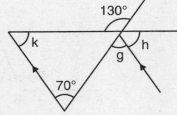

6.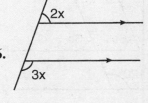

7.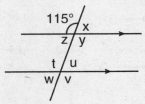

8.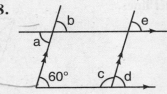

9.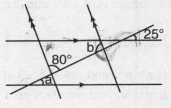

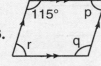

10. In the figure AB is parallel to CD, Find x.

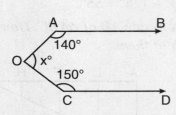

Fig. Q.10

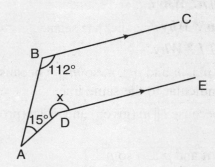

Fig. Q.11

11. In the given figure, $LM \parallel PQ$. Find the value of x.

12. In the given figure $AB \parallel CD$. Find the reflex $\angle PQR$.

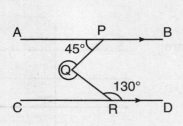

Fig. Q.12

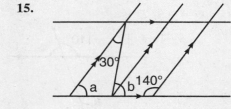

Fig. Q.13

13. In the given figure $BC \parallel DE$. Find x, *i.e.*, the reflex $\angle ADE$.

In the given figure find the lettered angles. (similar arrows shows set of parallel lines) :

14.

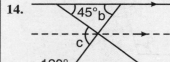

15.

16.

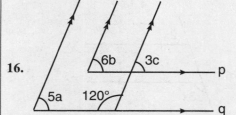

17.

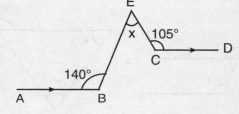

18. In the figure AB, CD, and EF are parallel lines.

(*a*) If $z = 69°$ and $w = \dfrac{2}{3}z$, find x.

(*b*) If $z = 85°$ and $y = 135°$, find x.

(*c*) If $y = 3w$ and $w = 2x$, find z.

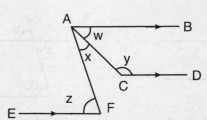

19. In the given figure show that $AB \parallel CD$, Give reasons.

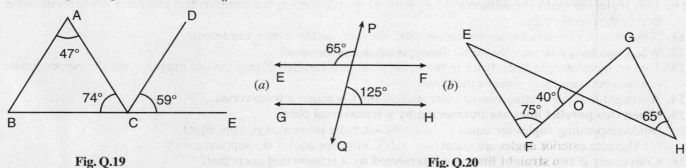

Fig. Q.19   (a)   (b)   Fig. Q.20

20. State giving reasons whether _EF_ ∥ _GH_ or not .

21. In the given figure, _AB_ ∥ _DC_ and _EF_ ∥ _AB_.

(a) In $EF \parallel DC$ also? Why?

(b) How many pairs of parallel line segments are there in the figure? Name each of them.

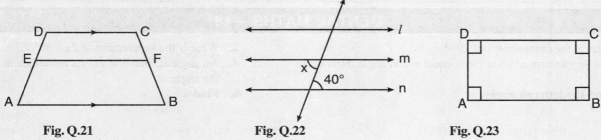

Fig. Q.21   Fig. Q.22   Fig. Q.23

22. In the given figure _l_ ∥ _m_ and _l_ ∥ _n_

(a) Is $m \parallel n$? Why?   (b) Find the value of x.

23. Each angle of a quadrilateral _ABCD_ is a right angle.

(a) Is $AD \parallel BC$? Why?   (b) Is $AB \parallel DC$? Why?

24. What value of x will make $AB \parallel CD$.

Fig. Q.24

LOOKING BACK
Summary of Key Facts

1. A point marks a location and has no magnitude.

2. Line is a straight path extending endlessly in both the directions having no fixed length.

3. Line segment is a part of a line having fixed length and two end points.

4. A ray is a line segment extending endlessly in one direction with one endpoint.

5. Two lines can be related to each other in four different ways:

   (i) Intersecting lines   (ii) Parallel lines

  (iii) Perpendicular lines   (iv) Skew lines;

6. Two rays sharing a common endpoint form an angle and the common endpoint is called the vertex,.

7. Types of Angles

   (i) **Straight Angle:** Measure = 180°   (ii) **Acute Angle :** Measure lies between 0° and 90°.

  (iii) **Right Angle :** Measure = 90°   (iv) **Obtuse Angle :** Measure lies between 90° and 180°.

   (v) **Reflex Angle:** Measure lies between 180° and 360°.

8. Two angles are called **complementary** if their sum = 90°

9. Two angles are called **supplementary** if their sum = 180°
10. Two angles are said to be **adjacent** if they have a common vertex, one common arm and other two arms on either side of the common arm.
11. If the sum of two adjacent angles equals 180°, they are said to form a **linear pair**.
12. When two lines intersect, the vertically opposite angles are equal.
13. Two or more straight lines lying in the same plane are parallel, if they do not intersect and the perpendicular distance between them remains the same.
14. A straight line intersecting two or more straight lines is called a **transversal**.
15. **When two parallel lines are intersected by a transversal then:**
    (*a*) Corresponding angles are equal   (*b*) Alternate interior angles are equal.
    (*c*) Alternate exterior angles are equal   (*d*) Co-interior angles are supplementary
16. **Conversely if two straight lines are intersected by a transversal such that:**
    (*a*) Corresponding angles are equal OR
    (*b*) Alternate angles are equal OR
    (*c*) Co-interior angles are supplementary, then the two lines are parallel to each other.
17. Two lines parallel to the same line are parallel to each other.
18. Two lines perpendicular to the same line are parallel to each other.

MENTAL MATHS – 18

1. What is the complement of 19° ?
2. What is the supplement of $2x - 30°$?
3. The supplement of an angle is equal to the angle. Find each.
4. An angle is four-fifths of its complement. Find the angle.

5. **Find the lettered angles**
6. **Find x :**

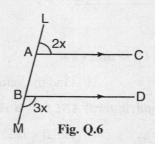

Fig. Q.5   Fig. Q.6

ANSWERS

EXERCISE 26 (a)

1. 28°, 62°   2. 67°   3. (*a*) 114° (*b*) 9°   4. 50°, 40°   5. 72°   6. 30°   7. 75°, 105°
8. 70°, 110°   9. $x = 20°$ 10. (*a*) $x = 25°$ (*b*) $\angle COA = 100°$ (*c*) $\angle COB = 80°$
11. $\angle AOC = 60°, \angle COD = 55°, \angle DOB = 65°$ 12. $x = 15°$ 13. $\angle AOB = 40°, \angle BOC = 60°, \angle COD = 100°, \angle DOA = 160°$
14. (*a*) $x = 115°, y = 65°, z = 115°$,   (*b*) $x = 40°, y = 60°, z = 120°$ 15. $a = 75°, b = 45°, c = 60°$
16. $x = 40°, y = 50°, \angle AOD = 50°$

EXERCISE 26 (b)

1. 35°   2. $a = 110°, b = 110°, c = 70°$ 3. $p = 65°, q = 115°, r = 65°$
4. $x = 75°, y = 75°, z = 105°, b = 105°$ 5. $g = 70° h = 60°, k = 60°$ 6. 72°, 108°
7. $x = 65°, y = 115°, z = 65°, t = 115°, u = 65°, v = 115°, w = 65°$ 8. $a = b = 60°, c = 120°, d = 60°, e = 60°$
9. $a = 25°, b = 100°$ 10. $x = 70°$ 11. $x = 20°$ 12. 265°
13. 233°   14. $a = 45°, b = 60°, c = 105°$ 15. $a = 40°, b = 70°$
16. $a = 12°, b = 10°, c = 20°$ 17. $x = 65°$ 18. (*a*) 23° (*b*) 40° (*c*) 67.5°
19. Yes $\angle ABC = \angle DCE = 59°$ (*corresponding angles*)   20. (*a*) No (*b*) Yes
22. (*a*) Yes (*b*) 40°   23. Yes, the sum of co-interior $\angle s$ is 180°.   24. $x = 16°$

MENTAL MATHS – 17

1. 71°   2. $210° - 2x$ 3. 90°   4. 40°   5. $x = 90°, y = 130°$ 6. $x = 36°$

27. Triangles

27.1 Triangle

A triangle is the simplest polygon (closed figure) having three sides and three angles. The adjoining figure shows a triangle ABC usually written as $\triangle ABC$, with the three sides AB, BC and CA, the three angles $\angle BAC$, $\angle ABC$, $\angle ACB$ and three vertices A, B and C. The three sides and three angles of a triangle are called its **elements** or **parts**.

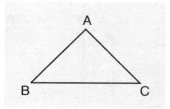

27.2 Classification of Triangles

Triangles can be classified in two general ways :

- **By sides**
  1. **Scalene Triangle** is a triangle with three sides of different lengths.

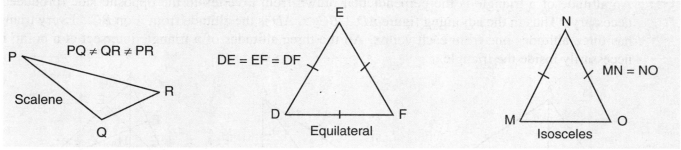

  2. **Isosceles Triangle** is a triangle with just two equal sides called legs. The third side is called the base. The angles that are opposite the equal sides are also equal.
  3. **Equilateral Triangle** is a triangle having all three sides equal. In this type of triangle, all the three angles are also equal, so it can also be called an equiangular triangle.

- **By angles**
  1. An **Acute Triangle** has three acute angles, or three angles with a measure of less than 90°.

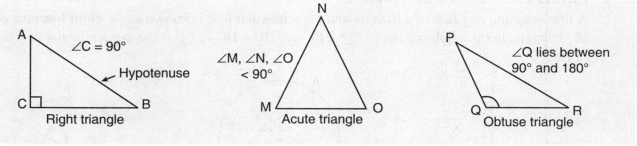

  2. An **Obtuse Triangle** has **one** obtuse angle (whose measure lies between 90° and 180°).
  3. A **Right Triangle** has one of the angles equal to a right angle. The side opposite the right angle is called the **hypotenuse.** In the figure given above $\triangle ABC$ is a right triangle, right angled at C with AB as the hypotenuse.

27.3 Some More Terms Related to a Triangle

■ **Medians of a Triangle :**

A median of a triangle is a line segment joining a vertex to the mid-point of the side opposite to that vertex.

Thus in the adjoining figure D is the mid-point of BC and hence AD is a median. Every triangle has three medians, one from each vertex.

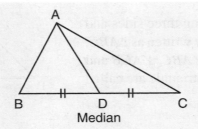
Median

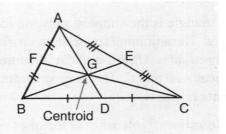
Centroid

All the three medians of a triangle meet at a point inside the triangle.

The point at which the medians of a triangle meet is called the **centroid** of the triangle.

■ **Altitudes of a triangle :**

An altitude of a triangle is the perpendicular drawn from a vertex to the opposite side (produced if necessary). Thus in the adjoining figure $AD \perp BC$. ∴ AD is the altitude from A on BC. Every triangle has three altitudes one from each vertex. All the three altitudes of a triangle intersect at a point, not necessarily inside the triangle.

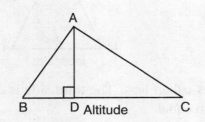
Altitude

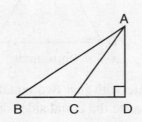

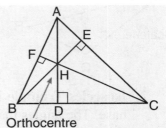
Orthocentre

The point of intersection of the altitudes of a triangles is called the orthocentre of the triangle.

In the adjoining figure the point of intersection H of the three altitudes AD, BF and CE of the $\triangle ABC$ is the **orthocentre.**

■ **Circum-centre and Circum circle**

A line bisecting any side of a triangle and perpendicular to it is known as the **right bisector** of the side of a triangle. In the adjoining figure $PQ \perp BC$ and $BD = DC$ ∴ PQ is the perpendicular or right bisector of BC.

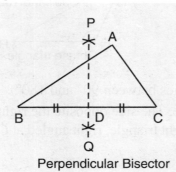
Perpendicular Bisector

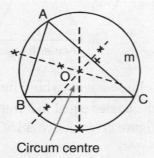
Circum centre

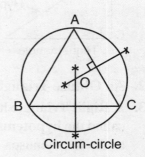
Circum-circle

The point of intersection of the perpendicular bisectors of the sides of a triangle is called the circumcentre of the triangle. O is the circumcentre of $\triangle ABC$.

Here $OA = OB = OC$ and the circle drawn through A, B and C with O as centre and OA or OB or OC as radius is called the **circum-circle**. OA or OB or OC is called the **circum-radius**.

In-centre and Incircle

An angle bisector of a triangle is a ray which bisects an interior angle of a triangle. In the figure below, PX bisects $\angle QPR \Rightarrow \angle 1 = \angle 2$.

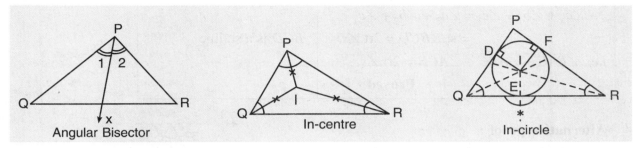

The point of intersection of the three angle bisectors of the interior angles of a triangle is called the incentre of a triangle. I is the in-centre of $\triangle PQR$.

If we draw ID, IE and IF perpendiculars to sides PQ, QR and PR respectively then we find $ID = IE = IF$.

The circle drawn with I as the centre and ID or IE or IF as the radius, touching the sides of the circle is called the **incircle**. ID or IE or IF is called the **inradius**.

■ **Exterior and interior Opposite Angles**

When any side of a triangle is extended beyond the vertex, it forms an exterior angle with the other side at the same vertex.

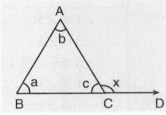

In the adjoining triangle BC is extended is BD. Thus it forms exterior angle $\angle x$ with AC. $\angle a$ and $\angle b$ are called the interior opposite angles to the exterior angle $\angle x$.

■ **Axiom:** A statement which is assumed as being true without any need for an explanation of how it is true.

Theorem: A theorem is a statement of mathematical truth, which is proved by using facts which, are already proved or assumed true.

Corollary: A statement whose truth can be derived from a theorem is called its corollary.

27.4 The Angle Sum Property of a Triangle

Theorem 1 : *The sum of the three angles of triangle is $180°$.*

Given: A $\triangle ABC$.

To prove that : $\angle BAC + \angle ABC + \angle ACB = 2\text{rt.}\angle s$.

Construction : Produce BC to D, and through C draw $CK \parallel BA$.

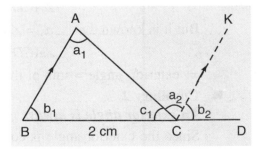

Proof :

Statements	Reasons
$\angle a_1 = \angle a_2$	$AB \parallel KC$; alt. $\angle s$
$\angle b_1 = \angle b_2$	$AB \parallel KC$; corr. $\angle s$
$\therefore \ \angle a_1 + \angle b_1 = \angle a_2 + \angle b_2$	Adding
To each side add $\angle c_1$	
$\therefore \ \angle a_1 + \angle b_1 + \angle c_1 = \angle a_2 + \angle b_2 + \angle c_1$	
$\qquad\qquad = $ st.$\angle BCD = 2$rt.$\angle s.$	BCD is a st. line
i.e. $\angle BAC + \angle ABC + \angle ACB = 2$rt.$\angle s.$	
Proved	

Alternative proof :

Given : A $\triangle ABC$

To prove : $\angle 1 + \angle 2 + \angle 3 = 180°$

Construction: Through A, draw a line $l \parallel BC$.

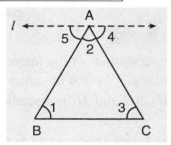

Proof :

Statements	Reasons
$\angle 1 = \angle 5$	Alt. $\angle s$; $l \parallel BC$ and AB is the transversal
$\angle 3 = \angle 4$	Alt. $\angle s$; $l \parallel BC$ and AC is the transversal
Adding, $\angle 1 + \angle 3 = \angle 5 + \angle 4$	
$\Rightarrow \angle 1 + \angle 3 + \angle 2 = \angle 5 + \angle 4 + \angle 2$	Adding $\angle 2$ to both sides
$\Rightarrow \angle 1 + \angle 3 + \angle 2 = \angle 5 + \angle 2 + \angle 4$	
But $\angle 5 + \angle 2 + \angle 4 = 180°$	Being a st. $\angle$
$\Rightarrow \angle 1 + \angle 3 + \angle 2 = 180°.$ **Proved**	

■ **Corollary 1**

An exterior angle of a triangle = sum of the interior opposite angles.

As we can see in the figure of the first proof of the above theorem. $\angle ACD$ is the exterior angle of $\triangle ABC$ at C.

$$\angle ACD = \angle a_2 + \angle b_2$$

But it is known that $\angle a_2 = \angle a_1$ and $\angle b_2 = \angle b_1$,

$$\therefore \qquad\qquad \angle ACD = \angle a_1 + \angle b_1$$

$\Rightarrow$ exterior angle = sum of the interior opposite angles.

■ **Corollary 2**

An exterior angle is always greater than either of the two interior opposite angles.

Since the exterior angle is equal to sum of the interior opposite $\angle s$, it follows that it is greater than either of the interior opposite $\angle s$.

$$\angle ACD = a_1 + b_1 \Rightarrow \angle ACD > a_1 \text{ and } \angle ACD > b_1.$$

27.5 Some Properties of an Isosceles Triangle and an Equilateral Triangle

Property 1. *If two sides of a triangle are equal , then the angles opposite those sides are equal.*

Proof. Isosceles $\triangle ABC$ is given and $AB = BC$. We wish to prove that $\angle A = \angle C$. We begin by drawing the bisector of $\angle B$, namely BD.

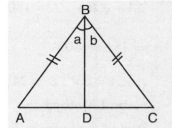

Statements	Reasons
$AB = CB$	*Given*
$\angle a = \angle b$	*Construction*
$BD = BD$	*Common*
$\therefore \triangle ABD \cong \triangle CBD$	*(SAS)*
$\therefore \angle A = \angle C$	*(Corr. $\angle$s of cong. $\triangle$s)*

Property 2. *If two angles of a triangle are equal the sides opposite those angles are also equal.*

Proof. A $\triangle ABC$ is given in which $\angle A = \angle C$. It is to be proved that $AB = BC$. In this case also, we begin by drawing the bisector of $\angle B$, namely BD.

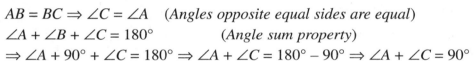

Statements	Reasons
$\angle A = \angle C$	*Given*
$\angle a = \angle b$	*Construction*
$BD = BD$	*Common*
$\therefore \triangle ABD \cong \triangle CBD$	*(AAS)*
$\therefore AB = CB$	*(Corr. sides of Cong. $\triangle$s)*

Property 3. *The angles of an isosceles right angled triangle are 45°,45° and 90°.*

Proof. $\triangle ABC$ is right angled isosceles triangle with $AB = BC$ and $\angle B = 90°$.

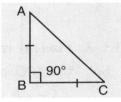

$AB = BC \Rightarrow \angle C = \angle A$ (*Angles opposite equal sides are equal*)

$\angle A + \angle B + \angle C = 180°$ (*Angle sum property*)

$\Rightarrow \angle A + 90° + \angle C = 180° \Rightarrow \angle A + \angle C = 180° - 90° \Rightarrow \angle A + \angle C = 90°$

But it is given that $\angle A = \angle C$ $\therefore$ $\angle A = \angle C = 45°$.

Property 4. *In an equilateral triangle all the three angles are equal and each angle is equal to 60^0.*

Proof : $\triangle ABC$ is an equilateral triangle with $AB = BC = CA$

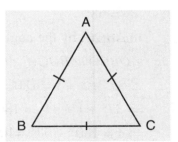

$AB = AC \Rightarrow \angle C = \angle B$ ...(i)

$AB = BC \Rightarrow \angle C = \angle A$ ...(ii)

and $BC = CA \Rightarrow = \angle A = \angle B$ ... (iii)

     ($\because$ *Angles opp. equal sides are equal*)

From (i) and (ii) it follows $\angle A = \angle B = \angle C$.

Also $\angle A + \angle B + \angle C = 180°$ (*Angle sum property of a $\triangle$*)

$\therefore$ From $\angle A = \angle B = \angle C$ it follows that $\angle A = \angle B = \angle C = 60°$.

Property 5. *If all the three angles of a triangle are equal, it is an equilateral triangle.*

Proof : $\triangle ABC$ is a triangle with $\angle A = \angle B = \angle C$

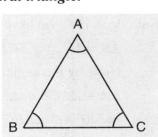

$\angle A = \angle B \Rightarrow BC = AC$ …(i)

$\angle B = \angle C \Rightarrow AC = AB$ ...(ii)

(*Sides opposite equal angles are equal*)

From (i) and (ii)

$AB = BC = AC \Rightarrow \triangle ABC$ is an equilateral triangle.

27.6 Solved Examples

Ex. 1. *In the triangle ABC, $\angle A : \angle B : \angle C = 2 : 5 : 8$. Find the angles of the triangle.*

Sol. Let $\angle A = 2x$, $\angle B = 5x$ and $\angle C = 8x$. By the angle sum property of a triangle.

$\angle A + \angle B + \angle C = 180° \Rightarrow 2x + 5x + 8x = 180°$

$\Rightarrow 15x = 180° \qquad \Rightarrow x = \dfrac{180°}{15} = 12°$

$\therefore \angle A = 2 \times 12° = \mathbf{24°}$, $\angle B = 5 \times 12° = \mathbf{60°}$ and $\angle C = 8 \times 12° = \mathbf{96°}$

Second Method :

Sum of the ratios $= 2 + 5 + 8 = 15$, Sum of the angle of the triangle $= 180°$

$\therefore$ Angles of the triangle are $\dfrac{2}{15} \times 180°$, $\dfrac{5}{15} \times 180°$ and $\dfrac{8}{15} \times 180°$.

i.e., $2 \times 12°$, $5 \times 12°$, $8 \times 12°$ i.e., $\mathbf{24°, 60°, 96°}$.

Ex. 2. *From the adjoining figure find x, given that AD bisects $\angle BAC$.*

Sol. Given AD bisects $\angle BAC$

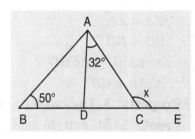

$\therefore \angle BAD = \angle DAC = 32°$

$\Rightarrow \angle BAC = \angle BAD + \angle DAC = 32° + 32° = 64°$

$\angle ACE = x = \angle BAC + \angle ABC$

$\qquad\qquad$ (ext. $= \angle$sum of int. opp. $\angle s$)

$\qquad\qquad = 64° + 50° = \mathbf{114°}$.

Ex. 3. *Find the value of x and y in the given figure.*

Sol. In ΔABC, by the angle sum property of a triangle

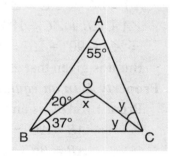

$\angle A + \angle B + \angle C = 180°$

$\because 55° + 57° + 2y = 180° (\because \angle B = \angle ABO + \angle CBO)$

$\Rightarrow 112° + 2y = 180° \Rightarrow 2y = 180° - 112°$

$2y = 68° \qquad\qquad \Rightarrow y = 34°$

In ΔBOC, by the angle sum property of a triangle

$\angle OBC + \angle BOC + \angle OCB = 180°$

$\therefore 37° + x + y = 180$

$\Rightarrow 37° + x + 34° = 180° \Rightarrow 71° + x = 180°$

$\Rightarrow x = 180° - 71° = 109° \therefore x = \mathbf{109°}$ and $y = \mathbf{34°}$.

Ex. 4. *In the adjoining figure, ΔABC is isosceles with $AB = AC$. If $\angle A = 40°$, what are the values of x and y ?*

Sol. In ΔABC, we have

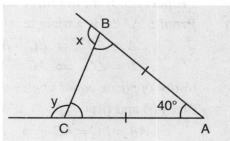

$AB = AC \Rightarrow \angle ACB = \angle ABC$.

Now, by the angle sum property of a Δ,

$\angle A + \angle ACB + \angle ABC = 180°$

$\Rightarrow 40° + 2 \angle ABC = 180°$ or $2\angle ABC = 180° - 40° = 140°$

$\Rightarrow \qquad \angle ABC = \dfrac{140°}{2} = 70° \qquad\qquad \therefore \qquad \angle ABC = \angle ACB = 70°$

But $\quad \angle ABC + \angle x = 180° \qquad\qquad$ (*Linear pair*)

or $\qquad 70° + \angle x = 180° \qquad\qquad \therefore \quad \angle x = 180° - 70° = \mathbf{110°}$

Also $\quad \angle ACB + \angle y = 180° \qquad$ or $\qquad 70° + \angle y = 180° \qquad \therefore \quad \angle y = 180° - 70° = \mathbf{110°}$

Ex. 5. *In the adjoining figure, measures of some angles are indicated. Find measures of $\angle B$ and $\angle C$. Is $\triangle ABC$ isosceles? If so, name the two sides that are equal.*

Sol. $\angle ABX + \angle ABC = 180° \qquad\qquad$ (*Linear pair*)

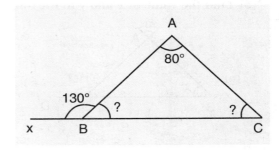

or $\qquad 130° + \angle ABC = 180°$

$\therefore \qquad \angle ABC = 180° - 130° = 50°$

Now, by angle sum property of a $\triangle$,

$\qquad \angle A + \angle ABC + \angle C = 180°$

or $\qquad 80° + 50° + \angle C = 180°$

$\Rightarrow \qquad \angle C = 180° - 130° = \mathbf{50°}.$

Thus $\angle ABC = \angle C = \mathbf{50°}$

Now, in $\triangle ABC$, we have $\angle ABC = \angle C \Rightarrow AC = AB$

Hence, $\triangle ABC$ is isosceles.

Ex. 6. *Find the value of x and y in the adjoining diagram where similar markings show equal sides and similar arrowheads show parallel lines.*

Sol. In $\triangle ABE$, $AB = AE \Rightarrow \angle AEB = \angle ABE = 64°$

$\qquad\qquad\qquad\qquad$ (*$\angle$s opp. equal sides are equal.*)

$\therefore \quad \angle BAE + \angle AEB + \angle ABE = 180°$ (*By angle sum property*)

$\angle BAE + 64° + 64° = 180° \Rightarrow \angle BAE = 180° - 128° = 52°$

$\angle AEF = \angle BAE = 52°$ ($\because$ alt. $\angle$s, $AB \parallel EF$ and AE is the transversal).

In $\triangle ABC$

$\angle ACD = \angle ABC + \angle BAC \qquad\qquad$ (*ext $\angle$ = sum of int. opp. $\angle$s*).

$\qquad = 64° + \angle BAE + \angle EAF = 64° + 52° + \angle EAF = 116° + \angle EAF$

$\Rightarrow 138° = 116° + \angle EAF \Rightarrow \angle EAF = 138° - 116° = 22°$

In $\triangle AEF$, by angle sum property of a $\triangle$

$\qquad \angle EAF + \angle AFE + \angle FEA = 180°$

$\Rightarrow \qquad 22° + \angle AFE + 52° = 180°$

$\Rightarrow \qquad \angle AFE + 74° = 180°$

$\Rightarrow \qquad \angle AFE = 180° - 74° = 106°$

$\Rightarrow \qquad y + \angle AFE = 180° \qquad\qquad$ (linear Pair).

$\Rightarrow \qquad y + 106° = 180° \quad \Rightarrow \quad y = 180° - 106° = \mathbf{74°}.$

$\therefore \qquad x = \angle AEB + \angle AEF = 64° + 52° = \mathbf{116°}.$

EXERCISE 27 (a)

1. Two angles of a triangle are 80° and 62°. Find the third angle.

2. The three angles of a triangle measure $(2x - 10°)$, $(x + 31°)$ and $(5x + 7°)$. Find the value of x and hence all the angles of the triangle.

3. One of the exterior angles of a triangle is 153° and the interior opposite angles are in the ratio 5 : 4. Find the three interior angles of the triangle.

4. If the three angles of a triangle are $(x + 15°)$, $\left(\frac{6x}{5} + 6°\right)$ and $\left(\frac{2x}{3} + 30°\right)$, prove that the triangle is an equilateral triangle.

5. **Find the value of x and y in the following figures :**

(a)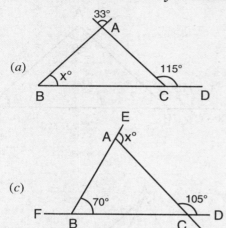

(b)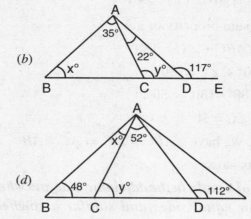

(c)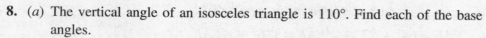

(d)

6. In the given figure $\angle A = 54°$. BO and CO are the bisectors of $\angle B$ and $\angle C$. Find $\angle BOC$.

   (**Hint:** In $\triangle ABC$ $2x + 2y + 54° = 180°$) $\Rightarrow$ $2(x + y) = 126°$
                                                           $\Rightarrow$ $x + y = 63°$

   In $\triangle BOC$ $x + y + z = 180°$).

   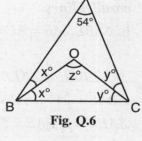

   Fig. Q.6

7. Find the value of x in the given figure.

   (**Hint:** Join AO and produce it to D. Then use exterior angle property).

   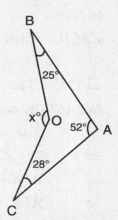

8. (a) The vertical angle of an isosceles triangle is 110°. Find each of the base angles.

   (b) In an isosceles triangle each base angle is 30° greater than the vertical angle. Find the measure of all the three angles of the triangle.

9. In the figure given below $AN = AC$, $\angle BAC = 52°$, $\angle ACK = 84°$, and BCK is a st. line. Prove that $NB = NC$.

10. In the figure $AB = AC$. Prove that $BD = BC$.

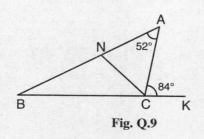

Fig. Q.9

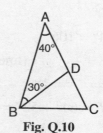

Fig. Q.10

Fig. Q.7

11. Calculate the measure of the angles marked by letters in the following figures:

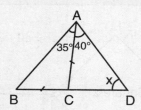 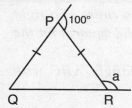 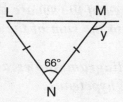

12. The ratio between the vertical angle and base angle of an isosceles triangle is 2 : 5. Find the angles of the triangle.

(**Hint:** $\dfrac{\text{Vertical angle}}{\text{base angle}} = \dfrac{2}{5}$ i.e., $\dfrac{v}{b} = \dfrac{2}{5} \Rightarrow v = \dfrac{2}{5}b$ (v denotes vertical angle and b denotes base angle)

Now, $v + b + b = 180° \Rightarrow \dfrac{2}{5}b + b + b = 180°$)

13. Prove that the sum of the exterior angles of a triangle taken in order is 360° i.e. $x + y + z = 360°$.

(**Hint :** Let int. $\angle A = a°$, int. $\angle B = b°$, int. $\angle C = c°$) $\Rightarrow a + b + c = 180°$

By ext. $\angle$ Property $x = a + b,\ y = b + c,\ z = a + c$

$x + y + z = a + b + b + c + a + c = 2(a + b + c)$.

14. Find the lettered angles in each of the following figures :

(*a*)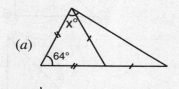

(*b*)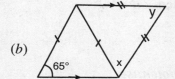

(*c*)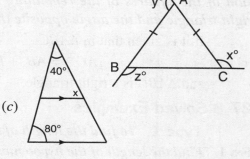

(*d*)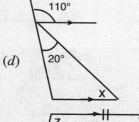

(*e*)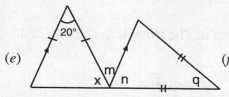

(*f*)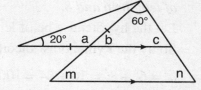

(*g*)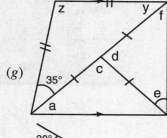

(*h*)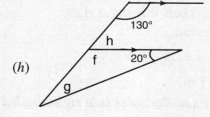

(*i*)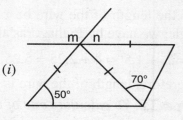

(*j*)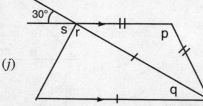

(*k*)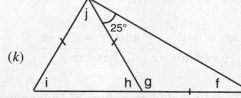

15. In the adjoining figure, $AE \parallel BC$. With the help of the given information find the value of x and y. (**Hint :** $\angle DAE = \angle ABC \Rightarrow x + 19 = y - 11 \Rightarrow x - y = -30$ ...(*i*)

$2x + y + y - 11 + x + 11 = 180 \Rightarrow 3x + 2y = 180$ ...(*ii*). Solve (*i*) and (*ii*).

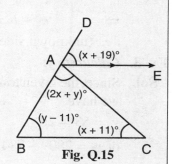

Fig. Q.15

PYTHAGORAS' THEOREM

Theorem: *The area of the square on the hypotenuse of a right angled triangle is equal to the sum of the areas of the squares on the other two sides.*

The adjoining diagram shows a right triangle ABC with $\angle C = 90°$, *and AB as the hypotenuse.*

By Pythagoras' theorem, we have

Area of sq z = Area sq x + Area of sq y

We know that area of a square = side^2

$\therefore \qquad AB^2 = BC^2 + AB^2$

or $\qquad c^2 = a^2 + b^2$

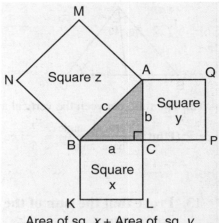

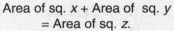
Area of sq. x + Area of sq. y = Area of sq. z.

27.7 Converse of Pythagoras' Theorem

If, in any triangle, the square of the longest side is equal to the sum of the squares of the remaining two sides, then the triangle is a right triangle and the angle opposite the longest side is a right angle.

If it is given that in $\triangle ABC$

$\qquad AC^2 = AB^2 + BC^2$, then $\angle B = 90°$

and $\triangle ABC$ is a right triangle.

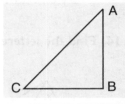

27.8 Solved Examples

Type I. *To find the length of the hypotenuse*

Ex. 1. *Find the length of the hypotenuse of a right triangle having other sides of lengths 6 and 8.*

Sol. Let the hypotenuse be of length a. The triangle is right-angled.

So by the Pythagoras' theorem

$a^2 = 6^2 + 8^2 = 36 + 64 = 100 \therefore a = \sqrt{100} = \mathbf{10}.$

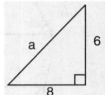

Ex. 2. *Calculate the length of the wire supporting the tree.*

Sol. Let the length of the wire be x m. Then it being a right angle, we have by Pythagoras' theorem

$x^2 = 2^2 + 1.5^2 = 4 + 2.25 = 6.25 \therefore x = \sqrt{6.25} = 2.5$

Therefore, length of the wire is **2.5 m.**

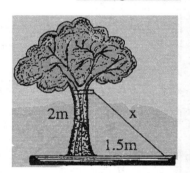

Type II. *To calculate one of the smaller sides in a right angled triangle.*

Method.

$\qquad c^2 = a^2 + b^2$

$\Rightarrow \qquad a^2 + b^2 = c^2 \Rightarrow a^2 = c^2 - b^2$ and $b^2 = c^2 - a^2$

i.e., (unknown side)^2 = (Hypotenuse)^2 – (other side)^2

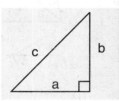

Ex. 3. *Calculate y.*

Sol. Since, the given triangle is right angled, therefore, by Pythagoras' theorem, we have

$y^2 = 53^2 - 28^2 \qquad$ (Hyp^2 – given side^2)

or $y^2 = 2809 - 784 = 2025 \Rightarrow y = \sqrt{2025} = \mathbf{45}.$

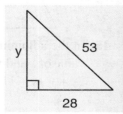

Type III. *Problem solving*

Ex. 4. *AB = 8 m. If the ladder is 10 m long, how far above B can it reach ?*

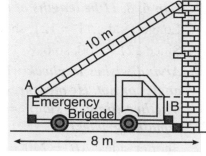

Sol.   Let the required height be h m

Then $h^2 = 10^2 - 8^2 = 100 - 64 = 36$

$\Rightarrow$ $h = \sqrt{36} = 6$

$\Rightarrow$ The ladder will reach **6 m** above B.

Ex. 5. *In the adjoining figure, it is given that PR $\perp$ QS, PQ = 15 cm, PS = 13 cm, RS = 5 cm. Find*
(a) PR   (b) QR   (c) QS.

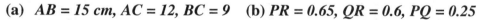

Sol :   (*a*)   In $\triangle PRS$, $\angle PRS = 90°$

$\therefore$ $PS^2 = PR^2 + RS^2$ (*Pythagoras' Theorem*)

$\Rightarrow$ $13^2 = PR^2 + 5^2$

$\Rightarrow$ $169 = PR^2 + 25 \Rightarrow PR^2 = 169 - 25 \Rightarrow PR^2 = 144$

$\Rightarrow$ $PR = \sqrt{144} = $ **12 cm.**

(*b*)   In $\triangle PQR$, $\angle PRQ = 90°$

$\therefore$ $PQ^2 = PR^2 + QR^2$ (*Pythagoras' Theorem*)

$\Rightarrow$ $15^2 = 12^2 + QR^2$

$\Rightarrow$ $225 = 144 + QR^2$

$\Rightarrow$ $QR^2 = 225 - 144 \Rightarrow QR^2 = 81 \Rightarrow QR = \sqrt{81} \Rightarrow QR = $ **9 cm.**

(*c*) $QS = QR + RS = 9$ cm $+ 5$ cm $= $ **14 cm.**

Type IV. *Based on converse of Pythagoras' theorem*

Ex. 6. *The lengths of the sides of some triangles are given below. Which of them is right angled. In case of a right angle, name the angle that measures 90°.*

(*a*) *AB = 15 cm, AC = 12, BC = 9*   (*b*) *PR = 0.65, QR = 0.6, PQ = 0.25*

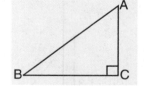

Sol.   (*a*)   Longest side $= AB$.

$AB^2 = 15^2 = 225$, $AC^2 = 12^2 = 144$, $BC^2 = 9^2 = 81$

Also $12^2 + 9^2 = 144 + 81 = 225$

$\Rightarrow$ $AC^2 + BC^2 = AB^2$

$\therefore$ $\triangle ABC$ is right angled and the angle opposite the longest side AB (hypotenuse) is $\angle C$. Hence, $\angle C = $ **90°**

(*b*)   Longest side $= PR = 0.65$

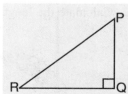

$PR^2 = (0.65)^2 = 0.4225$, $QR^2 = (0.6)^2 = 0.36$, $PQ^2 = (0.25)^2 = 0.0625$

Also $(0.6)^2 + (0.25)^2 = 0.36 + 0.0625 = 0.4225$

$\Rightarrow$ $QR^2 + PQ^2 = PR^2$

$\therefore$ $\triangle PQR$ is right angled. The angle opposite the longest side PR (hypotenuse) is $\angle Q$ and $\angle Q = $ **90°**

Ex. 7. *Can 6, 8, 11 be lengths of the sides of a right triangle?*

Sol. Longest side: $11^2 = 121$, shorter sides: $6^2 + 8^2 = 36 + 64 = 100$

Since $121 \neq 100$, so 6, 8, 11 cannot be the lengths of the sides of a right triangle.

Ex. 8. *Arvind wishes to check whether the walls are at right angles or not. He measures AB, BC and CA and checks whether (longest side)² = sum of the squares of the remaining sides?*

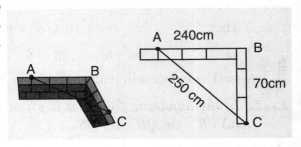

Sol. Shorter sides: $AB^2 = 240^2 = 57600$, $BC^2 = 70^2 = 4900$

$AB^2 + BC^2 = 62500$

Longest side: $AC^2 = 250^2 = 62500$

Since $AB^2 + BC^2 = AC^2$.

So $\angle B = 90°$, by the converse of Pythagoras' Theorem.

Ex. 9. *Sudhir wishes to check that the lamp-post is at right angles to the pavement. He measures as shown and applies converse of Pythagoras' theorem.*

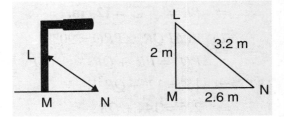

Sol. Shorter sides: $LM^2 = 2^2 = 4$

$MN^2 = 2.6^2 = 6.76$

$LM^2 + MN^2 = 4 + 6.76 = 10.76$

Longest side: $LN^2 = 3.2^2 = 10.24$

Since $LN^2 \neq LM^2 + MN^2$, so $\angle M$ is not $90°$.

EXERCISE 27 (b)

1. Two sides being given, calculate the third side marked by letter in each right angled triangle :

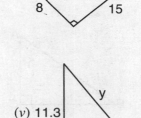
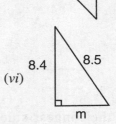
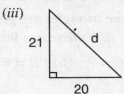
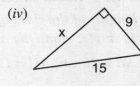
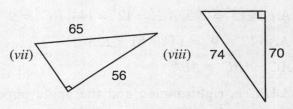

2. Calculate the length of the ramp.

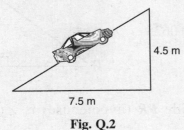

Fig. Q.2

3. Calculate the length of the wire.

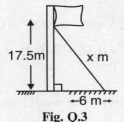

Fig. Q.3

4. Look at the diagram at the right. If you walk at the speed of 8 m/sec, how much longer will take you to walk from *A* to *B* and then from *B* to *C*, then directly from *A* to *C* ?

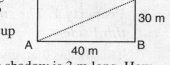

5. A 10 m ladder is placed against a wall at a distance of 8 m from its base. How high up on wall is the upper end of the ladder ?

6. When the sun is directly overhead, a 4 m rod is held in an inclined position so that its shadow is 3 m long. How much higher is one end of the rod than the other ?

7. To find the distance from point *A* to point *B* on opposite ends of a lake, a surveyor constructed the figure as shown. How far is it from *A* to *B* ?

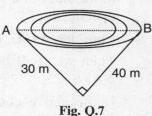

Fig. Q.7

8. A tree is broken by the wind as shown in the figure. If the point from where it broke is 5m above the ground and its top touches the ground at a distance of 12 m from its foot, find the total height of the tree before it broke. (**Hint :** *CD = AC*)

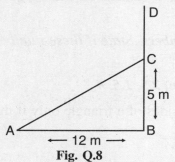

Fig. Q.8

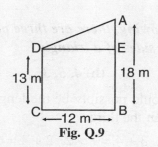

Fig. Q.9

9. Two chimneys 18 m and 13 m high stand upright in a ground. If their feet are 12 m a part, then find the distance between their tops. (**Hint :** Find *AD*)

10. **Determine if a triangle with sides of the given lengths is a right triangle. If the triangle is not right angled say whether it is acute angled or obtuse angled.**
    (*a*) 9, 12, 15   (*b*) 15, 20, 25   (*c*) 5, 8, 9   (*d*) 10, 24, 26   (*e*) 16, 30, 34   (*f*) 20, 40, 60
    (*g*) 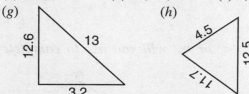   (*h*) 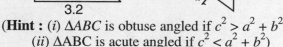   (*i*) 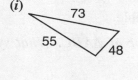   (*j*)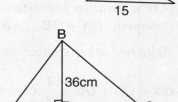

    (**Hint :** (*i*) $\triangle ABC$ is obtuse angled if $c^2 > a^2 + b^2$
    (*ii*) $\triangle ABC$ is acute angled if $c^2 < a^2 + b^2$)

11. (*a*) Calculate the lengths of
       (*i*) *AB*   (*ii*) *BC*
    (*b*) Prove the triangle *ABC* is right - angled.

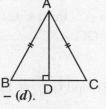

Fig. Q.11

12. **The following problems relate to an isosceles triangle.**
    Recall that if *AD* is drawn perp. to *BC*, then *BD = DC*.
    Also *AD* is the axis of symmetry.
    Calculate the lengths marked with letters in Figures (*a*) – (*d*).

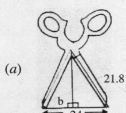

(*a*)

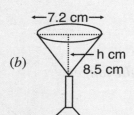

(*b*)

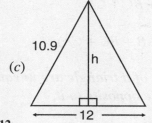

(*c*)

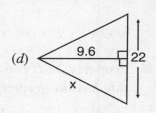

(*d*)

Fig. Q.12

13. Given that $\sqrt{3}$ = 1.732, find the altitude of an equilateral triangle whose one side measures 6 cm.

27.9 Triangle Inequality Properties

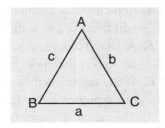

■ **Property 1:** *The sum of any two sides of a triangle is greater than the third side.*

This means that, given three numbers, they would possibly be the lengths of the sides of a triangle only if the sum of any two of them is greater then the third.

Consider $\triangle ABC$, Let $BC = a$, $AC = b$ and $AB = c$

Then we shall be able to construct a triangle with a, b, c only if $a + b > c$, $a + c > b$ and $b + c > a$.

If the above condition is not satisfied then a, b, c cannot be the lengths of the sides of a triangle.

Ex. 1. *In each of the following, there are three positive numbers. State if these numbers could possibly be the lengths of the sides of a triangle.*

     (a) 2, 3, 4   **(b) 4, 5, 3**   **(c) 2.5, 1.5, 4**

Sol. These numbers would possibly be the lengths of the sides of a triangle only if the sum of any two of them is greater than the third.

     (*a*) $2 + 3 = 5 > 4$, $3 + 4 = 7 > 2$, $2 + 4 = 6 > 3$

          $\therefore$ Triangle is possible.

     (*b*) $4 + 5 = 9 > 3$, $5 + 3 = 8 > 4$, $4 + 3 = 7 > 5$

          $\therefore$ Triangle is possible.

     (*c*) $2.5 + 1.5 = 4$ (the third number)

          $\therefore$ Triangle is not possible.

Ex. 2. *O is a point in the exterior of $\triangle ABC$. What symbol '>', '<' or '=' will you use to complete the statement: OA + OB ... AB.*

Write two other similar statements and show that

$$OA + OB + OC > \frac{1}{2} (AB + BC + CA).$$

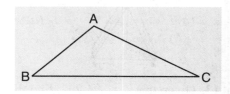

Sol.   In $\triangle OBA$, $OA + OB > AB$ ...(*i*)

(Sum of any two sides of a $\triangle$ > third side)
Similarly, in $\triangle OBC$, $OB + OC > BC$ ...(*ii*)

In $\triangle OAC$, $OA + OC > AC$ ...(*iii*)

Adding inequalities (i), (ii), and (iii) we have

$2(OA + OB + OC) > AB + BC + CA$

or $OA + OB + OC > \frac{1}{2} (AB + BC + CA)$.

■ **Property 2 :** *If two sides of a triangle are unequal, the longer side has the greater angle opposite to it.*

i.e., $BC > AC \Rightarrow \angle A > \angle B$.

- **Property 3 :** *If two angles of a triangle are unequal, the greater angle has the longer side opposite to it.*

  i.e., $\angle A > \angle B \Rightarrow BC > AC$.

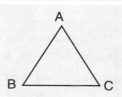

- **Property 4 :** *The difference of any two sides, of a triangle is always less than the third side.*

  i.e., $AB - AC < BC$.

Ex. 3. *The adjoining figure shows a* $\triangle ABC$ *with* $\angle ACD = 115°$ *and* $\angle CAB = 55°$. *show that* $AB > AC$.

Sol. $\angle ACB = 180° - 115°$ (Linear pair) $= 65°$

In $\triangle ABC$, by the angle sum property of a triangle

$\angle ACB + \angle CAB + \angle ABC = 180°$

$\Rightarrow \quad 65° + 55° + \angle ABC = 180°$

$\Rightarrow \quad 120° + \angle ABC = 180°$

$\Rightarrow \quad \angle ABC = 180° - 120° = 60°$

Now, $\angle ACB = 65°$ and $\angle ABC = 60°$

$\Rightarrow \quad \angle ACB > \angle ABC \Rightarrow AB > AC$

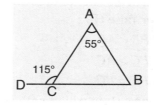

> $\because$ Side opp. to $\angle ACB$ is AB. Side opp to $\angle ABC$ is AC,
>
> Side opp. greater angle is longer

Ex. 4. **In a** $\triangle ABC$, $\angle A : \angle B : \angle C = 2 : 3 : 5$. **Without finding the angle name (i) the greatest side (ii) smallest side.**

Sol. The adjoining figure shows $\triangle ABC$

$\because \angle A : \angle B : \angle C = 2 : 3 : 5$

$\angle C$ is the greatest angle $\Rightarrow$ Side AB opposite $\angle C$ is the greatest side.

Similarly, $\angle A$ being the smallest angle $\Rightarrow$ Side BC opposite $\angle A$ is the smallest side.

Ex. 5: **In** $\triangle PQR$, **PQ = 6 cm, QR = 7.2 cm and PR = 8.1cm. Arrange the angles of the given triangle in asccending order.**

Sol : Given : $PR > QR > PQ$. $\therefore$ By the property that longest side has the greatest angle opposite to it, we have

$\angle Q > \angle P > \angle R$

$\therefore$ The angles of $\triangle PQR$ in ascending order are $\angle R$, $\angle P$, and $\angle Q$.

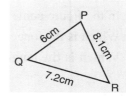

EXERCISE 27 (c)

1. **State with reasons, in which of the following cases triangles are not possible:**

   (*a*) $\triangle ABC$, $AB = 7$ cm, $BC = 3$ cm, $AC = 8$ cm

   (*b*) $\triangle XYZ$, $XY = 5$ cm, $YZ = 12$ cm, $XZ = 7$ cm

   (*c*) $\triangle PQR$, $PQ = 54$ m, $QR = 105$ m, $PR = 45$ m

   (*d*) $\triangle LMN$, $LM = 3.9$ cm, $MN = 4.11$ cm, $NL = 6.8$ cm

(e) ΔRST, $RS = 6.4$ cm, $ST = 2.9$ cm, $RT = 11.7$ cm

(f) ΔDEF, $DE = 5.6$ cm, $EF = 6.7$ cm, $DF = 7.8$ cm

2. O is any point within a ΔABC whose sides are 4 cm, 5 cm, and 7 cm respectively. Prove that $(OA + OB + OC) > 8$ cm.

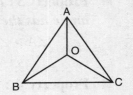

3. In ΔABC, P is a point on the side BC. Complete each of the statements below using symbol '=' '<' or '>' so as to make a true statement:

(a) AP .... $AB + BP$;

(b) AP .... $AC + PC$;

(c) AP .... $\dfrac{1}{2}(AB + AC + BC)$.

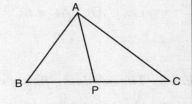

4. P is a point in the interior of ΔABC. State which of the following statements are **true (T) or false (F) :**

(a) $AP + PB < AB$

(b) $AP + PC > AC$

(c) $BP + PC = BC$

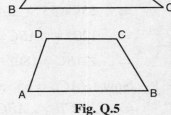

5. **In the figure, state which path is shorter.**

(a) A to D or (b) From A to D via B and C

Fig. Q.5

6. In the figure, name the sides of ΔABC in the order of their magnitudes.

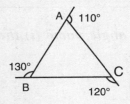

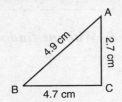

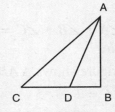

Fig. Q.6   **Fig. Q.8**   **Fig. Q.9**

7. With the data given below in each case find the unknown angle and fill in the blanks.

(a) $\angle A = 65°$, $\angle B = 69°$, $\angle C = $ ...., greatest side = ...

(b) $\angle A = 79°$, $\angle B = 31°$, $\angle C = $ ...., smallest side = ...

8. In the figure name the angles in descending order of magnitude.

9. Which is the longest side in the figure and why ?

10. **Which is the longer ?**

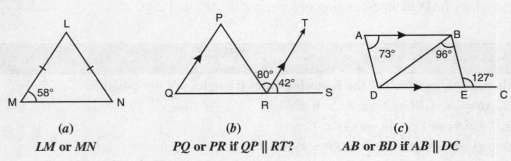

(a)   (b)   (c)

LM or MN   **PQ or PR if QP ∥ RT?**   **AB or BD if AB ∥ DC**

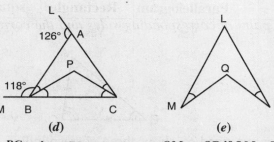

(d)

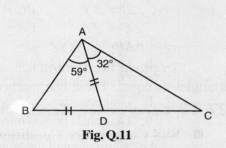

(e)

PB or PC, where *PB, PC* bisect   *QM or QR* if *LM > LR*

∠*B* and ∠*C* respectively   and ∠*LMQ* = ∠*LRQ*

11. In the adjoining figure which is not drawn accurately, ∠*BAD* = 59°, ∠*DAC* = 32° and *AD* = *BD*. Calculate the value of the angle *ACB* and state, giving reasons, which is greater, *BD* or *DC*.

Fig. Q.11

12. The side *BC* of a triangle *ABC* is produced to *D* so that *CD* = *AC*. If the angle *BAD* = 109° and the angle *ACB* = 72°, prove that *BD* is greater than *AD*.

CONGRUENCE OF TRIANGLES

27.10 Congruent Figures

■ **Recall that**

    Two figures having exactly the same shape and size are said to be congruent.

    They fit over each other exactly , when superposed.

1. Two line segments are congruent, if they have the same length.

    $AB = CD \Rightarrow AB \cong CD$

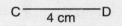

2. Two angles are said to be congruent, if they have the same measure.

    $\angle ABC = \angle PQR = 45°$

    $\Rightarrow \angle ABC \cong \angle PQR$

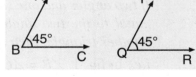

3. Two circles are congruent if they have the same radius.

    i.e. radius (r_1) of circle A = radius (r_2) of circle B $\Rightarrow$ circle A $\cong$ circle B.

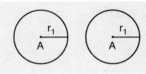

4. Two squares are congruent if they have the same side length.

    Thus, sq *ABCD* $\cong$ sq *PQRS*

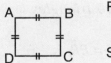

5. Two rectangles are congruent if they have the same length and breadth.

    Thus rect. *ABCD* $\cong$ rect. *PQRS*

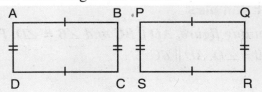

27.11 Congruent Triangles

Two triangles are said to be congruent if pairs of corresponding sides and the corresponding angles are equal.

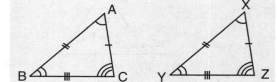

$$i.e., \quad \angle A = \angle X, \quad AB = XY$$
$$\angle B = \angle Y, \quad BC = YZ$$
$$\angle C = \angle Z, \quad CA = ZX$$
$$\Rightarrow \quad \triangle ABC \cong \triangle XYZ$$

To prove the congruence of two triangles we need to show three corresponding parts of the two triangles as equal. These congruence conditions are categorised as under.

27.12 Congruence Conditions

■ **SSS Congruence Condition**

If three sides of a triangle are equal respectively to the corresponding three sides of the other triangle, then the triangles are congruent.

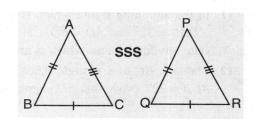

i.e., $AB = PQ$, $AC = PR$ and $BC = QR$

$\Rightarrow \quad \triangle ABC \cong \triangle PQR$ by **SSS**

■ **SAS Congruence Condition**

If two sides and the included angle of a triangle are respectively equal to the corresponding two sides and included angle of the other triangle, then the triangles are congruent.

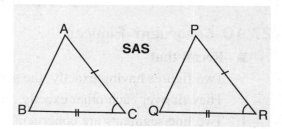

i.e., $AC = PR$, $BC = QR$ and $\angle C = \angle R$

$\Rightarrow \quad \triangle ABC \cong \triangle PQR$ by **SAS**

■ **ASA or AAS Congruence Condition**

If two angles and one side of one triangle are respectively equal to the two angles and the corresponding side of another triangle, then the two triangles are congruent.

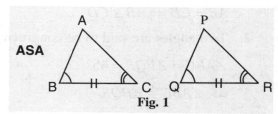

i.e., In fig. 1, $\angle B = \angle Q$, $\angle C = \angle R$ and $BC = QR$

$\Rightarrow \quad \triangle ABC \cong \triangle PQR$ by **ASA**

In fig 2, $\angle A = \angle P$, $\angle B = \angle Q$ and $BC = QR$

$\Rightarrow \quad \triangle ABC \cong \triangle PQR$ by **AAS**

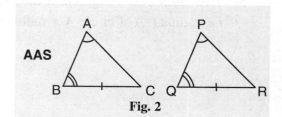

■ **RHS Congruence Condition**

If the hypotenuse and a side of a right angled triangle are equal to the hypotenuse and the corresponding side of another right angled triangle, then the two triangles are congruent to each other.

i.e., $\angle C = \angle R = 90°$, hyp $AB =$ hyp. PQ, $AC = PR$

$\Rightarrow \triangle ABC \cong \triangle PQR$ by **RHS**

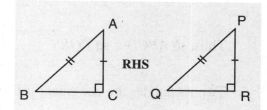

27.13 Solved Examples

Ex. 1. *In the adjoining figure, AD ∥ BC and $\angle B = \angle D$. Prove that $\triangle ABC \cong \triangle ADC$.*

Sol. **Given :** $\angle B = \angle D$, $AD \parallel BC$

To prove : $\triangle ABC \cong \triangle ADC$

Proof : In $\triangle$'s ABC and ADC

$\angle B = \angle D$	(Given)
$\angle DAC = \angle ACB$	($AD \parallel BC$, alt . $\angle$s are equal)
$AC = AC$	(common)
$\therefore \triangle ABC \cong \triangle ADC$	(AAS)

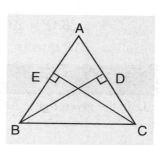

Ex. 2. *In the figure, it is given that AB = CD and AD = BC. Prove that $\triangle ADC \cong \triangle CBA$*

Sol.   **Given :** $AB = CD$ and $AD = BC$

To Prove: $\triangle ADC \cong \triangle CBA$

Proof : In $\triangle$'s ADC and CBA

$CD = AB$	(Given)
$AD = BC$	(Given)
$CA = AC$	(Common)
$\therefore \triangle ADC \cong \triangle CBA$	(SSS)

Ex. 3. *In the figure, it is given that BD and CE are two altitudes of a $\triangle ABC$, such that BD = CE. Prove that $\triangle ABC$ is isosceles.*

Sol.   **Given :** A $\triangle ABC$ in which altitudes BD and CE are equal.

To Prove: $\triangle ABC$ is an isoscels triangle

Proof : In $\triangle BCD$ and $\triangle BCE$.

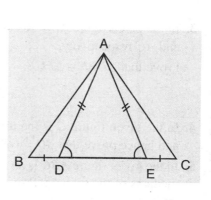

$BD = CE$	(Given)
$\angle BDC = \angle BEC$	(each equal to 90°, $BD \perp AC$ and $CE \perp AB$)
$BC = BC$	(Common)
$\therefore \quad \triangle BCD \cong \triangle BCE$	(RHS)
$\Rightarrow \quad \angle EBC = \angle DCB$	(c.p.c.t)
$\Rightarrow \quad \angle ABC = \angle ACB$	
$\Rightarrow \quad \triangle ABC$ is isosceles.	(In a $\triangle$, sides opposite equal angles are equal).

Remark : *c.p.c.t means corresponding parts of congruent triangles.*

Ex 4: *In the given figure D and E are points on the base BC of a $\triangle ABC$ such that BD = CE, AD = AE and $\angle ADE = \angle AED$. Prove that $\triangle ABE \cong \triangle ACD$ and $\triangle ABC$ is an isosceles $\triangle$.*

Sol.   **Given :** A $\triangle ABC$ with $AD = AE$,

$BD = CE$ and $\angle ADE = \angle AED$

To prove : (i) $\triangle ABE \cong \triangle ACD$

(ii) $\triangle ABC$ is an isosceles $\triangle$.

Proof : $\angle ADE = \angle AED$ (Given)

$\Rightarrow \quad 180° - \angle ADE = 180° - \angle AED$

$\Rightarrow \qquad \angle ADB = \angle AEC$ ...(i)

Now, In $\triangle$'s ABD and AEC

$AD = AE$	(Given)
$\angle ADB = \angle AEC$	(From (i))
$BD = EC$	(Given)
$\therefore \quad \triangle ABD \cong \triangle AEC$	(SAS)
$\Rightarrow \quad \triangle ABC$ is isosceles.	**Proved.**

Ex. 5. *ABC is a triangle in which AB = AC. P is any point in the interier of the triangle such that ∠ABP = ∠ACP. Prove that AP bisects ∠BAC.*

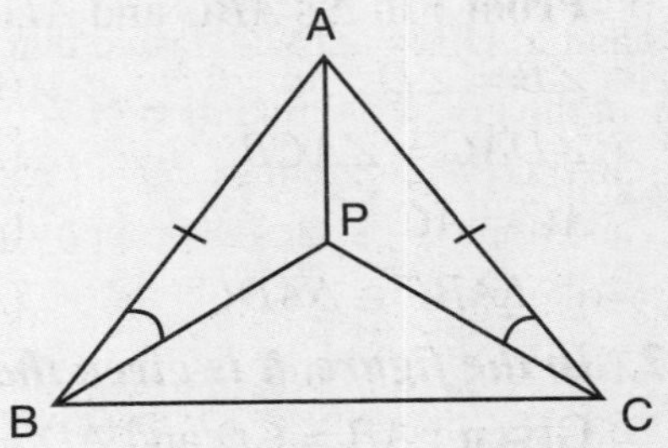

Sol.   **Given :** A $\triangle ABC$ with $AB = AC$ and $\angle ABP = \angle ACP$

       To Prove : AP bisects $\angle BAC$, i.e., $\angle BAP = \angle CAP$

       Construction : Join AP

       Proof : $AB = AC \Rightarrow \angle ABC = \angle ACB$ (*i*)

            (*Angles opp. equal sides are equal*)

       Given $\angle ABP = \angle ACP$ (*ii*)

   ∴   From (*i*) & (*ii*)

         $\angle ABC - \angle ABP = \angle ACB - \angle ACP$

   ⇒ $\angle PBC = \angle PCB$

   ⇒ $PB = PC$ (*sides opp. equal ∠s are equal*)

   ⇒   In $\triangle ABP$ and $\triangle ACP$

       $AB = AC$ (*Given*)

       $\angle ABP = \angle ACP$ (*Given*)

       $PB = PC$ (*Proved above*)

   ∴ $\triangle ABP \cong \triangle ACP$ (*SAS*)

   ⇒ $\angle BAP = \angle CAP$ (*c.p.c.t*)

   ⇒ AP bisects $\angle BAC$

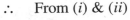

EXERCISE 27 (d)

1. In the given figure AX bisects $\angle CAB$ and $\angle BDC$, show that $\triangle ABD \cong \triangle ACD$.

2. In the given figure ABC is a triangle with BD and CE perpendiculars to AC and AB respectively, such that $BD = CE$. Prove that $\triangle BCD \cong \triangle CBE$.

3. In the given figure $AB = AC$ and D, E and F are the midpoints of sides AB, BC and AC respectively.

Prove that $\triangle DBE \cong \triangle FCE$.

4. In the given figure O is the midpoint of PQ, $PS \parallel RQ$. Prove that $\triangle POS \cong \triangle ROQ$ and hence prove that $SO = OR$.

5. In the given figure ABC is an isosceles triangle with $AB = AC$. BD and CE are two medians of the triangle. Prove that $BD = CE$.

(**Hint :** ∵ BD & CE are medians ⇒, D & E are mid-points of AC & AB respectively.

∴ $AB = AC \Rightarrow \dfrac{1}{2} AB = \dfrac{1}{2} AC \Rightarrow BE = CD$)

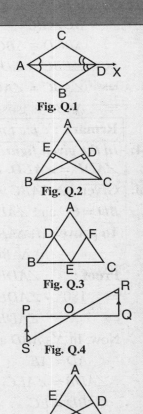

Fig. Q.1

Fig. Q.2

Fig. Q.3

Fig. Q.4

Fig. Q.5

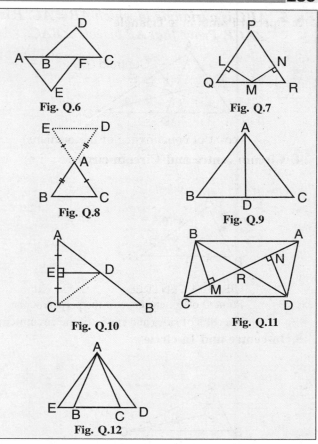

Fig. Q.6

Fig. Q.7

Fig. Q.8

Fig. Q.9

Fig. Q.10

Fig. Q.11

Fig. Q.12

6. In the given figure, it is given that $AB = CF$, $EF = BD$ and $\angle AFE = \angle DBC$. Prove that $\triangle AFE \cong \triangle CBD$.

7. In the given figure, $LM = MN$, $QM = MR$, $ML \perp PQ$ and $MN \perp PR$. Prove that $PQ = PR$ (**Hint :** Prove $\angle Q = \angle R$ and apply isosceles $\triangle$ property).

8. The sides BA and CA have been produced such that $BA = AD$ and $CA = AE$. Prove that $DE \parallel BC$.

9. Prove that perpendicular AD drawn to the base BC of an isosceles triangle ABC from the vertex A bisects BC i.e. $BD = DC$.

10. In a $\triangle ABC$, the perpendicular bisector of AC meets AB at D. Prove that $AB = BD + DC$. (**Hint:** Prove $\triangle AED \cong \triangle CED \Rightarrow AD = DC$ *Then $AB = AD + DB = DC + DB$*).

11. In the given figure, BM and DN are both perpendicular to the segment AC and $BM = DN$. Prove that AC bisects BD (**Hint:** Prove $\triangle BMR \cong \triangle DNR$).

12. In the adjoining figure ABC is an isosceles triangle with $AB = AC$ and also given that $EC = BD$. Prove that $AE = AD$.

LOOKING BACK
Summary of Key Facts

1. **Classification of triangles.**

With respect to sides			With respect to angles		
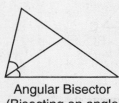 All sides different	2 sides equal	All sides equal	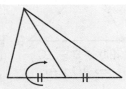 All $\angle s$ acute	One $\angle$ obtuse	One $\angle = 90°$
Scalene	Isosceles	Equilateral Each $\angle = 60°$	Acute $\angle d$	Obtuse $\angle d$	Rt. $\angle d$

2. **Special lines in a triangle**

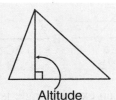

Angular Bisector (Bisecting an angle of the triangle)

Median (A line from a vertex to the mid point of the opposite side.)

Altitude (A line from a vertex perpendicular to the opposite side.)

Note : A triangle has three angular bisectors, three medians and three altitudes. They are all concurrent, *i.e.*, they meet in a point.

3. Special Points in a Triangle

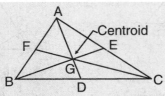 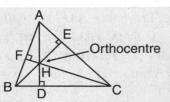

(point of concurrence of the medians)   (Point of concurrence of the altitudes)

4. Circum-centre and Circum-circle

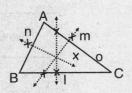 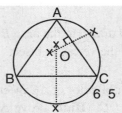

CIRCUM-CENTRE   **CIRCUM-CIRCLE**

Point O of concurrence of the perpendicular   Circle with centre O passing through

bisectors of sides and centre of the circum-circle   the vertices of the triangle OA = OB = OC

5. In-centre and In-circle

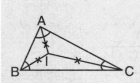 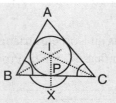

IN-CENTRE   **IN-CIRCLE**

Point of concurrence **I** of the angular bisectors   Circle with centre **I** touching the three

and centre of the incircle   sides of the triangle

6. Pythagoras' Theorem

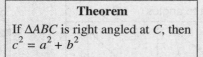 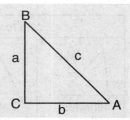

Theorem	**Converse**
If $\triangle ABC$ is right angled at C, then $c^2 = a^2 + b^2$	If in a $\triangle ABC$ $c^2 = a^2 + b^2$, then $\angle C$ is a right angle

7. Inequalities

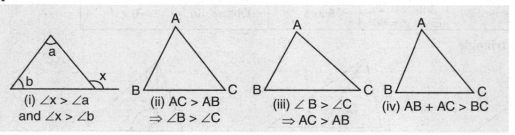

(i) $\angle x > \angle a$ and $\angle x > \angle b$ (ii) AC > AB $\Rightarrow \angle B > \angle C$ (iii) $\angle B > \angle C$ $\Rightarrow$ AC > AB   (iv) AB + AC > BC

(*a*) In a triangle, an exterior angle is greater than either opposite interior angle.

(*b*) If two sides of a triangle are unequal, the greater side has the greater angle opposite it.

    [**Note** : The largest angle of a triangle is opposite the longest side and the smallest angle opposite the smallest side.]

(*c*) If two angles of a triangle are unequal, the greater angle has the greater side opposite it.

(*d*) The sum of any two sides of a triangle is greater than the third side.

(*e*) The hypotenuse is the longest side of a right-angled triangle.

(*f*) The perpendicular is the shortest line from a given external point to a given line.

8. Tests for congruence of triangles. Two triangles are congruent if

   1. Two sides and the included angle of one triangle are equal to the corresponding parts of the other.

(S.A.S. = S.A.S.)

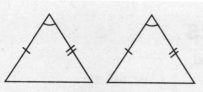 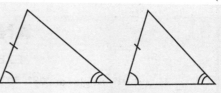

Fig. Test 1   **Fig. Test 2**

   2. Two angles and a side of one triangle are equal respectively to two angles and a correspondiong side of another.

(A.A.S. = A.A.S.)

   3. Three sides of one triangle are equal to three sides of another.

(S.S.S. = S.S.S.)

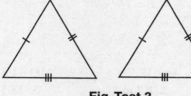 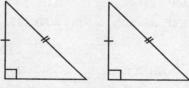

Fig. Test 3   **Fig. Test 4**

   4. The triangles are right angled and the hypotenuse and one side of one are equal to the hypotenuse and corresponding side of the other.

(R.H.S. = R.H.S.)

MENTAL MATHS – 19

1. Find *x*

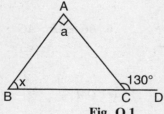

Fig. Q.1

2. Find the value of a

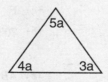

Fig. Q.2

3. In the given figure arrange the sides of $\triangle ABC$ in ascending order.

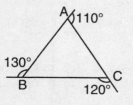

Fig. Q.3

4. Find *p*

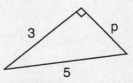

Fig. Q.4

5. Is the triangle right angled.

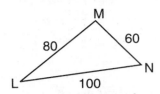

7. True and false ! AAS is the same as ASA.

6. The point of concurrency of the three medians of a triangle is known as the ....

8. *ABC* is an isosceles triangle such that $AB = AC. AD \perp BC$. Is $\triangle ABD \cong \triangle ACD$. If yes, name the congruence condition.

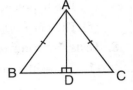

ANSWERS

EXERCISE 27(a)

1. 38°

2. $x = 19°$, Angles are 28°, 50°, 102°

3. 85°, 68°, 27°

5. (a) $x = 82°$ (b) $x = 60°, y = 95°$ (c) $x = 145°$ (d) $x = 12°, y = 60°$

6. $z = 117°$

7. $x = 105°$

8. (a) 35° (b) 40°, 70°, 70°

11. $x = 70°, a = 130°, y = 123°$

12. 30°, 75°, 75°

14. (a) $x = 87°$ (b) $x = 65°, y = 50°$ (c) $x = 60°$ (d) $x = 50°$ (e) $x = 80°, m = 20°, n = 80°, q = 20°$

    (f) $a = 140°, b = 40°, c = 80°, m = 40° n = 80°$ (g) $y = 35°, z = 110°, a = 35°, c = 110°, d = 70°, e = 55°, f = 55°$

    (h) $h = 50°, f = 130°, g = 30°$ (i) $m = 120°, n = 60°$ (j) $p = 120°, q = 30°, r = 75°, s = 75°$

    (k) $f = 25°, g = 130°, h = 50°, i = 50°, j = 80°$ **15.** $x = 24°, y = 54°$.

EXERCISE 27 (b)

1. (i) 17   (ii) 13   (iii) 29   (iv) 12   (v) 11.2

    (vi) 1.3   (vii) 33   (viii) 24   **2.** 8.7 m   **3.** 18.5 m

4. 2.5 sec   **5.** 6 m   **6.** 2.6 m   **7.** 50 m   **8.** 18 m

9. 13 m   **10.** (a) yes   (b) yes   (c) No, acute angled   (d) yes

    (e) yes   (f) No, obtuse angled   (g) yes   (h) No, acute angled   (i) yes

    (j) No, obtuse angled   **11.** (a) $AB = 45$ cm, $BC = 60$ cm

12. (a) 18.2   (b) 7.7 cm   (c) 9.1   (d) 14.6   **13.** 5.2 cm

EXERCISE 27 (c)

1. (b), (c), (e)   **3.** (a) <, (b) <, (c) <

4. (a) F   (b) T   (c) F   **5.** (a) A to D   **6.** $BC > AB > AC$

7. (a) $\angle C = 46°, AC$ (b) 70°, AC

8. $\angle C, \angle A, \angle B$ **9.** AC

10. (a) MN   (b) PQ   (c) AB   (d) PB   (e) QM

11. $\angle ACB = 30°, DC > BD$

MENTAL MATHS – 19

1. $x = 40°$ **2.** 15°   **3.** $AC < AB < BC$ **4.** $p = 4$ **5.** yes

6. centroid   **7.** False   **8.** AAS

FOR SHARP THINKERS

Pythagorean Triplets

The Pythagorean property relates the lengths, a and b, of the two legs of a right triangle with the length c of the hypotenuse by the equation : $a^2 + b^2 = c^2$.

If three natural numbers a, b and c are related so that $a^2 + b^2 = c^2$ then a, b and c are called a pythagorean triplet.

Thus, 5, 12 and 13 are a pythagorean triplet because $5^2 + 12^2 = 13^2$.

8, 9 and 12 are not a Pythagorean triplet because $8^2 + 9^2 \neq 12^2$

Note : You can show that if n is any positve real number, then $3n$, $4n$ and $5n$ represent sides of a right triangle

$(5n)^2 = 25n^2$

$(3n)^2 + (4n)^2 = 9n^2 + 16n^2 = 25n^2$

Therefore, $(5n)^2 = (3n)^2 + (4n)^2$

In general, if (a, b, c) is a pythagorean triplets and k is any positve number, then ak, bk and ck represent the three sides of a right triangle.

Note : one method of obtaining some Pythagorean triplets is to choose two relatively prime natural numbers m and n so that $m > n$, and taking $a = m^2 - n^2$, $b = 2mn$, $c = m^2 + n^2$

For example

m	n	$2mn$	$m^2 - n^2$	$m^2 + n^2$
3	2	12	5	13
4	3	24	7	25

12, 5, 13 and 24, 7, 25 are Pythagoran triplets.

Just for your Information :

The following table gives a few Pythagorean triplets

m	n	$2mn$	$m^2 - n^2$	$m^2 + n^2$	m	n	$2mn$	$m^2 - n^2$	$m^2 + n^2$
2	1	4	3	5	6	5	60	11	61
3	1	6	8	10	7	6	84	13	85
3	2	12	5	13	8	4	64	48	80
4	1	8	15	17	9	8	144	17	145
4	2	16	12	20	10	7	140	51	149
4	3	24	7	25	11	9	198	40	302
5	1	10	24	26	12	7	168	95	193
5	2	20	21	29	13	10	260	69	269
5	3	30	16	34	14	5	140	171	221
5	4	40	9	41	15	8	240	161	289

28. Special Types of Quadrilaterals

28.1 Introduction

You have learnt the definition of a quadrilateral, the various definitions related to a quadrilateral and the angle sum of a quadrilateral in class VII. Here you will study the properties of special types of quadrilaterals.

28.2 Recall that

A quadrilateral is a plane figure bounded by four line segments such that :

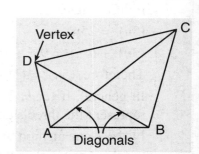

(i) No two line segments cross each other, and

(ii) No two line segments are collinear .

AB, BC, CD and *DA* are the **sides** and *A, B, C,* and *D* are the **vertices** of the quadrilateral.

Line segments *AC* and *BD*, joining two non consecutive vertices are called **diagonals**.

Two sides like *AB* and *AD* having a common end point are called **adjacent sides**.

28.3 Types of Quadrilaterals

There are various types of Quadrilaterals whose description is given below :

1. *A quadrilateral with both pairs of opposite sides parallel is a **parallelogram.***

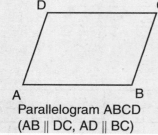

Parallelogram ABCD
(AB ∥ DC, AD ∥ BC)

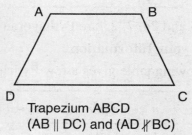

Trapezium ABCD
(AB ∥ DC) and (AD ∦ BC)

2. *A quadrilateral with exactly one pair of parallel sides is called a **trapezium**. An isosceles trapezium is a trapezium in which two non-parallel sides are equal.*

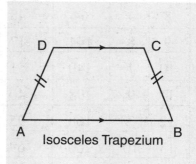

Isosceles Trapezium

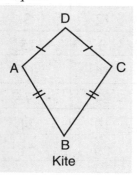

Kite

3. *A **kite** is a quadrilateral in which two pairs of adjacent sides are equal.*

4. *A parallelogram in which all angles are right angles is called a **rectangle**.*

5. *A parallelogram whose all four sides are equal is a called **rhombus**.*

6. *A rectangle with all sides equal, or, a rhombus in which all angles are right angles is called a* ***square.***

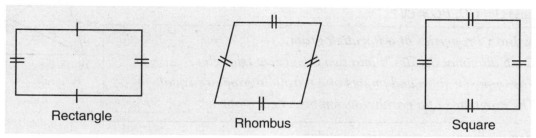

Rectangle   Rhombus   Square

This chart shows how special parallelograms are related.

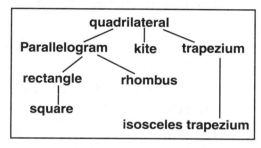

EXERCISE 28 (a)

1. Name the word used for a figure having four sides out of which two opposite sides are parallel.

2. Name the word used for a figure having four sides, the opposite sides parallel and the angles at the corners right angles.

3. Name the word used for a figure having four equal sides, the opposite sides parallel and the angles at the corners right angles.

4. What shape is a one-rupee currency note?

5. Answer true or false :

(*a*) Every quadrilateral is a parallelogram.   (*b*) Every parallelogram is a rhombus.

(*c*) Every square is a rhombus.   (*d*) Every square is a rectangle.

(*e*) No parallelogram is a square.   (*f*) Every square is a parallelogram.

6. ABCD is a parallelogram. What special name will you give it, if the following additional facts are known:

(*a*) $AB = AD$ (*b*) $\angle BAD$ is a right angle.   (*c*) $AB = AD$ and $\angle BAD = $ rt. $\angle$

7. *D, E* are points on sides *AB, AC* of $\triangle ABC$ such that $DE \parallel BC$. What is quadrilateral *BCED* called?

8. How does a trapezium differ from a parallelogram?

28.4 Properties of a Parallelogram

Activity 1. Draw a parallelogram *ABCD* and measure all its sides and angles. You will find on measurement that

   (*i*) $AB = CD$, $AD = BC$,

   (*ii*) $\angle A = \angle C$, $\angle B = \angle D$.

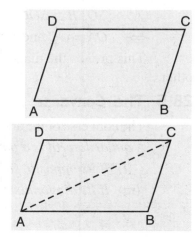

Activity 2. Cut out a parallelogram from a piece of paper. Join one diagonal say, *AC*. Cut along diagonal *AC* and place one of the triangles so obtained on the other. You will see that they exactly fit each other. This shows that the two triangles are equal in all respects.

Activity 3. Draw a parallelogram *ABCD* and draw its diagonals *AC* and *BD*. Label their point of intersection as *O*. Measure *AO*, *OC*, *BO* and *OD*. You will find that *AO* = *CO*, *BO* = *OD*.

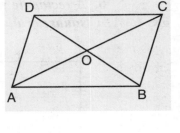

> **Conclusion :** *Properties of a Parallelogram.*
> 1. *Each diagonal divides it into two congruent triangles.*
> 2. *The opposite sides and angles of a parallelogram are equal.*
> 3. *The diagonals of a parallelogram bisect each other.*

We can prove the above properties as under:

Proof : Consider a parallelogram *ABCD*. Draw its diagonal *AC*. Then,
In triangles *ABC* and *CDA*, we have

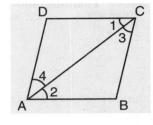

$\angle 1 = \angle 2$	*Alternate angles, AB ∥ DC and AC is the transversal*
$\angle 3 = \angle 4$	*Alternate angles, AD ∥ BC and AC is the transversal*
$AC = AC$	*common*
$\therefore \quad \triangle ABC \cong \triangle CDA$	*ASA property of congruence of Δs.*
$\Rightarrow \quad AB = CD$ and $BC = DA$	*Corresponding parts of congruent triangles.*

Also, $\angle B = \angle D$

Similarly, by drawing the diagonal *BD*, we can prove that

$$\triangle ABD \cong \triangle CDB \quad \Rightarrow \angle A = \angle C$$

Hence, properties 1 and 2 are proved.

To prove property 3 : Consider parallelogram *ABCD* and draw its diagonals *AC* and *BD*. Let these diagonals intersect each other at a point *O*.

Then, in triangles *OAB* and *OCD*, we have

$AB = CD$	*Opposite sides of a parallelogram*
$\angle AOB = \angle COD$	*Vertically opposite angles*
$\angle OAB = \angle OCD$	*Alternate angles; AB ∥ DC and transversal AC cuts them.*
$\therefore \quad \triangle OAB \cong \triangle OCD$	*AAS property of congruence of triangles.*
$\Rightarrow \quad OA = OC$ and $OB = OD$	*Corresponding parts of congruent Δs*

This proves the diagonal property of a parallelogram, i.e. the diagonals of a parallelogram bisect each other.

28.5 The Converse

The converse of the above properties is also true. Thus

A quadrilateral is a parallelogram,

> (i) *If its opposite sides are equal.*   (ii) *If its opposite angles are equal.*
>
> (iii) *If its diagonals bisect each other.*   (iv) *If it has one pair of opposite sides parallel and equal.*

28.6 Solved Examples

Ex. 1. *ABCD is a parallelogram : If ∠A = 70°, Calculate ∠B, ∠C and ∠D.*

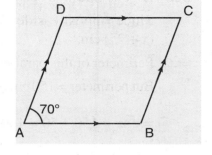

Sol. ∠A + ∠B = 180°　　　Co-interior angles, AD ∥ BC and AB is a transversal

i.e., 70° + ∠B = 180°

⇒ ∠B = 180° − 70° = 110°

Also, ∠C = ∠A = 70°　　　Opposite angles of a Parallelogram

∠D = ∠B = 110°　　　Opposite angles of a Parallelogram

Ex. 2. *The adjacent angles of a parallelogram are as 2 : 3. Find the measures of all its angles.*

Sol. Suppose ABCD is a parallelogram and the two adjacent angles A and B are as 2 : 3.

Suppose ∠A = 2x and ∠B = 3x

Since ∠A and ∠B are a pair of adjacent interior angles and AD ∥ BC.

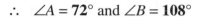

∴ ∠A + ∠B = 180°　or　2x + 3x = 180°

⇒ 5x = 180° ⇒ x = $\frac{180}{5}$ = 36°

∴ ∠A = **72°** and ∠B = **108°**

Again, since opposite angles of a ∥gm are equal, so ∴ ∠C = ∠A = 72° and ∠D = ∠B = 108°.

Ex. 3. *The ratio of two sides a ∥gm is 3 : 5, and its perimeter is 48 cm. Find the sides of the ∥gm.*

Sol. Let the two sides of the ∥ gm be 3x cm and 5x cm.

Since the opposite sides of a ∥ gm are equal, therefore, the other two sides are 3x cm and 5x cm.

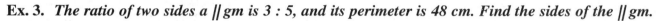

Now, perimeter of ∥ gm = 48 cm

∴ 3x + 5x + 3x + 5x = 48　⇒　16x = 48　∴　x = $\frac{48}{16}$ = 3

Hence the sides of the ∥gm are **9 cm, 15 cm, 9 cm and 15 cm.**

Ex. 4. *The point of intersection of diagonals of a quadrilateral divides one diagonal in the ratio 2 : 3. Is it a ∥gm? Why or why not?*

Sol. No, it is not a ∥gm, because in a ∥gm the diagonals of a ∥gm are bisected at their point of intersection.

Ex.5. *In a parallelogram ABCD, diagonals AC and BD intersect at O and AC = 12.8 cm and BD = 7.6 cm. Find the measures of OC and OD.*

Sol. Given : AC = 12.8 cm, BD = 7.6 cm.

We know that the diagonals of a parallelogram bisect each other, therefore,

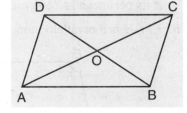

$AO = OC \Rightarrow OC = \frac{1}{2} AC = \frac{1}{2} \times 12.8$ cm = **6.4 cm.**

$BO = OD \Rightarrow OD = \frac{1}{2} BD = \frac{1}{2} \times 7.6$ cm = **3.8 cm.**

Ex. 6. *The perimeter of a parallelogram is 150 cm. One of its sides is greater than the other by 25 cm. Find the lengths of all the sides of the parallelogram.*

Sol. Let one side of the parallelogram $= x$ cm. Then its other side $= (x + 25)$ cm.

Since opposite sides of a parallelogram are equal so its remaining two sides are x cm and $(x + 25)$ cm.

∴ Perimeter of this parallelogram $= x + (x + 25) + x + (x + 25) = (4x + 50)$cm.

But perimeter $= 150$ cm (given) ∴ $4x + 50 = 150$

$\Rightarrow 4x = 150 - 50 = 100 \Rightarrow x = \dfrac{100}{4} = 25$

∴ Lengths of all the sides of the parallelogram are

$x, x + 25, x, x + 25$ cm, *i.e.,* **25 cm, 50 cm, 25 cm, 50 cm.**

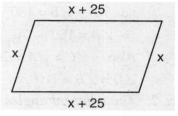

Ex. 7. *Diagonals of a ∥ gm ABCD intersect at O. XY contains O, and X, Y are points on opposite sides of the ∥ gm. Give reasons for each of the following statements.*

(a) *OB = OD;*   **(b)** *∠OBY = ∠ODX*

(c) *∠BOY = ∠DOX;*   **(d)** *ΔBOY ≅ ΔDOX.*

Now, state if XY is bisected at O.

Sol. In ΔBOY and ΔDOX

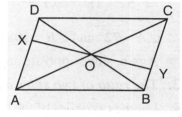

$\angle OBY = \angle ODX$ (*Alt. ∠s, AD ∥ BC*)

$OB = OD$ (*Diagonals of a ∥ gm bisect each other*)

$\angle BOY = \angle DOX$ (*Vert. Opp. ∠s*)

∴ $\Delta BOY \cong \Delta DOX$ (*ASA congruence condition*)

∴ $OY = OX$ Hence, XY is bisected at the point O.

EXERCISE 28 (b)

1. In a parallelogram $PQRS$, $\angle S = 75°$, determine the measures of $\angle P$ and $\angle Q$.

2. The measures of two adjacent angles of a parallelogram are in the ratio $2 : 7$. Find the measure of each angle of the parallelogram.

3. Two opposite angles of a parallelogram are $6x - 17°$ and $x + 63°$. Find the measure of each angle of the parallelogram.

4. Can a quadrilateral $ABCD$ be a parallelogram if :

(*i*) $AB = DC = 5$ cm, $AD = 3.8$ cm and $BC = 3.6$ cm

(*ii*) $\angle A = 95°$, $\angle B = 75°$ (*iii*) $\angle B = 105°$, $\angle D = 75°$

5. The shorter side of a parallelogram is 25 cm less than its longer side. Find the lengths of the sides of the parallelogram if its perimeter is 266 cm.

6. *EFGH* is a parallelogram. Find x, y and z. Also, state the properties you use to find them.

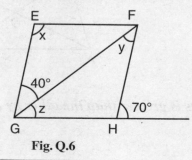

Fig. Q.6

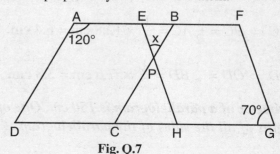

Fig. Q.7

7. *ABCD* and *EFGH* are parallelograms. Find the measure of *x*.

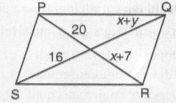

8. *PQRS* is a parallelogram. Find *x* and *y*. The given lengths are in cm.

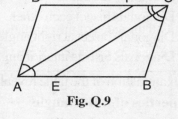

9. *ABCD* is a parallelogram. *CE* bisects ∠*C* and *AF* bisects ∠*A*. In each of the following, if the statement is true, give a reason for the same.

   (*a*) ∠*A* = ∠*C*   (*b*) ∠*FAB* = $\frac{1}{2}$ ∠*A*

   (*c*) ∠*DCE* = $\frac{1}{2}$ ∠*C*.   (*d*) ∠*FAB* = ∠*DCE*

   (*e*) ∠*DCE* = ∠*CEB*   (*f*) ∠*CEB* = ∠*FAB*

   (*g*) *CE* ∥ *AF*   (*h*) *AE* ∥ *FC*.

Fig. Q.9

10. In a △*ABC*, *D*, *E*, *F* are respectively, the mid-points of *BC*, *CA* and *AB*. If the lengths of side *AB*, *BC* and *CA* are 17 cm, 18 cm and 19 cm respectively, find the perimeter of △*DEF*.

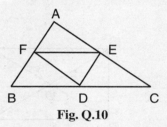

Fig. Q.10

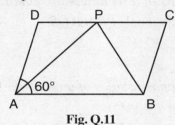

Fig. Q.11

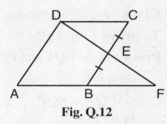

Fig. Q.12

11. In the figure, *ABCD* is a parallelogram in which ∠*A* = 60°. If the bisectors of ∠*A* and ∠*B* meet at *P*, prove that *AD* = *DP*, *PC* = *BC* and *DC* = 2*AD*.

12. In the figure, *ABCD* is a parallelogram and *E* is the mid-point of side *BC*. If *DE* and *AB* when produced meet at F, prove that *AF* = 2*AB*.

28.7 Properties of a Rectangle, Square and Rhombus

    Activity : Using a ruler and a set square, draw a parallelogram, a rhombus, a rectangle and a square. Draw the diagonals of each figure. Study each figure carefully (using a ruler and a protractor, if necessary) and then answer the following questions:-

    (*a*) Are the diagonals perpendicular to each other?

    (*b*) Do the diagonals bisect each other?

    (*c*) Do the diagonals bisect the interior angles ?

    (*d*) Are the diagonals equal in length ?

    (*e*) Are the opposite interior angles equal ?

    Put your results in the form of a table as under :

Properties	Parallelogram	Rectangle	square	Rhombus
1. Opposite sides are parallel	Yes	Yes	Yes	Yes
2. Opposite sides are equal	Yes	Yes	Yes	Yes
3. Adjacent sides are equal	No	No	Yes	Yes
4. Opposite angles are equal	Yes	Yes	Yes	Yes
5. Each interior angle is 90°	No	Yes	Yes	No
6. Diagonals are equal	No	Yes	Yes	No
7. Diagonals bisect each other	Yes	Yes	Yes	Yes
8. Diagonals bisect at right angles	No	No	Yes	Yes
9. Diagonals bisects interior angles	No	No	Yes	Yes

An examination of the table reveals the following :

Properties of a Rectangle

A rectangle being a parallelogram has all the properties of a parallelogram and some more, *i.e.*,

> *All angles of a rectangle are right angles. The diagonals of the rectangle are equal.*

Proof : *To prove that the diagonals of a rectangle are equal.*

Given : $PQRS$ is a rectangle with diagonals PR and QS.

To prove : $PR = QS$.

Proof : In $\Delta s\ PQS$ and PQR

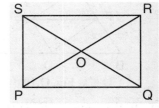

$PS = QR$	(*Opposite sides of a rectangle*)
$\angle SPQ = \angle RQP$	(*each* = 90°)
$PQ = QP$	(*common*)
$\Delta PQS \cong \Delta PQR$	(*S.A.S*)
$\Rightarrow\ QS = PR$	(*c.p.c.t.*)

■ **Properties of a Square**

A square has all the properties of a rectangle and some more, *i.e.*,

> 1. *All the sides of a square are equal.*
> 2. *The diagonals of a square are equal and bisect each other at right angles.*
> 3. *The angle which a diagonal makes with a side of the square is 45°.*

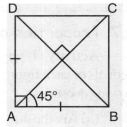

■ **Properties of a Rhombus**

A rhombus has all the properties of a parallelogram and some more.

Activity. Cut a piece of a paper into a rhombus and fold it about a diagonal. It will be seen that both parts exactly fit each other.

On opening it out it will be found that the crease along the diagonal bisects the angles at the opposite corners. The same will be found to hold true for the other diagonal when folded about it. Now if it is folded again so that AB falls on its equal AD, the two parts of BD will be seen to fall on each other, thus forming a right angle corner at O, the mid-point of BD. On opening it out, it will be found that the line of crease along AC is perpendicular to BD. This

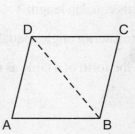

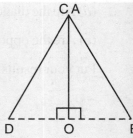

shows that the diagonals of a rhombus are perpendicular to each other. Summarising the above results and also from the table, we have the following properties of a rhombus.

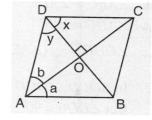

> **1.** *All the sides of a rhombus are equal.*
> **2.** *The diagonals of a rhombus bisect the interior angles.*
> **3.** *The diagonals of a rhombus bisect each other.*
> **4.** *The diagonals of a rhombus cut at right angles.*

Thus, in rhombus *ABCD*, we have

(1) $AB = BC = CD = DA$

(2) $\angle a = \angle b, = \angle x = \angle y$

(3) $AO = OC, BO = OD,$

(4) $\angle AOB = \angle AOD = \angle BOC = \angle COD = 90°.$

Maths Alert : The diagonals of a rhombus are not equal.

Proof : *To prove that the diagonals of a rhombus bisect each other at right angles.*

Given : A rhombus *ABCD* with diagonal *AC* and *BD* intersecting at *O*.

To prove : $OA = OC$; $OB = OD$; $\angle AOB = \angle COB = 90°$

Proof : In Δ's *OAB* and *OCD*

$\angle OAB = \angle OCD$	*(AB ∥ CD, Alternate ∠s)*
$\angle OBA = \angle ODC$	*(AB ∥ CD, Alternate ∠s)*
$AB = CD$	*(Opp. sides of a rhombus)*
$\Delta OAB \cong \Delta ODC$	*(ASA)*
⇒ $OA = OC, OB = OD$	*(c.p.c.t)*

Again in ΔOAB and OBC

$OA = OC$	*(Proved)*
$OB = OB$	*(Common)*
$AB = BC$	*(Sides of a rhombus)*
$\Delta OAB \cong \Delta OBC$	*(S.S.S.)*
⇒ $\angle AOB = \angle COB$	*(c.p.c.t.)*
But $\angle AOB + \angle COB = 180°$	*(Linear pair)*
∴ $\angle AOB = \angle COB = 90°.$	

28.8 Solved Examples

Ex. 1. *ABCD is a rectangle with* $\angle BAC = 28°$. *Determine* $\angle DBC$.

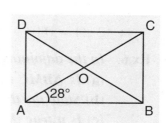

Sol. $AO = \dfrac{1}{2} AC$ and $BO = \dfrac{1}{2} BD$ *(Diagonals of a rectangle bisect each other.)*

But $AC = BD$ *(Diagonals of a rectangle are equal.)*

∴ $AO = BO \Rightarrow \angle OBA = \angle OAB = 28°$ *(In a Δ, angles opposite equal sides are equal)*

Now, $\angle ABC = 90°$ *(angle of rectangle)*

∴ $\angle DBC = 90° - \angle OBA = 90° - 28° = $ **62°**.

Ex. 2. *ABCD is a rhombus with* $\angle ABC = 126°$. *Determine* $\angle ACD$.

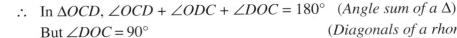

Sol. $\angle ABC = \angle ADC$ *(Opposite angles of a rhombus)*

$\therefore$ $\angle ADC = 126°$ $(\because \angle ABC = 126°,\ given)$

$\therefore$ $\angle ODC = \dfrac{1}{2}(\angle ADC) = \dfrac{1}{2} \times 126° = 63°$ *(Diagonals of a rhombus bisect interior angles)*

$\therefore$ In $\triangle OCD$, $\angle OCD + \angle ODC + \angle DOC = 180°$ *(Angle sum of a $\triangle$)*

But $\angle DOC = 90°$ *(Diagonals of a rhombus bisect at right angles)*

$\therefore$ $\angle OCD + 63° + 90° = 180°$

$\Rightarrow$ $\angle OCD = 180° - 63° - 90° = 180° - 153° = 27° \Rightarrow \angle ACD = \mathbf{27°}$.

Ex. 3. *One of the diagonals of a rhombus is congruent to one of its sides. Find the angles of the rhombus.*

Sol. Let *ABCD* be a rhombus in which diagonal

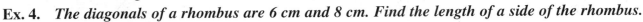

$BD = AB = AD$

$\therefore$ $\triangle ABD$ is an equilateral triangle

$\therefore$ $\angle BAD = 60°$ $(\because each\ angle\ of\ an\ equilateral\ \triangle\ is\ 60°)$

Also, $\angle BAD + \angle ABC = 180°$ *(adj. int. angles, AD $\parallel$ BC)*

$\therefore$ $\angle ABC = 180° - \angle BAD = 180° - 60° = 120°$

Since opposite angles of a rhombus are equal

$\therefore$ $\angle BCD = \angle BAD = 60°$ and $\angle ADC = \angle ABC = 120°$.

Hence, the angles of the rhombus are **60°, 120°, 60°** and **120°**.

Ex. 4. *The diagonals of a rhombus are 6 cm and 8 cm. Find the length of a side of the rhombus.*

Sol. **Given :** Rhombus *ABCD* in which $AC = 8$ cm and $BD = 6$ cm. Let these diagonals intersect at *O*. Since the diagonals of a rhombus bisect each other at right angles, therefore

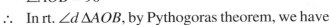

$AO = \dfrac{1}{2} AC = \dfrac{1}{2} \times 8$ cm $= 4$ cm, $BO = \dfrac{1}{2} BD = \dfrac{1}{2} \times 6$ cm $= 3$ cm,

$\angle AOB = 90°$

$\therefore$ In rt. $\angle$d $\triangle AOB$, by Pythogoras theorem, we have

$AB^2 = AO^2 + OB^2 = 4^2 + 3^2 = 16 + 9 = 25$

$\therefore$ $AB = \sqrt{25}$ cm $= 5$ cm. Hence, the length of each side of the rhombus is **5 cm.**

Ex. 5. *ABCD is a square. Determine* $\angle DCA$.

Sol. Since *ABCD* is a square therefore, $AD = DC$ and $\angle ADC = 90°$

Now, in $\triangle ADC$, we have

$AD = DC \Rightarrow \angle 1 = \angle 2$ (*In a $\triangle$, angles opposite equal sides are equal.*)

Also, $\angle 1 + \angle 2 + \angle ADC = 180°$ *(Angle sum of a $\triangle$)*

or $\angle 1 + \angle 1 + 90° = 180°$ $(\because \angle 2 = \angle 1\ and\ \angle ADC = 90°)$

$\Rightarrow$ $2\angle 1 = 180° - 90° = 90° \Rightarrow \angle 1 = \dfrac{90°}{2} = 45°$. *i.e,* $\angle ACD = \mathbf{45°}$.

Ex.6. *In the adjoining figure, ABCD is a rectangle. BM and DN are perpendiculars from B and D on AC.*

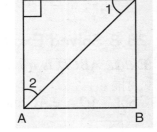

  (a) *Is $\triangle BMC \cong \triangle DNA$?*

  (b) *State the three pairs of matching parts you used to answer (i).*

  (c) *Is it true that* **BM = DN?**

Sol. (*a*) Yes, $\triangle BMC \cong \triangle DNA$

Reason :	$\angle BCM = \angle DAN$	(*Alt.* $\angle s$, $AD \parallel BC$)
	$\angle BMC = \angle DNA$	(*each* $= 90°$)
	$BC = AD$	(*opp. sides of rect.*)
$\therefore$	$\triangle BMC \cong \triangle DNA$	(*AAS*)

(*b*) $\angle MCB = \angle NAD$, $BC = DA$ and $\angle BMC = \angle DNA$

(*c*) Yes, it is true that $BM = DN$.　　(*corresponding parts of congruent triangles*)

EXERCISE 28(c)

1. For each of the statements given below, indicate whether it is true (T) or false (F).

(*a*) A rectangle is a parallelogram　　　　(*b*) A square is a rectangle

(*c*) A parallelogram is a rhombus　　　　(*d*) A square is a rhombus

(*e*) A rectangle is a square　　　　(*f*) A square is a parallelogram

2. What kind of a quadrilateral is the following :

(*a*) The diagonals cut each other perpendicularly at *X* such that $AX = XC$.

(*b*) The diagonals and the sides form four congruent right angled triangles.

3. What kind of a quadrilateral is *PQRS* if :

(*a*) *PQ* is parallel to *RS* and the diagonals are equal in length.

(*b*) *PQ* and *RS* are parallel and $\angle P = \angle R$.

4. Identify all the quadrilaterals that have

(*a*) four sides of equal length　　　　(*b*) four right angles.

5. Explain how a square is :

(*i*) a quadrilateral　　(*ii*) a parallelogram　　(*iii*) a rhombus　　(*iv*) a rectangle

6. Name the quadrilaterals whose diagonals

(*i*) bisect each other　　(*ii*) are perpendicular bisector of each other　　(*iii*) are equal.

7. *EFGH* is a rhombus. Find *a*, *b*, *c*

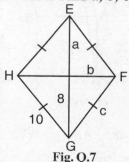

Fig. Q.7

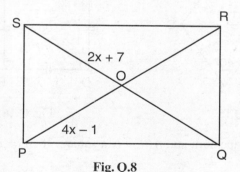

Fig. Q.8

8. *PQRS* is a rectangle whose diagonals intersect at point *O*. If $OP = 4x - 1$ and $OS = 2x + 7$, find the value of *x*.

9. The diagonals of a rectangle *ABCD* intersect at *O*. If $\angle BOC = 44°$, find $\angle OAD$.

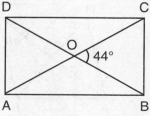

Fig. Q.9

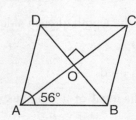

Fig. Q.10

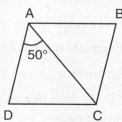

Fig. Q.11

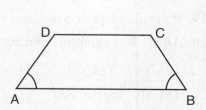

Fig. Q.12

10. *ABCD* is a rhombus with ∠*DAB* = 56°. Determine ∠*DBC*.

11. *ABCD* is a rhombus. If ∠*DAC* = 50°, **find** (a) ∠*ACD*   (b) ∠*CAB*   (c) ∠*ABC*.

12. (a) *ABCD* is a rhombus. ∠*BAC* = 37°. draw a sketch and find the four angles of the rhombus.

    (b) If an angle of a rhombus is 50°, find the size of the angles of one of the triangles which are formed by the diagonals.

13. *ABCD* is a trapezium in which *AB* ∥ *DC*. If ∠*A* = ∠*B* = 40°, what are the measures of the other two angles?

14. **Calculate the angles marked with small letters in the following diagrams.**

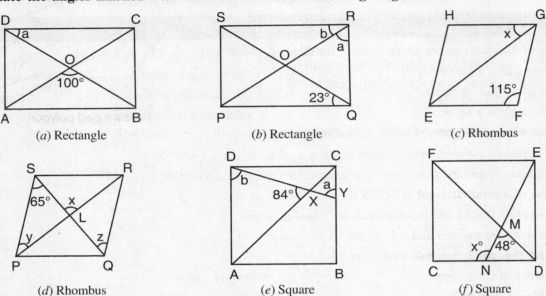

(a) Rectangle   (b) Rectangle   (c) Rhombus

(d) Rhombus   (e) Square   (f) Square

15. *ABCD* is a kite if ∠*BCD* = 40°, **find** (a) ∠*BDC* (b) ∠*ABC*.

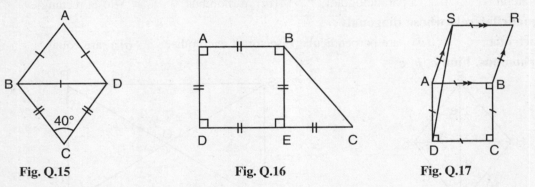

Fig. Q.15   Fig. Q.16   Fig. Q.17

16. *ABCD* is a trapezium and *ABED* is a square. If *BE* = *EC*, **find** (a) ∠*BAE* (b) ∠*ABC* (c) What shape is the figure *ABCE*.

17. *ABCD* is a square and *ABRS* is a rhombus. If ∠*SAD* = 120°, find (a) ∠*ASD* (b) ∠*SRB*.

18. *ABCD* is a kite and ∠*A* = ∠*C*. If ∠*CAD* = 70°, ∠*CBD* = 65°, find : (a) ∠*BCD* (b) ∠*ADC*.

19. If the diagonals of a rhombus are 12 cm and 16 cm, find the length of each side.

20. *ABCD* **is a rhombus and its diagonals intersect in** *O*.

    (a) Is Δ*BOC* ≅ Δ*DOC* ? State the congruence condition used.

    (b) Also state if ∠*BCO* = ∠*DCO*. Deduce that each diagonal of a rhombus bisects the angle through which it passes.

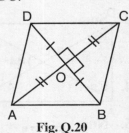

Fig. Q.20

28.9 Definitions

A rectilinear (closed) figure bounded by a number of line segments is called a polygon. The line segments are called the **sides** of the polygon and the point of intersection of adjacent sides of a polygon is called a **vertex**.

The angle which two consecutive sides make inside a polygon is called the **interior angle** of a polygon. A polygon is named according to the number of sides it has.

The line joining any two non-consecutive vertices of a polygon is called its **diagonal**.

If one of the sides is extended, then the angle formed by the extended side and the side adjacent to it is called the **exterior angle** of a polygon.

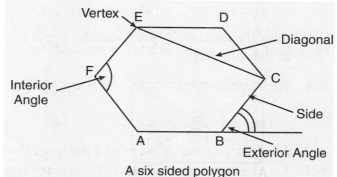

A six sided polygon

A polygon has the **same number of angles** (exterior as well as interior) **as it has sides**.

3 sides	4 sides	5 sides	6 sides	8 sides	9 sides	10 sides
Triangle	quadrilateral	Pentagon	Hexagon	Octagon	Nonagon	Decagon

A polygon, whose each interior angle is less than two right angles, is called a **convex polygon**.

A polygon whose one or more of the interior angles are reflex is called a **re-entrant or concave polygon**. A polygon is called **equilateral** when all its sides are equal, and *equiangular* when all its angles are equal.

A polygon is called **regular** if all its sides and also its angles are equal.

A polygon having *n* sides is called a *n*-gon.

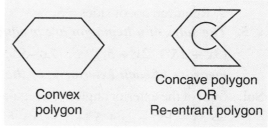

Convex
polygon

Concave polygon
OR
Re-entrant polygon

28.10 Formulas

1. **Interior angle + exterior angle at a vertex = 180°**

2. **Sum of the interior angles of a polygon of *n*-sides.**

    A polygon of *n*-sides can be divided into $(n-2)$ triangles

    ∴ sum of all the $\angle s$ of the polygon
    $$= (n-2) \times 180° = (n-2) \times 2 \times 90° = (2n-4) \text{ rt. } \angle s.$$

3. **Sum of the exterior $\angle s$ of a convex polygon = 360°.**

    Ext. $\angle s$ + Int. $\angle s = n \times 2$ rt. $\angle s = 2n$ rt. $\angle s \Rightarrow$ Ext. $\angle s + (2n-4)$ rt. $\angle s = 2n$ rt. $\angle s$

    ∴ Sum of Ext. $\angle s = 2n - (2n-4) = \mathbf{4}$ **rt.** $\angle s$, whatever *n* may be.

4. **Each exterior angle of a *n*-polygon =** $\dfrac{360°}{n}$, *n* denotes number of sides of the polygon.

5. **Number of side** $(n) = \dfrac{360°}{(\text{each ext. } \angle)}$.

28.11 Solved Examples

Ex. 1. *Find the sum of the interior angles of a 12 - sided polygon.*

Sol. Sum of the interior $\angle s$ of a 12 - gon

$$= (2n-4) \times 90° = (2 \times 12 - 4) \times 90° = (24-4) \times 90° = 20 \times 90° = \mathbf{1800°}.$$

$\boxed{\text{Here } n = 12}$

Ex. 2. *Find the measure of each exterior angle of a regular 15 - gon and hence find the measure of each of its interior angle.*

Sol. Each exterior angle of a regular n–gon $= \dfrac{360°}{n}$

$\therefore$ Here each exterior angle $\dfrac{360°}{15} = \mathbf{24°}$ $\therefore$ Each interior angle $= 180° - 24° = \mathbf{156°}.$

Ex. 3. *Find the number of sides of a polygon, the sum of whose interior $\angle s$ is 1440°.*

Sol. Let n be the number of sides of the given polygon.

$\therefore$ sum of interior $\angle s = (2n-4) \times 90° \Rightarrow (2n-4) \times 90° = 1440°$

$2n - 4 = \dfrac{1440°}{90°} \Rightarrow 2n - 4 = 16 \Rightarrow 2n = 16 + 4 = 20 \Rightarrow n = \mathbf{10}.$

$\therefore$ Required number of sides $= \mathbf{10}.$

Ex. 4. *Find the number of sides of a regular polygon, if each of its interior angle is 108°.*

Sol. Each interior angle $= 108° \Rightarrow$ Each exterior angle $= 180° - 108° = 72°$

Let the number of sides of the regular polygon be n.

Each ext. $\angle = \dfrac{360°}{n} \Rightarrow n = \dfrac{360°}{\text{each ext.} \angle} = \dfrac{360°}{72°} = 5$

$\therefore$ Required no. of sides $= \mathbf{5}.$

Ex. 5. *The sides of a heptagon are produced in order. If the measure of each exterior angle so obtained is (3x + 15°) (2x + 5°), x, (7x –5°), (8x – 10°),(6x –20°) and 3x. Find the value of x and hence the measure of each exterior $\angle$ of the heptagon :*

Sol. Sum of the exterior angles of a regular polygon $= 360°$

$\Rightarrow 3x + 15° + 2x + 5° + x + 7x - 5° + 8x - 10° + 6x - 20° + 3x = 360°$

$\Rightarrow 30x - 15° = 360° \Rightarrow 30x = 375° \Rightarrow x = \dfrac{375°}{30} = \mathbf{12.5°}$

$\therefore$ 1st angle $= 3x + 15° = 3 \times 12.5° + 15° = 37.5° + 15° = \mathbf{52.5°}$

2nd angle $= 2x + 5° = 2 \times 12.5° + 5° = 25° + 5° = \mathbf{30°}$

3rd angle $= x = \mathbf{12.5°}$

4th angle $= 7x - 5° = 7 \times 12.5° - 5° = 87.5° - 5° = \mathbf{82.5°}$

5th angle $= 8x - 10° = 8 \times 12.5° - 10° = 100° - 10° = \mathbf{90°}$

6th angle $= 6x - 20° = 6 \times 12.5° - 20° = 75° - 20° = \mathbf{55°}$

7th angle $= 3x = 3 \times 12.5° = \mathbf{37.5°}.$

Ex. 6. *The interior angles of a regular hexagon are in the ratio 1 : 2 : 3 : 5 : 6 : 7. Find the largest angle.*

Sol. Sum of the int. $\angle s$ of a regular hexagon

$$= (2n-4) \times 90° = (2 \times 6 - 4) \times 90° = (12-4) \times 90° = 8 \times 90° = \mathbf{720°}$$

Since the int. $\angle$s are in the ratio $1 : 2 : 3 : 4 : 5 : 6 : 7$

Let the angles be x, $2x$, $3x$, $5x$, $6x$ and $7x$.

Given $x + 2x + 3x + 5x + 6x + 7x = \mathbf{720°}$

$\Rightarrow 24x = 720° \Rightarrow x = \dfrac{720°}{24} = 30°$ $\qquad \therefore$ Largest angle $7x = 7 \times 30° = 210°$

$\because$ the largest angle $> 180°$, $\qquad \therefore$ it is a concave polygon.

Ex. 7. *Is it possible to have a regular polygon, the sum of whose interior $\angle$s is 1120°.*

Sol. Let n be the number of sides of the polygon, then

$$(2n - 4) \times 90° = 1120° \Rightarrow 2n - 4 = \dfrac{1120}{90} = 12\dfrac{4}{9}$$

$$2n = 12\dfrac{4}{9} + 4 = \dfrac{112}{9} + 4 = \dfrac{112 + 36}{9} = \dfrac{\mathbf{148}}{\mathbf{9}}.$$

Since n is a fraction so it is not possible to have a polygon having sum of int. $\angle$s $= 1120°$.

EXERCISE 28 (d)

1. Find the number of sides of a regular polygon in which each interior angle $= 162°$.

2. How many sides has a polygon the sum of the whose interior angles is 1980°?

3. The angles of a quadrilateral taken in order are $2x$, $3x$, $7x$, $8x$. Find x and prove that two opposite sides are parallel.

4. *ABCDE* is a regular pentagon. *AB*, *DC* are produced to meet at *P*; find $\angle BPC$.

5. Find the sum of the interior angles of a polygon which has (*a*) 30 sides, (*b*) 40 sides.

6. Prove that the sum of the interior angles of an octagon is twice the sum of the interior angles of a pentagon.

7. In a regular pentagon *ABCDE*, calculate the number of degrees in the angle *ABC* and prove that *BC* ∥ *AD*.

8. (*a*) **Is it possible to draw a regular polygon with exterior angle**

    (*i*) 72°, (*ii*) 32°, (*iii*) 40°, (*iv*) 55°, (*v*) 60°. Where possible give the number of sides.

  (*b*) **Is it possible to draw a regular polygon with interior angles**

    (*i*) 120°, (*ii*) 156°, (*iii*) 145°. Where possible, state the number of sides.

9. The number of sides of two regular polygons are in the ratio of 3 : 2 and their interior angles are in the ratio of 5 : 3. Find the number of their sides.

10. The sides of a pentagon are produced in order and the exterior angles so obtained measure $2x + 20°$, $x - 10°$, $3x + 30°$, $4x - 15°$, $5x - 10°$. Find the measure of x and find all the angles of the pentagon.

11. The ratio between the interior and exterior angle of a regular polygon is 8 : 1. Find :

   (*a*) The number of sides of the regular polygon   (*b*) each exterior angle of the polygon.

12. An octagon has two pairs of equal angles, one measuring 72° and the other 56° and 4 equal angles. Find the size of equal angles.

13. Each exterior angle of a regular polygon is two thirds of its interior angle. Find the number of sides in the regular polygon.

14. Each interior angle of a regular polygon is 160°. Find the interior angle of regular polygon which has double the number of sides as the given polygon.

15. Two interior angles of a polygon are right angles and sum of remaining angles is 720°. Find the number of sides of the polygon.

LOOKING BACK

Summary of Key Facts

1. The sum of the interior angles of a quadrilateral is 360°.

2. **Types of Quadrilaterals.**

    (*i*) Parallelogram   (*ii*) Trapezium   (*iii*) Rectangle

    (*iv*) Rhombus   (*v*) Square   (*vi*) Kite.

DEFINITIONS

3.   (*i*) A quadrilateral with exactly one pair of parallel sides is called a **trapezium**.

    (*ii*) A quadrilateral in which both pairs of opposite sides are parallel is called a **parallelogram**.

    (*iii*) A parallelogram in which all the sides are equal is called a **rhombus**.

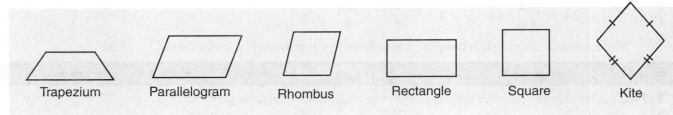

Trapezium   Parallelogram   Rhombus   Rectangle   Square   Kite

   (*iv*) A parallelogram in which each angle is a right angle is called **rectangle**.

    (*v*) A parallelogram in which all the sides are equal and each angle is equal to a right angle is called a **square**.

    (*vi*) A quadrilateral which has two pairs of equal adjacent sides but unequal opposite sides is called a kite.

4. **A quadrilateral is a parallelogram if**

    (*i*) its opposite sides are equal or

    (*ii*) its opposite angles are equal or

    (*iii*) its diagonals bisect each other or

    (*iv*) it has one pair of opposite sides equal and parallel.

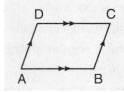

5. **PROPERTIES** : opposite sides and opposite angles of a parallelogram are equal.

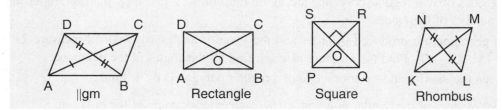

||gm   Rectangle   Square   Rhombus

6. The diagonals of a parallelogram bisect each other.

7. The diagonals of a rhombus bisect each other at right angles.

8. The diagonals of a rectangle are equal *i.e.*, *AC = BD*.

9. The diagonals of a square are equal and bisect each other at right angles (*PR = RS* and $\angle POQ = 90°$).

10.   The diagonals of a rhombus and a square bisect the internal angles.

11. Exterior $\angle s$ + interior $\angle s$ of a regular polygon = 180°

12. Sum of the interior $\angle s$ of a polygon of *n* sides = $(2n - 4)$ *rt* $\angle s$.

13. Each exterior angle of a regular *n*-gon = $\dfrac{360°}{n}$.

MENTAL MATHS – 20

1. One angle of a parallelogram is 60°. Find its opposite angle and the adjacent angle.
2. If one angle of a rhombus 70°, find other angles.
3. Every square is a rhombus –True or False?
4. Perimeter of a rhombus is 24 cm. Find the length of its sides.
5. The diagonals of a parallelogram are not perpendicular to each other. Is it a rhombus? Why?
6. Two opposite angles of a parallelogram are $(3x - 2)°$ and $(50 - x)°$. Find the measure of each angle of the parallelogram
7. The perimeter of a parallelogram is 60 cm. If the smaller side is 12 cm long, find the measure of the longer side.
8. In the figure, find the value of a and b and measure of $\angle Q$ of the parallelogram $PQRS$.
9. Each exterior angle of a regular polygon is 36°. Find the number of sides of the regular polygon.
10. If each interior angle of regular polygon is 90°, then find the numbers of sides of the regular polygon.
11. The exterior angle of a regular pentagon are x , $2x + 10°$, $3x - 15°$, $x - 10°$, $2x +15°$. Find the value of x.
12. If the given figure is a regular hexagon, DM bisects $\angle CDE$, $\angle CNM = 90°$. Find $\angle DMN$.

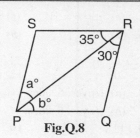

Fig.Q.8

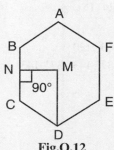

Fig.Q.12

ANSWERS

EXERCISE 28 (a)

1. Trapezium   2. Rectangle   3. Square   4. Rectangle

5. (*a*) False   (*b*) False   (*c*) True   (*d*) True   (*e*) False   (*f*) True

6. (*a*) Rhombus   (*b*) Rectangle   (*c*) Square   7. Trapezium

8. A trapezium has one pair of opposite sides parallel, while a parallelogram has two pairs of opposite sides parallel.

EXERCISE 28 (b)

1. $\angle P = 105°$, $\angle Q = 75°$,   2. 40°, 140°, 40°, 140°   3. 79°, 101°, 79°, 101°,

5. Longer side = 79 cm, Shorter side = 54 cm   6. $x = 110°, y = 40°, z = 30°$ 7. $x = 50°$,   8. $x = 3$ cm, $y = 13$ cm,

9. (*a*) True, opposite angles of a ∥gm   (*b*) True, AF bisects $\angle A$ (given)

   (*c*) true, CE bisects $\angle C$ (given)   (*d*) true, halves of opposite equal angles

   (*e*) True, Alternate angles   (*f*) True, $\angle FAB = \angle DCE$ and $\angle DCE = \angle CEB$

                                ∴ $\angle FAB = \angle CEB$

   (*g*) True, corresponding angles CEB and FAB are equal.

   (*h*) True, $AB \parallel CD \Rightarrow AE \parallel FC$ 10. 27 cm.

EXERCISE 28 (c)

1. (*a*) T   (*b*) T   (*c*) F   (*d*) T   (*e*) F   (*f*) T

2. (*a*) Square   (*b*) Rhombus   3. (*a*) Isosceles trapezium   (*b*) Parallelogram.

4. (*a*) Rhombus, Square   (*b*) Rectangle, square

5. (*i*) It has four sides and four angles   (*ii*) Opposite sides are parallel, opposite $\angle s$ are equal, adjacent $\angle s$ are supplementary.

   (*iii*) All four sides are equal, diagonals bisect each other at rt. $\angle s$ (*iv*) All four angles are at rt. $\angle s$, diagonals are equal.

6. (*i*) Parallelogram, Rhombus, Square, Rectangle   (*ii*) Rhombus, Square   (*iii*) Rectangle, Square

7. (*a*) $a = 8$ cm, $b = 6$ cm, $c = 10$ cm   8. $x = 4$ 9. 68°   10. 62°   11. 50°, 50°, 80°

12. (a) $\angle A = 74°, \angle B = 106°, \angle C = 74°, \angle D = 106°$ (b) $25°, 65°, 90°$ 13. $\angle C = \angle D = 140°$
14. (a) $40°$ (b) $a = 67°, b = 23°$ (c) $37.5°$ (d) $x = 90°, \ y = 25°, z = 65°$
  (e) $a = b = 51°$ (f) $93°$ 15. (a) $70°$ (b) $130°$
16. (a) $45°$ (b) $135°$ (c) parallelogram 17. $30°, 30°$ 18. $95°, 40°$ 19. 10 cm

EXERCISE 28 (d)

1. 20 2. 13 3. 18 4. $36°$ 5. (a) 56 rt $\angle s$ (b) 76 rt $\angle s$
8. (a) (i) yes, 5 sides (ii) No (iii) yes, 9 sides (iv) No (v) yes, 6 sides
  (b) (i) yes, 6 sides (ii) Yes, 15 sides (iii) No
9. $12, 8$ 10. $66°, 13°, 99°, 77°, 105°$
11. (a) 18 (b) $20°$ 12. $206°$ 13. 5 14. $170°$ 15. 7

MENTAL MATHS – 20

1. $60°, 120°$ 2. $110°, 70°, 110°$ 3. True 4. 6 cm each 5. No
6. $37°, 143°, 37°, 143°$ 7. 18 cm 8. $a = 30°, b = 35° \ \angle Q = 115°$ 9. 10
10. 4 11. $40°$ 12. $90°$

29. Construction of Special Types of Quadrilaterals

29.1 Construction of Quadrilaterals

Quadrilaterals are constructed by splitting up the figure into two triangles, the construction of which you have already learnt. You know that a quadrilateral has ten parts in all, four sides, four angles and two diagonals. To construct a quadrilateral, we shall need data about five specified parts out of ten.

You are *reminded to draw a rough free hand sketch* in every case before constructing the fair figure.

Case 1. Construction of a quadrilateral when four sides and one diagonal are given.

Ex. 1. *Construct a quadrilateral ABCD in which AB = 4.5 cm, BC = 4 cm, CD = 6.5 cm, DA = 3 cm and BD = 6.5 cm*

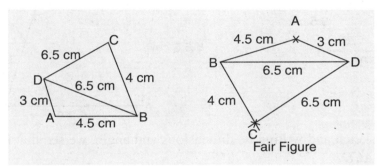

Fair Figure

Sol. Draw a rough sketch of the qudrilateral *ABCD*, and write down its dimensions as shown. Clearly, we may divide it into two triangles *ABD* and *BCD*. It is convenient to draw the diagonal *BD* and construct the two triangles.

Steps of Construction :

1. Draw *BD* = 6.5 cm
2. With *B* as centre and *BA* = 4.5 cm as radius, draw an arc on any side of *BD*.
3. With *D* as centre and *DA* = 3 cm as radius, draw another arc to intersect the arc of step (2) at *A*.
4. With B as centre and BC = 4 cm as radius draw an arc so that the arc and A are on opposite side of BD.
5. With D as centre and DC = 6.5 cm as radius draw another arc to intersect the arc of step (4) at C.
6. Join AB, BC, CD and AD. Then ABCD is the required quadrilateral.

Case 2. When three sides and two diagonals are given.

Ex. 2. *Construct a quadrilateral ABCD in which BC = 4.2 cm CA = 5.8 cm, AD = 4.7 cm, CD = 5.2 cm, and BD = 6.7 cm.*

Sol. We first draw a rough sketch and write the given dimension on it. As clear from the rough sketch, we can divide the quadrilateral into two triangles *DCA* and *DCB* with the three sides of each being known, So, to draw the required quadrilateral, we draw these two triangles.

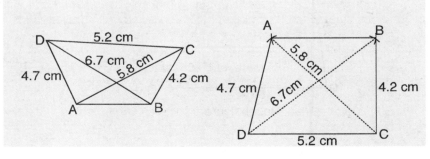

307

Steps of Construction :

1. Draw $DC = 5.2$ cm.
2. With D as centre and radius 6.7 cm draw on arc.
3. With C as centre and radius 4.2 cm, draw another arc intersecting the arc in (2) in B.
4. With D as centre and radius 4 .7 cm draw an arc.
5. With C as centre and radius 5.8 cm, draw an arc intersecting the arc in (4) in A.
6. Join CB, BA and AD.
7. Then $ABCD$ is the required quadrilateral.

Case 3. **When four sides and one angle are given**

Ex. 3. *Construct a quadrilateral ABCD in which AB = 4 cm, BC = 3.5 cm, CD = 5 cm, AD = 5.5 cm and B = 75°.*

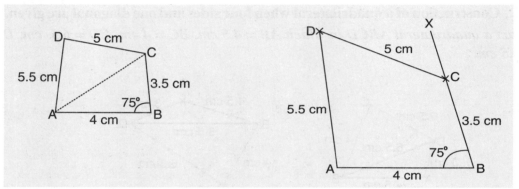

On drawing the rough sketch and writing its dimensions and angle, we see that it can be divided into two triangles ABC and ACD.

Steps of Constructionn :

1. Draw $AB = 4$ cm.
2. Make $\angle ABX = 75°$ and cut off $BC = 3.5$ cm from BX.
3. With A as centre and 5.5 cm radius, draw an arc.
4. With C as centre and radius 5 cm, draw another arc intersecting the arc in step (3) at point D.
5. Join CD and AD. Then $ABCD$ is the required quadrilateral.

Case 4. **When three sides and two included angles are given**

Ex. 4. *Construct a quadrilateral ABCD in which BC = 6 cm, CD = 6 cm, DA = 4 cm, $\angle C = 60°$ and $\angle D = 75°$.*

Sol.

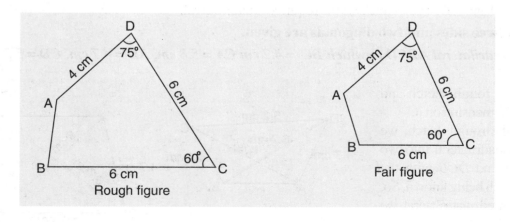

Steps of Construction :

Steps. 1 Draw $BC = 6$ cm.

Steps. 2 Construct $\angle BCD = 60°$ and cut off $CD = 6$ cm.

Steps. 3 Construct $\angle CDA = 75°$ and cut off $DA = 4$ cm.

Steps. 4 Join AB.

Then $ABCD$ is the required quadrilateral.

Case **5**. **When three angles and their included sides are given**

Ex. 5. *Construct a quadrilateral ABCD In which AB = 4.6 cm, BC = 5.3 cm, ∠A = 60°, ∠B = 100° and ∠C = 120°.*

Sol.

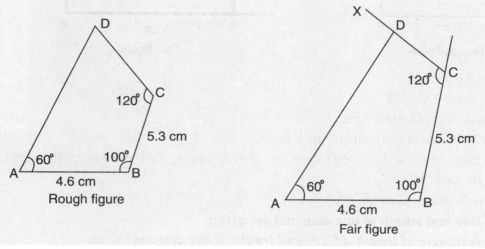

Rough figure   Fair figure

Steps of Construction :

1. Draw $AB = 4.6$ cm.
2. Draw $BC = 5.3$ cm making $ABC = 100°$.
3. Draw CX making $\angle BCD = 120°$.
4. At A draw a line AD making $\angle BAD = 60°$ and meeting CX at D.

Then $ABCD$ is the required quadrilateral.

EXERCISE 29 (a)

Construct a quadrilateral :

1. (*a*) $ABCD$ in which $AB = 3.6$ cm, $BC = 5.5$ cm, $CD = 4.9$ cm, $DA = 5.3$ cm and $AC = 7.2$ cm.

   (*b*) $PQRS$ in which $PQ = 3.5$ cm, $QR = 5.5$ cm, $QS = 5.5$ cm, $PS = 4.5$ cm, and $SR = 4.5$ cm.

2. (*a*) $ABCD$ in which $AB = 4.5$ cm, $BC = 3.5$ cm, $AD = 3$ cm, $AC = 5$ cm and $BD = 4.5$ cm.

   (*b*) Is it possible to construct a quadrilateral $ABCD$ in which $AD = 3$ cm, $CD = 3$ cm, $DA = 7.5$ cm $AC = 8$ cm and $BD = 4$ cm. If not, give reason.

3. (*a*) $ABCD$ in which $AB = 5$ cm, $BC = 4$ cm, $CD = 6$ cm, $AD = 7$ cm, and $\angle B = 80°$

   (*b*) $PQRS$ in which $PQ = QR = 3.5$ cm, $PS = RS = 5.2$ cm and $\angle PQR = 120°$.

4. (*a*) $ABCD$ in which $AB = 4.5$ cm, $CD = 5$ cm, $DA = 3.5$ cm, $\angle C = 120°$ and $\angle D = 75°$.

   (*b*) $PQRS$ in which $PQ = PS = 5$ cm, $RS = 5.5$ cm, $\angle A = 90°$, and $\angle D = 120°$.

5. (*a*) $ABCD$ in which $AB = 5.8$ cm, $BC = 4.2$ cm, $\angle A = 70°$, $\angle B = 110°$ and $\angle C = 105°$

   (*b*) $ABCD$ in which $AB = 6$ cm, $BC = 5$ cm, $\angle A = 55°$, $\angle B = 110°$ and $\angle D = 90°$.

   (**Hints :** $\angle C = 360° - (\angle A + \angle B + \angle D)$)

29.2 Construction of Rectangles

Case 1. Sides are given

Ex. 1. *Construct a rectangle of length 5 cm and breadth 3 cm.*

Sol.

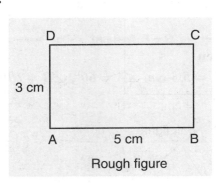

Rough figure

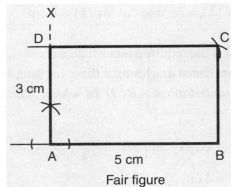

Fair figure

Step 1. Draw $AB = 5$ cm.

Step 2. At A draw $AX \perp AB$.

Step 3. From AX cut off $AD = 3$ cm.

Step 4. With 3 cm radius and centre B draw an arc.

Step 5. With radius 5 cm and centre D, draw another arc cutting the arc drawn in Step 4 at C.

Step 6. Join BC and DC.

Then $ABCD$ is the required rectangle.

Case 2. A side and length of one diagonal are given.

Ex. 2. *Construct a rectangle of length 4.5 cm and length of the diagonal 6 cm.*

Sol.

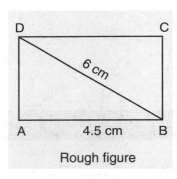

Rough figure

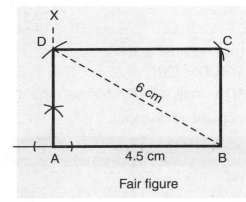

Fair figure

Step 1. Draw $AB = 4.5$ cm.

Step 2. At A draw $AX \perp AB$.

Step 3. With B as centre and radius 6 cm draw an arc cutting AX at D.

Step 4. With B as centre and radius equal to AD draw an arc. With D as centre and radius 4.5 cm draw an arc cutting the previous arc at C.

Step 5. Join BC and DC

Then $ABCD$ is the required rectangle.

29.3 Construction of Squares

Case 1. One side given

Ex.3. *Construct a square of side 4 cm.*

Sol. You can construct a square of given side length in the same manner as you constructed a rectangle.

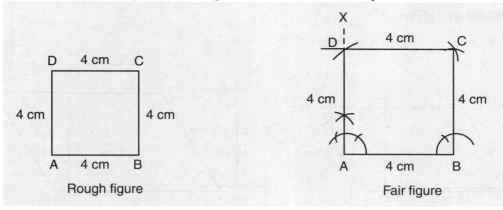

Rough figure   Fair figure

Step 1. Draw $AB = 4$ cm.

Step 2. At A, draw $AX \perp AB$.

Step 3. From AX, cut off $AD = 4$ cm.

Step 4. With B and D as centres and radii 4 cm each, draw two arcs cutting each other at C.

Step 5. Join BC and DC.

Then $ABCD$ is the required square.

Case 2. **A diagonal given.**

Ex. 4. *Construct a square whose one diagonal is 5 cm.*

Sol. *Use the fact that (i) the diagonals of a square are equal. (ii) They bisect each other at right angles.*

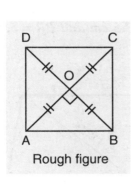

Rough figure

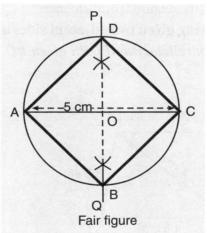

Fair figure

Step 1. Draw a diagonal $AC = 5$ cm.

Step 2. Draw PQ the perpendicular bisector of AC.

Step 3. Let PQ cut AC at O.

Step 4. With O as centre and OA radius draw a circle.

Let this circle cut QP at points B and D.

Step 5. Join AB, BC, CD and DA.

Then $ABCD$ is the required square.

29.4 Parallelogram

Case 1. **Having given adjacent sides and included angle.**

Ex. 5. *Construct a parallelogram ABCD in which AB = 4 cm, BC = 3 cm, ∠A = 60°.*

Sol. In constructing the parallelogram with the given measures, we will use the fact that the opposite sides of a parallelogram are equal.

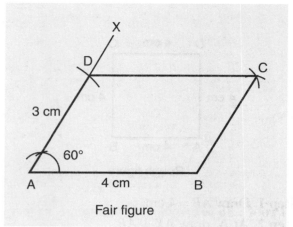

Rough figure   Fair figure

Step 1. Draw $AB = 4$ cm.

Step 2. Through A, draw AX making $\angle BAX = 60°$.

Step 3. From AX, cut off $AD = 3$ cm.

Step 4. With centre D and radius 4 cm, draw an arc.

Step 5. With B as centre and radius, 3 cm draw another arc cutting the arc drawn in Step 4. Name the point as C.

Step 6. Join BC and DC.

Then $ABCD$ is the required parallelogram.

Case 2. **Having given two adjacent sides and one diagonal.**

Ex. 6. *Construct a parallelogram PQRS given PQ = 4.5 cm, QR = 3.5 cm and PR = 5.4 cm.*

Sol.

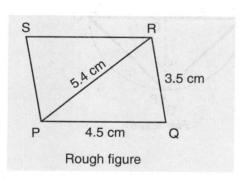 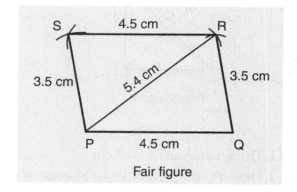

Rough figure   Fair figure

Step 1. Draw $PQ = 4.5$ cm.

Step 2. With Q as centre and radius 3.5 cm draw an arc.

Step 3. With P as centre and radius 5.4 cm, draw another arc cutting the arc drawn in Step 2. Name this point as R.

Step 4. Join QR and PR.

Step 5. With R and P as centres and radii 4.5 cm and 3.5 cm respectively draw two arcs cutting each other. Name this point as S.

Step 6. Join RS and PS.

Then *PQRS* is the required parallelogram.

Case 3. **Having given one side and two diagonals.**

Ex.7. *Construct a parallelogram ABCD with AB = 5 cm, AC = 4.8 cm and BD = 7 cm.*

Sol.

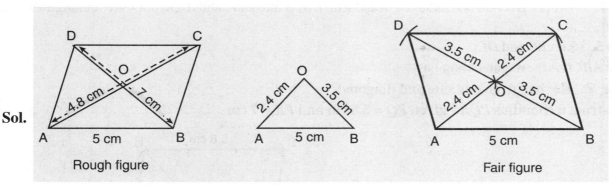

Rough figure   Fair figure

We will use the fact that the diagonals of a parallelogram bisect each other. Thus, $AO = \frac{1}{2}AC = \frac{1}{2} \times 4.8 = 2.4$ cm and $BO = \frac{1}{2}BD = \frac{1}{2} \times 7 = 3.5$ cm. We will, therefore, first construct $\triangle AOB$ with $AB = 5$ cm, $AO = 2.4$ cm and $BO = 3.5$ cm.

Step 1. Draw $AB = 5$ cm.

Step 2. With A as centre and radius 2.4 cm and with B as centre and radius 3.5 cm, draw arcs cutting each other at O.

Step 3. Join AO and BO.

Step 4. Produce AO to C such that $OC = OA = 2.4$ cm.

Step 5. Produce BO to D such that $OD = OB = 3.5$ cm.

Step 6. Join BC, CD and AD.

Then *ABCD* is the required parallelogram.

29.5 Rhombus

Recall that

The sides of a rhombus are equal. The construction of a rhombus is similar to that of a parallelogram. In case of parallelogram, the adjacent sides were given to be different. Here they are equal.

Case I. **Having given one side and an angle.**

Ex. 8. *Construct a rhombus of side 6 cm and ∠A = 60°.*

Sol.

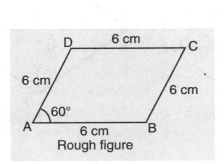

Rough figure

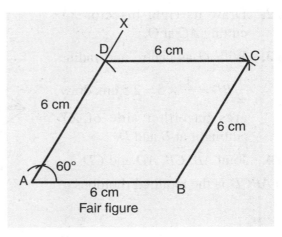

Fair figure

Step 1. Draw $AB = 6$ cm.

Step 2. At A, draw AX making $\angle A = 60°$.

Step 3. From AX, cut off $AD = 6$ cm.

Sep 4. With D as centre and radius 6 cm and with B as centre and radius 6 cm draw arcs cutting each other at C.

Step 5. Join BC and DC.

Then $ABCD$ is the required rhombus.

Case 2. **Having given one side and diagonal**

Ex. 9. **Construct a rhombus $PQRS$ given $PQ = 5.8$ cm and $PR = 7$ cm.**

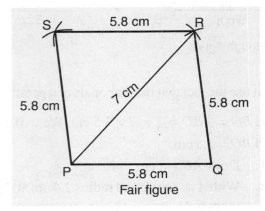

Sol.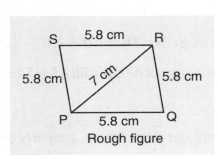

Step 1. Draw $PQ = 5.8$ cm.

Step 2. With P as centre and radius 7 cm and Q as centre and radius 5.8 cm, draw arcs cutting each other at R.

Step 3. With P as centre and radius 5.8 cm and R as centre and radius 5.8 cm, draw arcs cutting each other at S.

Step 4. Join PS and RS

Then $PQRS$ is the required rhombus.

Case 3. **Having given two diagonals.**

Ex.10. *Construct a rhombus ABCD in which AC = 7 cm. and BD = 5 cm.*

Sol. We use the fact that the diagonals of a rhombus bisect each other at right angles.

Step 1. Draw $AC = 7$ cm.

Step 2. Draw its right bisector XY cutting AC at O.

Step 3. With O as centre and radius $\dfrac{1}{2} BD = \dfrac{1}{2} \times 5 = 2.5$ cm, draw arcs on either side of XY cutting it at B and D.

Step 4. Joint AB, CB, AD and CD.

Then $ABCD$ is the required rhombus.

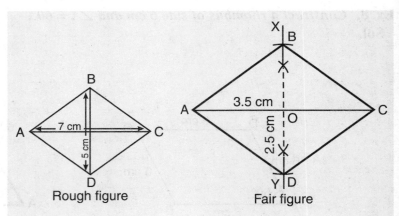

EXERCISE 29 (b)

I. Construct a rectangle *ABCD* given

1. *AB* = 6 cm, *BC* = 5 cm
2. *AB* = 5.8 cm, *BC* = 4.6 cm
3. *AB* = 6.3 cm, *BC* = 5.1 cm
4. *AB* = 7 cm, *BC* =5.5 cm
5. *AB* = 6 cm, *BD* = 8 cm
6. *AB* = 6.4 cm, *AC* = 7.8 cm
7. Construct a rectangle *WXYZ* where *WX* = 5 cm and *WY* = 7cm.
8. The sides of a rectangle are in the ratio 2 : 3, and perimeter is 20 cm. Draw the rectangle.

II. Construct a square *ABCD* :

1. Of side 4.5 cm
2. Of side 5.4 cm
3. *AB* = 6 cm
4. One diagonal = 7 cm
5. One diagonal = 8.3 cm
6. *BD* = 7.5 cm

III. Construct a parallelogram *ABCD* to the following measurements :

1. *AB*= 6.5 cm, *BC* = 5.2 cm and ∠*B* = 45°
2. *AB* = 6.5 cm, *AD* = 5.5 cm, ∠*DAB* = 70°
3. *AB* = 7 cm, *BC* = 5.8 cm, ∠*A* = 120°
4. *AB* = 6.8 cm, *AC* = 8 cm, *BD* = 7.3 cm
5. *AB* = 7 cm, *AC* = 6 cm, *BD* = 9 cm.
6. Construct a parallelogram *PQRS* given *PQ* = 8.2 cm, *PR* = 9.5 cm, *QS* = 10.8 cm.

IV. Construct a rhombus *ABCD* given :

1. *AB* = 6 cm and ∠*A* = 50°
2. *AB* = 7 cm and ∠*A* = 60°
3. *AB* = 7.4 cm and ∠*B* = 72°
4. *AB* = 6.5 cm and ∠*B* = 100°
5. *AB* = 6.8 cm, *AC* = 8 cm
6. *AB* = 7 cm, *AC* = 8.3 cm
7. *AB* = 6.3 cm, *BD* = 7.8 cm
8. *AC* = 6 cm, *BD* = 7cm
9. *AC* = 7 cm, *BD* = 8.5 cm
10. *AC* = 5.8 cm, *BD* = 6.4 cm

ENRICHMENT
Fibonacci Numbers

The first ten Fibonacci numbers are 1, 1, 2, 3, 5, 8, 13, 21, 34, 55, 89, 144,...... Fibonacci numbers are generated by adding together the two previous numbers in the sequence 1 + 1 = 2, 1 + 2 = 3, 2 + 3 = 5, 3 + 5 = 8, 5 + 8 =13, and so on.

Fibonacci numbers are named after Leonardo Fibonacci of Pisa (1170 – 1250) who lived in 13th century Italy. He was nicknamed Fibonacci since he was the son (figlio) of Bonaccio. Can you name next five numbers in the Fibonacci sequence?

Fibonacci numbers have many interesting mathematical properties and can be found in many aspects of the living world, especially in the world of biology.

If you look at the picture of a pine cone you can see a pattern of spirals coming out from the centre. They go in two directions. There are 13 spirals going anticlockwise and 8 going clockwise. Both 8 and 13 are Fibonacci numbers. If you count similar spiral patterns in other plants such as sunflowers you can count much larger Fibonacci numbers.

A very interesting fact is that the number of ancestors of a drone (a male bee) must in any generation be a Fibonacci number. A drone has a mother but no father, as the queen's unfertilised eggs hatch into drones. The queen's fertilised eggs produce either worker bees or queens.

30. Some Theorems on Area

30.1 Area

The amount of surface enclosed by the boundary of a plane closed figure is called its area and is measured in square units.

Congruent figures have equal area, *i.e.*, If ΔABC and ΔPQR are two congruent triangles, then $ar(\Delta ABC) = ar(\Delta PQR)$ but it is not necessary that two figures having equal areas are congruent.

For example :

Area of rectangle having sides 3 cm and 4 cm = 3 cm × 4 cm = 12 cm^2.

Area of a right triangle having base = 6 cm and height 4 cm = $\frac{1}{2}$ × 6 cm × 4 cm = 12 cm^2.

So the rectangle and triangle have equal area but they are not congruent.

30.2 Some Results on Area

Theorem 1: *A diagonal of a parallelogram divides it into two congruent triangles i.e. two triangles of equal area:*

The diagonal *AC* of the given parallelogram *ABCD* divides it into two congruent Δ's *ABC* and *ADC*. Congruent figures have equal area.

$\therefore \quad ar(\Delta ABC) = ar(\Delta ADC)$

Note:

Base of a parallelogram : A base of a parallelogram is any side of it.

Altitude of a parallelogram : For each base of a parallelogram, the corresponding altitude is the line segment from a point on the base, perpendicular to the line containing the opposite side.

If *AB* is the base of the ||gram then *BE* and *AF* are the altitudes.

If we take *AD* as the base then *BM* is the corresponding altitude

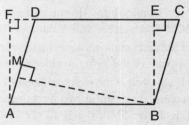

Theorem 2 : *Parallelograms on the same base and between the same parallels are equal in area.*

In the given figure *ABCD* and *ABEF* are two parallelograms on the same base *AB* and between the same parallels *AB* and *FC*.

Area (||gm *ABCD*)= Area (||gm *ABEF*)

Corollary 1: *A parallelogram and a rectangle on the same base and between the same parallels are equal in area. Since a rectangle is also a parallelogram, so the given result directly follows from Theorem 2.*

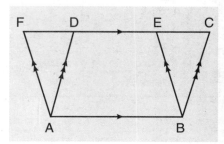

316

∴ Area of ||gm *ABCD*

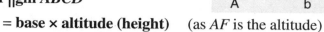

  = Area of rect ∠*ABEF*

  = *b* x *h*

where *AB* = *b*, *AF* = *h*.

⇒ **Area of ||gm *ABCD***

  = **base × altitude (height)**   (as *AF* is the altitude)

Corollary 2 : *Parallelograms with equal bases and between the same parallels are equal in area.*

Two ||grams *ABCD* and *PQRS* whose bases *AB* = *PQ* and they lie between the same ||s *m* and *n* have equal areas.

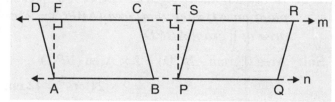

Area of ||gram $ABCD = AB \times AF$ (base × height)

Area of ||gram $PQRS = PQ \times PT$ (base × height)

$AF = PT$ (∵ ⊥ distance between two parallel lines remains the same)

∴   **Area (||gm *ABCD*) = Area (||gm *PQRS*)**

Theorem 3 : *If a triangle and a parallelogram are on the same base and between the same parallels, then the area of the triangle is equal to half the area of the parallelogram.*

Given : Δ*ABE* and ||gram *ABCD* are on the base *AB* and between the parallels *AB* and *DE*.

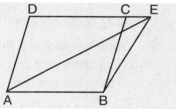

Then, Area (Δ*ABE*) = $\frac{1}{2}$ Area (||gm *ABCD*)

Theorem 4 : *Triangles on the same base and between the same parallels are equal in area.*

Triangles *ABD* and *ABC* are two Δ's on the same base *AB* and between the same parallels *AB* and *CD*.

By Th. 4 Area (Δ*ABD*) = Area (Δ*ABC*)

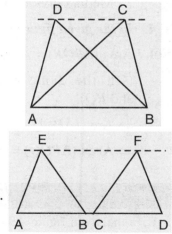

Corollary : *Triangles with equal bases and between the same parallels are equal in area.*

Δ*ABE* and Δ*CDF* have equal bases *AB* and *CD* and are between the same ||'s *AD* and *EF*.

Area (Δ*ABE*) = Area (Δ*CDF*)

(**Note** : The proofs of the above theorems are out of scope of this book).

30.3 Solved Examples

Ex. 1. *In the given figure, ABCD is a rectangle with AB= 6 cm and BC = 8 cm. Find the*

(a) *area of || gram ABEF*

(b) *area of ΔABF*

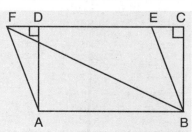

Sol. Area of rectangle *ABCD* = base × height

              = $AB \times BC = 6$ cm × 8 cm = 48 cm^2

(a)   ∵ The rectangle *ABCD* and ‖gm *ABEF* are on the same base *AB* and between the same parallels *AB* and *CF*,

         Area (‖gm *ABEF*) = Area (rect. *ABCD*)   ⇒ Area (‖gm *ABEF*) = **48 cm^2**.

(b)   Area (△*ABF*) = $\frac{1}{2}$ × Area (‖gm *ABEF*)   = $\frac{1}{2}$ × 48 cm^2 = **24 cm^2**.

> ∵ △*ABF* and ‖gm *ABEF* are on the same base AB and between the same parallels *AB* and *CF*.

Ex. 2. *In the adjoining figure, ABCD is a ‖ gram and P is a point on AD such that area (△BPC) = 21cm^2. Find the area of ‖ gram ABCD.*

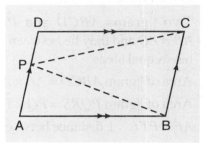

  Sol.   Area (‖gram *ABCD*) = 2 × Area (*BPC*)

                         = 2 × 21 cm^2 = **42 cm^2**.

     (Both are on the same base *BC* and between the same parallels *AD* and *BC*).

Ex. 3. *Show that the median of a triangle divides it into two equal parts.*

  Sol.   Let *AD* be the median of △*ABC*.

     ⇒ *D* is the midpoint of *BC*   ⇒ *BD* = *DC*

     Draw a line *EF* ‖ *BC* passing through *A*. Then △*ABD* and △*ADC* have equal bases *BD* and *DC* and are between the same parallels *EF* and *BC*, so they are equal in area.

     i.e., Area (△*ABD*) = area (△*ADC*).

     ⇒ Median divides a triangle into two △'s of equal area.

Ex. 4. *In the given figure PS ‖ QR. Prove that area (△SOR) = area (△PQO).*

  Sol.   Area (△*PQR*) = Area (△*SRQ*)

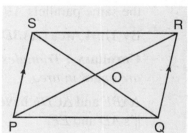

     (On the same base *QR* and between the same parallel *PS* and *RQ*).

     ⇒ Area (△*POQ*) + Area (△*ROQ*) = Area (△*SOR*) + Area (△*ROQ*)

     ⇒ **Area (△*POQ*) = Area (△*SOR*)**.

EXERCISE 30

1. In the given figure *ABCD* is a ‖gram and *ABEF* is a rectangle with *EF* = 7cm and *AF* = 4 cm. Find the area of ‖gram *ABCD*.

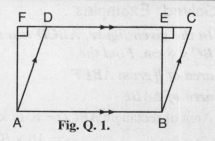

Fig. Q. 1.

2. $\triangle PQR$ is right angled $\triangle$ with $\angle P = 90°$ $PQ = 5$ cm and $PR = 3$ cm. Find the area of the obtuse angled triangle PSQ when $SR \parallel PQ$.

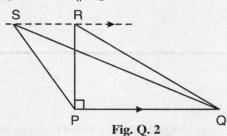

Fig. Q. 2

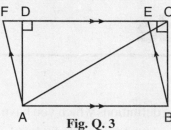

Fig. Q. 3

3. Given $ABCD$ a rectangle, $ABEF$ a ∥gram and a right triangle ADC. Given the area of the right $\triangle ADC = 17.5$ cm^2, Find (a) area (rectangle $ABCD$)   (b) area (∥gram $ABEF$).

4. In the given figure, $ST \parallel PQ$. Show that area $(\triangle PRT)$ = area $(\triangle QSR)$.

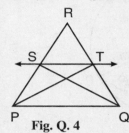

Fig. Q. 4

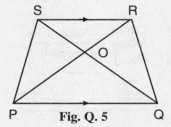

Fig. Q. 5

5. $PQRS$ is a trapezium with $PQ \parallel RS$, and the diagonals PR and QS intersect at O. Prove that area $(\triangle POS)$ = area (QOR).

6. In the figure, $ABCD$ and $ABEF$ are two parallelograms. Area of ∥gram $ABEF = 64$ cm^2. If $CD = 10$ cm, find the height of ∥gram $ABCD$.

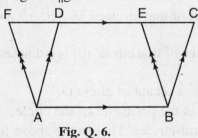

Fig. Q. 6.

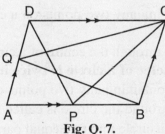

Fig. Q. 7.

7. In the adjoining figure $ABCD$ is a parallelogram. P is a point on AB and Q on AD. Prove that Area $(\triangle PDC)$ = area $(\triangle BQC)$.

LOOKING BACK
Summary of Key Facts

1. Parallelograms on the same base and between the same parallels are equal in area.

2. If a triangle and a parallelogram are on the same base and between the same parallels, then

    Area of the triangle = $\dfrac{1}{2}$ area of the parallelogram.

3. Two triangles on the same base and between the same parallels are equal in area.

ANSWERS

EXERCISE 30

1. 28 cm^2 2. 7.5 cm^2 3. (a) 35 cm^2 (b) 35 cm^2 6. 6.4 cm

31. Circle

31.1 Definitions

Recall the following definitions which you have learnt in earlier classes.

1. A **circle** is a simple closed curve all of whose points are at a constant distance from a fixed point in the same plane. The fixed point is called the **centre** of the circle.

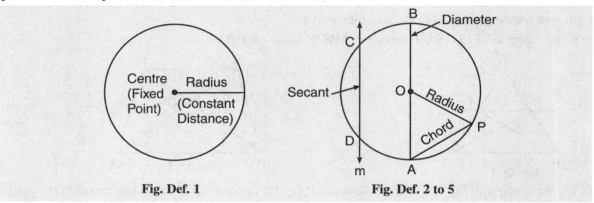

Fig. Def. 1   **Fig. Def. 2 to 5**

2. A line segment joining the centre of circle with any point on the circle is called a **radius** (plural radii) of that circle. *OA*, *OB*, *OP* are all radii of the circle *O*.
3. A line segment joining any two points on a circle is called a **chord** of that circle. *CD*, *AB*, *AP* are the chords of circle *O*.
4. A chord that passes through the centre of a circle is called a **diameter** of that circle, *AB* is a diameter of circle *O*. **The diameter of a circle is twice its radius.**
5. A **secant** is a line containing any two points on the circle. Line *m* is a secant of circle *O*.
6. The distance right around the circle is called its **circumference**. It is the perimeter of the circle.
7. A diameter divides a circle into two equal parts which are called **semi-circles**. Thus in the above figure *ACBOA* is one semi-circle and *APBOA* is the other semi-circle.
8. **Arc and segment.** An arc is a curved line which is part of the circumference. A chord *AB* of a circle divides the circle into two parts which are called **segments**. The smaller part is called the **minor segment** and the larger part **the major segment.** The chord also divides the circumference of the circle into two parts. The smaller part is called a **minor arc** because it is less than semi-circle and the larger part a **major arc** because it is greater that semi-circle.

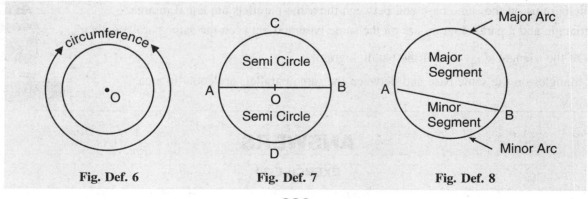

Fig. Def. 6   **Fig. Def. 7**   **Fig. Def. 8**

9. **Sector of a circle:** A sector of a circle is a region bounded by an arc of the circle and the two radii to the endpoints of the arc. One sector OAB (shaded region) is shown in this figure.

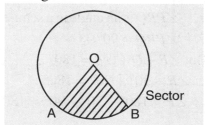

10. **Tangent of a circle :** A straight line which cuts a circle at two distinct points is called a **secant**.

A st. line which has one and only one point in common with a circle, however far either way it is produced, is called a **tangent** of the circle, and the common point is called the **point of contact.** *XY* in Fig. (*ii*) is a tangent and the point *A* is the point of contact.

> **Note :** (1) One and only one tangent can be drawn to a circle at a point on it.
>
> (2) We can draw tangents only from a point outside the circle.
>
> (3) Two tangents can be drawn from a point outside a circle. Thus in the above figure we have *XY* and *XZ* are two tangents to the given circle from the external point *X*.

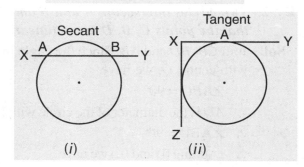

(i) (ii)

31.2 Angle in a Semi-circle

Draw a circle with centre *O*. Draw its diameter *AB*. Then *AXB* and *AYB* are two semi-circles. Mark any point *C* on the semi-circle *AXB*. Join *AC* and *CB*. Then, ∠*ACB* is said to be an angle in a semi-circle.

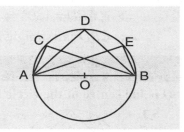

Activity. Draw two circles with centres *O* and *M*. Draw a diameter in each of these circles. Then each circle, is divided into two semi-circles.

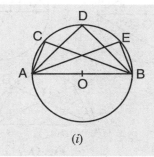

(i)

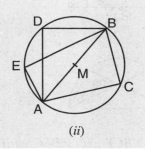

(ii)

Take any three different points *C*, *D* and *E* in each of these semi-circles. Join each of these points with *A* and *B*. Now, measure angles *C*, *D* and *E* and record your result as under :

Figure	∠C	∠D	∠E	Conclusion : Is ∠C = ∠D = ∠E = 90° ?
Fig. (*i*)	.....	.....	.....	yes/no
Fig. (*ii*)	.....	.....	.....	yes/no

Hence, we have the following result.

> *Angle in a semi-circle is a right angle.*

Ex. 1. *In the adjoining figure, O is the centre of the circle and ∠Q = 30°. Find ∠P.*

Sol. *PQ* passes through the centre *O* ∴ *PQ* is a diameter.

∴ ∠*PRQ* is an angle in a semi-circle

∴ ∠*PRQ* = 90°

But ∠*P* + *Q* + ∠*R* = 180° (angle sum property of a Δ)

∴ ∠*P* + 30° + 90° = 180°.

⇒ ∠*P* = 180° − 30° − 90° = 180° − 120° = **60°**.

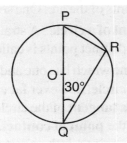

Ex. 2. *Two circles intersect in A and B and AC and AD are respectively the diameters of the circles, prove that the points C, B, D are collinear.*

Sol. Join *CB*, *BD* and *AB*. Since the angle in a semi circle is a right angle and *AC* is the diameter of the circle with centre *O*, we have

∠*ABC* = 90° ...(i)

AD is the diameter of the circle with centre *O′* ;

∴ ∠*ABD* = 90° ...(ii)

∴ Adding (i) and (ii) we have

∠*ABC* + ∠*ABD* = 90° + 90° = 180°

⇒ ∠*CBD* = 180° ⇒ ∠*CBD* is a straight angle

⇒ *CBD* is a straight line. ⇒ *C*, *B* and *D* are collinear.

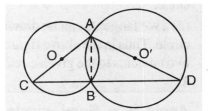

EXERCISE 31

O is the centre of the circle in each figure. Find the size of each lettered angle.

1.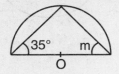
2.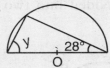
3.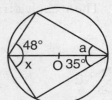
4.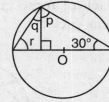

5.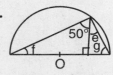
6.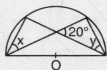

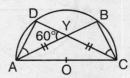

7. If AY = CY, find *(a)* ∠*DAY* *(b)* ∠*BCY* *(c)* ∠*BAC* *(d)* ∠*DCA* **Fig. Q. 7**

ANSWERS

EXERCISE 31

1. *m* = 55° 2. *y* = 62° 3. *a* = 42°, *x* = 55° 4. *p* = 60°, *q* = 30°, *r* = 60°

5. *e* = 40°, *f* = 40°, *g* = 50° 6. *x* = 70°, *y* = 70°

7. *(a)* 30° *(b)* 30° *(c)* 30° *(d)* 30°

32. Constructions

We shall review some basic constructions which are used quite often in geometry.

32.1 To Construct an Angle Equal to the Given Angle ABC at a Point Q Outside it.

Step 1: Draw a ray QR.

Step 2 : With B as centre and a convenient radius draw an arc which cuts AB at F and BC at E.

Step 3 : With Q as centre and the same radius as in step 2, draw an arc of sufficient length cutting QR at M.

Step 4 : With M as centre and radius = EF, draw an arc cutting the previous arc at N.

Step 5 : Join QN and extend it to form ray QP.

Then, $\angle PQR$ is the required angle, equal to $\angle ABC$.

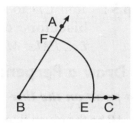

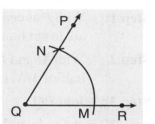

32.2 To Bisect a Given Angle ABC

Step 1: With B as centre and a suitable radius, draw an arc that intersects BA and BC. Name the points of intersection as P and Q.

Step 2 : With P as centre and a radius greater than half PQ draw an arc.

Step 3 : With Q as centre and the same radius draw another arc to cut the first arc. Name the point of intersection of the two arcs as R.

Step 4 : Join BR. The ray BR bisects $\angle ABC$. It is called the angle bisector.

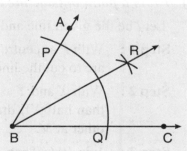

32.3 To Draw the Perpendicular Bisector of a Given Line Segment

Let AB be the given line segment.

Step 1: With A as centre and radius equal to more than half the length of AB draw two arcs one above AB and one below AB.

Step 2 : With B as centre and the same radius (as in step1), draw two arcs to cut the first two arcs. Name the points of intersection as P and Q.

Step 3 : Join PQ to cut AB at M. Measure AM and MB.

$AM = MB$ and $\angle PMA = \angle PMB = 90°$

$\therefore PQ$ is the perpendicular bisector of AB.

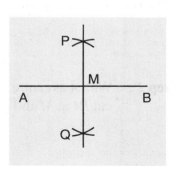

32.4 To Bisect a Given line Segment

Step 1 : Given a line segment *PQ*, draw any angle *APQ* at *P*.

Step 2 : At *Q*, construct ∠*PQB* = ∠*APQ* on the other side of line *PQ*.

Step 3 : With *P* as centre and any suitable radius, draw an arc to meet *PA* at *C*.

Step 4 : From *Q* cut off *DQ* = *PC*.

Step 5 : Join *CD* to meet *PQ* at *M*. Then *CD* is the bisector of the line segment *PQ*, i.e., *PM* = *MQ*.

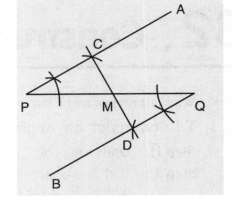

32.5 To Draw a Perpendicular to a Given Line

(a) *At a point on the line*

Let *AB* be the given line segment and *P* a point on it.

Step 1: With *P* as centre and any suitable radius draw an arc to cut line *AB* at points *M* and *N*.

Step 2 : With *M* and *N* as centres and radius more than half of *MN*, draw two arcs to intersect at *Q*.

Step 3 : Join *PQ*.

Ray *PQ* is the perpendicular to the line *AB* at *P*.

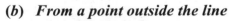

(b) *From a point outside the line*

Let *l* be the given line and *P* a point outside it.

Step 1 : With *P* as centre and a suitable radius, draw an arc to cut the line *l* at *X* and *Y*.

Step 2 : With *X* and *Y* as centres and a radius of more than half *XY*, draw two arcs to intersect each other at *M*.

Step 3 : Join *PM*. Then *PM* ⊥ *l*.

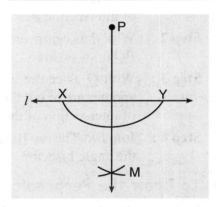

32.6 To Construct a Line Parallel to a Given Line From a Point Outside it

Let *l* be a given line and *P* a given point outside it.

Step 1: Mark any point *A* on *l* and join *PA*.

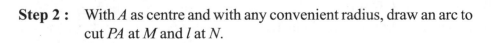

Step 2 : With *A* as centre and with any convenient radius, draw an arc to cut *PA* at *M* and *l* at *N*.

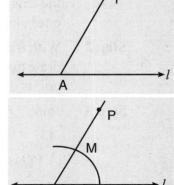

Step 3 : With P as centre and with the same radius draw an arc to cut PA at B.

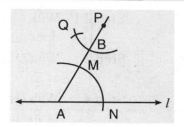

Step 4 : With B as centre and MN as radius draw an arc to cut the previous arc at Q.

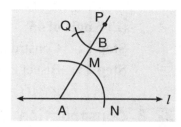

Step 5 : Joint PQ and produce it bothways. Then line m as shown is parallel to given line l.

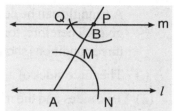

32.7 Construction of Angle 30°, 60°, 90° and 45°

- **Angle of 60°**
  Step 1 : Draw any line segment AB.
  Step 2 : With A as centre and any suitable radius draw an arc to meet AB at C.
  Step 3 : With C as centre and the same radius (as in step 2) draw an arc to meet the previous arc at D.
  Step 4 : Join AD and produce it to E. Then, $\angle EAB = 60°$

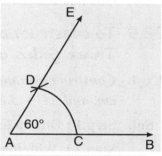

- **Angle of 30°**
  Step 1 : Draw a ray OA.
  Step 2 : With O as the vertex, construct $\angle AOB$ of 60°.
  Step 3 : Bisect $\angle AOB$. OC is the bisector. Then, $\angle AOC = 30°$, $\angle COB = 30°$.

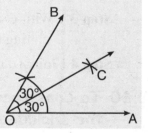

- **To construct angles of 90° and 45°.**

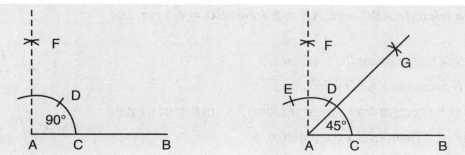

(i) **Angle of 90°**
Step 1 : With A as centre and any suitable radius draw an arc cutting AB at C.

Step 2 : With C as centre and the same radius as in step 1 draw an arc cutting the previous arc at D.

Step 3 : With D as centre and same radius, cut the arc again at E.

Step 4 : With D and E as centres and any convenient radius (same for both) draw arcs cutting at F. Join A and F. Then $\angle FAB = 90°$.

(ii) Angle of 45°

Step 1 : Construct $\angle FAB = 90°$.

Step 2 : Bisect $\angle FAB$. AG is the bisector.
$\angle FAG = \angle GAB = 45°$.

32.8 Construction of Triangles

A triangle can be constructed if three of its six elements are given. Therefore, for the construction of a triangle any of these three conditions should be fulfilled.

(i)   The three sides of a triangle are given.

(ii) Two sides and the included angle are given.

(iii) One side and two angles are given.

32.9 To construct a Triangle when the Lengths of Three Sides are Given.

Ex. 1. *Construct a triangle ABC with AB = 6.2 cm, BC = 5.2 cm, and AC = 5.8 cm.*

Sol. **Step 1 :** Draw a line segment $BC = 5.2$ cm.

Step 2 : With B as centre and radius 6.2 ($= AB$) cm draw an arc.

Step 3 : With C as centre and radius 5.8 cm ($= AC$) draw another arc cutting the previous arc at A.

Step 4 : Join AB and AC. Then $\triangle ABC$ is the required $\triangle$.

32.10 To Construct a Triangle when Length of Two Sides and the Included Angle are given

Ex.2. *Construct a triangle ABC with AB = 5.4 cm, BC = 4.5 cm and ∠B = 75°*

Sol. **Step 1:** Draw a line segment $BC = 4.5$ cm.

Step 2 : At B construct $\angle CBD = 75°$.

Step 3 : With B as centre draw an arc of radius 5.4 cm to cut BD at A.

Step 4 : Join AC. Then ABC is the required $\triangle$.

EXERCISE 32 (a)

1. **With the help of ruler and compasses construct the following angles:**
   (a) 30° (b) 45° (c) 105°
   (d) 135° (e) 75° (f) 37.5°

   (g) 150° (h) 15° (i) $22\frac{1}{2}°$

   (j) 52.5° (k) 172.5°

2. Construct a right angle and construct two lines dividing the right angle into three equal angles.

3. Draw an obtuse angle. Divide it into four equal angles.

4. Draw a line segment $AB = 6.4$ cm. Construct its perpendicular bisector.

5. **Draw a line segment AB = 5.6 cm. Draw a perpendicular to it.**
   (a) From a point P on it such that $AP = 2.4$ cm.
   (b) From a point P outside it.

6. Draw a line segment $PQ = 4$ cm. Construct a line segment parallel to it.

7. Draw a line segment $PQ = 4.8$ cm and divide it into two equal parts.

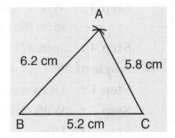

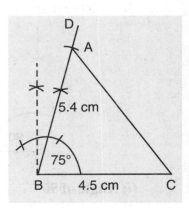

32.11 To Construct a Triangle When one Side and Two Angles are Given.

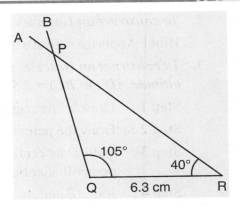

Ex. 3. *Construct a triangle PQR with QR = 6.3 cm* ∠Q = 105° *and* ∠R = 40°.

Sol. **Step 1:** Draw a line segment QR = 6.3 cm.

Step 2 : At Q, construct ∠BQR = 105°.

Step 3 : At R draw ∠ARQ = 40° with the protractor.

Step 4 : Let BQ and AR intersect at P. Then PQR is the required triangle.

32.12 Construction of Special Types of Triangles

A. **Equilateral Triangles**

1. **To construct an equilateral ΔABC when AB = 5 cm i.e. when the side is given.**

   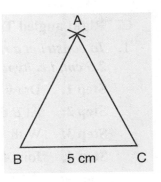

   Construction : Apply the case when the three sides of a triangle are given.

   Draw BC equal to 5 cm. With B and C as centres and radius equal to 5 cm draw arcs of circles cutting each other at A. Join AB and AC. Then ΔABC is the required equilateral triangle.

   > **Note :** In more complicated constructions it is advisable to draw a rough figure before constructing a fair figure.

2. **To construct an equilateral triangle having given the altitude, say, equal to 4 cm.**

   Construction : First we draw a rough figure and from the rough figure we evolve the following method:

   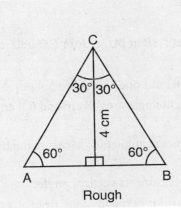
   Rough

   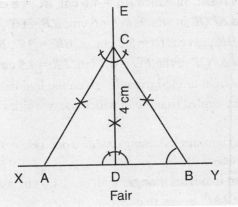
   Fair

   Construction :

   Step 1. Draw a st. line XY.

   Step 2. At any point D on it draw DE perpendicular to XY. Cut off DC = 4 cm.

   Step 3. At C, on each side of CD, construct angles DCA and DCB, each equal to 30°. Let CA and CB meet XY in A and B respectively. Then ΔABC is required equilateral triangle.

B. **Isosceles Triangles**

1. **To construct an isosceles triangle ABC with base BC = 4 cm and AB = AC = 5.3 cm.**

   Hint : Apply the case when the three sides of triangle are given.

2. *To construct an isosceles △ABC with base AB = 4.5 cm and each base angle of 45°.*

    Hint : Apply the case of a triangle with two angles and the included side.

3. *To construct an isosceles triangle ABC such that base BC = 4 cm and altitude AD (to BC) = 2.5 cm.*

    Step 1 :   Draw a line segment *BC* = 4 cm.

    Step 2 :   Draw the perpendicular bisector of *BC* meeting *BC* at *D*.

    Step 3 :   With *D* as centre cut off *DA* = 2.5 cm on the perpendicular bisector.

    Step 4 :   Join *AB* and *AC*.

    Then △*ABC* is the required triangle.

4. *To construct an isosceles triangle ABC with AB = AC = 5 cm and the vertical angle A = 75°.*

    Take *AB* as the base and then apply the case when two sides and included angle are given.

C. Right angled Triangles.

1. *To construct a rt, ∠d △ABC, rt. ∠d at B, when AC = 4.1 cm and AB = 2.5 cm, i.e. hypotenuse and one side are given.*

    Step 1.   Draw a st. line *AB* = 2.5 cm.

    Step 2.   At *B* draw the line *BE* perpendicular to *AB*,

    Step 3.   With *A* as centre and radius 4.1 cm, draw an arc to cut *BE* at *C*.

    Step 4.   Join *AC*.

    Then *rt. ∠d △ABC,* is the required triangle.

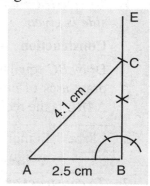

EXERCISE 32 (b)

1. Construct a △*ABC* in which *AB* = 4.6 cm, *BC* = 6 cm and *AC* = 5 cm.

2. Construct a △*PQR* in which *PQ* = 6 cm, ∠*P* = 60°, ∠*Q* = 75°.

3. Draw a △*ABC*, given *AB* = 5.2 cm, ∠*ABC* = 75°, *BC* = 4.7 cm. Bisect *AB* at pt. *M*. Join *CM* and measure it.

4. Construct a △*PQR* given *PQ* = 6.7 cm, *PR* = 4.5 cm, ∠*Q* = 60°.

5. Construct a right-angled triangle, given the hypotenuse, *BC* = 7.5 cm, and one side *AB* = 5.4 cm. Measure *AC*.

6. Draw a right-angled triangle in which the two sides containing the right angle are 4.8 cm and 6.9 cm. Measure the hypotenuse.

7. Construct a right-angled triangle whose one side = 3.2 cm and the adjacent angle 60°. Measure the hypotenuse and the other side.

8. Construct an isosceles triangle with base 4.6 cm, and height 5 cm. Measure its vertical angle.

9. Construct △*ABC*, given that ∠*A* = 70°, ∠*C* = 35° and the length of the perpendicular from *A* on *BC* is 5 cm. Measure *BC*.

10. Construct an equilateral triangle *ABC* having an altitude of 4.2 cm. Measure it sides.

11. Construct an isosceles triangle with equal sides as 5.2 cm each and the vertical angle as 60°.

12. Construct an isosceles right angled triangle with hypotenuse = 6 cm.

    (Hint : Take hyp. as the base and the base ∠s = 45° each)

13. Construct an equilateral triangle *ABC* with each side = 5 cm. Draw the three altitudes and show by measurement that they are equal.

14. Construct an isosceles triangle *PQR* with base = 6.5 cm and base angles as 45° and 30°.

32.13 Constructions of Circles

Ex. 1. *Construct two concentric circles of radii 2.5 cm and 3.5 cm.*

Construction

Step 1. With *O* as centre and radius 2.5 cm , draw a circle.

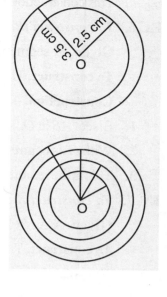

Step 2. With the same centre *O*, and radius 3.5 cm, draw another circle.

> **Note:** Taking the same centre *O*, and taking radii of different lengths you can draw as many concentric circles as you like.

Ex. 2. *Construct two circles of radii 2 cm and 3 cm touching externally.*

Sol. Since the circles touch externally, the distance between their centres = sum of their radii = 2 + 3 = 5 cm.

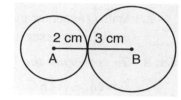

Step 1. Draw a line segment *AB* = 5 cm.

Step 2. With *A* as centre and radius 2 cm, draw a circle.

Step 3. With *B* as centre and radius 3 cm, draw another circle.

The second circle will touch the first circle externally.

Ex. 3. *Construct two circles of radius 1.5 cm and 1 cm touching internally.*

Sol. Since the two circles touch internally, therefore, distance between their centres = difference of their radii = 1.5 cm – 1 cm = 0.5 cm.

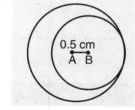

Step 1. Draw a line segment *AB* = 0.5 cm.

Step 2. With *A* as centre and radius 1.5 cm, draw a circle.

Step 3. With *B* as centre and radius 1 cm, draw another circle.

Then the second circle will touch the first circle internally.

Ex. 4. *To construct the centre of a circle, an arc of which is given.*

Given. An arc *AB* of the circle.

To construct. The centre of the circle.

Construction.

Step 1. Take any three points *P*, *Q* and *R* on the arc *AB*.

Step 2. Construct the perpendicular bisectors *LM* and *XY* of the chords *PQ* and *QR* respectively intersecting each other at *O*.

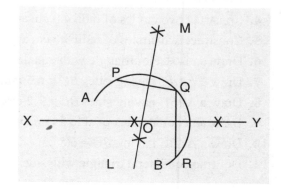

The *O* is the required centre.

Ex. 5. *To construct the circle passing through three non-collinear points.*

This construction is just like construction (2) above.

Ex. 6. *To construct the circle on a given segment as a diameter.*

Given. A segment *AB*.

To construct. The circle on *AB* as a diameter.

Construction.

1. Bisect *AB* at *O*.

2. With *O* as centre and radius equal to *OA* draw the circle.

3. This is the required circle.

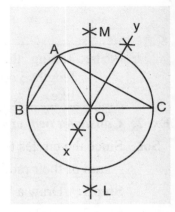

Ex. 7. *To construct the circumcircle of a given triangle.*

Given. A △*ABC*.

To construct. The circumcircle of △*ABC*.

Construction.

1. Draw *LM* and *XY* the perpendicular bisectors of *BC* and *AC* respectively meeting each other at *O*.

2. With *O* as centre and *OA* as radius draw the circle. Then this is the required circle that passes through *A*, *B*, *C*.

Ex. 8. *To construct the inscribed circle of a given triangle.*

Given. A △*ABC*.

To construct. The inscribed circle of △*ABC*.

Construction.

1. Draw *BE* and *CF* bisector of ∠*B* and ∠*C* respectively meeting each other at *I*. Draw *IL* perpendicular to *BC*.

2. With *I* as centre and *IL* as radius draw the circle.

Then this is the required inscribed circle of △*ABC*.

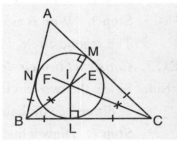

EXERCISE 32 (c)

1. Draw a circle with radius 6.4 cm.

2. Draw a circle with diameter 8.2 cm.

3. Draw concentric circles of radii 5.8 cm and 4.3 cm. Find the width of the ring.

4. Construct two circles of radii 4.3 cm and 5.7 cm touching externally.

5. Construct two circles of radii 3.5 cm and 2.4 cm touching internally.

6. Draw an isosceles triangle with equal sides as 5.5 cm and the vertical angle 60°. Draw its circum circle.

7. Draw a △*ABC* having sides *BC* = 6.5 cm, *AB* = 5.4 cm, *AC* = 7 cm. Draw its circum-circle.

8. Draw a △*ABC* having sides *BC* = 7.2 cm, *AB* = 6.3 cm, *AC* = 5.8 cm. Draw its incircle.

9. Draw an equilateral △ of side 5 cm. Draw its circum-circle.

10. Draw a △*ABC* having *BC* = 6.8 cm, ∠*B* = 70°, ∠*C* = 80°. Draw its in-circle.

11. Draw an equilateral triangle with side 5.6 cm. Draw its in-circle.

33. Linear Symmetry, Reflection and Rotation

SYMMETRY

33.1 Introduction

You have studied in detail about the concepts of symmetry, reflection and rotation in class VII. We intend to help you in this Chapter to revise and strengthen your understanding of what you have already learnt there.

33.2 Line Symmetry

The following pictures show objects which are symmetrical about the dotted line. Each part on the left of the dotted line has a mirror image on the right.

Activity 1. If you fold a rectangular sheet of paper *ABCD* along the line *PQ*, the one half *PQCD* will fit exactly over the other half *PQBA*.

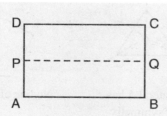 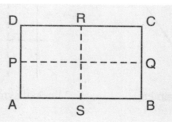

The rectangle *ABCD* is said to be symmetrical about the line *PQ* which is called the **line** or an **axis** of symmetry. Besides *PQ*, the line *RS* is another line of symmetry. Thus, a rectangle has two lines of symmetry.

Activity 2. Draw an isosceles trapezium *ABCD*. Draw line *EF* through points *E* and *F* which are the mid-points of *AB* and *DC* respectively.

Fold the figure about the line *EF*, you will find that

(*i*)   the points *A* and *D* coincide with the points *B* and *C* respectively;

(*ii*) the line segments *EA*, *AD* and *DF* coincide with the line segments *EB*, *BC* and *FC* respectively; and

(*iii*) the two angles *EAD* and *ADF* coincide with the two angles *EBC* and *BCF* respectively.

We therefore conclude that the portion *EADF* of the trapezium is exactly half of the trapezium *ABCD* and is equal (congruent) to the other half portion *EBCF*. Also, if you place a mirror MN along the line of symmetry *EF*, you will observe that

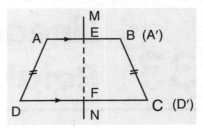

(a) the mirror images of *A* and *D* are *A'* and *D'*, which coincide with the points *B* and *C* respectively; and

(b) the mirror images of *EA*, *AD* and *DF* coincide with *EB*, *BC* and *CF* respectively.

> *When a straight line divides a shape into two identical (congruent) shapes the shape is symmetrical about the line. The line is called a line or axis of symmetry. It is usually shown by a dotted line. Each side of one portion is the mirror image of the other.*

33.3 Number of Lines of Symmetry

Take a square piece of paper. Find the several lines of symmetry through folding.

In (a) and (b) the line of symmetry separates the square into two symmetric rectangles. In (c) and (d) the line of symmetry separates the square into two equal (congruent) triangles.

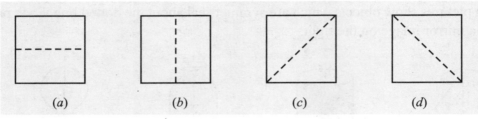

Thus, a square has four lines of symmetry.

> *A figure may have one line of symmetry, two lines of symmetry, three or more lines of symmetry or no line of symmetry.*

Ex. 1.

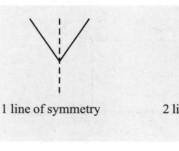

1 line of symmetry   2 lines of symmetry   An equilateral △ has 3 lines of symmetry   No line of symmetry

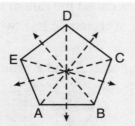 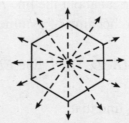 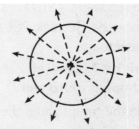

A regular pentagon has 5 lines of symmetry

A regular hexagon has 6 lines of symmetry (along the diagonals and mid-way lines)

A circle has infinite number of lines of symmetry (each line passing through the centre.

Ex. 2. *Part of a geometrical figure is given in each of the diagrams below. Complete the figures so that the dotted line in each case is a line of symmetry of the completed figure.*

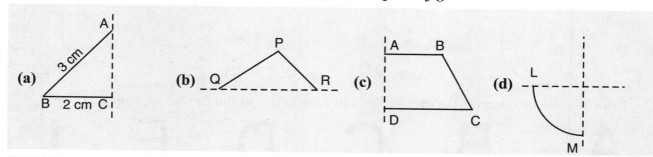

Sol.

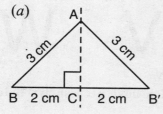 

EXERCISE 33 (a)

1. **Examine the following shapes and tell which of these have a line or lines of symmetry and which do not have any line of symmetry ?**

(a)   (b)   (c) 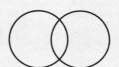 (d)

(e) **Y** (f) **N** (g)   (h) **O**

2. Draw the lines of symmetry in each of the following figures :

(a)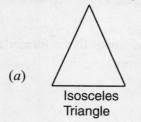
Isosceles
Triangle

(b)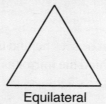
Equilateral
Triangle

(c)
Square

(d)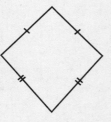
Kite

(e)
An arrowhead

(f)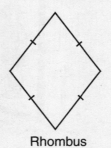
Rhombus

(g)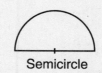
Semicircle

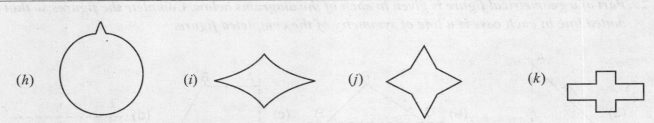

(h)   (i)   (j)   (k)

3. **Draw the line of symmetry in each of the following letters of the English alphabet.**

A   B   C   D   E   I

K   M   T   U   V   W

4. Name the seven letters of the English alphabet which have no line of symmetry.

5. Complete the following figures about the given lines of symmetry, which have been shown by dotted lines.

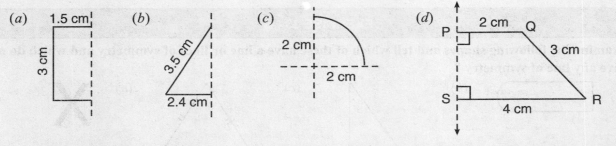

(a) 1.5 cm   3 cm   (b) 3.5 cm 2.4 cm   (c) 2 cm 2 cm   (d) P 2 cm Q 3 cm S 4 cm R

6. Construct a triangle in which $AB = 5.3$ cm, $\angle A = 45°$ and $\angle B = 90°$. Draw its line (or lines) of symmetry.

SECTION B

REFLECTION

33.4 Introduction

The child is looking into the mirror. The image that he sees behind the mirror is the image that is formed after reflection in the mirror. An image in the mirror is as far behind the mirror as the object in front.

The picture of butterfly given in the picture was made after reflecting a shape in the mirror.

You know from physics that if A' is the image of A upon reflection in mirror M then the line m is the **perpendicular bisector** of the line 'AA''. The line m is called the mirror line or the **reflection line.** If A' is the image of A after reflection in the line m then the point A is called the **pre-image** of the point A'.

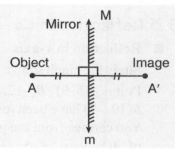

A **reflection** *in a line produces a* **mirror image.** *In a reflection the image is the same size and each point on it is the same perpendicular distance from the axis of reflection as the corresponding point on the object.*

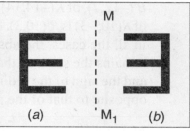

Ex. 1. *Draw the reflection of the given shape ABCDEF in the dashed mirror line.*

Sol. A and F which lie on the mirror line are their own images. The image of B is B' which is at the same perpendicular distance from the mirror line m as B. Similarly, points C', D' and E' are at the same distance from line m as C, D and E respectively.

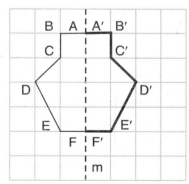

EXERCISE 33 (b)

1. **Copy the figure and show the images which result from reflection in the line m.**

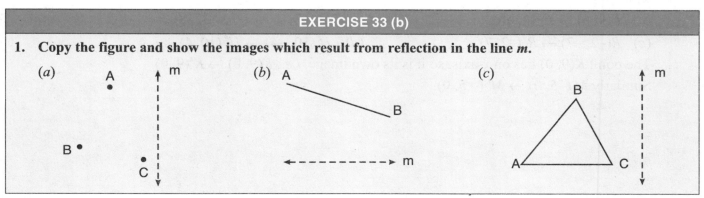

2. **Complete the given shapes after drawing the images of the given portions in the mirror line. Name the complete shape so formed.**

> **Ex.** The first one is a kite.

(a)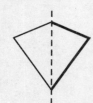

(b)

(c)

(d)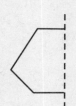

33.5 Reflection in Co-ordinate Axes

■ **Reflection in x-axis**

Study the graph shown here.

Points $A(5, 9)$, $B(-12, -7)$, $K(-14, 14)$ and $R(10, -3)$ have been reflected in the x-axis. You can see from the graph that the image of $A(5, 9)$ is $A'(5, -9)$, of $B(-12, -7)$ is $B'(-12, 7)$, of $K(-14, 14)$ is $K'(-14, -14)$ and of $R(10, -3)$ is $R'(10, 3)$. Do you observe that in all the cases, the abscissa in the image remains the same as that of the pre-image and the sign of the ordinate in the image is opposite to that of the pre-image.

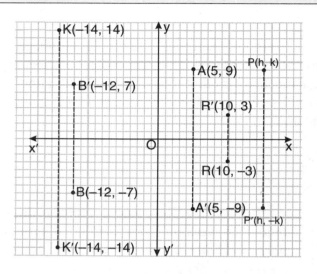

In general the image of any point $P(h, k)$ after reflection in x-axis is $P'(h, -k)$ that is the sign of the ordinate is changed.

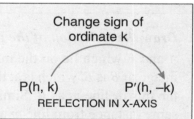

Change sign of ordinate k

$P(h, k)$ → $P'(h, -k)$

REFLECTION IN X-AXIS

Ex. 1. *Write the coordinates of the following points when reflected in x-axis.*

(a) $P(4, 6)$ (b) $Q(-3, 8)$ (c) $R(-2, -7)$
(d) $H(10, -4)$ (e) $K(9, 0)$ (f) $M(-5, 0)$

Sol. You know that after reflection in x-axis, the image of any point $A(h, k)$ is $A(h, -k)$. After reflection in x-axis

(a) $P(4, 6) \rightarrow P'(4, -6)$, (b) $Q(-3, 8) \rightarrow Q'(-3, -8)$
(c) $R(-2, -7) \rightarrow R'(-2, 7)$ (d) $H(10, -4) \rightarrow H'(10, 4)$

The point $K(9, 0)$ lies on x-axis, so it is its own image *i.e.*, $K(9, 0) \rightarrow K'(9, 0)$.
Similarly $M(-5, 0) \rightarrow M'(-5, 0)$.

33.6 Reflection in y-axis

Study the graph shown below :

The image of point P(8, 17) after reflection in y-axis is P(–8, 17), that of T(–5, 8) is T '(5, 8), that of G (10, –9) is G '(–10, –9) and of N(–14, –13) is N ' (14, –13).

In all these cases, the ordinate in the image remains the same as in the pre-image while the sign of the abscissa is opposite to that of the pre-image.

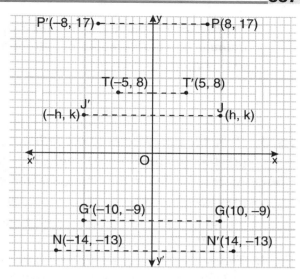

In general, the image of any point P(h, k) after reflection in y-axis is P'(–h, k), that is, the sign of the ordinate is changed.

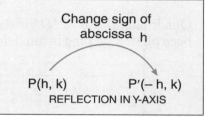

Ex. 2. *Write the coordinates of the following points when reflected in y-axis.*

    (a) *P* (3, 5)   **(b)** *Q* (–8, –6)   **(c)** *R* (7, –10)

    (d) *S* (0, –2)   **(e)** *T* (–2, 11)   **(f)** *M* (0, 4)

Sol. You know that after reflection in y-axis, the image of any point *A*(h, k) is *A*'(–h, k), *i.e.*, the sign of abscissa is changed and ordinate remains the same.

∴ After reflection in y-axis, P(3, 5) → P '(–3, 5), Q (–8, –6) → Q '(8, –6), R (7, –10) → R '(–7, –10), T (–2, 11) → T '(2, 11).

The point S(0, –2) lies on y-axis and so is its own image, *i.e.*, S(0, –2) → S '(0, –2).

Similarly, M(0, 4) → M '(0, 4).

33.7 Reflection in the Origin

Study the graph shown here :

The image of point P(2, 5) after reflection in the origin is P'((–2, –5), that of Q(–4, 4) is Q'(4, –4) and of R (5, –2) is R'(–5, 2).

In all these cases, the signs of both abscissa and ordinate are opposite to that of the pre-image.

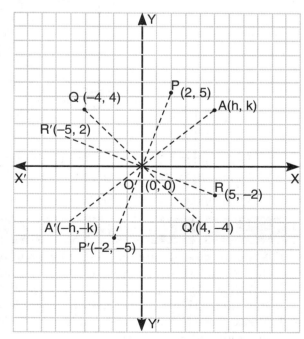

In general, the image of any point P(h, k) after reflection in the origin is P′(–h, –k), i.e., the sign of both abscissa and ordinate is changed.

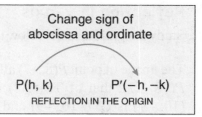

Change sign of abscissa and ordinate

P(h, k)   P′(–h, –k)

REFLECTION IN THE ORIGIN

Ex. 3. *Write the coordinates of the following points when reflected in the origin.*

    (a) *A(3, 7)*   **(b)** *B(–4, 8)*   **(c)** *C(7, –2)*   **(d)** *D(–11, –9)*   **(e)** *E(0, –3)*

Sol. After reflection in the origin, the image of any point $P(h, k)$ is $P′(–h, –k)$

∴   (*a*) $A(3, 7) \rightarrow A′(–3, –7)$ (*b*) $B(–4, 8) \rightarrow B′(4, –8)$

    (*c*) $C(7, –2) \rightarrow C′(–7, 2)$ (*d*) $D(–11, –9) \rightarrow D′(11, 9)$

    (*e*) $E(0, –3) \rightarrow E′(0, 3)$.

Ex. 4. *The vertices of a quadrilateral ABCD are A (8, 6), B (20, 6), C (20, 20) and D (5, 14). The figure is reflected in x-axis and then in y-axis. Find the coordinates of the vertices of the final image.*

Sol. Quadrilateral $A′B′C′D′$ is the reflection of the given quadrilateral $ABCD$ in x-axis. Its vertices have been plotted keeping in mind that a point (h, k) becomes $(h, –k)$ after reflection in x-axis.

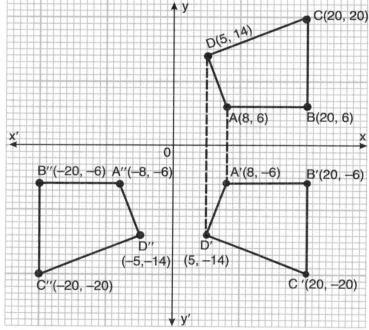

Quadrilateral $A″B″C″D″$ is the reflection of quadilateral $A′B′C′D′$ in y-axis obtained according to the rule 'point $(h, k) \rightarrow (–h, k)$ on reflection in y-axis.

Quadrilateral $A″B″C″D″$ is the final image of quadrilateral $ABCD$.

EXERCISE 33(c)

1. State the co-ordinates of image of each of the following points :

    (*a*) $P(5, 8)$, $Q(–7, 11)$, $R(10, –6)$, $T(–15, –7)$ after reflection in x-axis.

    (*b*) $A(11, 14)$, $B(–10, 15)$, $C(17, –12)$, $D(–6, –8)$ after reflection in y-axis.

    Plot all the above points and their images in separate grids.

2. Write down the coordinates of image of each the points $E(–7, –13)$ and $F(16, –21)$ when

    (*a*) reflected in the x-axis,   (*b*) reflected in the y-axis

    (*c*) reflected in the y-axis followed by reflection in the x-axis.   (*d*) reflected in the origin

3. (*a*) Point *H*(*a, b*) in reflected in the *x*-axis to $H_1(-7, 8)$. Write down the values of *a* and *b*.

(*b*) H_2 is the image of *H* when reflected in the *y*-axis. Write down the coordinates of H_2.

4. The vertices of a Δ*ABC* are *A*(–5,9), *B*(–10,5) and *C*(–2, 3). Find the coordinates of the vertices of the image of this triangle after reflection in the *x*-axis. Draw the given figure and its image.

5. The coordinates of a pentagon are *A*(–10, 10), *B*(–17, 6), *C*(–12, –5), *D*(–3, 2) and *E*(–3, 6). Draw this pentagon on a graph paper. Draw the image $A_1 B_1 C_1 D_1 E_1$ of the given shape under reflection in the *y*-axis.

6. On a graph paper plot the triangle *ABC* where *A* is (4, 4), *B* is (10, 10) and *C* is (18, 2). Now, draw the image of triangle *ABC* under reflection in the *y*-axis followed by a reflection in the *x*-axis.

7. On a graph paper draw a figure *ABCDEF* where *A* is (5, –6), *B* is (10, –4), *C* is (11, 2), *D* is (19, 2), *E* is (14, 6) and *F* is (5, 6). Draw its image under reflection in *y*-axis.

ROTATION

33.8 Introduction

Rotation is the movement (turning) of an object about a point through a given number of degrees in a clockwise or an anticlockwise direction. The adjoining figure below shows a rotation through 90^0 clockwise about the point *O*.

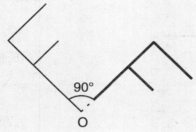

90°

O

Illustrations

1. The following pictures show the turning (rotation) of a disco light.

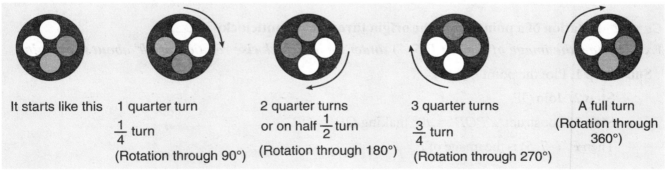

It starts like this	1 quarter turn	2 quarter turns	3 quarter turns	A full turn
	$\frac{1}{4}$ turn	or on half $\frac{1}{2}$ turn	$\frac{3}{4}$ turn	(Rotation through 360°)
	(Rotation through 90°)	(Rotation through 180°)	(Rotation through 270°)	

2. The following pictures show the different position of a flap after it has turned (*i*) $\frac{1}{4}$ turn clockwise, (*ii*) $\frac{1}{4}$ turn anticlockwise and (*iii*) $1\frac{1}{2}$ turns.

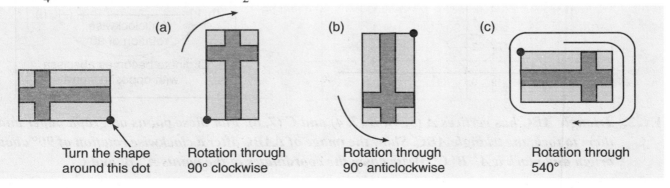

(a)

(b)

(c)

Turn the shape around this dot

Rotation through 90° clockwise

Rotation through 90° anticlockwise

Rotation through 540°

33.9 Describing Rotations

To describe a rotation fully you need to give the :

(*a*) **Centre of rotation,** *i.e., the point about which the object is turning or rotating.*

(*b*) **Angle of rotation**.

Case 1. **Rotation of a point about the origin through 90° clockwise.**

Ex. 1. *Show the image of a point P(8, 7) under a clockwise rotation of 90° about the origin.*

Sol. **1.** Plot the point *P*(8 ,7).

2. Join *OP*

3. Construct $\angle POP' = 90°$ making $OP' = OP$

Then *P'* (7, –8) is the image of *P*.

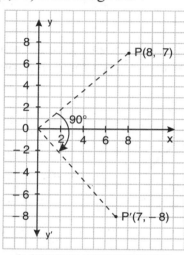

CLOCKWISE ROTATION OF 90°

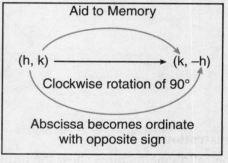

Notice that when rotated through 90° clockwise about the origin point $P(h, k)$ takes the position $P'(k, -h)$.

Aid to Memory

$(h, k) \longrightarrow (k, -h)$

Clockwise rotation of 90°

Abscissa becomes ordinate with opposite sign

Case 2. **Rotation of a point about the origin through 90° anticlockwise.**

Ex. 2. *Show the image of a point P(5, 7) under an anticlockwise rotation of 90^0 about the origin.*

Sol. **Step 1.** Plot the point *P* (5, 7).

Step 2. Join OP.

Step 3. Construct $\angle POP' = 90°$ making $OP' = OP$.

Then *P'* (–7, 5) is the image of *P*.

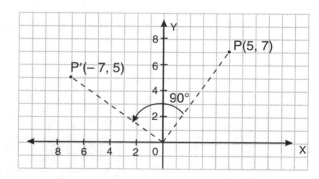

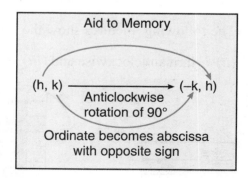

Aid to Memory

$(h, k) \longrightarrow (-k, h)$

Anticlockwise rotation of 90°

Ordinate becomes abscissa with opposite sign

Ex. 3. *Triangle ABC has vertices A (3, 4), B (7, 4) and C (7, 6). Plot these points on graph paper and join them to form the triangle ABC. Show the image of $\triangle ABC$ after a clockwise rotation of 90° about the origin and mark it A' B' C'. Write down the coordinates of the points A', B' and C'.*

Sol.

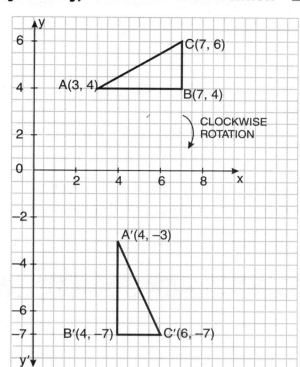

Plot the following points on a graph paper and show their images under the indicated rotation :

1. $A(4, 6)$ through 90° clockwise.
2. $B(-8, -10)$ through 90° clockwise.
3. $P(5, -9)$ through 90° clockwise.
4. $D(7, -11)$ through 90° anticlockwise.
5. $K(6, 4)$ through 90° anticlockwise.
6. $F(-7, -4)$ through 90° anticlockwise.
7. Construct the image of a $\triangle ABC$ with $A(5, -6)$, $B(5, -9)$, $C(8, -9)$ under an anticlockwise rotation of 90° about the origin.
8. Construct the image of a rectangle $ABCD$ having vertices $A(-5, 4)$, $B(8, 4)$, $C(-8, -3)$ and $D(-5, -3)$ under a clockwise rotation of 90° about the origin 0.

LOOKING BACK
Summary of Key Facts

1. When a straight line divides a shape into two identical (congruent) shapes, the shape is symmetrical about the line. The line is called a line of symmetry. It is usually shown by a dotted line.

2. A simple test to determine whether a figure has line of symmetry or not is to fold the figure along the supposed line of symmetry. If the two halves of the figure coincide, the figure has line symmetry about that line otherwise not.

3. The reflection (or image) of a point P in a line m is the perpendicular bisector of the line segment $PP^\wedge$.

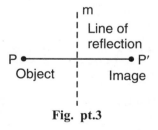

Fig. pt.3

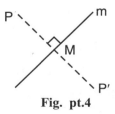

Fig. pt.4

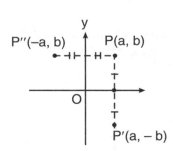

Fig. pt.5

4. To find the reflection (or image) of a point P in a line m, draw perpendicular PM from P on m and extend it to P' such that $MP' = PM$. Then, P' is the image of P and m is the reflection or mirror line.

5. (i) A point $P(a, b)$ has its image $P'(a, -b)$ when reflected in x-axis.
   (ii) A point $P(a, b)$ has its image $P''(-a, b)$ when reflected in y-axis.

6. A shape can be rotated from one position to another. The figure at the right shows the rotation of a circular shape about a point C in the clockwise direction.

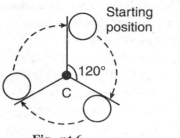   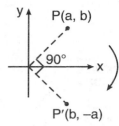   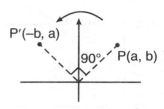

     Fig. pt.6   **Fig. pt.8(i)**   **Fig. pt.8(ii)**

7. A rotation is defined by the angle of rotation, direction of rotation and the centre of rotation.

8. (i) A point $P(a, b)$ takes the position $(b, -a)$ when rotated clockwise through $90°$.
   (ii) A point $P(a, b)$ takes the position $(-b, a)$ when rotated anticlockwise through $90°$.

UNIT REVIEW – 5

1. **Find the complement of :**
   (i) $47°$ (ii) $(90° - 2x°)$ (iii) $52°13'$

2. **Find the supplement of :**
   (i) $138°$ (ii) $(180 - x)°$ (iii) $87° \ 14' \ 23''$

3. If two angles are supplementary and one angle is $150°$ less than four times the other. Find the angles.

4. **Find the value of x from the following diagram :**

   (a) 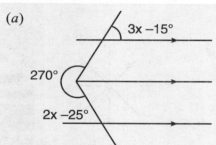   (b)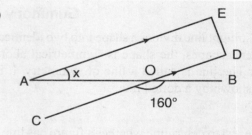

5. **Calculate the lettered angle in each case :**

   (a) 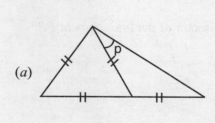   (b)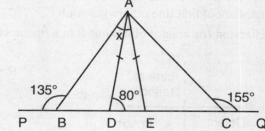

6. Find the value of $a + b + c$ from the diagram given below, where ABC is a right angled triangle and DEF an equilateral triangle.

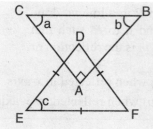

7. If the exterior angles of a triangle are $(2x - 20)°$, $(3x + 37)°$ and $(5x + 13)°$, find the value of x and hence all the interior angles of the triangle.

8. In the given figure, all the measurements are in centimetres. Find *(i)* PR *(ii)* RS. Also find ∠PRS.

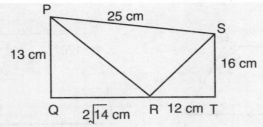

9. In a $\triangle ABC$, $\angle B = 90°$ and M is the midpoint of BC. Prove that $AC^2 = AM^2 + 3BM^2$.
    (**Hint :** $AC^2 = AB^2 + BC^2$
    In $\triangle ABM$ use Pythagoras Theorem to calculate AB^2.
    Also use $BM = MC$).

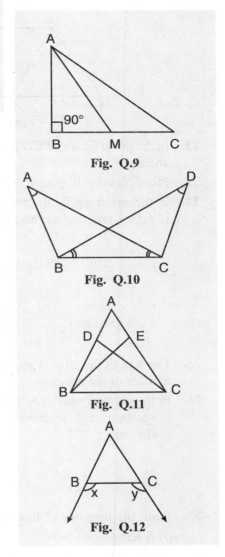

10. In the adjoining diagram it is given that $\angle BAC = \angle CDB$ and $\angle ACB = \angle DBC$. Prove that $AB = DC$.

11. In the adjoining figure ABC is a triangle with $AB = AC$ and $AD = AE$. Prove that $BE = CD$.
    (**Hint :** Prove $\triangle ABE \cong \triangle ACD$)

12. In the given figure, if $x > y$, show $AB > AC$.

13. Show that in a right triangle, hypotenuse is the longest side. (use triangle inequality property : Greatest side opp. Greatest angle)

14. In a $\triangle PQR$, $PQ = 6$ cm, $QR = 4.5$ cm and $PR = 7.2$ cm. Arrange the angles in descending order.

15. In the adjoining figure, $AB = BD$.
    $\angle BAD = 54°$, $\angle CAD = 32°$. **Show that**
    (i) $AC > AD$ *(ii)* $AD > BD$ *(iii)* $AC > AB$

16. Construct an equilateral triangle with altitude = 5.4 cm.

17. Construct an isosceles right angled triangle where hypotenuse = 6.2 cm.

18. Construct a rhombus whose diagonals are 5.2 cm and 6 cm.

19. Construct a triangle PQR with $PQ = 6.5$ cm and $\angle P = 60°$ and $\angle Q = 75°$. Also draw its in-circle.

20. If two angles of a quadilateral are 125° and 65° and out of the remaining two one angle is 25° more than the other, find these angles.

21. In the given figure *ABE* is an equilateral triangle and *BCDE* is a rhombus. Find ∠*x*.

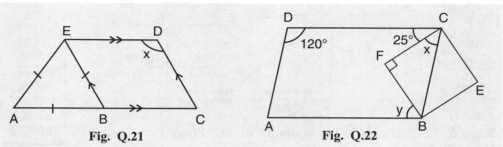

Fig. Q.21   **Fig. Q.22**

22. In the given figure *ABCD* is a parallelogram and *ECFB* is a rectangle. ∠*ADC* = 120° and ∠*DCF* = 25°. Find ∠*x* and ∠*y*.

23. Prove that the diagonals of rectangle are equal and bisect each other. (**Hint :** Use congruency)

24. In the adjoining figure it is given that *AH* ∥ *DC*. Area of ∥ gram *DCHG* = 64 cm². Find the area of Δ*AEB*. If *AB* = 8 cm, find the height of Δ*ABC*.

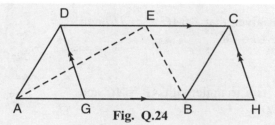

Fig. Q.24

25. The sum of the interior angles of a regular polygon is three times the sum of its exterior ∠*s*. Find the number of sides of the polygon.

26. In the given figure, *O* is the centre of the circle. Δ*ABC* is an isosceles triangle inscribed in the circle with *AB* = *AC*. Find ∠*ABC* and ∠*ACB*.

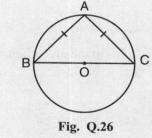

Fig. Q.26

27. **State the number of lines of symmetry of each of the following.**

 (*i*) A television screen   (*ii*) The figure eight   (*iii*) A rhombus.

28. The Point *Q*(*a*, *b*) is first reflected in *y*-axis and then reflected in *x*-axis to get *Q*". If the co-ordinates of *Q*" are (–6, –2), find the values of *a* and *b*.

29. **Find the images of the following points on a graph paper when it is rotated about the origin through 90° clockwise.**

 (*a*) *P* (–3, 5)   (*b*) *Q* (3, 0)

ANSWERS

EXERCISE 33 (a)

1. (*a*) Yes   (*b*) No   (*c*) Yes   (*d*) Yes   (*e*) Yes   (*f*) No   (*g*) Yes   (*h*) Yes

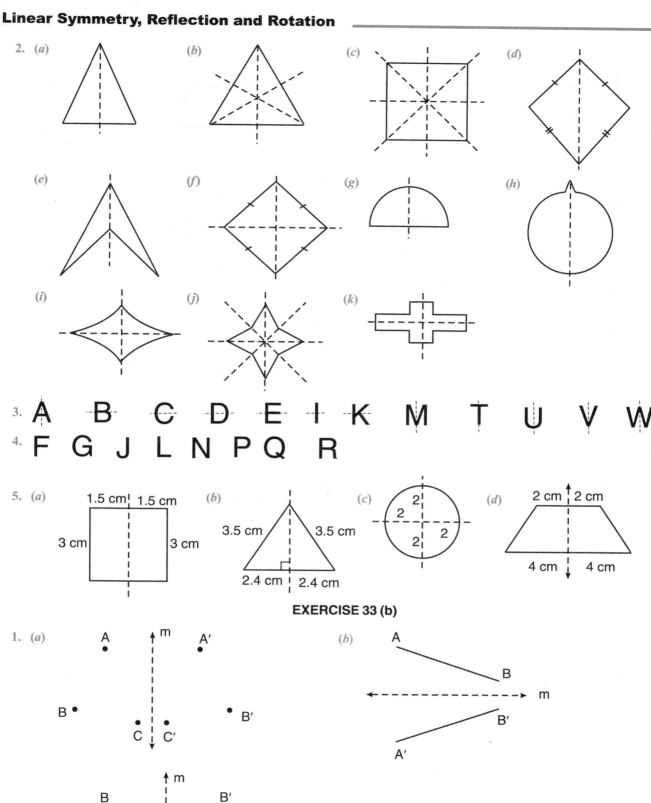

EXERCISE 33 (b)

2. (a) 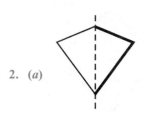 (b) 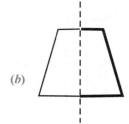 (c) 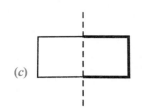 (d)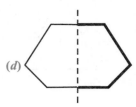

EXERCISE 33 (c)

1. (a) (i) P′ (5, –8), (ii) Q′ (–7, –11), (iii) R′ (10,6), (iv) T′(–15, 7)

(b) (i) A′(–11,14), (ii) B′(10,15), (iii) C′ (–17, –12), (iv) D′ (6,–8)

2. (a) E′ (–7,13), F′ (16,21) (b) E′ (7, –13), F′(–16, –21) (c) E′(7,13), F′(–16,21)

(d) E′(7, 13), F′(–16, 21)

3. (a) H(–7, –8) (b) H₂(7, –8) **4.** A′(–5, –9), B′(–10, –5), C′(–2, –3).

5. The vertices of the image are A′ (10,10), B′ (17,6), C′ (12,– 5), D′ (3,2) and E′ (3,6)

6. The vertices of the figure in the final image are A′ (–4, –4), B′ (–10, –10), C′(–18, –2).

7. The vertices of the image are $A'(-5, -6), B'(-10, -4). C'(-11, 2). D'(-19, 2). E'(-14, 6). F'(-5, 6)$.

EXERCISE 33 (d)

1. A′(6, –4) **2.** B′(–10,8) **3.** P′(–9 –5) **4.** D′(11,7) **5.** K′(–4, 6) **6.** (4, –7)

7. A′(6, 5), B′(9, 5), C′(9, 8) **8.** A′(4, 5), B′(4, –8), C′(–3, 8), D′(–3, 5),

UNIT REVIEW – 5

1. (i) 43° (ii) 2x° (iii) 37°47′ **2.** (i) 42° (ii) x° (iii) 92° 45′37″ **3.** 66°, 114°

4. (a) 26° (b) x = 20° **5.** (a) p = 30° (b) 55° **6.** 150° **7.** 134°, 44°, 2°

8. (i) 15 cm (ii) 20 cm, ∠PRS = 90° **14.** ∠Q > ∠R > ∠P 20. 72.5°, 97.5°

21. x = 120° **22.** x = 35°, y = 65° **24.** Area of ΔAEB = 32 cm², height = 8 cm. **25.** 8 **26.** 45° each

27. (i) 2 (ii) 2 (iii) 2

28. (6, 2) **29.** (a) (5, 3) (b) (0, –3)

34. Areas of Rectilinear Figures

34.1 Introduction

You have studied in previous class the formulas for finding out perimeter and area of different types of rectilinear figures. Revise the same with the help of the key facts and problems given in this chapter.

34.2 Key Facts

Abbreviations : mm = millimetre, cm = centimetre, dm = decimetre.

m = metre, dam = decametre, hm = hectometre, km = kilometre.

a = are, ha = hectare

■ **Relation between standard units of area**

Since	10 mm	= 1 cm therefore	$100 \text{ mm}^2 = 1 \text{ cm}^2$
	10 cm	= 1 dm therefore	$100 \text{ cm}^2 = 1 \text{ dm}^2$
	10 dm	= 1 m therefore	$100 \text{ dm}^2 = 1 \text{ m}^2 = (100 \times 100) \text{cm}^2 = 10\,000 \text{ cm}^2$
	10 m	= 1 dam therefore	$100 \text{ m}^2 = 1 \text{ dam}^2$
	10 dam	= 1 hm therefore	$100 \text{ dam}^2 = 1 \text{ hm}^2$
	10 hm	= 1 km therefore	$100 \text{ hm}^2 = 1 \text{ km}^2$

One dam^2 i.e. 100 m^2 is called **Are**. This is taken as the unit of measuring area of land.

1 Are = 100 m^2

The area of large pieces of land is generally expressed in **hectares** (ha)

1 hectare (1 ha) = $(100 \times 100) \text{ m}^2 = \textbf{10\,000 m}^2 = 100$ are

100 ha = 1 km^2

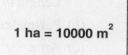

1 ha = 10000 m^2

■ **Area and perimeter of a rectangle**

If l is the length and b the breadth of a rectangle, then

Area = **length × Breadth** = $l \times b$ sq units

$\Rightarrow$ Length $(l) = \dfrac{\text{Area}}{\text{Breadth}} = \dfrac{A}{b}$ units.

Breadth $(b) = \dfrac{\text{Area}}{\text{Length}} = \dfrac{A}{l}$ units.

Perimeter = 2(length + breadth) = $2(l + b)$ units

Diagonal of a rectangle = $\sqrt{l^2 + b^2}$ units.

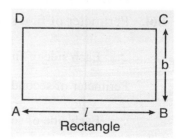

Rectangle

■ **Area and perimeter of a square**

If a be the side of a square then

Area of a square = $a \times a = \boldsymbol{a^2} = (\textbf{side})^2$ sq units

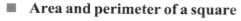

$\Rightarrow$ One side = $\sqrt{\text{Area}}$ units = a units

and perimeter = $4 \times a$ units = **4 × side** units

Diagonal of a square = $\sqrt{a^2 + a^2} = \sqrt{2a^2} = a\sqrt{2}$ = side $\sqrt{2}$ units.

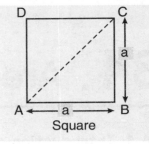

Square

■ **Area of the four walls and diagonal**

Area of the four walls = $2lh + 2bh = $ **2 $(l + b) \times h$ sq units**

= 2(length + breadth) × height sq units

Diagonal of a room = $\sqrt{l^2 + b^2 + h^2}$ units.

Ex. 1. *Find the perimeter and area of a rectangle whose diagonal is 17 cm and length = 15 cm.*

Sol. Let the breadth of the rectangle = b cm. Given diagonal = 17 cm, l = 15 cm.

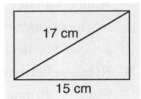

Then, diagonal (d) $= \sqrt{l^2 + b^2}$

$\Rightarrow$ $\qquad d^2 = l^2 + b^2 \Rightarrow b^2 = d^2 - l^2$

$\therefore$ $\qquad b^2 = 17^2 - 15^2 = 289 - 225 = 64 \Rightarrow b = 8$ cm.

Perimeter of the rectangle = $2(l + b) = 2(15 + 8)$ cm = 2×23 cm = **46 cm**

Area of the rectangle = $l \times b = (15 \times 8)$ cm^2 = **120 cm^2**.

Ex. 2. *The diagonal of a square is $9\sqrt{2}$ cm. Find :*

(a) *length of its side* **(b) *Perimeter*** **(c) *Area*.**

Sol. (*a*) Let the length of each side of the square = a cm.

Length of the diagonal = $9\sqrt{2}$ cm.

$\therefore$ $\qquad a\sqrt{2} = 9\sqrt{2} \Rightarrow$ **$a = 9$ cm.**

Length of each side = 9 cm.

(*b*) Perimeter of square = $4a = (4 \times 9)$ cm = **36 cm**.

(*c*) Area = $a^2 = (9 \times 9)$ cm^2 = **81 cm^2**.

Ex. 3. *The perimeters of two squares are 120 cm and 64 cm. Find the perimeter of a square whose area is equal to the sum of the areas of these two squares.*

Sol. Perimeter of first square = 120 cm

$\therefore$ Each side of first square = $\dfrac{120}{4}$ cm = 30 cm $\qquad$ $\boxed{\because P = 4a}$

Perimeter of second square = 64 cm

$\therefore$ Each side of second square = $\dfrac{64}{4}$ cm = 16 cm

Area of required square = Area of 1st square + Area of 2nd square

$\qquad\qquad = (30 \times 30 + 16 \times 16)$ cm^2

$\qquad\qquad = (900 + 256)$cm^2 = 1156 cm^2

$\therefore$ Each side of the required square = $\sqrt{1156}$ cm = 34 cm $\qquad$ $\boxed{A = s^2}$

Required Perimeter = 4×34 cm = **136 cm**

Ex. 4. *A path of uniform width 3 m runs around the outside of a square park of side 18 cm. Find the area of the path.*

Sol. Let *ABCD* represent the square path and the shaded region as shown in the figure, the path around it. Then,

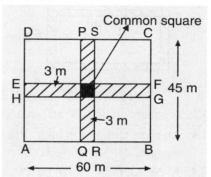

Area of path = (Area of square *EFGH*)
                  − (Area of square *ABCD*)

EF = EH = 18 + 3 + 3 cm = 24 cm.

Area of square *ABCD* = (18 × 18) cm² = 324 cm²

Area of square *EFGH* = (24 × 24) cm² = 576 cm²

∴   Area of path = (576 − 324) cm² = **252 cm²**.

Ex. 5. *Find the area of the cross-roads at right angle to each other through the centre of the rectangular field whose dimensions are 60 m × 45 m and the cross-roads are 3 m wide.*

Sol. *ABCD* is the rectangular field and *EFGH* and *PQRS* are the cross-roads at right angles, through the centre of the field.

Area of path *EFGH* = (60 × 3) m² = 180 m²

Area of path *PQRS* = (45 × 3) m² = 135 m²

Area of common space = (3 × 3) m² = 9 m²

∴   Total Area of the two cross paths = 180 m² + 135 m² − 9 m²

                                                = **306 m²**.

EXERCISE 34 (a)

1. (*a*) Find the perimeter and area of a square whose one side is 6.5 cm long.

   (*b*) Find the area of a square whose perimeter is 124 cm.

   (*c*) Find the perimeter and diagonal of a square whose area is 64 cm².

2. Find in hectares the area of a square-shaped village 14 km long.

3. **Copy and complete the following table for rectangles :**

	Length	Breadth	Area	Perimeter
(*a*)	4.4 cm	....	77 cm²	....
(*b*)	29 mm	....	....	104 mm
(*c*)	1.5 km	90 m	...ha	...
(*d*)	40 m	....	1 are	....
(*e*)	300 m	....	...ha	0.8 km

4. Find the area of a rectangular plot, one side of which is 48 m and its diagonal = 50 m.

5. The perimeter of a rectangle is 98 cm and its breadth is 9 cm. Find its (*a*) length, (*b*) length of diagonal and (*c*) area.

6. **The area of a square is 1 hectare. Calculate its :**

   (*a*) perimeter   (*b*) length of diagonal

7. How may tiles of area 15 cm² will be needed to cover a floor 5.85 m by 6.90 m?

8. The length and breadth of a rectangle are in the ratio 3 : 2. If the area of the field is 1350 cm², find the cost of fencing the field at the rate of Rs 5.50 per metre.

9. A room is 5.4 m by 4.8 m. A carpet is laid centrally, leaving a margin of 40 cm all around between the carpet and the walls of the room. Find the area of the carpet in square metres.

10. **Find the areas enclosed by Figs.(a) to (c). All corners are right-angled and dimensions are in cm.**

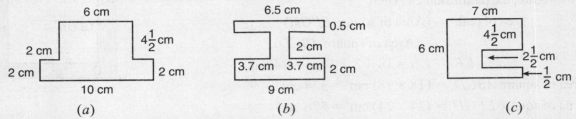

(a) (b) (c)

11. **Find the areas of the shaded parts in Figs. (a) to (c). All corners are right-angled and dimensions are given in metres.**

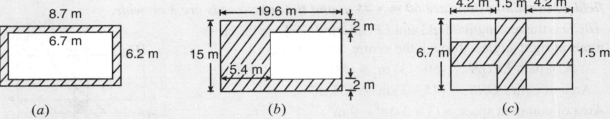

(a) (b) (c)

12. A square field has an area of 6.25 km^2. Find the cost of putting a fence round it at Rs 10.50 per metre.

13. An open tank is 3 m long, 2 m wide and 1 m 50 cm deep. Find the amount of paint required to paint its inside and outside, if 1 kg of paint covers 20 square metres. (Neglect the thickness of the material)

14. A photograph 25 cm by 20 cm is mounted on a card so that there is margin of 2.5 cm all the way round. What fraction of the card is covered?

15. The walls of a room are 5.2 m long, 3.8 m wide and 3 m high. There is a door 2 m by 1m and a window 1.5 m by 1 m. Find the cost of painting the walls (excluding the door and the window) at Rs 10 per square metre.

34.3 Area of a Triangle

I. **Area of a triangle = $\frac{1}{2}$ × base × height,**

where any side can be taken as the base and the length of perpendicular drawn from the opposite vertex to the base is the corresponding height.

As there are three sides of a triangle, the following three cases arise :

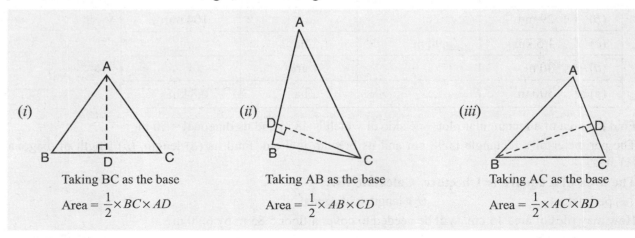

(i) Taking BC as the base
Area $= \frac{1}{2} \times BC \times AD$

(ii) Taking AB as the base
Area $= \frac{1}{2} \times AB \times CD$

(iii) Taking AC as the base
Area $= \frac{1}{2} \times AC \times BD$

As   Area of a triangle $= \dfrac{1}{2} \times$ base $\times$ height or altitude

$\therefore$ Base of a triangle $= \dfrac{2 \times \text{Area}}{\text{Altitude}}$, Height $= \dfrac{2 \times \text{Area}}{\text{Base}}$.

II. Heron's formula

A GREEK mathematician, Heron, gave the following formula :

Area of a triangle $= \sqrt{s(s-a)(s-b)(s-c)}$ sq units where a, b, c are the lengths

of the sides of the triangle and $s = \dfrac{a+b+c}{2}$ is the semi-perimeter of the triangle.

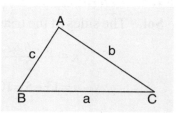

III. Area of an equilateral triangle

Let ABC be an equilateral triangle with side $= a$ cm. Then,

$$s = \frac{a+a+a}{2} = \frac{3a}{2}$$

$\therefore$ By Heron's formula,

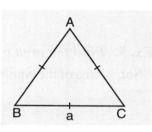

$$\text{Area of } \Delta ABC = \sqrt{s(s-a)(s-b)(s-c)} = \sqrt{\frac{3a}{2}\left(\frac{3a}{2}-a\right)\left(\frac{3a}{2}-a\right)\left(\frac{3a}{2}-a\right)}$$

$$= \sqrt{\frac{3a}{2} \times \frac{a}{2} \times \frac{a}{2} \times \frac{a}{2}} = \frac{\sqrt{3}}{4} a^2 = \frac{\sqrt{3}}{4} \times \text{side}^2.$$

IV. Area of a right-angled triangle

$$\text{Area of } \Delta ABC = \frac{1}{2} \times BC \times AB \qquad (\angle B = 90°)$$

$$= \frac{1}{2} \times \text{product of sides containing the right angle.}$$

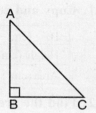

Ex. 1. *Find the area of a triangle, whose base in 9.6 cm, and the corresponding altitude is 5 cm.*

 Sol. Here, base $= 9.6$ cm, altitude $= 5$ cm

$\therefore$ Area of the $\Delta = \dfrac{1}{2} \times$ base $\times$ altitude $= \dfrac{1}{2} \times 9.6 \times 5 \text{ cm}^2 = \mathbf{24\,cm^2}$.

Ex. 2. *Find the altitude of a triangle whose area is 45 cm² and base 15 cm.*

 Sol. Area of the $\Delta = 45$ cm², base of the $\Delta = 15$ cm

Area of a $\Delta = \dfrac{1}{2} \times$ base $\times$ altitude $\therefore$ Altitude of the $\Delta = \dfrac{2(\text{Area})}{\text{Base}} = \dfrac{2 \times 45}{15} = \mathbf{6\,cm}$.

Ex. 3. *A field in the form of a parallelogram, has one of its diagonals 42 m long and the perpendicular distances of this diagonal from either of the outlying vertices is 10 m 8 dm. Find the area of the field.*

 Sol. Diagonal $AC = 42$ m,   10 dm $= 1$m

$BE = DF = 10$ m 8 dm $= 10.8$ m $\therefore$ 8 dm $= 0.8$ m $= \dfrac{8}{10}$ m

Area of $\|$ gm $ABCD =$ (Area of ΔABC) + (Area of ΔACD)

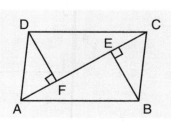

$$= \frac{1}{2} \times AC \times BE + \frac{1}{2} \times AC \times DF = \frac{1}{2}AC(BE + DF) = \frac{1}{2} \times 42 \times (10.8 + 10.8)\,\text{m}^2$$

$$= (21 \times 21.6)\,\text{m}^2 = \textbf{453.6 m}^2.$$

Ex. 4. *Determine the area of a triangle whose sides are 5 cm, 13 and 12 cm.*

Sol. The sides of the triangle are $a = 5$ cm, $b = 12$ cm, $c = 13$ cm

$$s = \frac{a+b+c}{2} = \frac{5+12+13}{2} = 15 \text{ cm}$$

$$s-a = 15-5 = 10 \text{ cm}, \quad s-b = 15-13 = 2 \text{ cm}, \quad s-c = 15-12 = 3 \text{ cm}$$

$\therefore$ Area of the triangle $= \sqrt{s(s-a)(s-b)(s-c)}$

$$= \sqrt{15 \times 10 \times 3 \times 2} = \sqrt{900} = \textbf{30 cm}^2.$$

Ex. 5. *Find the area of the equilateral triangle whose one side is 7 cm.*

Sol. Area of the equilateral Δ

$$= \frac{\text{side}^2\sqrt{3}}{4} = \frac{49\sqrt{3}}{4} = \frac{49 \times 1.732}{4} = \frac{84.868}{4} \text{ cm}^2$$

$$= 21.217 \text{ cm}^2 = \textbf{21.22 cm}^2 \ (\text{to 2 dp}).$$

```
   1732
   ×49
 ------
  15588
   6928
 ------
  84868
```

EXERCISE 34 (b)

1. **Copy and complete the table for a triangle.**

Base (cm)	6	8	5	x	16	?	?
Height (cm)	10	14	20	$2x$	?	5	11
Area (cm^2)	?	?	?	?	120	50	110

2. **Find the area of each triangle.**

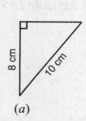
(a)

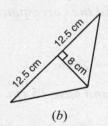
(b)

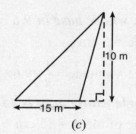
(c)

3. **Find the area, in square metres, of the triangle, whose base and altitudes are as under.**

(a) base = 1.5 cm, altitude = 8 cm
(b) base = 7.5 cm, altitude = 4 cm
(c) base = 1.5 m, altitude = 0.8 m
(d) base = 32 cm, altitude = 105 cm

4. **Find the area of each of the following figures. The measurements are in cm.**

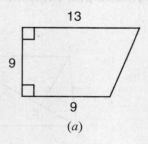
(a)

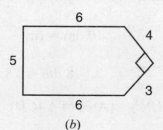
(b)

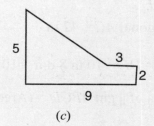
(c)

5. Find the area of an isosceles right triangle if one of the right sides is 20 cm long.
   (**Hint** : In the isos. Δ, base = altitude = 20 cm)

6. **Find the base of the triangle if**
   (*a*) Area is 50 cm^2 and altitude is 8 cm; (*b*) Area is 25 ares and height is 20 m;
   (*c*) Area is 16 hectares and height is 40 dam.

7. Find the altitude of the triangle if its area is 2.5 ha and base is 250 m.

8. The area of a triangle is equal to that of a square whose each side measures 60 m. Find the side of the triangle whose corresponding altitude is 90 m.

9. Find the area of a quadrilateral *ABCD* whose measurements are *AC* = 48 cm, *BF* = 10 cm, *DE* = 20 cm.

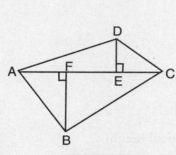

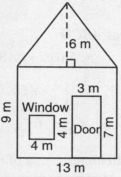

Fig. Q. 9   **Fig. Q. 10**

10. Ramu is going to paint the front of the house pictured above. He is not going to paint the window or the door. One litre of paint covers 80 square metres. How much paint will he need ?

11. **Find the area of the triangle whose sides are**
    (*a*) 26 cm, 28 cm, 30 cm,   (*b*) 48 cm, 73 cm, 55 cm,   (*c*) 21 cm, 20 cm, 13 cm.

12. Find the area of a triangle with base 5 cm and whose height is equal to that of a rectangle with base 5 cm and area 20 cm^2.

13. Find the area of the equilateral triangle whose each side is (*a*) 12 cm, (*b*) 5 cm.

14. The area of an equilateral triangle is 173.2 m^2. Find its perimeter. $\left(\text{given } \sqrt{3} = 1.732\right)$

34.4 Area of Parallelogram

Area of a parallelogram = Base × corresponding height

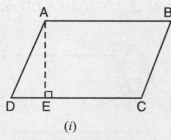

(*i*)

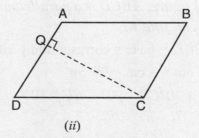

(*ii*)

Here *DC* is the base and   Here *AD* is the base and *CQ* the
AE the corresponding altitude   corresponding altitude
∴   Area = *DC* × *AE*   ∴   Area = *AD* × *CQ*.

Note : The corresponding altitude gives the distance between the base and the side parallel to it.

Area of parallelogram = base × height.

34.5 Area of a Rhombus

A parallelogram whose all sides are equal is called a rhombus. Its diagonals bisect each other at right angles.

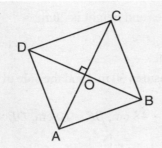 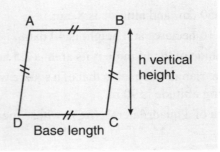

Area of the rhombus *ABCD*

$$= \Delta ADC + \Delta ABC = 2\Delta ADC$$

$$= 2\left(\frac{1}{2} \times AC \times DO\right) = AC \times DO$$

$$= AC \times \frac{1}{2} BD = \frac{1}{2} \times \text{ Product of diagonals.}$$

Also, being a parallelogram, area of rhombus = base × vertical height.

Area of rhombus = base × vertical height or $\frac{1}{2}$ (product of diagonals)

Ex. 1. *Find the area of a parallelogram with base 7 cm and the corresponding altitude 4.3 cm.*

Sol. Base of the ‖ gm = 7 cm, altitude = 4.3 cm.

∴   Area of the ‖ gm = base × altitude = 7 cm × 4.3 cm = **30.1 cm²**.

Ex. 2. *Find the altitude of a parallelogram of area 2.34 m² and base 18 dm.*

Sol. Area of the ‖ gm = 2.34 m². Its base = 18 dm = $\frac{18}{10}$ m = 1.8 m

∴   Area of a ‖ gm = base × altitude

∴   Altitude = $\frac{\text{Area}}{\text{Base}} = \frac{2.34}{1.8}$ m = 1.3 m = **13 dm.**

Ex. 3. *In the adjoining figure, ABCD is a parallelogram, CE ⊥ AB and BF ⊥ AD. If AB = 12 cm, AD = 10 cm and CE = 8 cm, find BF.*

Sol. Area of ‖ gm *ABCD* = base × corresponding altitude

$= AB \times CE = 12 \text{ cm} \times 8 \text{ cm} = 96 \text{ cm}^2.$ ... *(i)*

Also, area of ‖ gm *ABCD* = $AD \times BF = 10 \times BF$ ... *(ii)*

From *(i)* and *(ii)*, 10 × BF = 96

∴ $BF = \frac{96}{10}$ cm = **9.6 cm.**

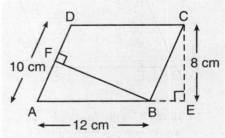

Ex. 4. *The base and the corresponding altitude of a parallelogram are 10 cm and 12 cm respectively. If the other altitude is 8 cm, find the length of the other pair of parallel sides.*

Sol. Given base = 10 cm, corresponding altitude = 12 cm

∴   Area = base × altitude = 10 cm × 12 cm = 120 cm²

Other altitude = 8 cm ∴ length of other side = $\dfrac{\text{Area}}{\text{Altitude}} = \dfrac{120}{8} = $ **15 cm.**

Ex. 5. *In the adjoining figure*

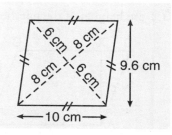

    (*a*) Area of rhombus   = base × vertical height
                          = 10 cm × 9.6 cm = **96 cm².**

    (*b*) Area of rhombus   = $\dfrac{1}{2}$ (product of diagonals)

                                  = $\dfrac{1}{2}(16 \times 12) = $ **96 cm².**

Ex. 6. *The area of a rhombus is 60 sq cm. One of its diagonals is 12 cm. Find the other diagonal.*

Sol.   Area of a rhombus = $\dfrac{1}{2}$ × product of the diagonals

    ∴ $60 = \dfrac{1}{2} \times 12 \times$ other diagonal   ⇒ other diagonal = $\dfrac{2 \times 60}{12} = $ **10 cm.**

Ex. 7. *The perimeter of a rhombus is 100 cm and one of its diagonals is 40 cm long. Find the length of the other diagonal.*

Sol.   Perimeter the rhombus = 100 cm.

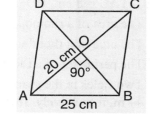

    ∴   One side of the rhombus = $\dfrac{100}{4} = 25$ cm

Since the diagonals of a rhombus bisect each other at right angles, therefore

$AO = \dfrac{1}{2} \times 40$ cm = 20 cm and $\angle AOB = 90°$

From rt $\angle d$ ΔAOB, $OB^2 = \sqrt{AB^2 - AO^2} = \sqrt{25^2 - 20^2} = \sqrt{625 - 400} = \sqrt{225} = 15$ cm

∴ Length of the diagonal $BD = 2 \times OB = 2 \times 15 = $ **30 cm.**

EXERCISE 34 (c)

1. Find the area of each parallelogram.

	(*a*)	(*b*)	(*c*)	(*d*)	(*e*)	(*f*)
Base	8 cm	2.8 cm	12 mm	6.5 m	1 m 5 cm	4.2 dm
Height	3 cm	5 cm	8.7 cm	4.8 m	45 cm	25 cm

2. Find the missing measures :

   (*a*) Area of ‖ gm *ABCD*
      = 48 cm²
      DE = 6 cm
      AB = ?

   (*b*) Area of ‖ gm *PQRS*
      = 252 cm²
      PQ = 9 cm
      RT = ?

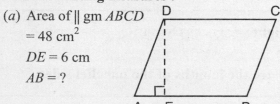

3. Find the altitude of a parallelogram of area 2.25 m² given that its base is 25 dm.

4. The adjacent sides of a parallelogram are 36 cm and 27 cm in length. If the distance between the shorter sides is 12 cm, find the distance between the longer sides.

5. The area of a parallelogram and a square are the same. If the perimeter of the square is 160 m and the height of the parallelogram is 20 m, find the length of the corresponding base of the parallelogram.

6. The area of a rhombus is 42 m^2. If its perimeter is 24 m, find its altitude.

7. AX and CY are heights of the parallelogram $ABCD$ whose area is $9\frac{1}{3}$ cm^2. What are the lengths of XA and CY ?

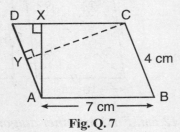

Fig. Q. 7

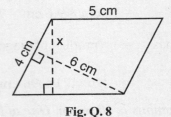

Fig. Q. 8

8. The figure above shows a ∥ gm. Find the value of x.

9. **Find the area of the rhombus in each case :**

	(a)	(b)	(c)	(d)	(e)
Base b	8 cm	6 cm	2.5 cm	40 cm	0.025 cm
Height h	3 cm	3.5 cm	13.2 cm	35 cm	0.04 cm

10. **Find the area of rhombus ABCD in Q. 10(a) to (c).**

   (a) AC = 8 cm, BD = 10 cm. (b) AC = 15 cm, BD = 36 cm. (c) AC = 30 cm, BD = 40 cm.

11. The area of a rhombus is 72 cm^2 . If one of its diagonals is 18 cm, what is the length of the other diagonal?

12. The area of a rhombus is 2016 cm^2 and its sides are each equal to 63 cm. Find its height.

13. The perimeter of a rhombus is 40 cm and the length of one of its diagonals is 16 cm. Find its area.

14. Two fields in the shape of parallelogram and rhombus are equal in area. The diagonals of rhombus are 110 m and 44 m, respectively. If one of the sides of the parallelogram is 88 m, find its altitude.

34.6 Area of a Trapezium

Area of trapezium $ABCD$ = area of ΔABC + area of ΔADC

$$=\left(\frac{1}{2}BC\times AE\right)+\left(\frac{1}{2}AD\times FC\right)$$

$$=\left(\frac{1}{2}BC\times AE\right)+\left(\frac{1}{2}AD\times AE\right) \quad \because \ AE=FC$$

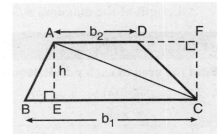

∴ Area of trapezium $ABCD=\frac{1}{2}(AD+BC)AE$

$$=\frac{1}{2}(\text{sum of parallel sides}) \times \text{height}$$

Area of trapezium $=\frac{1}{2}$ **(sum of parallel sides)** × **height**

$=\frac{1}{2} \times (b_1 + b_2) \times h$ where h is the height and b_1, b_2 are the lengths of the parallel sides.

Ex. 1. *Find the area of a trapezium with base 12 cm and height 6 cm, if the side parallel to the given base is 7 cm long.*

Sol. *Given* : Height (h) = 6 cm, Base b_1 = 12 cm, Base b_2 = 7 cm

   Area of trapezium $=\frac{1}{2}\times h\times(b_1+b_2)=\frac{1}{2}\times 6\times(12+7)$ cm^2 $=(3\times 19)$ cm^2 $= \mathbf{57\ cm^2}$.

Ex. 2. *Find the altitude of a trapezium, the sum of the lengths of whose bases is 8.5 cm and whose area is 34 cm².*

Sol. *Given* : sum of the bases $(b_1 + b_2)$ = 8.5 cm, Area = 34 cm²

Height $(h) = \dfrac{2 \times \text{Area}}{b_1 + b_2} = \dfrac{2 \times 34}{8.5} = \dfrac{2 \times 34}{\frac{85}{10}} = \dfrac{2 \times 34 \times 10}{85} = \textbf{8 cm}$.

Ex. 3. *Find the sum of the lengths of the bases of a trapezium whose area is 4.2 m² and whose height is 280 cm.*

Sol. *Given* : Area of the trapezium = 4.2 m²,

Height (h) = 280 cm = $\dfrac{280}{100}$ m = 2.8 m

Sum of the bases $(b_1 + b_2) = \dfrac{2 \times \text{Area}}{h} = \dfrac{2 \times 4.2}{2.8} = \dfrac{2 \times 42}{28} = \textbf{3 m}$.

$\dfrac{4.2}{2.8} = \dfrac{\frac{42}{10}}{\frac{28}{10}} = \dfrac{42}{28}$

■ **Aid to Quick calculation :**

Note that if there are equal decimal places in the numerator and denominator then you can just remove the decimal point. Thus $\dfrac{2.037}{0.194} = \dfrac{2037}{194}$. Here we have written $\dfrac{4.2}{2.8}$ as $\dfrac{42}{28}$.

Ex. 4. *The area of a trapezium is 143 cm² and its height is 11cm . If one of the parallel sides is longer than the other by 4 cm, find the two parallel sides.*

Sol. *Given* : Area of a trapezium = 143 cm², Height (h) = 11 cm.

Sum of the bases $(b_1 + b_2) = \dfrac{2 \times \text{Area}}{h} = \dfrac{2 \times 143}{11} = 2 \times 13 = \textbf{26 cm}$.

Let length of one base be x cm. Then the length of the other base is $(x + 4)$ cm.

∴ $x + (x + 4) = 26$ ⇒ $2x = 26 - 4$ ⇒ $2x = 22$ ⇒ $x = 11$

∴ one side = **11 cm** and the other side = 11 + 4 = **15 cm.**

Ex. 5. *In the figure, AB ∥ DC and DA is perpendicular to AB. Further, DC = 7 cm, CB = 10 cm and AB = 13 cm. Find the area of the quadrilateral ABCD.*

Sol. Draw $CM \perp AB$. Then AM = DC = 7 cm

$MB = AB - AM$ = 13 cm – 7 cm = 6 cm

From rt $\triangle CMB$,

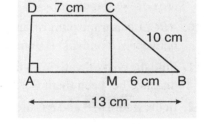

$CM = \sqrt{CB^2 - MB^2} = \sqrt{10^2 - 6^2} = \sqrt{100 - 36} = \sqrt{64}$ = 8 cm

Since $AB \parallel DC$, therefore, the quad. $ABCD$ is a trapezium.

Area of trapezium $ABCD = \dfrac{1}{2} \times$ height × sum of parallel sides

$= \dfrac{1}{2} \times 8 \times (13 + 7) = \dfrac{1}{2} \times 8 \times 20 = \textbf{80 cm}^2$.

Ex.6. *The parallel sides DC and AB of a trapezium are 10 cm and 20 cm respectively. Its non-parallel sides are each equal to13 cm. Find the area of the trapezium.*

Sol. Given DC = 10 cm, AB = 20 cm and $DA = CB$ = 13 cm.

Through C, draw CM parallel to DA meeting AB at M.

Now, $AM = DC$ = 10 cm, MB = 20 cm – 10 cm = 10 cm

Draw $CN \perp MB$.

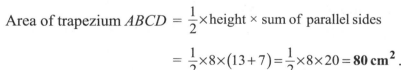
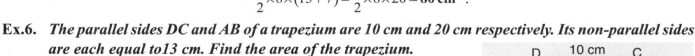
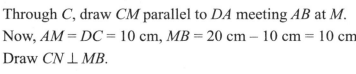

Since, $\triangle CMB$ is isosceles so, CN bisects MB $\therefore$ $MN = NB = 5$ cm

Now, from rt. $\triangle CMN$, $CN = \sqrt{CM^2 - MN^2} = \sqrt{13^2 - 5^2} = \sqrt{169 - 25} = \sqrt{144} = 12$ cm

$\therefore$ Area of trapezium $ABCD = \dfrac{1}{2} \times$ height $\times$ (sum of the parallel sides)

$$= \frac{1}{2} \times 12 \times (10 + 20) = 6 \times 30 = \mathbf{180\ cm^2}.$$

EXERCISE 34 (d)

1. **Find the area of the following trapeziums:-**

	Height	**Parallel sides**
(*a*)	7 cm	8 cm and 10 cm
(*b*)	15 cm	10 cm and 12 cm
(*c*)	2 cm	2.2 cm and 3.5 cm
(*d*)	4 cm	15 cm and 7.8 cm

2. A garden is in the form of a trapezium whose parallel sides are 40 m and 22 m and the perpendicular distance between them is 12 m. Find the area of the garden.

3. Two parallel sides of a trapezium are 85 cm and 63 cm and its area is 2664 cm². Find its altitude.

4. Find the height of the trapezium, the sum of the lengths of whose bases is 50 cm, and whose area is 500 cm².

5. Find the sum of the lengths of the bases of a trapezium whose altitude is 17cm and whose area is 0.85 m².

6. The area of a trapezium is 210 cm² and its height is 14 cm. If one of the parallel sides is double that of the other, find the two parallel sides.

7. The area of a trapezium is 300 m². The perpendicular distance between the two parallel sides is 15 m. If the difference of the parallel sides is 16 m. Find the lengths of the parallel sides.

8. Two parallel sides of an isosceles trapezium are 6 cm and 14 cm respectively. If the length of each non- parallel side is 5 cm, find the area of the trapezium. (**Hint :** Type solved Ex. 5)

9. The parallel sides of a trapezium are 25 cm and 13 cm, its non- parallel sides are equal, each being 10 cm. Find the area of the trapezium.

10. $ABCD$ is a trapezium of area 91 cm². CD is parallel to AB and CD is longer than AB by 8 cm. If the distance between AB and CD is 7cm, find AB and CD.

11. Find the cost of watering a trapezoidal field whose parallel sides are 10 m and 25 m respectively, the perpendicular distance between them is 15 m and the rate of watering is Rs 4 per m².

12. In the figure, AB and DC are parallel sides of a trapezium $ABCD$ and $\angle ADC = 90°$. Given $AB = 15$ cm, $CD = 40$ cm and diagonal $AC = 41$ cm, calculate the area of trapezium $ABCD$.

(**Hint :** In $\triangle ADC$, $AD = \sqrt{AC^2 - DC^2} = \sqrt{41^2 - 40^2} = 9$ cm

Now, Area of trap. $ABCD = \dfrac{1}{2} \times AD \times (AB + DC))$

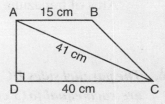

LOOKING BACK
Summary of Key Facts

1.   (i)   Area of a rectangle = length × breadth   (ii) Perimeter = 2(length + breadth)

    (iii)   Length = $\dfrac{\text{area}}{\text{breadth}}$, breadth = $\dfrac{\text{area}}{\text{length}}$, Diagonal = $\sqrt{(\text{length})^2 + (\text{breadth})^2}$

2.   (i)   Area of four walls of a room = 2(length + breadth) × height

    (ii)   Diagonal of a room = $\sqrt{(\text{length})^2 + (\text{breadth})^2 + (\text{height})^2}$

3.   (i)   Area of a square = $(\text{side})^2 = \dfrac{1}{2}(\text{diagonal})^2$ (ii)   Perimeter = 4 × side

    (iii)   Side of a square = $\sqrt{\text{area}}$ (iv)   diagonal of a square = side $\sqrt{2}$

4.   (i)   Area of a parallelogram = Base × Height (_i.e.,_ corresponding altitude)

         Base of the parallelogram = $\dfrac{\text{Area}}{\text{Height}}$, Height of the parallelogram = $\dfrac{\text{Area}}{\text{Base}}$.

5.   (i)   Area of a triangle = $\dfrac{1}{2}$ × Base × Altitude (or Height)

    (ii)   Base of a triangle = $\dfrac{2 \times \text{Area}}{\text{Altitude}}$ (iii)   Height (Altitude) of a triangle = $\dfrac{2 \times \text{Area}}{\text{Base}}$

    (iv)   Area of a triangle = $\sqrt{s(s-a)(s-b)(s-c)}$, where a, b, c are the lengths of the sides and

         s = semi-perimeter = $\dfrac{a+b+c}{2}$.

    (v)   Area of an equilateral triangle = $\dfrac{\sqrt{3}}{4}$ × side^2.

6. Area of a rhombus = $\dfrac{1}{2}$ × product of diagonals.

7.   (i)   Area of a trapezium = $\dfrac{1}{2}$ × (sum of parallel sides) × distance between them

        = $\dfrac{1}{2} \times h \times (b_1 + b_2)$ where h = height and b_1, b_2 are the two bases (parallel sides)

    (ii)   Height (h) = $\dfrac{2 \times \text{Area}}{\text{sum of parallel sides}} = \dfrac{2 \times \text{Area}}{b_1 + b_2}$.

    (iii)   Sum of parallel sides $(b_1 + b_2) = \dfrac{2 \times \text{Area}}{\text{Height}} = \dfrac{2 \times \text{Area}}{h}$.

MENTAL MATHS – 21

Find the area of :
1. a parallelogram whose base is 8 cm and the corresponding altitude 5 cm.
2. a triangle whose base is 7 cm and the corresponding altitude 4 cm.
3. an equilateral triangle of side 8 cm.
4. a rhombus whose diagonals are 8 cm and 5 cm.
5. a trapezium whose parallel sides are of length 8 cm and 5 cm and whose height is 4 cm.
6. a rhombus whose perimeter = 40 cm and altitude = 7 cm.

7. The area of a trapezium is 48 cm² and the sum of the its parallel sides is 16 cm. Find the distance between them.

8. Find the altitude of a triangle if its area is 48 cm² and base is 12 cm.

9. The area of a parallelogram is 35 cm² and the base is 7 cm. Find the corresponding altitude.

10. *ABCD* is a square. Find the area of the shaded region.

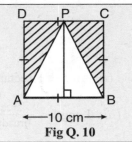

←—10 cm—→

Fig Q. 10

ANSWERS

EXERCISE 34 (a)

1. (*a*) 26 cm, 42.25 cm²   (*b*) 961 cm²   (*c*) 32 cm; $8\sqrt{2}$ cm   2. 19600 ha

3. (*a*) 17.5 cm ; 43.8 cm   (*b*) 23 mm, 667 mm²   (*c*) 13.5 ha; 3180 m   (*d*) 2.5 m, 85 m   (*e*) 100 m, 3 ha.

4. 672 m²   5. (*a*) 40 cm   (*b*) 41 cm   (*c*) 360 cm²   6. (*a*) 400 m   (*b*) $100\sqrt{2}$ m

7. 26910   8. Rs 825   9. 18.4 m²   10. (*a*) 47 cm²   (*b*) 24.45 cm²   (*c*) 30.75 cm²

11. (*a*) 25.8 m²   (*b*) 137.8 m²   (*c*) 22.65 m²   12. Rs 105 000   13. 2.1 kg   14. $\frac{2}{3}$ 15. Rs 505

EXERCISE 34 (b)

1. Base	6	8	5	x	16	20	20
Height	10	14	20	$2x$	15	5	11
Area	30	56	50	x^2	120	50	110

2. (*a*) 24 cm²   (*b*) 100 cm²   (*c*) 75 m²   3. (*a*) 0.0006 m²   (*b*) 0.0015 m²   (*c*) 0.6 m²   (*d*) 0.168 m²

4. (*a*) 99 cm²   (*b*) 36 cm²   (*c*) 27   5. 200 cm²   6. (*a*) 12.5 cm   (*b*) 250 m   (*c*) 800 m

7. 200 m   8. 80 m   9. 720 cm²   10. 1.49 *l*, approx

11. (*a*) 336 cm²   (*b*) 1320 cm²   (*c*) 126 cm²   12. 10 cm²

13. (*a*) 62.352 cm²   (*b*) 10.825 cm²   14. 60 m

EXERCISE 34 (c)

1. (*a*) 24 cm²   (*b*) 14 cm²   (*c*) 10.44 cm²   (*d*) 31.20 m²   (*e*) 4725 cm² or 0.4725 m²   (*f*) 1050 cm²

2. (*a*) 8 cm   (*b*) 28 cm   3. 9 dm   4. 9 cm   5. 80 m   6. 7 m

7. $1\frac{1}{3}$ cm, $2\frac{1}{3}$ cm   8. 4.8 cm   9. (*a*) 24 cm²   (*b*) 21 cm²   (*c*) 33 cm²   (*d*) 1400 cm² (*e*) 0.001 cm²

10. (*a*) 40 cm²   (*b*) 270 cm²   (*c*) 600 cm²   11. 8 cm   12. 32 cm

13. 96 cm²   14. 27.5 m

EXERCISE 34 (d)

1. (*a*) 63 cm²   (*b*) 165 cm²   (*c*) 5.7 cm²   (*d*) 45.6 cm²   2. 372 m²   3. 36 cm   4. 20 cm

5. 10 m   6. 10 cm, 20 cm

7. 28 m, 12 m (**Hint :** You will find $x + y$. *Given :* $x - y = 16$. Solve these two equations)

8. 30 cm²   9. 152 cm²   10. *AB* = 9 cm, *CD* = 17 cm   11. Rs 1050   12. 247.5 cm²

MENTAL MATHS – 21

1. 40 cm²   2. 14 cm²   3. $16\sqrt{3}$ cm²   4. 20 cm²   5. 26 cm²   6. 70 cm²

7. 6 cm   8. 8 cm   9. 5 cm   10. 50 cm²

35. Circumference and Area of a Circle

35.1 Circumference of a Circle

The length of the diameter D is twice the length of the radius r.

$$D = 2r$$

The distance around a circle is called the **circumference (C)** of the circle.

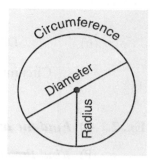

You can measure the circumference of a circular object by winding a piece of fine string round the curved surface of the object exactly once and then measuring the length of the string with a metre scale.

If you measure the circumference of a number of objects and find the value of the ratio $\dfrac{\text{Circumference}}{\text{Diameter}}$ in each

Circular object	Circumference (C)	Diameter (D)	Ratio $\dfrac{C}{D}$ i.e., $\dfrac{\text{Circumference}}{\text{Diameter}}$

case, you will find that the value of $\dfrac{C}{D}$ is almost the same in each case. This will be between 3.1 and 3.2. This constant ratio is named by the Greek letter π (pronounced "pi").

Thus,
$$\frac{C}{D} = \pi \quad \text{or} \quad C = \pi D = \pi(2r) = 2\pi r \qquad \because \quad D = 2r$$

> *i.e.* **Circumference = $\pi \times$ diameter**
>
> $$= 2\pi \times \textbf{radius}$$
> $$\therefore \qquad \textbf{C} = 2\pi r$$

- It has been proved that π is not a rational number. Some reasonably useful approximations of π are $3\frac{1}{7}$ *i.e.*, $\frac{22}{7}$, 3.14, 3.1416.

35.2 Area of a Circle

The area of a circle is found by using the formula
$$\textbf{A} = \pi r^2 \text{ or } \textbf{Area} = \pi \times \textbf{radius} \times \textbf{radius}$$

Note : In terms of diameter, area of circle $= \pi\left(\dfrac{D}{2}\right)^2 = \dfrac{1}{4}\pi D^2$

35.3 Area of a Circular Ring

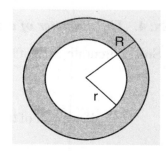

Area of the space enclosed between two concentric circles (shaded area)
$$= \pi(R^2 - r^2),$$
where R and r are the radii of the outer and inner circle respectively.

Ex. 1. *Find the circumference and area of a circle of* **(a)** *radius = 21 cm, using* $\pi = \frac{22}{7}$

       (b) *diameter = 28 cm, using* $\pi = 3.14$

Sol. *(a)*   Circumference $= 2\pi r = \left(2 \times \frac{22}{7} \times 21\right)$ cm $= \mathbf{132\ cm}$

             Area $= \pi r^2 = \left(\frac{22}{7} \times 21 \times 21\right)$ cm^2 $= \mathbf{1386\ cm^2}$

   (b)   Diameter $= 28$ cm $\Rightarrow$ Radius $= \frac{28}{2}$ cm $= 14$ cm

         Circumference $= 2\pi r = (2 \times 3.14 \times 14)$ cm $= \mathbf{87.92\ cm.}$

               Area $= \pi r^2 = 3.14 \times 14 \times 14 = \mathbf{615.44\ cm^2.}$

Ex. 2. **(i)** *Find the area of a circle whose circumference is 44 cm,* $\pi = \frac{22}{7}$?

        (ii) *Find the circumference of a circle whose area = 12474 cm*^{2}.

Sol. *(i)*   Let r be the radius of the given circle

$$C = 2\pi r \quad \therefore \quad 44 = 2 \times \frac{22}{7} \times r \quad \Rightarrow \quad r = \frac{44 \times 7}{2 \times 22} = 7 \text{ cm}$$

$$\therefore \qquad \text{Area} = \pi r^2 = \frac{22}{7} \times 7 \times 7 = \mathbf{154\ cm^2.}$$

(ii) Let r be the radius of the circle, then

$$A = \pi r^2 \quad \Rightarrow \quad 12474 = \frac{22}{7} \times r^2 \quad \Rightarrow \quad r^2 = \frac{12474 \times 7}{22}$$

$$\Rightarrow \qquad r^2 = 3969 \quad \Rightarrow \quad r = \sqrt{3969} = 63 \text{ cm.}$$

$$\therefore \text{Circumference} = 2\pi r = 2 \times \frac{22}{7} \times 63 = \mathbf{396\ cm.}$$

```
           6 3
      ┌─────────
   6  │ 39 69
      │ 36
      │ ──
  123 │   369
      │   369
      │   ──
      │     0
```

Ex. 3. *How many times will the wheel of a car rotate in a journey of 88 km if the diameter of the wheel is 56 cm?* $\left(Take\ \pi = \frac{22}{7}\right)$

Sol. Diameter of the wheel $(D) = 56$ cm

$$\therefore \quad \text{Circumference of the wheel} = \pi D = \frac{22}{7} \times 56 = 176 \text{ cm}$$

Length of the journey $= 88$ km $= 88 \times 1000 \times 100$ cm

$\therefore$ Number of times the wheel will rotate in covering the above journey

$$= \frac{88 \times 1000 \times 100}{176} = \mathbf{50,000.}$$

Ex. 4. *The diameter of a semi-circular protractor is 7 cm. Find its perimeter.* $\left(\pi = \frac{22}{7}\right)$

Sol. Circumference of the semi-circular protractor

$$= \frac{1}{2}\pi D = \frac{1}{2} \times \frac{22}{7} \times 7 \text{ cm} \left(\pi = \frac{22}{7}\right) = 11 \text{ cm}$$

$\therefore$ Perimeter of the protractor = Its circumference + diameter

$$= (11 + 7) \text{ cm} = \mathbf{18\ cm.}$$

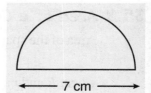

7 cm

Ex. 5. *A piece of wire is bent in the shape of an equilateral triangle of each side 6.6 cm. It is rebent to form a circular ring. What is the diameter of the ring ?*

Sol. ∴ Each side of the equi. $\Delta = 6.6$ cm

∴ Perimeter of the equi Δ

$$= 3 \times 6.6 \text{ cm} = 19.8 \text{ cm}$$

Circumference of the circular ring = Perimeter of the Δ

i.e., $\qquad \pi \times d = 19.8 \Rightarrow \dfrac{22}{7}d = 19.8 \Rightarrow \dfrac{22}{7} \times d = \dfrac{198}{10}$

$$d = \dfrac{198}{10} \times \dfrac{7}{22} \text{ cm} = \dfrac{63}{10} \text{ cm} = 6.3 \text{ cm}$$

Hence, the diameter of the ring $= 6.3$ cm.

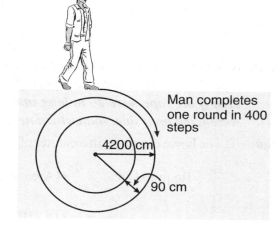

Ex. 6. *A circular pond has a 90 cm wide footpath along the edge. A man walks around the outer edge of the footpath with 66 cm long steps. In 400 steps, he makes a full round. What is the radius of the pond?*

Sol. Circumference of the outer edge $= 66 \times 400$

$$= 26400 \text{ cm}$$

We know that $C = 2\pi r$ ∴ $26400 = 2 \times \dfrac{22}{7} \times r$

$\Rightarrow \qquad\qquad r = \dfrac{26400 \times 7}{2 \times 22} = 4200 \text{ cm}$

∴ Radius of the outer edge $= 4200$ cm

∴ Radius of the pond = Radius of the outer edge

$$- \text{ width of the path}$$

$$= 4200 \text{ cm} - 90 \text{ cm}$$

$$= 4110 \text{cm} = \dfrac{4110}{100} = \mathbf{41.1\,m.}$$

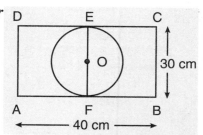

Man completes
one round in 400
steps

4200 cm

90 cm

Ex. 7. *A copper wire when bent in the form of a square encloses an area of 121 cm². If the same wire is bent in the form of a circle, find the area of the circle.*

Sol. Area of the square $= 121$ cm².

∴ One side of the square $= \sqrt{121} = 11$ cm

Circumference of the circle = Length of the wire = perimeter of the square $= 4 \times 11 = 44$ cm

∴ $2\pi r = 44$ or $2 \times \dfrac{22}{7} \times r = 44 \Rightarrow r = \dfrac{44 \times 7}{2 \times 22} = 7$ cm

∴ Area of the circle $= \pi r^2 = \dfrac{22}{7} \times 7 \times 7 = \mathbf{154\ cm^2.}$

Ex. 8. *From a rectangular metal sheet of sides 30 cm and 40 cm, a circular off. Find the area of the remaining sheet.*

Sol. Given : Sides of the rectangular metal sheet are 30 cm and 40 cm.

Area of rectangular metal sheet $= 30 \text{ cm} \times 40 \text{ cm}$

$$= 1200 \text{ cm}^2$$

Diameter of the biggest circular sheet that can be cut off from the rectangular sheet $= 30$ cm

30 cm

40 cm

Radius of this circular sheet $= \dfrac{30}{2} = 15$ cm

$\therefore$ Area of the circular sheet $= \pi r^2 = \dfrac{22}{7} \times 15 \times 15$ cm$^2 = \dfrac{4950}{7}$ cm$^2 = 707.14$ cm^2.

$\therefore$ Area of the remaining sheet $= 1200$ cm$^2 - 707.14$ cm$^2 = \textbf{492.86 cm}^2$.

Ex. 9. *A 7 m wide path is to be constructed all around, and outside a circular garden of diameter 112 m. Find the cost of constructing the path at Rs 50 per square metre.*

Sol. Radius of inner circle $= \dfrac{112}{2} = 56$ m

Radius of outer circle $= 56 + 7 = 63$ m

Area of path = Area of outer circle – area of inner circle

$= \pi \times 63^2 - \pi \times 56^2 = \pi \left(63^2 - 56^2\right) = \dfrac{22}{7}(63 + 56)(63 - 56)$

$= \dfrac{22}{7} \times 119 \times 7 = 22 \times 119 = 2618$ m^2

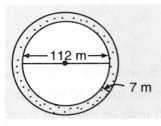
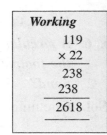

Working

$\begin{array}{r} 119 \\ \times\ 22 \\ \hline 238 \\ 238 \\ \hline 2618 \end{array}$

$\therefore$ Cost of constructing the path = Rs $(2618 \times 50) = \textbf{Rs 130900.}$

Ex.10. *A horse is tied to a pole fixed at one corner of a 30 m × 30 m square field of grass, by means of 10 m long rope. Find (i) the area of that part of the field in which the horse can graze (ii) the increase in the grazing area if the rope were 20 m long instead of being 10 m long. (iii) What will be the area in (i) if the pole were fixed on a side, somewhere near the middle.*

Sol. (*i*) The horse can graze in a quarter of the circular field of radius 10 cm, because the length of the rope is 10 m

$\therefore$ Required area $= \dfrac{1}{4} \times$ (Area of a circle with radius 10 m)

$= \dfrac{1}{4} \times (\pi \times 10^2) = \dfrac{1}{4} \times (3.14 \times 100) = \dfrac{314}{4} = \textbf{78.5 m}^2$

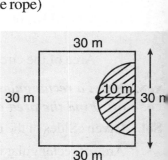

(*ii*) Now, the rope is of length 20 m, $\therefore$ radius = 20 m

$\therefore$ Area of the field in which the horse can now graze

$= \dfrac{1}{4} \times (\pi \times 20^2) = \dfrac{1}{4} \times 3.14 \times 400 = \textbf{314 m}^2$

$\therefore$ Increase in grazing area $= 314$ m$^2 - 78.5$ m$^2 = \textbf{235.5 m}^2$

(*iii*) In this case, the horse is tied to a pole fixed on the side of the field, near its middle. The area which the horse can graze is in the form of a semi-circle with radius 10 m (the length of the rope)

$\therefore$ Required area $= \dfrac{1}{2} \pi r^2 = \dfrac{1}{2}(3.14 \times 10^2) = \dfrac{1}{2} \times 3.14 \times 100$

$= \dfrac{1}{2} \times 314 = \textbf{157 m}^2.$

EXERCISE 35

1. **Find the circumference and area of a circle of :**

   (*i*) radius = 10.5 cm   (*ii*) radius = 35 cm   (*iii*) diameter = 9.8 cm   (*iv*) diameter = 56 cm

2. **Taking $\pi = \dfrac{22}{7}$, find the diameter of the circle whose,**

   (*i*) circumference = 61.6 cm   (*ii*) area = 154 cm^2.

3. The circumference of a flower bed is 88 cm. Find its area.

4. The ratio of the radii of two wheels is 3 : 4. What is the ratio of their circumferences?

5. A wire is in the form of a circle of radius 42 cm. It is bent into a square. Find the side of the square. $\left(\text{Take } \pi = \dfrac{22}{7} \right)$

6. In the adjoining figure, the radius is 3.5 cm. Find the perimeter of the quarter of the circle.
   $\left(\text{Take } \pi = \dfrac{22}{7} \right)$

3.5 cm

7. **Find the perimeter of the following shapes to 1 d.p. Take π =3.14.**

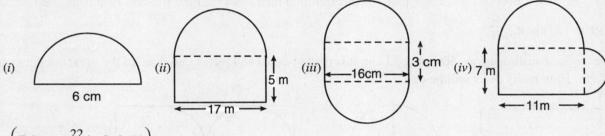

(*i*)   6 cm   (*ii*)   5 m, 17 m   (*iii*)   16cm, 3 cm   (*iv*) 7 m, 11m

$\left(\text{Take } \pi = \dfrac{22}{7} \text{ in Q. 8–11} \right)$

8. The diameter of a bicycle wheel is 28 cm. What distance will it cover in 100 revolutions?

9. The radius of a circular field is 24.5 m. Find the distance run by a boy in making 4 complete turns.

10. The radius of a racing ground is 280 m. How many rounds will one have to make in running a distance of 17.6 km?

11. A wheel, 14 cm in diameter, makes 3000 revolutions per minute. Find its speed in m/sec.

12. The circumference of the front wheel of a car is 10 dm and that of the hind wheel in 16 dm. How may revolutions more will the first wheel make than the second in covering a distance of 96 km?

13. A circular road runs round a circular ground. if the difference between the circumferences of the outer circle and the inner circle is 66 metres, find the width of the road.

14. The radius of a circle is 35 cm. A quadrant (*i.e.* $\dfrac{1}{4}$ of the circle) is cut away from the circle. Find the perimeter of the cut out portion. $\left(\text{Take } \pi \text{ for } \dfrac{22}{7} \right)$

15. The area of a circle is 15400 m^2. Find its circumference. $\left(\text{Take } \pi \ \dfrac{22}{7} \right)$

Fig. Q. 14

16. **Find the area of each shape correct to 1 d.p. (Use 3.14 for π)**

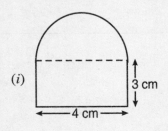

(*i*)   3 cm, 4 cm

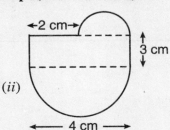

(*ii*)   2 cm, 3 cm, 4 cm

Fig. Q. 16

17. Find the shaded area correct to 1 d.p. (π = 3.14).

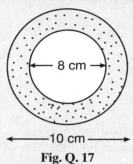

Fig. Q. 17

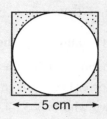

Fig. Q. 18

18. Covers for cans are stamped out of sheets of metal. How many square centimetres of waste material are there when the covers are cut from a square 5 cm wide ? (Use 3.14 for π)

19. The radius of a circular field is 20 m. Inside it runs a path 5 m wide all around. Find the area of the path.

(Take $\pi = \frac{22}{7}$)

20. A road 3.5 m wide surrounds a circular plot whose circumference is 44 m. Find the cost of paving the road at

Rs 20 per m². (Take $\pi = \frac{22}{7}$)

21. A sheet of metal has dimensions 56 cm by 33 cm. It is melted down and recast into discs of the same thickness and radius 7 cm. How many discs will be cast ?

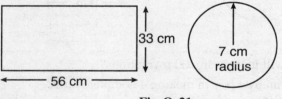

Fig. Q. 21

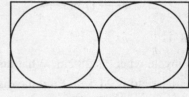

Fig. Q. 22

22. The area of two equal circles in the figure is 308 cm². Find the perimeter of the rectangle.

23. The shaded portion in the given figure shows a circular path enclosed by two concentric circles. If the outer circumference of the path is 88 cm and the uniform width of the path is 3.5 cm; find the area of the path.

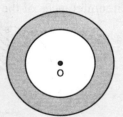

Fig. Q. 23

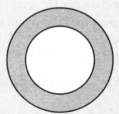

Fig. Q. 24

24. The area enclosed between two concentric circles is 1386 cm². If the radius of the inner circle is 28 cm. Calculate the radius of the outer circle.

LOOKING BACK
Summary of Key Facts

For a circle of radius r units,

1. diameter $d = 2r$ units

2. Circumference (C) $= \pi \times$ diameter $= \pi d = 2\pi r$ units

   π is not a rational number. An approximate value of π is taken as $\frac{22}{7}$ or 3.14 or 3.1416.

3. Area of a circle $= \pi \times (\text{radius})^2 = \pi r^2$ sq units.

4. Area of a semi-circle of radius $r = \frac{1}{2}\pi r^2$.

5. Area of a quadrant of circle of radius $r = \frac{1}{4}\pi r^2$.

MENTAL MATHS – 22

Find the circumference of a circle whose

1. diameter is 14 cm $\left(\pi = \frac{22}{7}\right)$ 2. radius is 21 cm $\left(\pi = \frac{22}{7}\right)$.   3. diameter is 10 cm ($\pi = 3.14$)

Find the area of a circle whose

4. radius 7 cm $\left(\pi = \frac{22}{7}\right)$ 5. radius is 10 cm ($\pi = 3.14$).

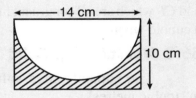

6. What is the radius of a circle whose area is 25π.
7. The circumference of a circle is $4\pi r$. Find its area.
8. What is the area of a quadrant of a circle of radius $2r$.
9. A water sprinkler in a field sprays water as far as 7 cm in all directions. Find the length of the outer edge of wet grass.
10. Find the area of the shaded portion.

Fig. Q. 10

ANSWERS

EXERCISE 35

1. (i) $C = 66$ cm; $A = 346.5$ cm^2 (ii) $C = 220$ cm; $A = 3850$ cm^2 (iii) $C = 30.8$ cm; $A = 75.46$ cm^2
   (iv) $C = 176$ cm; $A = 2464$ cm^2 2. (i) $d = 19.6$ cm   (ii) $d = 14$ cm.

3. 616 cm^2 4. 3 : 4   5. 66 cm   6. 12.5 cm

7. (i) 15.5 cm   (ii) 53.7 cm   (iii) 56.24 cm   (iv) 46.3 m

8. 88 m   9. 616 m   10. 10   11. 22 m/sec   12. 36000   13. 10.5 m

14. 125 cm   15. 440 m   16. (i) 18.3 cm^3 (ii) 19.9 cm^2 17. 28.3 cm^2 18. 5.4 cm^2

19. 550 m^2 20. Rs 3850   21. 12   22. 84 cm   23. 269.5 cm^2 24. 35 cm.

MENTAL MATHS – 22

1. 44 cm   2. 132 cm   3. 31.4 cm   4. 154 cm^2 5. 314 cm^2 6. 5

7. $4\pi r^2$ 8. πr^2 9. 44 cm   10. 63 cm^2

36. Volume and Surface Area of Solids

36.1 Cuboid

A **cuboid** is a rectangular solid. A brick, a book, a match box and an almirah all are the forms of a cuboid.

The figure here shows a cuboid having vertices $A, B, C, D,$ E, F, G and H. It has **six faces** which are the rectangles $ABCD$, $EFGH$, $CDHG$, $ABFE$, $ADHE$ and $BCGF$. It has **twelve edges** which are the line segments $AB, BC, CD, DH, HG, GC, GF, AE,$ DA, HE, BF and EF. The vertices $A, B, F, E, D, C, G, F, H$ are its **corners.**

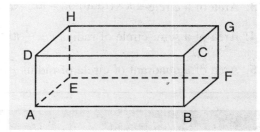

36.2 Cube

A cube is a rectangular solid whose all sides are equal. A chalk-box, a die, a packing case having all sides equal, a room measuring 4 m $\times$ 4 m $\times$ 4 m all are in the form of a cube. The figure at the right shows a cube whose six faces are the squares $ABCD$, $CDEF$, $EFGH$, $ABGH$, $BCFG$ and $ADEH$.

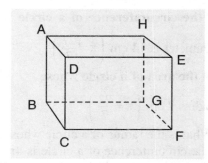

Its sides are $AB, BC, CD, DE, EF, FG, GH, HA, AD, HE, BG$ and CF which are all congruent line segments. Cube is a special case of a cuboid where $l = b = h$.

36.3 Volume of a Solid

The capacity of a solid is called its volume and is measured in cm^3 (cubic centimetres) or m^3 (cubic metres)

Total Surface Area : The sum of the surface areas of the six faces of the cuboid or cube is its total surface area.

36.4 Key Facts

1. The volume of a cube of 1 cm side is 1 cm $\times$ 1 cm $\times$ 1 cm *i.e.*, **1 cm^3**, read as **1 cubic centimetre.**

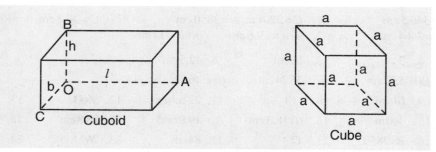

Cuboid   Cube

2. 1000 mm^3 = 1 cm^3; **1 litre = 1 dm^3 = 1000 cm^3**
   1000 cm^3 = 1 dm^3; 1 ml = 1 cm^3
   1000 dm^3 or 10^6 cm^3 = 1 m^3; 1 kl = 1000 l = 10^6 cm^3.

3. **Formulae**

A. **Cuboid :** Length $= l$ units, breadth $= b$ units, height $= h$ units

1. *Volume= (l × b × h) cubic units*

2. *Diagonal of the cuboid =* $\sqrt{l^2 + b^2 + h^2}$ *units.*

3. *Total Surface Area = 2 (l b + bh + l h) sq units*

4. *Lateral Surface Area or Area of 4 walls of a room = 2 (l + b) × h sq units.*

B. **Cube :** each edge $= a$ units

1. *Volume = a^3 cubic units*   2. *Diagonal of the cube = a $\sqrt{3}$ units.*

3. *Total Surface Area = 6 a^2 sq units.*   4. *Lateral Surface Area = 4 a^2 sq units.*

36.5 Solved Examples

Ex. 1. *Find the volume, total surface area and lateral surface area of a cuboid whose dimensions are length = 10 cm, breadth = 12 cm and height = 15 cm.*

Sol. Given : $l = 10$ cm, $b = 12$ cm, $h = 15$ cm

Volume of the cuboid $= (l \times b \times h)$ cubic units $= (10 \times 12 \times 15)$ cm^3 = **1800 cm^3**

Total Surface Area of the cuboid $\qquad = 2(lb + bh + lh)$ sq units

$\qquad\qquad\qquad\qquad\qquad\qquad\qquad = 2(10 \times 12 + 12 \times 15 + 10 \times 15)$ cm^2

$\qquad\qquad\qquad\qquad\qquad\qquad\qquad = 2(120 + 180 + 150)$ cm$^2 = 2(450)$ cm$^2 = $ **900 cm^2.**

Lateral Surface Area of the cuboid $= 2(l + b) \times h$ sq units

$\qquad\qquad\qquad\qquad\qquad = 2(10 + 12) \times 15$ cm$^2 = 2 \times 22 \times 15$ cm$^2 = $ **660 cm^2.**

Ex. 2. *How many planks each of which is 2 m long, 14 cm broad and 5 cm thick can be prepared from a wooden block 8 m long, 70 cm broad and 45 cm thick?*

Sol. Length of the wooden block $= 8$ m $= 800$ cm, breadth $= 70$ cm, thickness $= 45$ cm.

$\therefore$ Volume of the wooden block $= (800 \times 70 \times 45)$ cm^3.

Length of the plank $= 2$ m $= 200$ cm, breadth $= 14$ cm, thickness $= 5$ cm.

$\therefore$ Volume of one plank $= (200 \times 14 \times 5)$ cm^3.

Number of planks $= \dfrac{\text{Volume of the wooden block}}{\text{Volume of one plank}} = \dfrac{(800 \times 70 \times 45)}{(200 \times 14 \times 5)} = $ **180.**

Ex. 3. *A cuboid has a total surface area of 55 m^2 and its lateral surface area is 27 m^2. Find the area of its base.*

Sol. Total surface area of a cuboid $= 2$(Area of its base) + Lateral Surface Area

$\qquad\qquad\therefore\qquad\qquad 55$ m$^2 = 2$ (Area of base) $+ 27$ m^2

$\Rightarrow 2$ (Area of base) $= 55$ m$^2 - 27$ m$^2 = 28$ m$^2 \qquad \Rightarrow \qquad$ Area of base $= \dfrac{28}{2}$m$^2 = $ **14 m^2.**

Ex. 4. *The outer dimensions of a closed wooden box are 14 cm by 10 cm by 8 cm. Thickness of wood is 1.5 cm. Find the total cost of wood required to make the box if 1 cm^3 of wood costs Rs 2.50.*

Sol. External dimensions of the box are : Length $= 14$ cm, Breadth $= 10$ cm, Height $= 8$ cm.

∴   External Volume of the box = $(14 \times 10 \times 8)$ cm^3 = 1120 cm^3.

Thickness of wood = 1.5 cm.

∴   Internal Length = $14 - 3 = 11$ cm, Internal Breadth = $10 - 3 = 7$ cm, ∴ Internal Height = $8 - 3 = 5$ cm.

∴   Internal Volume = $(11 \times 7 \times 5)$ cm^3 = 385 cm^3

∴   Volume of wood = External Volume – Internal Volume = 1120 cm^3 – 385 cm^3 = 735 cm^3

∴   Total cost of wood required to make the box = Rs (735×2.50) = **Rs 1837.50.**

Ex. 5. *Find the volume, total surface area and length of the diagonal of a cube whose edge is 1.2 m.* **(Given $\sqrt{3}$ = 1.732 approx)**

Sol.   Volume of a cube = (side)^3 cubic units = $(1.2)^3$ m^3 = 1.728 m^3

Total Surface Area = $6 \times$ (side)^2 sq. units = $6 \times (1.2)^2$ m^2 = 6×1.44 m^2 = 8.64 m^2

Length of diagonal = (side) $\sqrt{3}$ units = $1.2 \times \sqrt{3}$ units = 1.2×1.732 = 2.0784 units

$= \textbf{2.08 m}$ (correct to 2 d.p)

Ex. 6. *Three cuboids of dimensions 2 cm × 5 cm × 7 cm, 4 cm × 4 cm × 5 cm and 2 cm × 3 cm × 11 cm, are melted and a cube is formed. Find the side of the cube.*

Sol.   Total volume of the three cuboids

$= (2 \times 5 \times 7)$ cm^3 + $(4 \times 4 \times 5)$ cm^3 + $(2 \times 3 \times 11)$ cm^3 = 70 cm^3 + 80 cm^3 + 66 cm^3 = 216 cm^3

∴   Volume of the cube formed = 216 cm^3

Let a cm be length of the side of the cube so formed.

Then $a^3 = 216$ cm^3 $\Rightarrow$ $a = \sqrt[3]{216}$ cm = 6 cm

∴   Length of one side of the cube = **6 cm.**

EXERCISE 36

1. **Find the surface area and volume of a cuboid whose dimensions are**
   (*i*) 3 m, 4 m and 5 m   (*ii*) 36 m, 12 m and 1 m   (*iii*) 12 cm, 16 cm and 8 cm

2. Find the surface area and volume of a cube whose edge is (*i*) 8 cm (*ii*) 4 m.

3. The surface area of a cube is $32\frac{2}{3}$ m^2. Find the volume of the cube.

4. (*a*) **Express** (*i*) 2.5 m^3 in cm^3 and (*ii*) 30 000 cm^3 in m^3.

   (*b*) Find the volume of a tank 1 m long, $\frac{1}{2}$ m wide and 75 cm deep in m^3.

5. What is the area of the cardboard needed to make a rectangular box 12 cm long, 8 cm wide and 6 cm high?

6. A beam 9 m long, 50 cm wide, and 20 cm deep is made of wood which weighs 30 kg per m^3; find the weight of the beam.

7. The bottom of a petrol tin measures 25 cm by 25 cm. It is 36 cm high. How many litres of petrol will it hold if filled to 6 cm from top?

8. How many match-boxes 50 mm by 40 mm by 25 mm can be picked into a carton $\frac{1}{2}$ m by 40 cm by 25 cm ?

9. A stack of bricks is 4.5 m long, 6.75 m wide, and 5.4 m high. If each brick is 18 cm × 9 cm × 6 cm, find the number of such bricks in this stack.

10. Find in tonnes the weight of water which a tank 8 m long, 7 m wide and 5 m deep will hold if 1 litre of water weighs 1 kg. (1 tonne = 1000 kg)

11. Find the length of the side of a cube which has a volume equal to half that of a box 10 cm × 4 cm × 3.2 cm.

12. A metal cube of 9 cm is melted and formed into three smaller cubes. If the edge of two smaller cubes are I cm and 6 cm, find the side of the third smaller cube.

13. The whole surface of a rectangular block is 846 cm². Find the length , breadth and height if these dimensions are proportional to 5 : 4 : 3 .

14. 50 students sit in a class room. Each student requires 9 m² on floor and 108 m³ in space. If the length of the room is 25 m, find the breadth and height of the room.

15. The outer dimension of a closed wooden box are 42 cm × 30 cm × 27 cm. If the thickness of the wood is 1 cm, find the capacity of the box.

16. The dimensions of a room are 12.5 m by 9 m by 7 m. There are 2 doors and 3 windows in the room. Each door measures 2.4 m by 1.5 m and each window 1.4 m by 1.2 m. Find the cost of painting the walls at Rs. 3.50 per square metre.

17. Find the volume of a cube (in m³) whose diagonal is 6 m.

18. A rectangular water reservoir is 11 m by 4 m at the base. Water flows into it at the rate of 16 m per second through a pipe having a cross-section 7.7 cm × 2 cm. Find the height to which the water will rise in the reservoir in 30 minutes.

    (**Hint :** Volume of water flowing in 30 mins. = (0.077 × 0.02 × 16 × 60 × 30) m³

    Area of base = (11 × 4) m²   ∴   Height = $\frac{\text{Volume of water}}{\text{Area}}$)

19. The length of a cold storage is double its breadth. Its height is 3 metres. The area of its four walls (including doors) is 108 m². Find its volume.

20. A field is 200 m long and 120 m wide. A plot (outside the field) 60 m long and 50 m wide is dug to a depth of 12 m and the earth taken out from the plot is spread evenly in the field. By how much is the level of field raised?

    (**Hint :** Level of field raised = $\frac{\text{volume of the earth dug out}}{\text{Area of field}}$)

21. A box is tightly packed with tins of soft drink of the same size. These tins are arranged in 2 layers contains 3 rows of 5 tins as shown. If the diameter of each tin is 6 cm and it is 12 cm high, find the volume of the box.

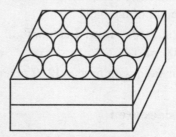

    (**Hint :** Length = 6 × 5 = 30 cm, Breadth = 6 × 3 = 18 cm, Height = 12 × 2 (being 2 layers) = 24 cm)

LOOKING BACK
Summary of Key Facts

1. Volume of a cuboid = $(l \times b \times h)$ cubic units.

   Volume of a cube = a^3 cubic units.

2. Total surface area of a cuboid = $2(lh + bh + lb)$ square units.

   Total surface area of a cube = $6a^2$ square units.

3. Lateral surface area of a cuboid (Area of 4 walls of a room)= $2(l+b) \times h$ square units.

   Lateral surface area of a cube = $4a^2$ square units.

4. Diagonal of a cuboid = $\sqrt{l^2 + b^2 + h^2}$ units,

   Diagonal of a cube = $a\sqrt{3}$ units.

MENTAL MATHS – 23

1. The volume of a cube is 64 m^3. Find its total surface area.

2. The number of rectangular faces of a cuboid are ....

3. Ratios of the surface areas of two cubes is 16 : 25. What is the ratios of their sides ?

4. The area of four walls of a room is 128 m^2. The perimeter of the floor is 32 m. What is the height of the room ?

5. **The volume of a cuboid whose length, breadth and height are in the ratio 5 : 1 : 4 is**

   (a) 10 × length^3 (b) 10 × breadth^3 (c) 20 × breadth^3 (d) 20 × height^3.

6. Find the surface area of cubical box whose each side is 1 cm assuming that the box has no lid.

7. A room is 10 m long, 7 m wide and 4 m high. How many persons can be accomodated in it if each person requires 8 m^3 of space.

8. A container is 100 cm long, 80 cm wide and 60 cm high. How many litres of water can it hold if 1000 cm^3 = 1 litre.

UNIT REVIEW – 6

1. The length and breadth of a rectangular field are in the ratio 4 : 3. If the area of the field is 5292 m^2, find the cost of fencing the field at Rs 4 per metre.

2. The length of a rectangle is 30 cm and its diagonal is 34 cm. Find the breadth and area of the rectangle.

3. The perimeters of two squares are 256 cm and 192 cm. Find the perimeter of a square whose area is equal to sum of the areas of these two squares.

4. A room is 38 m long and 32 m broad. Allowing 60 m^2 for doors and windows, the cost of repairing the walls at the rate of Rs 7.20 is Rs 4608. Find the height of the hall.

5. A square field has an area of 7.29 ares. Find the cost of putting a fence around it at the rate of Rs 10.50 per metre (**Hint :** 1 Are = 100 m^2).

6. Find in hectares the area of a triangular field with base = 1210 m and height = 800 m.
   (**Hint :** 10000 m^2 = 1 hectare)

7. **Find the area of a triangle whose sides are :**

   (a) 17m, 25m, 26m   (b) equilateral triangle of side 12 cm $\left(\sqrt{3} = 1.732\right)$

8. The sides of a triangle are 25cm, 39 cm and 56 cm. Find the altitude to the longest side.

9. Find the area of a right-angled triangle with hypotenuse 26 cm and base = 10 cm.

10. The base of an isosceles triangle is 12 cm and its perimeter is 32 cm. Find its area.

11. Find the area of the shaded region in the given figure.

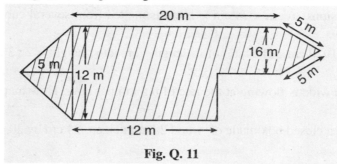

Fig. Q. 11

12. The base of a parallelogram is thrice its height. If the area is 867 cm², find the base and height of the parallelogram.

13. Find the area of a rhombus having each side = 15 cm and one of whose diagonals is 24 cm.

14. Two sides of a parallelogram are 22 cm and 25 cm. If the altitude corresponding to side 22 cm is 15 cm, find the attitude corresponding to the other side.

15. The area of a trapezium is 460 cm². The lengths of the parallel sides are respectively 22 cm and 24 cm. Find the distance between them.

16. If the perimeter of a trapezium is 64 cm, its non-parallel sides are equal to 12 cm each and its altitude is 10 cm, find the area of the trapezium.

17. The area of a trapezium is 164 cm² and its height is 8 cm. If one side is 5 more than 2 times the other side, find the two parallel sides.

18. Find the area enclosed by the given figure as the sum of the areas of a rectangle and a trapezium.

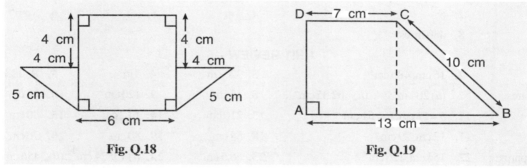

Fig. Q.18   **Fig. Q.19**

19. In the above figure $AB \parallel DC$ and $DA \perp AB$. Given, $DC = 7$ cm, $CB = 10$ cm and $AB = 13$ cm., find the area of the trapezium $ABCD$.

20. A bicycle wheel makes 5,000 revolutions in moving 11 km. Find the diameter of the wheel. $\left(\text{Take } \pi = \dfrac{22}{7}\right)$

21. The circumference of a circular plot is 220 m. A 15 m wide concrete track runs around outside the plot. Find the area of the track. $\left(\text{Use } \pi = \dfrac{22}{7}\right)$

22. The sum of the radii of two circles is 140 cm and the difference of their circumference is 88 cm. Find the diameters of the circles.

(**Hint :** $r_1 + r_2 = 140$; $2\pi r_1 - 2\pi r_2 = 88$)

23. In the figure, AB and PQ are perpendicular diameters of the circle whose centre is O

and radius $OA = 7$cm. Find the area of the shaded portion. $\left(\text{Use } \pi = \dfrac{22}{7}\right)$

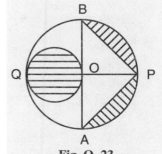

Fig. Q. 23

24. The lateral surface area of a cube is 2304 cm^2. **Find its** (*i*) volume (*ii*) total surface area.

25. A block of metal of dimensions 36 cm × 24 cm × 16cm is melted from several cubes of side 8 cm each. Find the number of cubes formed.

26. The volume of a cuboid is 1920 cm^3. The ratio of its length : breadth : height = 2 : 3 : 5. Find the dimensions of the cuboid.

27. A river 3 m deep and 35 m wide is flowing at the rate of 6.5 km per hour. How many cubic metres of water flows into sea per minute ?

28. The internal dimensions of a closed box made of wood 2 cm thick are 24 cm by 20 cm by 16 cm. Find the volume of wood in the box.

ANSWERS

EXERCISE 36

1. (*i*) 94 m^2, 60 m^3 (*ii*) 960 m^2, 432 m^3 (*iii*) 832 cm^2, 1536 cm^3

2. (*i*) 384 cm^2, 512 cm^3 (*ii*) 96 m^2, 64 m^3 3. $12\frac{19}{27}$ m^3

4. (*a*) (*i*) 2.5×10^6 cm^3 (*ii*) 0.03 m^3 (*b*) 0.375 m^3

5. 432 cm^2 6. 27 kg   7. 18.75 *l*   8. 1000   9. 168750   10. 280 *t*

11. 4 cm   12. 8 cm   13. 15 cm, 12 cm, 9 cm   14. breadth = 18 m, height = 12 m

15. 28,000 cm^3 16. Rs 1010.66   17. $24\sqrt{3}$ m^3 18. 1.008 m   19. 216 m^3 20. 1.5 m   21. 12,960 cm^3

MENTAL MATHS – 23

1. 96 m^2 2. 6   3. 4 : 5   4. 4 m   5. (*c*)   6. 5 cm^2

7. 35   8. 480 litres.

UNIT REVIEW – 6

1. Rs 1176   2. 16 cm, 480 cm^2 3. 320 cm   4. 5 m   5. Rs 1134

6. 48.4 hectares   7. (*a*) 204 m^2 (*b*) 62.35 cm^2 8. 15 cm   9. 120 cm^2 10. 48 cm^2

11. 326 m^2 12. *b* = 17 cm, *h* = 51 cm   13. 216 cm^2 14. 13.2 cm   15. 20 cm

16. 200 cm^2 17. 12 cm, 29 cm   18. 54 cm^2 19. 80 cm^2 20. 70 cm

21. 4007 m^2 approx.   22. 154 cm, 126 cm   23. 66.5 cm^2 24. (*i*) 13824 cm^3, (*ii*) 3456 cm^2

25. 27   26. 8 cm, 12 cm, 20 cm   27. 11,375 m^3 per minute   28. 5760 cm^3.

37. Statistics

SECTION-A

FREQUENCY DISTRIBUTION

37.1 Data

The test scores shown at the right are those obtained by 10 students in each of the two tests given in a mathematics course. These marks have been arranged in tables in such a way that whatever information we may wish to obtain about these tests may be obtained easily. We call such a collection of facts a **set of data**. Each member of a set of data is called a datum. (**Data** is plural of **datum**)

	Test 1	Test 2
Pradeep	77	96
Shekhar	40	70
Ranjan	45	70
Amit	81	86
Rakesh	69	70
Sunil	81	91
Vinod	94	96
Harish	51	70
Asha	87	89
Rekha	50	58

> *A collection of numerical facts about objects or events is called data.*
>
> *Statistics is the science of collecting, organising, and analyzing sets of data in order to reveal information.*

EXERCISE 37 (a)

1. **The following is a listing of the names, heights, and weights of five boys in a seventh-grade basket-ball team**

   Devendra 167 cm, 66 kg; Narendra 160 cm, 61 kg; Sanjay 165 cm, 65 kg; Piyush 175 cm, 68 kg; Girish 155 cm, 60 kg

   Organise these data as follows :

   (*a*) Ascending order of heights   (*b*) Ascending order of weights,   (*c*) Alphabetical order.

2. **Some Particulars of four pupils are shown below :**

   Pawan's height is 155 cm.   Hema's height is 140 cm.
   He is 12-years-old.   She is 14-years-old.
   He weighs 48 kg.   She weighs 45 kg.
   His hobby is stamp-collecting.   Her hobby is gardening.
   Vivek's height is 145 cm.   Shyam's height is 158 cm.
   He is 11-years-old.   He is 13-years-old.
   He weighs 42 kg.   He weighs 46 kg.
   His hobby is painting.   His hobby is photography.

   Use the above data to complete the table below :

Name	Age	Height	Weight	Hobby
Pawan				
Hema				
Vivek				
Shyam				

37.2 Frequency

The marks scored by 35 students in a Mathematics test were as under :

60, 65, 100, 70, 85, 75, 95, 90, 65, 70, 80, 95, 70, 75, 75, 70, 80, 80.

70, 75, 85, 85, 70, 90, 75, 75, 80, 80, 85, 85, 90, 75, 75, 80, 80.

As in the above case, it often happens that some scores or measures occur more than once in a set of data. The number of times each score or measure occurs in the set is called its **Frequency**.

The score of 75 occurs 8 times in the set above, therefore its frequency is 8. What is the frequency of a score of 65? of 80 ? of 95 ?

It may be important to know the frequency of each score in a set. A convenient way to determine the frequency of each score by constructing a **frequency table** is shown at the right.

Such a table is called a **frequency distribution**. The column of tally marks is not necessary, but is a convenient way to determine the frequency of each score. How many students took the test? Notice that the sum of the frequencies is the same number as the number of members in the set of data.

Score (s)	Tally	Frequency (f)
60			1
65				2
70								6
75										8
80									7
85							5
90					3
95				2
100	I	1

37.3 Range

The difference between the greatest and the least values of observations, in a set of data is called the *range* of the set of data. Thus the range of the set of data given above is $100 - 60 = 40$.

Ex. 1. *The scores (out of 100) obtained by 33 students in a Mathematics test are, 70, 49, 85, 59, 85, 49, 74, 84, 49, 67, 59, 67, 65, 72, 65, 67, 70, 67, 84, 67, 70, 72, 82, 72, 74, 70, 67, 67, 65, 59, 65, 70, 70.*

Prepare a frequency table for the above scores.

Sol. Arranging the data in ascending order, we have

49, 49, 49, 59, 59, 59, 65, 65, 65, 65, 67, 67, 67, 67, 67, 67, 67, 70, 70, 70, 70, 70, 70, 72, 72, 72, 74, 74, 82, 84, 84, 85, 85, counting how many times a particular score occurs, e.g., the score 49 occurs 3 times, we form the frequency table as under :

Score	49	59	65	67	70	72	74	82	84	85
Frequency	3	3	4	7	6	3	2	1	2	2

Remark : We can also use tally marks to count the various items in the given data.

Ex. 2. *Given below are the ages of 25 students of a class in a school. Prepare a frequency distribution.*

13, 15, 12, 13, 15, 16, 12, 15, 13, 16, 14, 12, 13, 15, 16, 12, 15, 16, 14, 12, 16, 13, 15, 14, 12

Sol. For counting, we use tally marks and prepare the frequency table as given below. We make bundles of 5 tally marks by crossing the four tally marks by the fifth one.

Age	Tally marks	Frequency
12								6
13							5
14					3
15								6
16							5
Total		25

EXERCISE 37 (b)

1. Write true or false. Use the following frequency table.

Age	13	14	15	16	17	18	19
Frequency	3	2	7	2	3	2	1

(*i*) The frequency of 19 is 1;   (*ii*) The frequency of 14 is 3.   (*iii*) 17 has the lowest frequency;

(*iv*) 16 has a frequency of 2;   (*v*) 15 has the highest frequency   (*vi*) The frequency of 13 is 3.

2. Make a frequency distribution for the given data.

15, 14, 11, 16, 12, 17, 15, 15, 18, 16, 13, 12, 14, 16, 15, 18, 16, 15, 14, 13.

3. A total of 20 patients admitted to a hospital have blood sugar levels as given below :

67, 69, 74, 73, 70, 70, 71, 67, 73, 74, 73, 75, 69, 72, 70, 70, 72, 70, 73, 74. Make a frequency table.

4. The marks obtained by 30 students of a class in a test out of 10 marks are as follows :

4, 6, 5, 1, 5, 4, 3, 6, 8, 10, 7, 1, 8, 5, 4, 9, 7, 10, 3, 2, 4, 5, 3, 6, 7, 8, 4, 10, 3, 9.

Make a frequency distribution table for the above data. Use the table to find :

(*i*)   The number of students passed, if the minimum pass marks are 40%.

(*ii*) How many students failed ?

(*iii*) How many students secured the highest marks?

(*iv*) How many students secured more than 60% marks?

[**Hint :** Pass marks = 40% of 10 = 4, 60% of 10 = 6].

5. The weight (in kg) of 30 students of a class are 50, 49, 45, 49, 49, 50, 50, 54, 55, 44, 44, 42, 44, 56, 57, 49, 49, 42, 41, 50, 50, 50, 57, 45, 45, 45, 50, 54, 43 and 49.

Prepare a frequency table for the above data and answer the following questions :

(*i*)   What is the least weight ?

(*ii*) Find the number of students having the least weight in the above data.

(*iii*) Find the number of students having the maximum weight in the above data.

(*iv*) Which weight do the maximum number of students have ?

6. The value of π upto 50 decimal places is given below :

3.1415926535   8979323846   2643383279   50288841971   6939937510

Write the frequencies of the following digits in the decimal part of the above number.

(*i*) 2   (*ii*) 3   (*iii*) 5   (*iv*) 6   (*v*) 9   (*vi*) 1

SECTION-B

ARITHMETIC MEAN

37.4 Introduction

The idea of an arithmetic average or mean is not new to you. You have probably heard such statements as : "My average on tests is 70%" . " Tendulkar averaged 63 runs in the test series". "The average speed during the trip was 65 km per hour". What does each of the above statements mean? An average of 76% on tests means that while some marks were higher and some were lower, the scores on tests clustered around a score of 76%. Tendulkar most likely did not score 63 runs in any inning. However, the runs made probably grouped themselves around 63. If the average speed on a trip was 65 kilometres per hour, at times it was less than 65 and, at other times it was above 65 kilometres per hour. The speed was usually about 65 kilometres per hour.

Suppose Pradeep was practising for the pole vaulting event in the annual athletic meet. He made vaults of the following heights.

3.2 m, 3.3 m, 3.2 m, 3.3 m, 3.6 m, 3.3 m, and 3.2 m. His coach calculated the average height for the 7 vaults by adding the heights and dividing by the number of heights. The sum of the heights = 23.1 m. The mean is 23.1 ÷ 7 or 3.3 m.

> *The arithmetic mean of a set of data is found out by dividing the sum of all the data by the total number of data. If we denote the arithmetic mean by $\bar{x}$ (read "x bar"),*
>
> *Then* $\qquad \bar{x} = \dfrac{\text{Sum of all data}}{\text{Number of data}}$
>
> *The mean is also called the "average".*

Ex. 1. *Find the arithmetic mean of the numbers 3, 0, –1, 7, 11.*

Sol. The list has 5 entries. Therefore, $\bar{x} = \dfrac{3 + 0 + (-1) + 7 + 11}{5} = \dfrac{20}{5} = 4.$

Ex. 2. *The heights of 10 girls were measured in cm and the results were as follows :*
143, 148, 135, 150, 128, 139, 149, 146, 151, 132

   (i) *What is the height of the tallest girl ?*

   (ii) *What is the height of the shortest girl?*

   (iii) *What is the range of the data?*

   (iv) *Find the mean height.*

   (v) *How many girls are there whose heights are less than the mean height?*

Sol. Heights in ascending order are :
128, 132, 135, 139, 143, 146, 148, 149, 150, 151.

   (*i*) Height of the tallest girl = 151 cm

   (*ii*) Height of the shortest girl = 128 cm.

   (*iii*) Range of the data = 151 cm – 128 cm = **23 cm.**

   (*iv*) Total sum of given heights = 128 + 132 + 135 + 139 + 143 + 146 + 148 +149 + 150 + 151
                              = 1421 cm.

Number of girls = 10 ∴ Mean height = $\dfrac{1421}{10}$ = **142.1 cm.**

   (*v*) Number of girls whose heights are less than the mean height = **4.**

Ex. 3. *A group of students were given a special test. The test was completed by various students in the following time (in minutes) : 18, 20, 21, 23, 25, 25, 29, 31, 31, 37.*

   (i) *Find the mean time taken by the students to complete the test.*

   (ii) *How many students took more than the mean time to complete the test ?*

   (iii) *If the student who took 37 minutes had taken only 23 minutes to complete the test, what would have been the mean time?*

Sol. The time taken by students (in minutes) are 18, 20, 21, 23, 25, 25, 29, 31, 31, 37;
Number of students = 10

∴ Mean time

$$= \frac{18+20+21+23+25+25+29+31+31+37}{10} = \frac{260}{10} = \textbf{26 minutes.}$$

(ii) Number of students who took more than mean time, *i.e.*, more than 26 minutes to complete the test = **4**.

(iii) Replacing 37 by 23, new mean time

$$= \frac{18+20+21+23+25+25+29+31+31+23}{10}$$

$$= \frac{246}{10} = 24.6 \text{ minutes} = \textbf{24 min. 36 sec.}$$

Ex. 4. *The mean of 5 observations is 15. If mean of the first three observations is 14 and that of the last three is 17, then find the third observation.*

Sol. The mean of 5 observations = 15

Total sum of 5 observations = 5 × 15 = 75

Mean of first 3 observations = 14

Total sum of first 3 observations = 3 × 14 = 42

Mean of last three observations = 17

Total sum of last three observations = 3 × 17 = 51.

∴ Third observation = 42 + 51 − 75 = 93 − 75 = **18**.

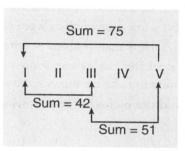

37.5 Arithmetic Mean of an Ungrouped Frequency Distribution

$$\textbf{Mean} = \frac{\textbf{Sum of the } fx \textbf{ column}}{\textbf{Sum of the } f \textbf{ column}}$$

$$= \frac{\sum fx}{\sum f} = \frac{\sum fx}{N} \text{ where } N = \sum f$$

Note : The symbol Σ is pronounced 'sigma' and is used for the phrase 'the sum of' *f* is the frequency.

Ex. 5. *Find the mean of the following distribution :*

x	5	15	25	35	45
f	7	8	20	10	5

Sol. Mean $(\bar{x}) = \dfrac{\sum fx}{\sum f}$

$$= \frac{1230}{50} = \frac{123}{5} = \textbf{24.6.}$$

x	f	f.x
5	7	35
15	8	120
25	20	500
35	10	350
45	5	225
Total	50	1230

EXERCISE 37 (c)

1. Find the mean of the following sets of numbers :

(a) 4, 5, 7, 8　　　　　　　　　　　(b) 3, 5, 0, 2, 8

(c) 2.5, 2.4, 3.5, 2.8, 2.9, 3.3, 3.6　　(d) −6, − 2, −1, 0, 1, 2, 5, 9.

2. The weights of six students in kg were 56, 54, 44, 35, 45, 36, Find the mean weight.

3. Daisy received 85, 73, 92, 61 and 89 marks in five tests. What are her mean marks?

4. Madhu practiced on her sitar 45 minutes, 30 minutes, 60 minutes, 50 minutes, and 20 minutes. What was her mean practice time?

5. Find the mean of the first ten natural numbers.

6. Find the mean of the first ten prime numbers.

7. Nisha secured 73, 86, 78 and 75 marks in four tests. What is the least number of points she can secure in her next test if she is to have an average of 80 ?

8. The mean of 5 numbers is 20. If one number is excluded, mean of the remaining numbers becomes 23. Find the excluded number.

9. **The weights of new born babies (in kg), in a hospital on a particular day are as follows:**

   2.3, 2.2, 2.1, 2.7, 2.6, 3.0, 2.5, 2.9, 2.8, 3.1, 2.5, 2.8, 2.7, 2.9, 2.4

   (*i*) Re-arrange the weights in ascending order.   (*ii*) Determine the highest weight.

   (*iii*) Determine the lowest weight.   (*iv*) Determine the range.

   (*v*) How many babies were born on that day?   (*vi*) How many babies weigh below 2.5 kg?

   (*vii*) How many babies weigh more than 2.8 kg?   (*viii*) How many babies weigh 2.8 kg?

10. A cricketer has a mean score of 60 runs in ten innings. Find out how many runs are to be scored in the eleventh inning to raise the mean score to 62.

11. **Find the mean of the following distributions.**

(*i*)	*x*	:	4	6	9	10	15		(*ii*)	*x*	:	10	30	50	70	89
	f	:	5	10	10	7	8			*f*	:	7	8	10	15	10

12. In an English Test, the marks obtained out of 10 by 50 students are given in the table below :

Marks (*x*)	:	0	1	2	3	4	5	6	7	8	9	10
Frequency (*f*)	:	2	1	3	5	6	3	3	7	8	8	4

   Find the average marks.

13. The following table gives the height in cm and the number of plants of each height. Compute the mean height of the plants.

Height in cm (*x*)	:	50	53	61	64	67	70
Number of plants (*f*)	:	15	10	18	12	25	20

14. The following data gives the number of boys of a particular age in a class of 50 students. Calculate the mean age of the students.

Age in years (*x*)	:	15	16	17	18	19	20
Number of students (*f*)	:	5	10	12	12	6	5

SECTION-C

GROUPED FREQUENCY DISTRIBUTION

37.6 Introduction

So far we have talked about ungrouped frequency distributions. If the data extends over a wide range, such tables become lengthy and unwieldy. In such cases, statisticians usually condense the data into more usable form, *i.e,* in groups or classes. **For example,** consider the following ungrouped marks out of 50 awarded to 30 students.

3, 5, 8, 15, 25, 30, 16, 7, 35, 40, 49, 40, 30, 15, 14, 21, 23, 22, 25, 27, 29, 32, 15, 1, 9, 11, 14, 42, 43, 8.

Let us arrange them in the following array, *i.e.,* in ascending order

1, 3, 5, 7, 8, 8, 9, 11, 14, 14, 15, 15, 15, 16, 21, 22, 23, 25, 25, 27, 29, 30, 30, 32, 35, 40, 40, 42, 43, 49.

(Arrangement in ascending or descending order is called an array.)

We can classify these marks into groups or classes as shown in the table given below.

Marks	No. of students	Marks	No. of students
0-5	2	25-30	4
5-10	5	30-35	3
10-15	3	35-40	1
15-20	4	40-45	4
20-25	3	45-50	1

The groups 0-5, 5-10 etc. are called the **class intervals.**

Each class interval is bounded by two figures which are called the **class limits**. The **class limits** of the **first class**, for example, are the numbers 0 and 5 and those of the second class are 5 and 10. The larger of these numbers namely 5 is called the **upper limit**, and the number 0 is the **lower limit.** Similarly, the upper and the lower limits of the second class are 10 and 5 respectively, and so on.

It may be noted that :

(*i*) the upper limit of one class coincides with the lower limit of the next class, and

(*ii*) **the class 0 and 5 means 0 and less than 5 ; 5 – 10 means 5 and less than 10,** and so on. Here, the upper limit 5 belongs to the next class 5 – 10 and not to the class 0 – 5. Similar is the case in other classes.

> **Maths Alert :** Marks '5' are included in the class interval 5–10 and not 0–5. Similarly, marks '15' are counted in the class interval 15–20 and not 10–15 and so on.

37.7 Class Size, Class-mark and Class Frequency

1. The difference between the upper and the lower class limits is called the **size** or **width** of the class interval. For example, in the table, the size of the class interval $0 - 5$ is $5 - 0 = 5$, of $5 - 10$ is $10 - 5 = 5$, of $10 - 15$ is
$15 - 10 = 5$, and so on.

2. The mid-value of a class-interval is called its **class-mark**. Thus, the class-mark of the class interval 10 – 15 is
$$\frac{10+15}{2} = \frac{25}{2} = \textbf{12.5}$$

3. The frequency of a class interval is called its **class frequency**. Thus, the class frequency of the class interva
$1 0 - 5$ is 2, of $5 - 10$ is 5, of $10 - 15$ is 3 and so on.

Ex. 1. *In an examination, 40 boys secured the following marks :*

8, 11, 20, 37, 40, 15, 29, 31, 27, 8, 7, 13, 29, 25, 42, 37, 30, 10, 9, 27, 18, 25, 9, 2, 17, 47, 32, 11, 29, 6, 15, 41, 37, 10, 40, 21, 39, 13, 15, 3.

Represent the data by a frequency table.

Sol. Arranging the given marks in ascending order, we have

2, 3, 6, 7, 8, 8, 9, 9, 10, 10, 11, 11, 11, 13, 13, 15, 15, 15, 18, 20, 21, 25, 25, 27, 27, 29, 29, 29, 30, 31, 32, 37, 37, 37, 39, 40, 40, 41, 42, 47.

Here, the maximum marks secured = 47,

The minimum marks secured = 2   ∴ Range = 47 – 2 = **45**

Classes	Tally	Frequency (*f*)
0-10	Ж|| |||	8
10-20	Ж|| Ж||		11
20-30	Ж|| ||||	9
30-40	Ж|| ||	7
40-50	Ж||	5
Total		40

Suppose we want to form 5 classes, then the class interval should be $\frac{45}{5}$, *i.e.* 9 or roughly 10 as we prefer 5 or 10 or 20, etc. Therefore the class intervals are 0-10, 10-20, 20-30, 30-40, 40-50. The frequency distribution is as given in the table.

Ex.2. *Construct a frequency distribution table for the following data of the maximum temperature (in °C) using equal class intervals-one of them being 28 – 30 (30 not included).*

32.5, 30.3, 33.8, 31.0, 28.0, 33.9, 33.3, 32.4, 30.4, 32.6, 34.7, 34.9, 31.6, 35.2, 35.3, 35.5, 36.4, 35.6, 37.0, 34.3, 32.0, 34.0, 34.4, 36.0, 37.3, 38.0, 36.9, 37.0, 36.3, 38.0, 36.7.

Sol. Arranging the given data in ascending order, we have

28.0, 30.3, 30.4, 31.0, 31.6, 32.0, 32.4, 32.5, 32.6, 33.3, 33.8, 33.9, 34.0, 34.3, 34.4, 34.7, 34.9, 35.2, 35.3, 35.5, 35.6, 36.0, 36.3, 36.4, 36.7, 36.9, 37.0, 37.0, 37.0, 37.3, 38.0, 38.0.

The highest temperature = 38.0°C,

The lowest temperature = 28.0°C

Range = 38.0°C – 28.0°C = 10°C

Size of the class interval = 2

$\therefore$ No. of class intervals = $\frac{10}{2} + 1 = 6$

Temperature (in °C)	Tally	Frequency (f)
28-30	I	1
30-32	IIII	4
32-34	JHI II	7
34-36	JHI IIII	9
36-38	JHI IIII	9
38-40	II	2
Total	Σf	32

$\therefore$ The class intervals covering the given data are 28-30, 30-32, 32-34, 34-36, 36-38, and 38-40.

37.8 Arithmetic Mean of Grouped Data

Ex. 1. *Calculate the arithmetic mean of the marks scored by students of a class in a class test from the following data.*

Marks	0-10	10-20	20-30	30-40	40-50	50-60	Total
Number of students	12	18	27	20	17	6	100

Sol. We find the class-mark of each class interval and represent it by *x*. Then we proceed to find the arithmetic mean as in case of tabulated data.

i.e.,   **Mean** $= \dfrac{\sum fx}{\sum f}$

Marks	Frequency (f)	Class-Mark (x)	f.x
0-10	12	5	12 × 5 = 60
10-20	18	15	18 × 15 = 270
20-30	27	25	27 × 25 = 675
30-40	20	35	20 × 35 = 700
40-50	17	45	17 × 45 = 765
50-60	6	55	6 × 55 = 330
Total	100		2800

Mean $= \dfrac{\sum fx}{\sum f} = \dfrac{2800}{100} =$ **28 marks.**

	EXERCISE 37 (d)

1. Fill in the blanks :

    (*i*) The difference between the maximum and the minimum observations in a data is called the .... of the data.

    (*ii*) The number of observations in a particular class interval is called the .... of the class interval.

2. Fill in the blanks :

    (i) lower limit of the class interval 26-33 is ....   (*ii*) upper limit of the class interval 20-25 is ....

    (*iii*) The range of the data 5, 8, 15, 21, 7, 10, is ....

    (*iv*) The range of the data 15, 13, 14, 17, 19, 16, 14, 15, is ....

3. Fill in the blanks in the following table :

Weights in kg	10-20	20-30	30-40	40-50	50-60
Class marks	-	-	-	-	-

Sol. Hint : Class-mark for 1st class interval $= \dfrac{10+20}{2} = \dfrac{30}{2} = 15$.

    Similarly, the class marks of other class intervals are obtained.

4. The following are the monthly rents (in rupees) of 30 shops :

    42, 49, 37, 82, 37, 75, 62, 54, 79, 84, 75, 63, 44, 74, 36, 69, 54, 48, 74, 39, 48, 45, 61, 71, 47, 38, 80, 51, 31, 47.

    Using the class intervals of equal width in which one class interval being 40-50 (excluding 50), construct a frequency table for the above data.

5. Construct a frequency table for the following marks obtained by 45 students using equal class intervals, one of them being 16-24 (24 not included).

    12, 35, 6, 10, 8, 24, 37, 32, 61, 52, 63, 7, 41, 48, 15, 16, 25, 29, 62, 40, 33, 46, 18, 20, 34, 28, 24, 56, 55, 12, 50, 56, 48, 47, 38, 26, 60, 42, 39, 40, 43, 25, 13, 46, 20.

6. The following list shows the weights in kg of 22 male students in a class :

    37.48   61.93   58.72   49.78   51.70   68.20

    49.87   38.75   69.10   65.39   36.49   65.62

    54.63   49.17   48.80   57.35   62.25

    38.50   62.82   59.73   56.60   50.15

    [Hint : Since observations like 37.48, 62.25, 59.73, do not fit in any intervals, the class intervals have to overlap in such a way that all values fit in. You may take the intervals as 35-40, 40-45, 45-50, ..., 65-70.]

Find the mean of each of the following frequency distributions :

7.

Class	0-10	10-20	20-30	30-40	40-50	50-60	60-70
Frequency	4	4	7	10	12	8	5

8.

Class interval	25-35	35-45	45-55	55-65	65-75
Frequency	6	10	8	12	4

9.

Class interval	0-8	8-16	16-24	24-32	32-40
Frequency	5	6	4	3	2

MEDIAN

37.9 Median

    A group of students took a spelling test. After evaluation, the teacher announced that " on the average" each of the five students mis-spelt 18 words.

Shown at the right is the actual number of words mis-spelt by each student. Is 18 the mean of these scores? (Yes). How many mis-spelt at least 18 words? (one). Does 18 satisfactorily represent the five scores ? (No)

Sunil	25
Manish	15
Ashok	10
Subodh	9
Rekha	6

The five scores are arranged in order. Which score has the same number of score above it as below it ? (**Ans :** 10) Is 10 a more satisfactory representative score? (Yes) Why or Why not? (**Ans :** It is more representative of all of the scores than 18.)

If a set of data contains a few very high scores or very low scores, the mean does not satisfactorily represent the data. In situations such as these, it is often more desirable to use the middle score, called the median, as the representative score.

> *The median of a set of numbers is the middle number when all the numbers are arranged in order of size. i.e. in descending or ascending orders.*
>
> *To find the median of a set of numbers, arrange them in order of size and select the middle number. If there is no middle number, it occurs when the number of numbers in the data is even, then the mean of the two middle scores is the median.*

Ex. 1. *What is the median weekly salary of workers in a firm whose salaries are Rs 84, Rs 60, Rs 50, Rs 40, Rs 45, Rs 42, Rs 38, Rs 65, Rs 71?*

Sol. **1.** First arrange the salaries in order :   Rs. 84, 71, 65, 60, [50], 45, 42, 40, 38.
                                                                                              4 terms   4 terms

2. Next, count the number of workers. It is 9.

The fifth salary (Rs 50) has four salaries which are less than it and four salaries above it. Therefore, Rs 50 is the middle or median salary.

Ex. 2. *Find the median salary of the following salaries of workers : Rs 56, Rs 89, Rs 121, Rs 38, Rs 98, Rs 70, Rs 70, Rs 72.*

Sol. Arrange the salaries in order : Rs 121, 98, 89, 72, 70, 70, 56, 38.

Count the number of workers. It is 8.

Find the salary which has the same number of salaries above and below it.

In this case, there is no single such salary. We shall, therefore, select as the median the mean of the fourth and fifth salaries.

121, 98, 89,   [72, 70]   70, 56, 38
      3 terms   Two   3 terms
                       middle
                       terms

Thus, Rs $\frac{72+70}{2} = $ Rs $\frac{142}{2}$, *i.e.,* **Rs 71** is the median salary.

MODE

37.10 Mode

Miss Gita observed at a club meeting that three of the girls wore red dresses, seven wore black dresses and four wore pink dresses. "Since more girls wore black than any other colour she said, "Black is the mode or fashion."

The mode is another kind of average and it is found by observing the frequency with which each number in a set of numbers occurs. Since the mode can be found by inspection, it is the easiest of the measures of central tendency to obtain. However, as you will soon see it is not an especially reliable index of clustering.

> **The mode** _of a set of numbers is the number which occurs most frequently in the set. If no number occurs more than once, the set of data is said to have no mode. If different numbers occur the same number of times, the set of data has more than one mode._

For example,

6, 7, 8, 9, 14   52, 58, 58, 58, 65, 73, 73, 73

no mode   two modes : 58 and 73

Ex. 1. *Find the mode of the following years of experience of teachers in a school : 10, 12, 5, 4, 7, 6, 7, 4, 2, 7, 1, 2, 3, 10, 1, 7, 5, 4.*

Sol. By inspection, the largest frequency is 4. Therefore, 7 years of experience is the mode. More teachers have 7 years of experience than any other number of years.

Years of experience	Frequency
12	1
10	2
7	4
6	1
5	2
4	3
3	1
2	2
1	2

Note that if the number of teachers with 7 years were only 3, and with 3 years were 2, then table would represent the situation.

Years of experience	Frequency
12	1
10	2
7	3
6	1
5	2
4	3
3	2
2	2
1	2

The mode would now be 4 years and 7 years. When two scores appear with the same highest frequency, we call such a frequency distribution **bimodal**.

EXERCISE 37 (e)

Find the median of the following :

1. 2, 3, 5, 7, 9

2. 4, 8, 12, 16, 20, 24, 28, 32

3. 60, 33, 63, 61, 44, 48, 51

4. 13, 22, 25, 8, 11, 19, 17, 31, 16, 10

5. 15 students secured the following marks in a test in Statistics. Find the median marks.

   35, 28, 13, 17, 20, 30, 19, 29, 11, 10, 29, 23, 18, 25, 17

6. Determine the mode(s) for each of the following sets of data :

   (*a*) 5, 3, 5, 2, 3, 5, 1, 7   (*b*) 1, 7, 13, 19, 25

   (*c*) 4, 6, 8, 4, 10, 4, 6, 12, 6, 10   (*d*) 51, 68, 70, 76, 55, 70, 73, 68, 70, 81

   (*e*) 8, 4, 8, 4, 8, 4, 8, 4, 8, 4, 8, 4   (*f*) 29, 29, 10, 10, 3, 3, 14, 14, 2, 10

   (*g*) 26, 32, 26, 21, 83, 26, 83, 67, 53, 83, 85

7. Find the mode of the following distributions :

(*a*) Size	:	2	3	4	5	6	7
Frequency	:	4	6	2	5	3	1
(*b*) Size of shoes	:	6	7	8	9	10	
No. of persons	:	12	20	40	15	7	

8. Determine (*a*) the mode (*b*) the median, and (*c*) the mean for each of the following sets of data :

   (*i*) 1, 16, 11, 6, 11, 8, 14, 11, 21   (*ii*) 5, 10, 10, 12, 13, 16, 15, 18, 18, 23

   (*iii*) 23, 2, 42, 6, 36, 11, 29, 9, 15   (*iv*) 8, 8, 8, 8, 18, 18, 18, 18

9. Find the mode, and the mean for the set of data below.

   Number of fiction books read by 28 eight-grade pupils :

   4, 6, 1, 7, 3, 9, 5, 7, 8, 5, 4, 6, 10, 6, 9, 5, 6, 6, 8, 6, 8, 5, 10, 7, 2, 5, 3, 7.

10. Find the mode, and the mean of the following set. Number of hours of operating life of 25 flashlight batteries :

   20, 21, 19, 22, 18, 23, 25, 22, 23, 20, 23, 20, 22, 21, 24, 21, 22, 23, 19, 21, 22, 22, 24, 26, 22.

SECTION-D

BAR GRAPHS

37.11 Bar Graphs

Bar graphs consist of axes and a series of labelled horizontal or vertical bars that give different information for each bar. We give below two examples to help you revise the concept of bar graphs which you have already learnt in detail in classes VI and VII.

Ex. 1. *The table given below shows the sale of some fruits in one day by a local market.*

Fruit	Papaya	Pears	Mangoes	Oranges	Apples
Sale (in kg)	16	8	24	40	52

   Represent the data by a bar graph.

Sol.

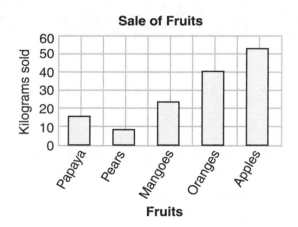

Ex. 2. *The table shows the marks scored by Rahul in the four terminal exams. Represent the data by a bar graph.*

Term	I	II	III	IV
Marks	65	75	50	85

Sol.

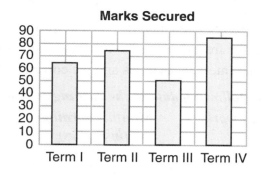

Marks Secured

HISTOGRAMS

37.12 Introduction

You have learnt what we mean by a frequency distribution and how to make a frequency distribution table from the given data. You have also learnt how to draw bar graphs. Now, we will tell you about another kind of graph which can be used to display a given data. This is called a histogram. A histogram is very similar to a bar chart. The bars of a histogram are also vertical, but unlike a bar graph and there are no gaps between the bars. Also, the data must be grouped into class intervals of equal width.

This table shows how long an audience's applause lasted for 67 jokes told by a comedian.

Duration of applause in seconds	Frequency
0 to less than 5	6
5 to less than 10	10
10 to less than 15	17
15 to less than 20	14
20 to less than 25	8
25 to less than 30	12

We convert the given table into a grouped frequency distribution with class intervals as under :

Duration of applause in seconds	Frequency
0-5	6
5-10	10
10-15	17
15-20	14
20-25	8
25-30	12

The data can be displayed in a histogram as shown below.

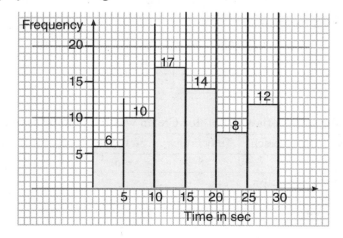

37.13 Drawing a Histogram

Method. 1. On the horizontal axis, mark off the class intervals on a uniform scale.

2. On the vertical axis mark off the frequencies, also on a uniform scale.

3. Construct rectangles with class intervals as bases and the corresponding frequencies as heights.

Ex. 1. *Draw a histogram to represent the following data of the earnings of workers :*

Monthly earnings (in rupees)	Number of workers	Monthly earnings (in rupees)	Number of workers
80-120	4	200-240	8
120-160	7	240-280	5
160-200	13	280-320	2

Sol.

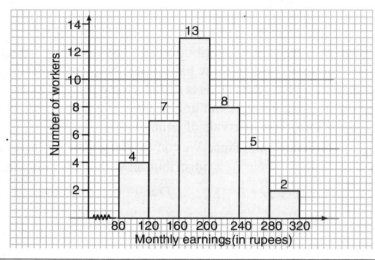

Note : When the scale along the x-axis does not start at the origin, we show it by a kink (break) or a zig-zag curve near the origin.

EXERCISE 38 (f)

1. The percentage of marks obtained by a student in different subjects are given below :

English	Hindi	Science	Maths	Social Studies
75	60	80	95	85

Represent the above data by a bar graph.

2. In a particular month, the number of accidents reported in a city by the various modes of transport are as below :

Scooter	Motorcycle	Car	Van	Bus
25	40	20	15	10

Represent the above data by a bar graph.

3. In a class, the preference for various flavours of Ice Cream was found to be as under :

Vanilla	Chocochip	Butterscotch	Tutty Fruity	Strawberry
14	12	9	8	5

Represent the above data by a bar-graph.

4. During the festive season, the sales of the various gadgets is as under :

Mixer	Microwave	Toaster	DVD Player	IPod
250	180	200	260	50

5. Represent the following distribution of ages (in years) of 35 teachers in a school by means of a histogram.

Age (in years) :	25-30	30-35	35-40	40-45	45-50
Number of Teachers :	12	11	8	1	3

6. Draw histogram for the following frequency distribution.

Size :	0-10	10-20	20-30	40-50	50-60
Frequency :	5	10	20	25	30

LOOKING BACK
Summary of Key Facts

1. A collection of numerical facts about objects is called **data.**
2. **Frequency** is the number of times each score occurs in a set.
3. For ungrouped frequency distribution   4. For a grouped frequency distribution :

$$\text{Arithmetic Mean} = \frac{\text{Sum of all data}}{\text{Number of data}} ; \quad \text{Mean} = \frac{\Sigma fx}{\Sigma f} = \frac{f_1 x_1 + f_2 x_2 + \dots\dots + f_n x_n}{f_1 + f_2 + \dots\dots + f_n}$$

where the frequencies of n observations $x_1, x_2, x_3, \dots\dots, x_n$ are $f_1, f_2, f_3, \dots\dots, f_n$ respectively.

5. The **median** of a set of numbers is the middle number when all the numbers are arranged in order of size *i.e.,* either ascending or descending.
6. In case the set of numbers has even number of values, **median** is the mean of the two middle scores.
7. The number which occurs most frequently in a set of numbers is known as the **mode.**

ANSWERS

EXERCISE 37 (a)

1. (*a*) 155, 160, 165, 167, 175,   (*b*) 60, 61, 65, 66, 68
   (*c*) Devendra, Girish, Narendra, Piyush, Sanjay

2.

Name	Age	Height	Weight	Hobby
Pawan	12 yrs.	155 cm	48 kg	Stamp-collecting
Hema	14 yrs.	140 cm	45 kg	Gardening
Vivek	11 yrs.	145 cm	42 kg	Painting
Shyam	13 yrs.	158 cm	46 kg	Photography

EXERCISE 37 (b)

1. (*i*) T   (*ii*) F   (*iii*) F   (*iv*) T   (*v*) T   (*vi*) T

2.

Number	11	12	13	14	15	16	17	18
Frequency	1	2	2	3	5	4	1	2

3.

Blood sugar level	67	69	70	71	72	73	74	75
Frequency (No. of patients)	2	2	5	1	2	4	3	1

4.

Marks	1	2	3	4	5	6	7	8	9	10
No. of students (Frequency)	2	1	4	5	4	3	3	3	2	3

(*i*) 23   (*ii*) 7   (*iii*) 3   (*iv*) 11

5.

Weight in kg.	41	42	43	44	45	49	50	54	55	56	57
No. of students (Frequency)	1	2	1	3	4	6	7	2	1	1	2

    (i) 41 kg   (ii) 1   (iii) 2   (iv) 50 kg

6. (i) 5   (ii) 9   (iii) 5   (iv) 4   (v) 8   (vi) 5

EXERCISE 37 (c)

1. (a) 6   (b) 3.6   (c) 3   (d) 1

2. 45 kg   3. 80 marks   4. 41 minutes   5. 5.5   6. 12.9   7. 88 marks   8. 8

9. (i) 2.1, 2.2, 2.3, 2.4, 2.5, 2.5, 2.7, 2.7, 2.8, 2.8, 2.9, 2.9, 3.0, 3.1   (ii) 3.1 kg   (iii) 2.1 kg

    (iv) 1.0 kg   (v) 15   (vi) 4   (vii) 4   (viii) 2   10. 82 runs.

11. (i) 9   (ii) 55   12. 6.08   13. 62.21 cm   14. 17.38 years

EXERCISE 37 (d)

1. (i) range   (ii) frequency

2. (i) 26   (ii) 25   (iii) 16   (iv) 6

3.

Weight in kg	10-20	20-30	30-40	40-50	50-60
Class-mark	15	25	35	45	55

4.

Monthly rent (in rupees) :	30-40	40-50	50-60	60-70	70-80	80-90
f :	6	8	3	4	6	3

5.

Marks :	0-8	8-16	16-24	24-32	32-40	40-48	48-56	56-64
Number of Students (f) :	2	6	4	7	7	8	4	7

6.

Weight (in kg) :	35-40	40-45	45-50	50-55	55-60	60-65	65-70
f :	4	0	4	3	4	3	4

7. 38.2   8. 49.5   9. 16.4

EXERCISE 37 (e)

1. 5   2. 18   3. 51   4. 16.5

5. 20 marks   6. (a) 5   (b) no mode   (c) 4 and 6   (d) 70

    (e) 4 and 8   (f) 10   (g) 26 and 83

7. (a) 3   (b) 8

8. (i) (a) 11   (b) 11   (c) 11

    (ii) (a) 10 and 18 ;   (b) 14 ;   (c) 14

    (iii) (a) no mode   (b) 15   (c) $19\frac{2}{9}$

    (iv) (a) 8 and 18   (b) 13   (c) 13

9. mode 6; mean 6   10. mode 22; mean 21.8

EXERCISE 38 (f)

1.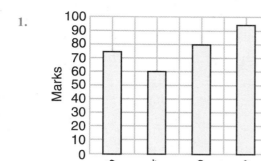

2.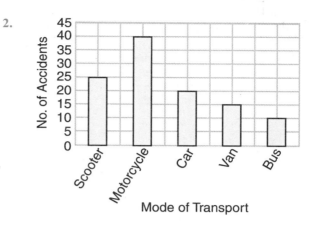

3.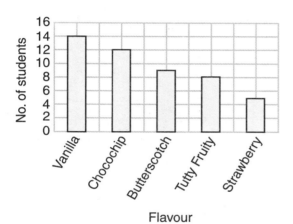

4.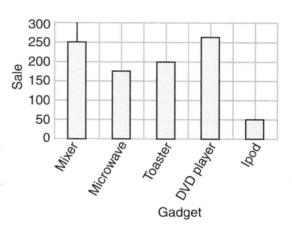

5.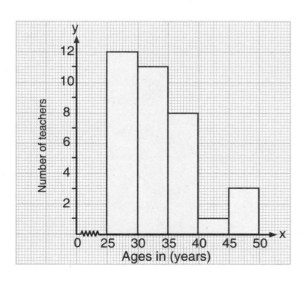

6.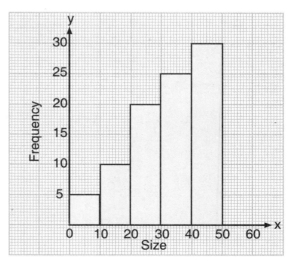